AEROSPACE:
The Journey of Flight

AEROSPACE EDUCATION
CIVIL AIR PATROL

3RD EDITION

AEROSPACE:
The Journey of Flight

Executive Editor: Dr. Jeff Montgomery
Design and Production: Barb Pribulick
Publishing Director: Jim Mallett
Associate Editor: Dr. Ben Millspaugh

Writers: Dr. Jeff Montgomery, Dr. Ben Millspaugh
Gary Dahlke, Lawrence Trick, Randall Carlson,
Ken Arteaga, Chris Charles, Lou Kaelin, Dave Landfair,
Damian McCarthy, Tom Sobieski, Barry Spink,
Kent Stitt, and James Wertz

Project Editor: Lydia Drennan
Contributing Editors: Debbie Dahl, Susan Mallet, Angie St. John,
Judy Stone and Paul Wescott

Photographic support: Dr. Ben Millspaugh and Bob Sharpe
Graphic support: Barb Pribulick

Cover Art: "One Man's Lifetime" by Roland O. Powell. Courtesy of NASA

Civil Air Patrol National Headquarters
Maxwell Air Force Base, Alabama 36112-6332

Published 2013

ACKNOWLEDGEMENTS

A tremendous amount of cooperation and teamwork accompanied the production of this book, and we are extremely grateful to the many dedicated people and organizations who contributed their time, talents, and resources.

We sincerely thank the team of writers from the United States Air Force Air Command and Staff College located at Maxwell Air Force Base, Alabama. Their dedicated research efforts produced an excellent manuscript of critical importance to the overall product.

We gratefully acknowledge the following organizations for their photographic contributions: Boeing Corporation, Experimental Aircraft Association (EAA), Lockheed Martin Astronautics, National Aeronautics and Space Administration (NASA), San Diego Air and Space Museum, National Oceanic and Atmospheric Administration (NOAA), Raytheon Corporation and the Smithsonian Institute, National Air and Space Museum (NASM).

We especially want to thank Peggy Greenlee for her dedication to the original project and to Barb Pribulick for devoting her tremendous talents to the 2nd and 3rd editions. We also thank Dr. Ben Millspaugh for providing much of the additional writing for the 2nd edition and to Gary Dahlke for lending his considerable skills to the third edition.

Finally, we certainly thank Jim Mallett, Director of Education, National Headquarters Civil Air Patrol (CAP), for his extraordinary vision and outstanding leadership in making this textbook a reality. He has superbly led the CAP Aerospace Education Program into the 21st century.

Dr. Jeff Montgomery

Contents

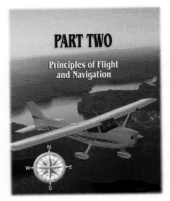

PART FOUR: The Rich History of Air Power

PART FIVE: Rockets

PART SIX: Space

PART ONE

The Rich History
of Air Power

1 INTRODUCTION TO AIR POWER

What is unique about the air and space domain? Can you drive or fly faster from home to school? Is it easier to turn around in a plane or a ship? Can you see farther from your car or from a plane? The answer to these questions and many more tell us that the air and space domain is special and unique. That is why we study it.

Objectives

Describe what makes air power unique.
Define air and space power.
Recognize the various legends of flight.
Identify the Chinese invention that solved one of the major problems of air power.
Identify the contributions the Chinese made to advance air and space power.
Identify the significant contributions that advanced air and space power.
Recall the individual scientists and researchers and their experiments.

Speed and Perspective Unique

The ability to move people, cargo and information quickly through air and space is unmatched. For example, what if you want to deliver medicine to a place across the ocean? Would it be faster to take a ship across the ocean, or to fly? What if you had to get to a town hundreds of miles away? Would it be faster to take a car or a plane? The answer to these questions, of course, is to fly.

Another aspect of air and space power that makes it unique is elevation. Not only can you fly over an obstacle that is in your way, you can see over it. Elevation gives you the ability to see objects that are far away.

In this chapter, you will discover why we should care so much about air and space domain. Its very uniqueness and our ability to use it is an interesting story.

At first there were problems that had to be overcome. Learning to fly was a very difficult task. The very first questions that had to be answered are fairly obvious. Just think about it. How would you go about figuring out how to fly? Would you ask a bird? Could you tell a bird how you are able to run or walk? Why are you able to run faster and jump higher than someone else? It isn't as easy as you may think, is it?

Believe it or not, both subjects are related. Walking and flying have several things in common. For instance, you need some sort of power to get you going. You will also need more

Men tried to imitate the flight of birds.

power as your load gets heavier. You will also need some place to store that power. This only adds to your problem because when you add a storage container you also add weight.

Air does not flow freely over a surface without some sort of reaction. Are there road signs in the sky? How do those airline pilots know where they are going? This is getting complicated and we haven't even started talking about the more advanced problems such as lift and navigation.

Virtually Unlimited Possibilities

Just think. In the last 100 years we have gone from gliders, to rotary aircraft, to jets. We have gone from traveling just a few miles to traveling unlimited distances. We have gone from building our planes from wood to building them from stealthy, man-made composite materials. We have gone from moving a few miles per hour to flying at multiples of the speed of sound and beyond.

The uses of air and space power have expanded as well. We have gone from using balloons to see a few miles ahead, to using satellites to monitor weather patterns from space. We have gone from carrying one or two people, to moving hundreds. We have gone from small loads to cargo loads large enough to carry a helicopter, tank or even another plane. We have gone from navigating by sight, to relying totally on instruments to tell us where we are going. The result of all this success is even higher expectations for bigger and better things in the future.

However, before we examine the future of air and space power, we should examine how we got to where we are today. The lessons learned developing air and space power are very interesting. More importantly these lessons should be examined so that we do not repeat the mistakes of the past. This will let us expand our horizons and reach out even farther, faster and better than we do today.

In the following chapter, we will look at the lessons learned and the development of air and space power. What is air and space power? It is the ability to take advantage of air and space to do many things. We can move people, cargo and information farther, faster and cheaper than ever before. We can now move all the information in the Library of Congress from Washington DC to Los Angeles faster than a blink of an eye. We can do this because of our satellites in space.

The Growth of Air Power from Balloons to Rockets

Our ability to use air and space did not come easy. Many lessons were learned the hard way, and they cost many lives along the way. Mistakes were made while we experimented with new engines, wings and life support systems. We don't want to repeat costly mistakes. We want to build on what we learned from them so we can get even better. The following chapter looks at many of the major developments in the history of air and space power. Additionally, the chapter points out why these are important to the continuing development of our air and space power.

The Heritage of Flight

Long before people appeared on this planet, other forms of life, which included birds, mammals (bats) and reptiles (pterodactyls) learned to travel through the air. Some imaginative people even believe that, many centuries ago, life from other planets may have traveled through space.

For people here on Earth, however, air and space travel is a very recent occurrence. Only within the last century have we been able to fly. In another sense, however, people have probably traveled through air and space for as long as they have been on Earth—at least, in their imagination they have.

Legends About Flight

Among the earliest recorded stories of man in flight is the Chinese legend of Emperor Shun. According to this legend, nearly 4,000 years ago, Emperor Shun escaped from prison by "donning the work clothes of a bird."

The Chinese have always been particularly enchanted by flight. Legends tell us that Kei Kung, the Chinese god of thunder and lightning, flew using the wings of a bat. Also, 1,800 years before Christ, legend has it that Ki-Kung-Shi built a flying chariot that had no visible means of support.

Wan Hoo

Although we don't know how truthful these legends are, we do know that the Chinese built the first devices that enabled us to fly. About 500 BC, the Chinese invented the kite. Some of the kites were very large and may have carried man aloft. We are fairly certain the Chinese used man-carrying kites to watch enemy troops in the seventeenth century.

About 900 AD, the Chinese invented gunpowder, and by 1100 AD, they were using gunpowder to build simple rockets. These early rockets were used for celebrations and in warfare. There is at least one Chinese legend of manned flight using rocket power. According to this legend, a Chinese official named Wan Hoo attempted a flight to the Moon using a large wicker chair to which were fastened 47 large rockets. When the rockets were ignited, Wan Hoo disappeared in a large ball of smoke and fire—never to be seen again. The Chinese legend concludes that maybe Wan Hoo is the man in the Moon.

It is from ancient Greece and Rome (800 BC—500 AD), however, that we get our most familiar legends and art showing flight. The Greek god Hermes and the Roman god Mercury traveled on winged sandals. Eros and his Roman counterpart, Cupid, are both pictured as winged children. The Greeks also gave us Pegasus, the winged horse.

Of course, the most famous myth of all is that of Icarus and Daedalus. According to this myth, Daedalus (an architect and mechanic) and his son, Icarus, were imprisoned by King Minos of Crete. Determined to escape, Daedalus made a large set of wings for himself and his son. The wings were made of feathers. They attached them to their bodies with wax. With these wings, they glided away from the island prison. Despite his father's warning, Icarus flew too close to the Sun. The wax melted, and Icarus fell to his death into the sea.

Daedalus and Icarus

One of the earliest illustrations of flight is found on a seal from Babylonia that was made in about 3500 BC. This seal pictures King Etena flying to heaven on the back of an eagle.

Another example is from 1500 BC. The Persian King, Kai Kawus, was supposed to have had a flying throne that was carried aloft by four eagles. In addition, Alexander the Great, King of Macedon in 336 BC, is said to have ridden in a cage drawn by winged griffins (a mythical animal—half eagle and half lion).

In tracing the history of flight, there are two trends that appear over and over in all parts of the world. First, it seems that people have always had the desire to fly. Second, since they did not have the natural ability to fly like the birds, flight depended on their ability to build machines to carry them aloft. The history of flight is really a history of people's ability to invent and perfect these machines.

Early Scientific Research

Leonardo da Vinci, (1452 – 1519), the great Italian artist, architect and man of science made the first scientific experiments in the field of aviation. He devoted many years of his life to understanding the mysteries of flight and left the world 160 pages of descriptions and sketches of flying machines.

Among these descriptions and pictures are the world's first known designs of the parachute and the helicopter.

He understood and wrote about the importance of the center of gravity, center of pressure and streamlining. These principles are vital in designing and building modern aircraft and spacecraft.

It seems certain that if da Vinci had concentrated his research only in these areas, he could have constructed a workable manned

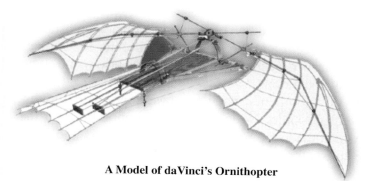

A Model of daVinci's Ornithopter

glider 400 years before the first one was actually built and flown. However, like so many before and since, he was obsessed with the idea of man flying like a bird.

He described, sketched and built models of many types of *ornithopters* (flying machines that are kept aloft and propelled by flapping wings). He left detailed sketches of wing mechanisms that used levers and pulleys to allow human muscle power to flap the artificial wings.

It is important to note that Leonardo da Vinci was a brilliant scientist whose work could have changed the entire history of flight—except for one tragic fact. It was more than 300 years after his death before his manuscripts were published and made known to the world. As a result, this knowledge was temporarily lost to the world and likely delayed the progress of manned flight.

Leonardo da Vinci

Basic Scientific Research

Beginning in the late 1500s and through the 1700s, there were many stories and books written about flight. Some were partially based on scientific principles. In the 1600s, a great deal of scientific research took place that was not directly related to flight. This research provided knowledge that would be used later to accomplish flight.

Three European scientists (Torricelli from Italy, Von Guericke from Germany and a Frenchman named Pascal) performed scientific studies of the atmosphere. They learned that the atmosphere is a fluid and that atmospheric pressure decreases the higher you climb. They invented the barometer, which measures the pressure of the atmosphere, and the air pump, which allowed them to study vacuums. This knowledge eventually led to successful lighter-than-air flight.

Francesco de Lana's Aerial Ship

In 1670, a Jesuit priest, Francesco de Lana, a professor of mathematics, wrote about an "aerial ship." This airship would be carried aloft by four large spheres from which all air had been removed to make them lighter than the surrounding air. He proposed to make the spheres out of very thin copper. The principle was sound but the spheres would have been immediately crushed by the pressure of the surrounding air. Francesco de Lana's writings are the first scientific records of a "vacuum balloon."

He also discussed the need for ballast (a heavy substance) for controlling ascent and the need to let air enter the spheres gradually to control descent. Francesco de Lana also wrote about military uses for balloons.

Several developments made the first successful lighter-than-air flight possible. None were more important than the developments that reduced the cost of printing, which made the wide distribution of books and other written documents possible. For the first time, scientists throughout Europe could compare notes, and benefit from the work done by each other.

Another Jesuit priest, Laurenco de Gusmao, is credited with inventing the hot-air balloon. In 1709, he demonstrated a small hot air balloon for the King of Portugal. Records of this demonstration were printed and widely read throughout Europe.

In 1766, an English chemist named Henry Cavendish made an important contribution to flight when he discovered a gas, which he called "flammable air." Later named hydrogen, this gas is important because it is lighter than air. Cavendish himself didn't recognize its importance to flight.

However, Dr. Joseph Black, Professor of Chemistry at Glasgow University, did. He realized that if this light gas were enclosed in a thin bladder, it would weigh less than the surrounding air and would therefore rise. Dr. Black's records show that he intended to experiment with this idea, but dropped it due to his heavy teaching schedule.

Finally, two brothers, who were papermakers in Annonay, France, achieved manned flight. Joseph and Etienne Montgolfier were well-educated eighteenth century gentlemen who enjoyed researching science and flight. They read all about the work of English scientist Joseph Priestley. Priestly discovered oxygen and had written scientific papers on the properties of air.

In 1782, Joseph Montgolfier was watching a fire in his fireplace and noticed an example of Priestley's work. He saw a force cause the sparks and smoke in the fireplace to rise. He then made a small bag out of fine silk and lit a fire under the opening at the bottom. The bag swelled and rose to the ceiling of the room. The Montgolfiers soon moved their experiments outdoors, building and flying larger and larger bags made of paper and linen.

In June 1783, the Montgolfier brothers were ready for a public demonstration using a paper-lined linen bag 38 feet in diameter. On June 5, in the marketplace, they built a fire of straw and wood under their balloon. The balloon rose to an altitude of 6,000 feet and traveled over a mile before landing.

The Montgolfiers had no idea that their balloon rose because it contained heated air that was lighter than the surrounding air. They thought a lighter-than-air gas that was created by the burning fuel caused the balloon's ascent. They called this gas "Montgolfier gas."

An account of this demonstration was sent to the Academy of Science in Paris. This led to an invitation for the Montgolfiers to demonstrate their balloon. Once again, the demonstration was a success.

Montgolfier's Hot Air Balloon

They were then asked to demonstrate their balloon before King Louis XVI and Marie Antoinette on September 19, 1783. For this demonstration, the Montgolfiers attached a cage to their balloon and the first living passengers—a sheep, a rooster and a duck—were carried aloft and returned safely to Earth.

The first men to fly in a lighter-than-air craft rode a Montgolfier balloon into the air over Paris on November 21, 1783. These two men were Pilatre de Rozier, a young physician, and the Marquis d'Arlandes, a young infantry officer. The flight lasted 25 minutes and covered a little more than 5 miles.

After centuries of dreaming, flight had become a reality. However, we were still a long way from mastering air and space power.

The problem with these hot air balloons was that they only stayed aloft as long as a fire continued to heat the trapped air. This made them very dangerous. It also limited the duration of the flight because a great deal of wood and straw had to be carried as fuel.

Later, the Montgolfiers hired a young scientist, J. A. C. Charles, to carry out further research on balloons. Charles was familiar with the "flammable air" isolated by Cavendish. He also realized that whatever "Montgolfier gas" was, it was not as light as hydrogen.

Charles was aware of the difficulties in containing hydrogen; therefore, for his balloon he developed a small globe of rubberized silk. On August 27, 1783, the globe was inflated with hydrogen and rose into the air.

One of the spectators at this event was Benjamin Franklin. He was so impressed that he immediately wrote to scientists in the United States stressing the military importance of this new invention. On December 1, 1783, Charles and another passenger made the first manned flight in a hydrogen balloon. This flight lasted over 2 hours and covered more than 27 miles.

Following these early flights, ballooning became very popular in Europe. Between 1783 and 1790, 76 flights were recorded in France alone. In 1793, the French government formed an air arm to their Army, and used balloons for reconnaissance during the French Revolution.

Andre-Jacques Garnerin's first parachute jump from a balloon.

In 1797, Andre-Jacques Garnerin made the first parachute jump from a balloon flying at an altitude of 3,000 feet.

During this time period, the hydrogen balloon became much more popular than the hot air balloon. In fact, by the end of the 1700s, the hot air balloon disappeared and its popularity would not return until the advent of modern-day sport balloons.

On January 7, 1785, a French aeronaut (balloonist), Jean Pierre Blanchard, and an American passenger, Dr. John Jeffries, made the first balloon flight from one nation to another. They flew across the English Channel from England to France. The flight covered about 30 miles and required almost two hours to complete.

On November 10, 1798, Jeanne-Genevieve Garnerin, wife of Andre-Jacques Garnerin, became one of the earliest woman to fly in a balloon. She was also the first woman to ascend solo and on October 12, 1799, the first woman to make a parachute descent; from an altitude of 900 meters.

The first woman to make ballooning a career was Jean Blanchard's wife, Madeleine Sophie Blanchard. From 1805-1819, she performed exhibitions of ballooning throughout Europe. Madame Blanchard was also the first woman to be killed in a ballooning accident (1819, in Paris).

The first balloon flight in the United States took place in Philadelphia, Pennsylvania, on January 9, 1793. The pilot was the same Jean Pierre Blanchard who had flown across the English Channel. President George Washington and thousands of spectators witnessed the flight. The balloon lifted off at 10 o'clock in the morning and landed safely near Woodbury, New Jersey, about 46 minutes later.

The first use of balloons by the United States military occurred during the Civil War. Several professional aeronauts, including Thaddeus S. C. Lowe, volunteered their services to the Union Army.

Lowe was unable to convince General Scott, of the Union Army, that there was a real military need for balloons. He told his friend Joseph Henry, first Secretary of the Smithsonian Institution, of his disappointment at the General's reaction. Henry made an appointment with President Abraham Lincoln and went with Lowe to tell the President of the advantages of aerial observation.

To show how well aerial reporting could work, Lowe went up in his balloon from the Smithsonian grounds. He used a telegraph wire that extended from his balloon basket to the White House to describe the scene to President Lincoln. After the dramatic show and the discussion with Lowe and Henry, President Lincoln sent General Scott a note asking him to seriously consider Lowe's offer.

Lowe was finally allowed to organize the Balloon Signal Service of the Union Army. He and a few other Army aeronauts served in the balloon corps for the first 2 years of the war. The aeronauts furnished valuable information to Union forces during several battles.

The aerial observers also had some frustrating experiences. They had to struggle to get their salaries, supplies, ground and maintenance crews. They even had to get permission to make aerial ascents. Lowe headed the corps, but he was never given an official title. He often had to pay for his own ballooning supplies. He eventually resigned from the corps. Later, the balloon corps was disbanded due to the lack of manpower and money for upkeep.

An Observation Balloon in the American Civil War

The South was well aware of the value of the aeronauts' services to the Union and wanted to start a Confederate balloon force. They made their first balloon of varnished, polished cotton and raised it with air heated over a fire of turpentine and pine knots. The second Confederate balloon had to be made from silk dresses donated by Southern women. Each day the crew filled this patchwork balloon at the Richmond, Virginia, gas plant. They took it by rail to the battle lines east of the city. Once, they mounted the balloon on a James River steamer, but the steamer ran aground. When the Union troops spotted the helpless vessel, they captured the balloon and ended Confederate hopes for a balloon corps.

While the use of hydrogen gas overcame the major disadvantages of hot air balloons, hydrogen gas was highly flammable an many people were killed before the use of a safer gas, helium, came into use.

However, hydrogen also had a serious disadvantage—it was highly flammable and many people were killed before a safer gas (helium) came into use.

In either case, the balloon's real major problem was steering it. The problem of changing a free balloon into a *dirigible* (a lighter-than-air craft that can be propelled and steered) would stump scientific minds for almost a century.

In 1785, a French general, Jean Baptiste Meusnier, made several suggestions that eventually led to successful *dirigibles*. First, he suggested changing the shape of a balloon from a sphere to the shape of a football. This would reduce air resistance and also establish a front and rear for the balloon.

He also suggested an envelope (container for the gas) made of several compartments and a passenger car shaped like a boat attached to the bottom of the dirigible by a system of ropes. The one problem Meusnier did not solve was how to power the dirigible. He suggested a large propeller turned by 80 men!

The next breakthrough came in 1852 by another Frenchman, Henri Giffard. He built a cigar-shaped *dirigible* 114 feet long and 39 feet in diameter. The *dirigible* was powered by a 3- horsepower steam engine that pushed it at a speed of about 5 mph. This *dirigible* is generally credited as being the first successful one in the world.

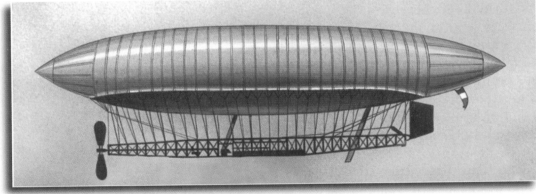

Renard's *Dirigible*

Another *dirigible*, which is sometimes credited as being the first successful one, was the LaFrance, built by Charles Renard and A. C. Krebs in 1884. This airship was powered by electric motors. It was the first *dirigible* to be steered back to its takeoff point.

However, the early *dirigibles* had limited range. It was not until the invention of the internal combustion engine that *dirigibles* became a real success.

A German engineer, Paul Haenlein, built the first *dirigible* powered by an internal combustion engine in 1872. This engine used coal gas taken from the balloon envelope as its fuel. The big problem with this was the longer the *dirigible* flew, the less lift it had because the engine was using the gas from the balloon.

These early *dirigibles* were nonrigid, which meant that only the pressure of the gas inside maintained the shape of the envelope. If the airship exceeded a certain speed, or if the pressure of the gas went down below a certain point, the balloon envelope would buckle or become distorted.

As balloon technology improved, an internal rigid keel (a long, reinforcing piece on the bottom of the balloon) stiffened the envelope. This keel extended along the length of the airship and carried the load of the engines and the passenger compartment. These were known as semi-rigid airships.

As a practical flying machine, the *dirigible* made its most noteworthy advances with the contributions of Alberto Santos-Dumont, a Brazilian, and Count Ferdinand von Zeppelin, a German. Both men successfully used internal combustion engines to power lighter-than-air crafts.

It was Santos-Dumont who ushered in the era of the powered gasbag. His first non-rigid airship was a small vessel 82 feet long driven by a 3-horsepower gasoline motor. On its first flight, it reached a height of 1,300 feet and was steered by movements of its rudder.

During the period between 1898 and 1907, Santos-Dumont constructed and flew 14 gasoline-powered, non-rigid airships. On his largest airship of 157 feet, he used a 20-horsepower engine.

Santos-Dumont became the idol of Paris in 1901, when he piloted an airship driven by a 12-horsepower motor, around the Eiffel Tower, a distance of nine miles. Despite a side wind of 12 to 13 mph, he developed a speed of 19 mph and covered the distance in less than 1/2 hour. For this accomplishment, Dumont won a 100,000 franc award put up by Henri Deutsch, a French petroleum magnate.

In July 1900, Ferdinand von Zeppelin built and flew the world's first successful rigid *dirigible*, the *LZ*-1. This began a long period of German domination of this type of aircraft. In fact, Germany so dominated the development of rigid airships, they became known as Zeppelins. These were rigid-type airships with an internal framework of steel or aluminum girders to support the *dirigible* and give it its shape.

Zeppelin built many large rigid airships for the German government. On June 22, 1910, the

The *LZ*-1 was built by Ferdinand von Zeppelin in 1900.

Deutschland (*LZ*-7) became the world's first commercial airship. Between 1910 and the beginning of World War I in 1914, German *Zeppelins* flew 107,208 miles and carried 34,028 passengers and crew—entirely without injury.

Developing the Airplane

The developments that finally led to the airplane of today were not easy. There were many basic problems of flight to be solved by both lighter-than-air and heavier-than-air fliers. First, they had to develop the lift necessary to get into the air. Second, they had to figure a way to sustain that lift. Third, they had to develop a way to control the aircraft once it was flying.

The balloonists overcame the first two problems by building their aircraft lighter than air. They kept them lighter than air by either dumping ballast or maintaining a fire to heat the trapped air. Therefore, they were faced only with the problem of control. Since the airplane would not have the balloon to keep it aloft, pioneers of the airplane had to struggle with all three problems.

The first airplane pioneer in the nineteenth century was a young Englishman named George Cayley. He was 9 years old when the Montgolfiers made their first flight. It was then that he began experimenting with small paper balloons.

His interest in flight continued into his teens, and he built small model helicopters. He applied what is called the "airscrew" concept to his models. Like Leonardo da Vinci, Cayley also studied the flight of birds. In 1804, he constructed a whirling-arm device. He used it to test the behavior of air pressure on various types of wings. He later built and flew small model gliders.

In 1809, he published the conclusions of his research in a scientific paper. The most important part of his paper was stated in one single sentence, which laid the whole foundation for modern aeronautics. It said, "The whole problem is confined within these limits, namely, to make a surface support a given weight by the application of power to the resistance of air."

Cayley identified the forces of lift, drag and thrust. He developed the cambered (curved) upper surface on a wing to increase lift. He also worked on propellers and power plants, and developed the concept of biwinged and triwinged aircraft. In 1850, he built the first successful full-sized, manned glider.

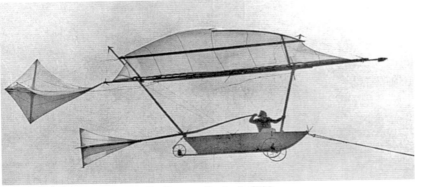

Sir George Cayley's Glider

Other Europeans, particularly the French, tried to unlock the secrets of the airplane in the nineteenth century. In 1871, Frenchman Alphonse Penaud developed a twisted rubber band to power workable helicopter models and to fly his planaphore. It was a 20-inch model airplane that flew 131 feet in 11 seconds. The planaphore contained Penaud's greatest contribution to aviation. It had automatic longitudinal (front to back) stability. To do this, he placed a small tail wing well behind the main wings. Penaud ranks close to Cayley as one of the most significant nineteenth century aeronautical thinkers.

Toward the end of the century, Clement Ader built the first manned aircraft to take off from level ground under its own power (1890). The craft looked like a huge bat and was powered by a 20-horsepower engine. Although it rose to a height of 8 inches and traveled through the air some 165 feet, it was not able to sustain flight. Seven years later he built a better model, which he called the *Avion III*. Unfortunately, it never got off the ground.

During the second half of the nineteenth century, flying became very popular and many people tried designing gliders and airplanes. Most of the gliders were unsuccessful, but from these failures came a lot of knowledge that would later contribute to the success of aviation.

For example, Francis H. Wenham had little practical success with his own gliders, but he became the first person to build a wind tunnel to test various wing shapes (1871). In time, both his invention and his glider work would become useful to Octave Chanute and the Wright brothers. During this period, three men made significant contributions to real gliding: an American, John J. Montgomery; a German, Otto Lilienthal; and a French-born American, Octave Chanute. These men all conducted very successful gliding experiments.

In 1884, 26-year-old John Montgomery, secretly built a 440-pound, man-carrying glider with wings like a sea gull. To avoid the ridicule of neighbors, he and his brother chose to try their first flight in the dead of night.

They had to wait until dawn before a breeze came in from the sea. To take off, Montgomery faced the wing surface of the glider into the 12 mph breeze, with his brother along side carrying a rope that was attached to the glider. The glider then carried Montgomery's 130 pounds aloft 600 feet before easing to Earth again.

Montgomery made several flights in his glider before it was wrecked in an accident. He built two other gliders: one with flat wings and one with wings that pivoted to the rear. Neither flew as well as his first.

From 1886 through 1892, Montgomery made thousands of experiments and studies of the wings of soaring birds. He gave every moment he could spare from his job, as professor of physics at Santa Clara College in California, to conduct these experiments.

By 1893, Montgomery had done enough research to design a glider that he thought would be successful. Yet, he had to wait 9 years before he had the time and money to turn the plans into a real flying craft.

In 1905, he unveiled his glider to the public. Fifteen thousand people gathered at Santa Clara, California, to watch Daniel Maloney, known for his parachute jumps from hot air balloons at county fairs, pilot Montgomery's craft.

Montgomery left and Maloney standing beside glider *Santa Clara*.

Maloney climbed aboard the glider, which Montgomery had hitched to a hot-air balloon. After the balloon was cut loose, it rose to 4,000 feet where Maloney cut the glider loose. Twenty minutes and 8 air miles later, Maloney brought the ship down to a pre-selected spot, 3/4 of a mile from where the ascent had started.

During the flight, he had whipped the craft into sharp dives and turns and had reached speeds estimated at 68 mph. Everyone in attendance was thrilled with Montgomery's successful glider.

During the next year, Montgomery exhibited his glider throughout California, raising funds for additional experiments. He built five more gliders and trained men to pilot them. These craft were all extremely maneuverable and capable of all sorts of twists, turns and somersaults. Then on April 18, 1906, his 20 years of labor were demolished in an earthquake. It was the same earthquake that destroyed San Francisco.

Montgomery was unable to resume his experiments until 1911. On October 31, 1911, his lifelong

Poster Advertising Aerial Exhibition

devotion to gliding and aviation ended. As he was landing his glider, a gust of wind flipped it and hurled him to his death.

The next pioneer, Otto Lilienthal, has been called the "Father of Modern Aviation." This German engineer was the first practical aviator. He built many single- and two-winged gliders, which he flew by running downhill until sufficient speed was built up to allow them to fly. His gliders had cambered (curved) wings and fixed-tail surfaces. Between 1891 and 1896, he made over 2,000 glides, many of which covered over 700 feet.

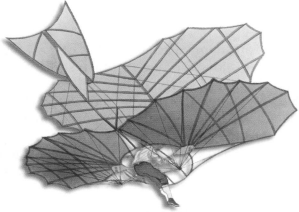

Lilienthal's Glider

In 1896, Lilienthal explored powered flight. He chose to use a biplane patterned after a double-winged glider he had flown successfully the year before.

He built an engine to link to the wingtips, which were hinged for flapping. He built a pilot control system into both the old and the new biplane for elevating the surfaces of the tail plane. The pilot's head worked the controls by a headband and rope that connected him to the tail. When the pilot lowered his chin, the plane rose, and when he lifted his chin, the plane dropped.

Before trying his powered biplane, Lilienthal flew the older biplane glider one last time to practice with the new elevating controls. He took off in a gusty wind. At 50 feet, his glider stalled and suddenly dropped like a rock. The fall broke Lilienthal's back, and he died the next day.

Lilienthal's book on flying informed and inspired pioneers in many countries. The development of photography allowed pictures to accompany his writings. The photos of his aircraft were seen throughout the world and helped create a great deal of interest in aviation.

One of the people who read Lilienthal's works was an American civil engineer, Octave Chanute. By 1896, Chanute was performing gliding experiments on the sand dunes around Lake Michigan.

Chanute was in his sixties when he became interested in flight. Because of his age, he did no flying himself. He designed the gliders, which were flown by another engineer named A. M. Herring. Chanute is not noted for any outstanding advancement in aeronautics, although he did improve on Lilienthal's work. Chanute is noted for his careful study of aviation history and collection and distribution of aviation information.

Two Englishmen made additional contributions to the development of heavier-than-air flight. They read the works of Cayley which were published and widely read by scientists and aviation enthusiasts throughout the world. The two Englishmen were W. S. Henson, an inventor, and John Stringfellow, a skilled engineer. In 1843, they drew up plans and received a patent for a man-carrying powered aircraft. This aircraft, named the *Ariel,* was to be a monoplane with a 150-foot wingspan. It was powered by a steam engine, which drove two six-bladed propellers. This aircraft was never built, but the plans were masterpieces of aviation engineering.

Octave Chanute

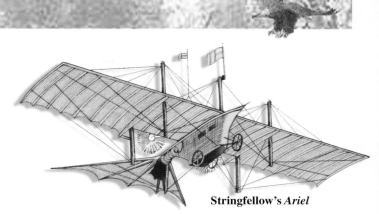

The plans for the wing structure showed a front and a rear spar with connecting ribs. This same type structure is used for making aircraft wings today.

A small model of the *Ariel* was built and tested, but it failed to fly. Later, Stringfellow built a steam-driven model which did fly (1848). This was the first successful powered flight of a heavier-than-air craft.

Stringfellow's *Ariel*

Another American who entered the field of aviation at this time was Samuel Pierpont Langley. Langley was an astronomer and the director of the Smithsonian Institution in Washington, D.C. His major contributions to flight involved attempts at adding power to a glider.

In 1896, he successfully built a steam-powered model that flew for 3/4 of a mile before it ran out of fuel. He then set out to build a full-size, man carrying aircraft. He received a $50,000 grant from Congress to build it.

One problem Langley encountered was the extremely heavy weight of steam engines. He was convinced that the internal combustion gasoline engine held the greatest promise for a lightweight, powerful engine for aircraft.

Charles M. Manly, Langley's assistant, designed such an engine. It was a 5-cylinder, radial engine that weighed only 125 pounds, but produced an amazing 53-horsepower. By October 1903, the engine had been placed in a full-size copy of his successful model, and Langley was ready for flight-testing.

The *Aerodrome,* as Langley called his aircraft, was to be launched by catapult from a barge anchored in the Potomac River .

Langley's *Aerodrome* speeds from its launch track atop a houseboat, only to plunge instantly into the Potomac.

The first flight was conducted on October 7, with Manly at the controls. The *Aerodrome* left the catapult; however, it did not fly and fell into the Potomac.

The test was repeated on December 8, with exactly the same results. Unfortunately, both attempts were well attended by the press. The reporters' critical writings caused the government to withdraw its support and Langley gave up his project.

Langley made some important contributions to flight. However, he spent far too much time on the power plant and too little time on how to control the aircraft once it was flying. Just 9 days after

Langley's last failure, two brothers succeeded. They had approached the problem from the opposite direction (control first and then power) and succeeded with powered flight on the sand dunes of North Carolina.

The Wright Brothers

A combination of factors helped Orville and Wilbur Wright achieve success in controlled, sustained and powered flight. First, they had access to the knowledge about flight gained by the others before them. The lessons learned by their predecessors contributed greatly to the success of the Wright brothers.

Secondly, they lived at a time when the first practical power plant (the gasoline engine) had been developed. Finally, they were patient in their approach to solving problems. They possessed a combination of attitudes and skills that allowed them to bring the work of their predecessors together and combine it into a successful product.

The Wright brothers develop controlled flight.

The Wright brothers' approach to flight was to first develop an aircraft that would fly and could be controlled in flight, and then to add a power plant. Their observations led them to believe that birds maneuvered in flight chiefly by twisting their wings. Using this information, they built a large box kite with four cords attached to the wingtips. They found by pulling these cords, and thus twisting (warping) the wings, they could maneuver the kite from the ground.

Following these successful kite flights, the brothers realized that the next step must be to get into the air themselves to further test their "wing-warping technique." Before beginning their glider tests, they requested information from the Weather Bureau to determine a site for conducting their tests. They needed a location that would have steady winds and plenty of open space. They were advised to try the beaches just south of Kitty Hawk, North Carolina.

They selected Kill Devil Hills, North Carolina, for their tests. In October 1900, their first glider was ready. This glider was a biplane with a horizontal elevator in front, no tail and cords attached to the wingtips for warping them. To reduce wind resistance, the pilot rode lying down between the wings.

They made a few successful glides during that first winter, but the winds were generally too light for manned flights. For the most part, this first aircraft was flown as a kite.

The following July, they returned with their second glider which had much larger wings. They also had fastened the wing-warping cables to a cradle in which the pilot lay. The aircraft was controlled by shifting this cradle with the hips, thus tightening the cables and causing the wings to warp.

The Wright brothers' crowded shack, at Kill Devil Hills, N .C., that sheltered the 1901 glider.

The cables were arranged so that as the rear of one wingtip was warped downward, the wingtip on the opposite side was warped upward. This caused the aircraft to turn. This was the first of two great contributions the Wright brothers made toward controlling flight.

The Wrights had so many problems with the control of their second glider, that after only 1 month, they stopped their tests and returned home to Dayton, Ohio.

During the winter of 1901, they built a small wind tunnel and tested many different shapes of wings. These tests gave them the knowledge they needed to overcome the control problems of their second glider.

By September 1902, they built a third glider and returned to North Carolina. This aircraft was almost the same as the first two. The only difference was the addition of two fixed vertical fins at the rear. It performed well except for its turns.

This is the Wright brothers' workshop at Dayton, Ohio, which was reconstructed at the Henry Ford Museum in Dearborn, Michigan. Their wind tunnel stands between an aircraft engine (far right) and a workbench cluttered with wing ribs. The overhead shaft was turned by an engine that the brothers built. It also ran the shop machinery.

The wing, which was warped downward, would tend to drag and the aircraft would begin to slide sideways through the air. This was corrected by changing the two fixed vertical fins to a single moveable rudder that was connected with the wing-warping cables. This allowed the rudder to be turned so that the air pressure against it would cause the body of the airplane to pivot toward the downward wing. The pivoting action caused the airplane to enter turning flight more quickly and smoothly, putting an end to the sliding sideways action. This was the second great contribution they made toward controlling flight.

By the time the Wright brothers returned to Dayton, Ohio, in October, they had performed over 1,000 successful flights and had solved all the major problems of control in the air. Now, all that remained was to add a suitable power plant.

On their quest for powered flight, the Wrights found no suitable lightweight engines that would meet their needs. Although they had no experience in power plants, they designed and built a four cylinder, water-cooled gasoline engine that produced about 12 horsepower.

Next, they designed and built the two propellers that would be turned by the engine. The propellers were connected to the engine by two bicycle chains and turned in opposite directions.

By September 1903, the engine had been installed and the Wrights returned to North Carolina with their powered aircraft, which they named the *Flyer*. The *Flyer* had no wheels, but landed in the sand on a pair of skids.

For takeoff, they constructed a long wooden rail upon which ran a small trolley. The skids were set on the trolley, and a wire held the trolley until the aircraft's engine was running at full power. When the wire was released, the aircraft and trolley ran smoothly down the track until the aircraft lifted off, leaving the trolley behind.

Their first attempt to fly was on December 14, 1903, with Wilbur at the controls. The *Flyer* became airborne but stalled and fell back into the sand. It was slightly damaged.

Three days later the damage was repaired. The wind was blowing at over 20 mph. It was Orville's turn, so he fitted himself into the cradle. The engine was started, turned up to full power, and the wire was released.

The *Flyer* began picking up speed as it moved down the track with Wilbur running alongside. As the *Flyer* neared the end of the track, it rose into the air and flew for 12 seconds. One hundred and twenty feet from the end of the track, it slowly settled back onto the sand. It was 10:35 a.m., December 17, 1903.

Three more times that day the *Flyer* left the Earth. The final flight with Wilbur at the controls lasted 59 seconds and covered 852 feet.

Following the last flight, a gust of wind tipped the Flyer and badly damaged it. This small, flimsy, wood and cloth airplane made a place in history, but it never flew again. Its total useful lifetime was 1 day.

Prior to the Wright brothers' success with the *Flyer,* Stringfellow had flown a powered model airplane, but he was not aboard to control it. Lilienthal created controlled flight with his glider, but it was not sustained flight because it was not powered. Clement Ader created a manned craft that flew under its own power, but it was not controllable, nor could it sustain flight. With the flight of the *Wright Flyer*, mankind's age-old dream of controlled, sustained and powered heavier-than-air flight was finally a reality.

Summary

This chapter has pointed out the major milestones in the development of flight and the significant accomplishments of the men and women around the world who helped make the flight of the *Wright Flyer* possible. With the *Wright Flyer*, controlled, sustained, and powered heavier-than-air flight was finally achieved. Real flight was born.

However, it would be a number of years before the powered airplane would be developed to the point of being accepted as a practical, useful tool. In the next chapter, we will examine how the flying machine continued to evolve.

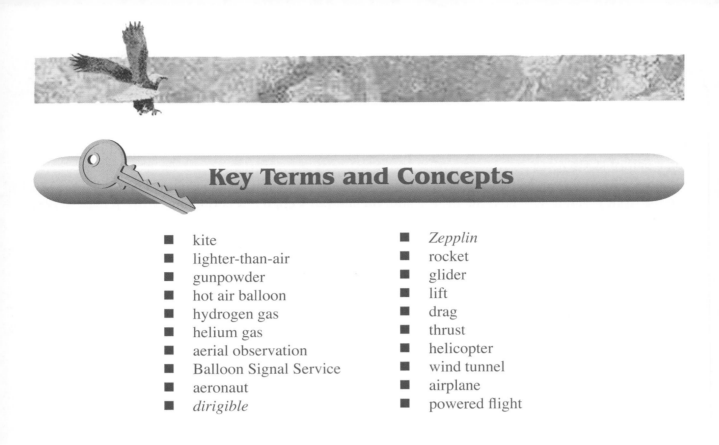

Key Terms and Concepts

- kite
- lighter-than-air
- gunpowder
- hot air balloon
- hydrogen gas
- helium gas
- aerial observation
- Balloon Signal Service
- aeronaut
- *dirigible*

- *Zepplin*
- rocket
- glider
- lift
- drag
- thrust
- helicopter
- wind tunnel
- airplane
- powered flight

? Test Your Knowledge ?

SELECT THE CORRECT ANSWER

1. *According to legend,* **(Wan Hoo / Daedalus)** *built two sets of wings so he and his son could escape imprisonment.*
2. *The* **(Greeks / Chinese)** *invented gunpowder.*
3. *The* **(Chinese / Persians)** *may have used man-carrying kites to spy on their enemies.*

MATCHING

4. *Developed first known principles of flight.*
5. *Invented the hot air balloon.*
6. *First human passengers flew on their balloon.*
7. *Organized Balloon Signal Service of the Union Army.*
8. *First successful rigid dirigible.*
9. *"Father of Modern Aviation."*
10. *First success in controlled, powered and sustained flight.*

a. **Otto Lilienthal**
b. **Thaddeus S. C. Lowe**
c. **Laurenco deGusmano**
d. **Wright brothers**
e. **Montgolfier brothers**
f. **Leonardo da Vinci**
g. **Ferdinand von Zepplin**

TRUE OR FALSE

11. *The* dirigible *was an important improvement over the balloon because it could be steered.*
12. *Hydrogen, as a lifting gas in balloons, was a major advancement in ballooning because of its safety.*
13. *Three European scientists — Toricelli, von Guericke, and Pascal — learned that atmospheric pressure decreases the higher you climb.*
14. *The three basic problems of flight are (1) developing necessary lift, (2) sustaining that lift and (3) controlling the aircraft once it is flying.*
15. *George Caley laid the foundation for modern aeronautics when he wrote, "The whole problem is confined within these limits; namely, to make a surface support a given weight by the application of power to the resistance of air."*
16. *Alphonse Penaud's greatest contribution to aviation was the development of the cambered wing.*
17. *John Montgomery was known as "The Father of Modern Aviation."*
18. *Wings having a front and a rear spar, with connecting ribs, were developed by John Stringfellow.*
19. *Samuel Pierpont Langley's aircraft* Aerodrome *was the first airplane to successfully fly after being launched from a catapult.*
20. *The Wright brothers solved the three basic problems of flight when their* Flyer *flew on December 17, 1903.*

Chapter 2 — THE ADOLESCENCE OF AIR POWER: 1904-1919

This chapter will look at the development of air power between 1904 and 1919 when aviation was in its adolescence. Many people were very interested in and enthusiastic about flying. Most people in the United States still looked at airplanes as toys and didn't understand that they could be put to practical use.

Meanwhile, in Europe, air power progressed more rapidly and there was a far greater understanding that aviation could be used in lots of ways.

Objectives

List significant aviation events occurring between 1904 and 1911.
Describe the development of new aircraft engines.
Recall Louis Bleriot's aviation contributions.
Discuss early attempts at vertical flight.
Discuss the story of the world's first regularly scheduled airline service.
Discuss air power preparations towards World War I.
Discuss the military role of the airplane in World War I.
Describe the use of bomber and fighter aircraft in World War I.
Identify several World War I aces.
Describe the impact Billy Mitchell had on the development of air power.

Developments in the United States

The Wright brothers' first successful powered flight went almost unnoticed throughout the world. Only one newspaper published an account of the flight and it was poorly written and misleading. The Wright brothers issued a public statement to the Associated Press on January 5, 1904. Unfortunately, this statement was either ignored or hidden deep inside the papers.

From 1904-1905, the Wright brothers continued trial flights from a pasture just outside Dayton, Ohio. They experimented and perfected their flying machines. In October 1905, they made a flight, which lasted 38 minutes and covered over 24 miles. It ended when the fuel supply was exhausted.

In 1905, the Wright brothers wrote a letter to the United States Government in Washington, D.C. They offered to build aircraft that would meet government needs. The response to their offer was unenthusiastic. After the Langley failures, the War Department did not want to be embarrassed again. When the War Department failed to accept their third offer, the Wright Brothers gave up trying to sell their invention to their own government.

When Theodore Roosevelt became President of the United States in 1904, he directed the Secretary of War to look into the possibility of testing the Wrights' new flying machines.

President Roosevelt's interest set into motion the contracting process with the War Department. With Wilbur Wright's help, the department drafted a public request for bids for an aircraft that could do seven things. It had to carry a pilot, a passenger and have fuel for a 125-mile trip. It also had to fly at least 36 mph under perfect control, and take off and land in any likely war zone without damage. Lastly, it had to be disassembled

The Wright brothers in Pau, France, in 1909 demonstrating their airplane, which had not attracted much attention in the United States.

Orville Wright tests plane for Army at Fort Myer, Virginia, September 9, 1908. The flight lasted 1 hour 2 1/2 minutes.

for transport by wagon and be reassembled in 1 hour.

In addition, the contract called for the Wrights to train two pilots for the Army. This public request for bids was merely a "red tape" formality. The Wrights were the only people with the knowledge to build such a craft at that time, and now they were in business.

As Orville got busy building a new plane for the Army tests, Wilbur went to France. There he demonstrated the Wright brothers' flying machine for European governments and businessmen. These demonstrations resulted in Wilbur signing a $100,000 contract to form a French

aircraft building company.

In September, Orville began his tests at Fort Myer, Virginia. His first flight took official Washington by storm. During the next 2 weeks, Orville completed 11 more flights. Every flight was more successful than the last.

Then tragedy struck on the thirteenth test. While conducting a test carrying Army Lieutenant Thomas Selfridge as a passenger, a propeller broke and the airplane crashed. Lieutenant Selfridge was killed. He was the first man to lose his life in a powered airplane. Orville was seriously hurt in the crash. He later recovered and completed the tests.

On August 2, 1909, the Army bought its first airplane from the Wright

Lieutenant Frank P. Lahm

brothers. The price was $25,000 plus a $5,000 bonus because the airplane exceeded the speed requirements. This was the Army's first heavier-than-air flying machine.

In October of that year, Wilbur met the final requirements of the United States Army contract by teaching Lieutenants Frank P. Lahm and Frederic E. Humphreys how to fly.

During this same time, another aviation pioneer was entering the scene. Glenn Curtiss (who, as a teenager in Hammondsport, New York, had tuned his natural engineering talents by building gasoline engines for the motorcycles he loved to race) was beginning to catch the interest of men in other fields. In 1907, Curtiss became known as the "Fastest Man on Earth" when he set the motorcycle speed record of 136.3 mph.

Glenn H. Curtiss

Curtiss' motorcycle engines were so light and powerful that Thomas Baldwin, a balloonist, asked Curtiss to build an engine for use on an airship. Baldwin's airship, with its Curtiss engine, became the first powered *dirigible* in the United States. Other balloonists soon followed Baldwin's lead and turned to Curtiss for engines for their ships. Another of his engines was used to power the first US Army aircraft—the *dirigible SC*-1.

It wasn't long until airplanes replaced motorcycles as Glenn Curtiss' first love, and the "fastest man on Earth" went into the business of making flying machines.

In 1907, Curtiss and Alexander Graham Bell (the inventor of the telephone) founded an organization

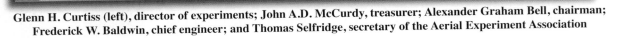

Glenn H. Curtiss (left), director of experiments; John A.D. McCurdy, treasurer; Alexander Graham Bell, chairman; Frederick W. Baldwin, chief engineer; and Thomas Selfridge, secretary of the Aerial Experiment Association

called the Aerial Experiment Association that designed and built several aircraft. One of them was the first American aircraft to be equipped with ailerons. Ailerons are small flaps on the wings that help control the plane.

Another one of their aircraft was the first seaplane to be flown in the United States. This plane could land and takeoff from water.

In 1908, Curtiss won the Scientific American Trophy in an aircraft called the *June Bug*. The *June Bug* made the first public flight of over one kilometer in the United States.

In 1909, at the Rheims Air Meet in France, Curtiss won the Gordon Bennett Trophy for flying the *Golden Flyer*, a plane he had just completed. He won the trophy for flying the fastest two laps around a triangular 6.21-mile course averaging 47 mph.

Glenn Curtiss wins the Scientific American trophy on July 4, 1908, by flying over a measured course of one-kilometer.

In 1910, both the Wrights and Curtiss opened flying schools. The Wright brothers had delivered their airplane to the Army and trained the first two Army pilots.

In November 1910, Eugene Ely made the first flight from the deck of a ship at Hampton Roads, Virginia, in a Curtiss biplane. He later accomplished the more difficult feat of landing his aircraft on a wooden platform on the United States naval ship *U.S.S. Pennsylvania*.

Also in 1910, former President Theodore Roosevelt took an airplane ride in St. Louis, Missouri. He became the first US President to fly.

In 1911, William Randolph Hearst, publisher of the *Hearst* newspapers, offered a prize of $50,000 for a flight across the United States completed in 30 days. Calbraith Perry Rodgers, grandnephew of Commodore Oliver H. Perry, US naval hero of the War of 1812, decided to try for the prize.

Rodgers persuaded a company that made a popular soft drink called Vin Fiz, to sponsor and help pay for the attempt. The company thought it would make great publicity value for Vin Fiz and agreed to help pay for a Wright plane. Rodgers named the plane the *Vin Fiz Flyer*. A specially trained team, with spare parts, followed him across the country.

Rodgers knew the trip would be hard, so he looked for a superior mechanic who could be relied upon to keep his plane in good repair. He asked Charles Taylor, the Wright brothers'

The Curtiss *Golden Flyer*, powered by a 50 hp engine, won the first Gordon Bennett Cup in 1909.

mechanic, to take the job. The Wrights were extremely reluctant to let Taylor go, but Rodgers had offered him considerably more money than he was getting from the Wrights. Taylor was so eager to go that Orville finally agreed, but only on the condition that Taylor consider himself on loan so that he would come back to work for the Wright brothers.

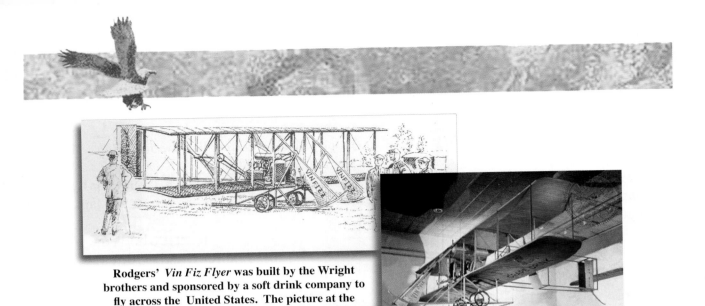

Rodgers' *Vin Fiz Flyer* was built by the Wright brothers and sponsored by a soft drink company to fly across the United States. The picture at the right shows the *Vin Fiz* in the Smithsonian.

Rodgers' flight started from Sheepshead Bay, on Long Island, on September 17, 1911. The sponsoring company helped plan the route. It went roughly from New York to Chicago, Kansas City, San Antonio, El Paso, Yuma, and then Pasadena, California. The trip planned to cover more than 3,390 miles. Rodgers had some problems with the route. For example, the small 40-horsepower engine would have problems

A poster distributed by the soda pop manufacturer traces Rodgers' 1911 transcontinental marathon and lists the statistics.

getting over the huge Rocky Mountains. Rodgers learned that there were only a few places where he could fly across the Rockies.

Rodgers took off from Long Island and flew day after day. Some days he had trouble making 40 mph because of head winds. Before the trip ended, he had made 68 landings—some of them severe crack-ups. His plane had to be repaired so many times that the only a very few pieces of the orginial Vin Fiz made it all the way.

Rodgers' actual flying distance was 4,251 miles. His longest single flight was 133 miles, and his average flying speed was just under 52 mph. After reaching Pasadena on November 5, he flew on to the ocean where he rolled his plane along the beach and wet the wheels in the Pacific. Unfortunately, he missed the prize because the trip had taken 49 days.

An automobile or a train would have made much better time. However, Rodgers made it. He made the first airplane crossing of the United States from coast to coast.

By today's standards, this flight may not sound like much of an achievement. However, in 1911, it was a remarkable feat. Rodgers' plane would not compare favorably with today's sturdy aircraft. Plus, he had no prepared landing fields, no advance weather information, no special instruments, and inadequate supplies and facilities. Calbraith Perry Rodgers was indeed a skillful and heroic pilot.

During this same time period, American women entered the field of flying. It was during the Belmont Park Aviation Meet in October 1910, that a young woman writer, Harriet Quimby, became interested in aviation. She signed up for flying lessons with an instructor named Alfred Moisant.

In August 1911, Harriet Quimby became America's first licensed female pilot. She also became a member of the Moisant International Aviators, an organization designed to advance the science of aviation.

Harriet Quimby became America's first licensed female pilot.

She became a strong advocate of aviation. Believing the United States was falling behind other nations in the field of aviation, she used her writing talents to urge the country to give more attention to commercial aviation and aeronautical development.

Later, she made history again. On April 16, 1912, Harriet Quimby took off from the English Coast into a cold and foggy sky, and landed about 30 minutes later at Hardelot, France. With this flight, she became the first woman to fly solo across the English Channel.

Unfortunately, in July 1, 1912, she died when she was flying with a passenger at the Harvard-Boston Aviation Meet. Harriet Quimby lost control of a Bleriot monoplane, and both she and her passenger fell to their deaths.

Progress in Europe

The Wright brothers' wing-warping technique was a clumsy method to control the airplane. In Europe, a Frenchman named Robert Esnault-Pelterie built a Wright-style glider in 1904 and used ailerons to replace the wing-warping technique. Although Matthew P. W. Boulton had described the operation of ailerons in his 1868 British patent (No. 392), no one had actually built the devices to control lateral balance and control until Esnault-Pelterie's 1904 glider. His use of ailerons encouraged designers in several nations to experiment with their own aileron designs. It was Esnault-Pelterie who also built the first fully enclosed fuselage airplane.

Alberto Santos-Dumont flew the first powered airplane in Europe. His aircraft, the 14-*bis* biplane, which looked like two huge box kites, was successfully flown in Paris, France, on October 23, 1906.

Two weeks later, he again flew his airplane — this time traveling 722 feet. Unlike the negative press reaction that flying was receiving in the United States, the press reported this flight favorably. As a result, all of Europe was excited by the news.

**The first successful powered flight in Europe was made by
Alberto Santos-Dumont in the 14-*bis* biplane on October 23, 1906.**

In 1907, Louis Bleriot, built and flew the world's first powered monoplane. Then in 1909, two major events attracted worldwide attention to aviation. The first was the flight across the English Channel by Bleriot in his *Bleriot* XI, and the second was the first international air meet held in Rheims, France.

Bleriot, a man of great determination, built 11 planes before getting one that was good enough to make the trip across the English Channel. While testing his planes, he had almost 50 crashes, but he refused to give up.

For his flight across the English Channel, he took off from the coast of France, near Calais. Unfortunately, he had no compass for the 25-mile trip, and 10 minutes after his takeoff, he was lost. All he could see was sky and water—not a landmark in sight.

When he finally saw the cliffs of Dover in the distance, he noticed that his engine was running hot. As Bleriot listened to the roar of his overheated engine, he searched the water below him hoping to find a ship that would be close enough to pick him up if he had to ditch before he could reach the coast of England.

He saw no ship, but he saw a small storm and flew into a rain shower. The rain cooled the overheated engine. Thirty-seven minutes after taking off in France, Bleriot landed not far from the spot that had been the starting point for the balloon crossing of the English Channel by Jeffries and Blanchard 124 years earlier. Word of his historic flight soon spread throughout Europe and the United States, and he became quite famous.

Louis Bleriot, the *Bleriot* XI builder, is pictured just prior to his flight across the English Channel.

The *Bleriot* XI was the world's first monoplane.

Less than a month later, the first international air meet was held in Rheims, France, August 22-28, 1909. Thirty-six planes competed in the contest. During the week of the meet, several of the planes crashed, but luckily no one was killed or seriously injured. Many of these pilots broke several records. One was an endurance record, set by Henri Farman, who stayed in the air 3 hours 4 minutes 56 seconds. Meanwhile, Bleriot made the best time for a single lap—47.8 mph.

Another aviation accomplishment during this time was the development of the first multiengine aircraft.

There are two reasons for building aircraft with more than one engine. One is to increase the aircraft's power, and the second is to improve reliability and safety. Two engines can provide more

power than one, and if one engine fails in flight, there is another to provide power until a safe landing can be made.

During the early days of aviation, both of these reasons were justified. The engines did not supply that much power for their relative weight and often stopped while the aircraft was in flight.

In 1911, the Short brothers of England were granted patents for the world's first multiengine aircraft. It had two engines and three propellers, and was called the *Triple Twin*. The two engines were mounted in tandem, one in front of the cockpit and one behind. The front engine drove two propellers attached to the wings. The rear engine drove a single pusher propeller.

The first four-engine aircraft was built and flown by the great Russian designer and pilot, Igor Sikorsky, on May 13, 1913. This aircraft was a giant of its time. It had a wingspan of 92 feet. Four 100-horsepower engines powered the aircraft, and because of its large size, its landing gear had 16 wheels.

Igor Sikorsky designed and flew the first 4-engine aircraft named *LeGrand*. This painting of *LeGrand* once hung in the Canadian National Aviation Museum.

Other innovations included a fully enclosed cockpit. It protected the pilot from the weather. It also had a passenger cabin with portholes for windows. The *LeGrand,* as this aircraft was called, was an imaginative forerunner of the modern airliner.

Another important development in aircraft engines also occurred during this time period. Early aircraft engines were manufactured out of steel, cast iron, and brass and were water-cooled. This resulted in engines that were very heavy. They generally weighed about 10 pounds for every horsepower they produced. These large heavy engines not only reduced performance, but also required a heavy structure to support the weight of the engine.

In an effort to overcome this problem, in 1907, two French brothers, Laurent and Gustav Seguin, developed an engine they called the *Gnome.* The *Gnome* was an air-cooled engine with the cylinders arranged in a radial (round) fashion. The cylinders had cooling fins that helped bleed the heat into the surrounding air.

The Seguins realized they had to have some way to circulate the air around the cylinders even while the aircraft was sitting still. They accomplished this by fastening the crankshaft solidly to the airframe, and allowing the engine and the attached propeller to spin around the fixed crankshaft. This is exactly the opposite of modern radial engines where the engine is fixed and the propeller is attached to the rotating crankshaft. Because of this unique method of operation, these engines were called rotary engines.

Rotary engines, like the *Gnome* and the later *Le Rhone*, were an instant success and weighed only about 3 pounds for each horsepower produced. It was later discovered that it was not necessary to rotate the cylinders to achieve cooling, but many World War I aircraft, such as the Sopwith *Pup* and Sopwith *Camel* were powered by rotary engines.

Moving Up - Flying Vertical

While the balloon and airplane pioneers were building their "flying machines," others were experimenting in another area of flight. These pioneers dreamed of being able to takeoff and land vertically. Their experiments would lead to the modern-day helicopter.

We have already mentioned the three basic problems of flight in Chapter 1. Later on you will study how lift is produced and sustained in heavier-than-air crafts. Here we will simply say that in heavier-than-air crafts, the lift is produced by the wing. Also, in order to sustain lift, the wing must continuously move through the air.

In a fixed-wing aircraft, the forward motion of the aircraft causes the wing to move through the air and produce lift. For helicopters, there is another method of moving the wing through the air. The large rotor (propeller) on top of a helicopter is made up of a number of blades. Each of these rotor blades is just like a wing. As the rotor whirls, the blades move through the air causing lift. Helicopters are called rotary-wing aircraft because of the way that the wings (blades) rotate.

Paul Cornu's Helicopter

Many aviation pioneers already mentioned, such as Roger Bacon, Leonardo da Vinci, and George Cayley, experimented with helicopters. None of them, however, went any further than building and flying models. But it was these models that validated the rotary-wing concept.

In 1842, W. H. Phillips built and successfully flew a model helicopter powered by steam jets at the rotor tips. The first helicopter to lift a man into the air was flown in 1907. This machine was built and flown by a Frenchman named Louis Breguet. Although it lifted him, it was held steady by four assistants.

In that same year, another Frenchman, Paul Cornu, also "flew" a helicopter. In 1909, a father and son—Emile and Henry Berliner— became the first Americans to build and fly a helicopter.

All of these early experimenters were plagued by problems of controlling the helicopter while in flight. The major control problem to be overcome was counteracting the torque of the rotor blade. When the rotor of a helicopter is turning, the rest of the machine tends to spin in the opposite direction.

One way to overcome the torque is to have two rotors that rotate in opposite directions. Another is to provide a small propeller at the end of a long tail boom (tail rotor), which provides thrust to counteract the torque of the main rotor. This problem of control would continue to haunt the designers for more than 30 years before being solved.

Commercial Flying - The Beginning

On January 1, 1914, the world's first regularly scheduled airline service using heavier-than-air craft was started in the United States. This airline was called the "St. Petersburg - Tampa Airboat Line." It was flown by Tony Jannus in a twin-engine *Benoist* XIV flying boat, which carried two passengers. The 22-mile flight across Tampa Bay cost $5 and took about 20 minutes. The airline flew the route twice a day for about 5 months and carried a total of 1,200 passengers.

The first regularly scheduled airline flew the *Benoist* XIV flying boat.

Preparing for War

By 1912, all the major modern countries of the world had formed a military flying service. In the United States, it was present in name only. While other nations of the world made advances in military aviation, almost no progress was made in the United States.

The US Army had purchased a single Wright biplane in 1908, and for 3 years, this one airplane was the entire "Air Force." Then, in 1911, Congress appropriated funds to purchase five more airplanes. By the end of 1913, there were 19 aircraft and 29 pilots in the US Army.

In 1914, when World War I started in Europe, Germany had about 200 aircraft in its Air Force. Britain and France possessed about 450. More importantly, they also had the industry needed to make more aircraft.

The Wright Brothers' Military Flyer Known as *Signal Corps No. 1*

The United States did not enter World War I until 1917. Even with 3 years to prepare, the United States still did not have a single combat-worthy aircraft when it entered the war. To make the situation even worse, Curtiss Aircraft was the only company in the United States that could be considered an aviation industry.

In 1917, Congress appropriated $64 million for construction of aircraft—boasting that we would "darken the skies over Europe with US aircraft." Congress promised that 263 American squadrons equipped with 22,625 aircraft would be in action by June 1918. However, when the war ended in November 1918, there were only 45 American squadrons in action, and they were all flying British and French aircraft. Not a single American-designed combat aircraft saw action in World War I.

The United States wound up building some British-designed *DH*-4 aircraft that saw some action from September 1918 until the end of the war in November.

This was the first example of the shortsightedness of the United States Congress with regard to aviation. Unfortunately, this mistake would be repeated over and over again. What Congress overlooked was that the United States did not possess the engineers to design the aircraft, the industry to build them or the instructors and planes with which to train the pilots. Without these resources, there would be no strong US aviation industry.

World War I

Military Role of the Airplane

Throughout the history of aviation, the greatest progress in flight has been made during times when either war or the threat of war was present. When the war started in 1914, the average airplane had a speed of 70 to 80 mph and could not go higher than about 10,000 feet. By the time World War I ended, the speed of aircraft had increased to 140 to 150 mph, and they could operate up to about 24,000 feet.

There have been very few revolutions in military affairs. It is rare when a new weapon or a new way of thinking completely changes the way wars are fought. The airplane was one of those few weapon systems that changed warfare, but it took a while to do it. In World War I, the real revolution

in military affairs took place with the advent of the tank and the machine gun. These weapons changed the way wars were fought.

Large armies that tried to destroy the enemies' weakest link by either out maneuvering them or destroying them head-on typically fought wars. These large armies would face off in large open battlefields. The advent of the machine gun and later the tank changed the way wars were fought.

Armies could no longer line up and merely fight it out. They had to dig in. So the airplane also changed the way wars were fought. When the enemy started to dig in, an airplane could fly overhead and use its mastery of the air and space domain to gain a new and previously unknown advantage.

The German *Fokker D-7* of World War I *(EAA)*

The airplane was first used in the same role as balloons had been in earlier wars. They were used for observation. This role required aircraft that were slow and stable. The pilot or observer could study and photograph activity on the ground. Aircraft, such as the British *BE*-2 and *Avro* 504, the French *Morane* and *Farman*, and the German *Taube* and *Albatros*, were excellent for this type of mission.

These airplanes usually carried no guns. If an allied observer met an enemy aircraft, the pilots would salute each other with a respect for each other's skill and mastery of the sky.

As war progressed, there were a few bombing attempts. Bomber aircraft were observation aircraft with the pilot or an observer carrying small bombs on his lap. These bombs were released by hand with very poor accuracy.

The German *Albatros D*-II had a plywood fuselage and two machine guns. *(EAA)*

During the war, the first long-range strategic bombing raid was made by three British *Avro* 504s against the German *Zeppelin* storage sheds at Lake Constance in southern Germany. There was little damage done, but the raid did cause the Germans to form their first bombing squadron.

By 1915, the Germans were raiding behind allied lines in France, and later began bombing London using both dirigibles and airplanes.

Europe in World War I

At the beginning of World War I, the German Army had 20 large *dirigibles*, 9 built by Zeppelin and 11 by other German manufacturers. During the war an additional 88 *Zeppelins* were produced. Germany's plans were to use these airships as strategic bombers against French and English cities. On August 9, 1915, they made their first raids over London.

Early German Airship

The raids were very accurate with their bombing, but because the airships were filled with highly flammable hydrogen, the slightest damage caused them to burst into flames. Because of their vulnerability to anti-aircraft fire from the ground and the air, they began flying only at night.

By 1916, it was clear that a replacement was necessary, and it came in the form of a large twin-engine bomber called the *Gotha* IV. Beginning in April 1917, these bombers dropped tons of bombs on English cities and factories.

Although these raids caused considerable damage and many deaths, the most important impact was that the English had to recall some of their fighter squadrons from France to protect the homeland.

Another outcome of the German air raids was the formation of the Independent Bombing Force within the British Royal Flying Corps. This was the first and only Allied flying force during World War I that was not under the command of an infantry trained general officer.

This same organization went on to later become the Royal Air Force (RAF) that we know today. It was created independent of and equal to the British Army and Navy.

By the time the war ended, strategic bombing (bombing enemy territory) had grown from a few observation planes with the pilots dropping small handheld bombs to large, specially designed bombers capable of carrying up to 6,000 pounds of bombs.

Fighter Development

As more and more bombing raids took place, it became clear that control of the air was needed. Fighter or pursuit aircraft were needed to drive off the bombers.

At first, the armament of these "fighters" consisted of the pilot shooting at the enemy with a pistol or rifle. In 1915, a French pilot, Roland Garros, mounted an automatic rifle on his aircraft so he could fire forward through the propeller. To keep from shooting off his own propeller, the rear of the prop was armored with steel plates to deflect the bullets.

As primitive as this device was, it was quite effective because, for the first time, the pilot could aim his guns by flying directly at the enemy.

April 1915, Garros was shot down behind the German lines, and his aircraft was captured. After examining his armored propeller, the Germans gave a Dutch airplane designer, Anthony Fokker, the task of improving this device.

Fokker designed an interrupting gear which connected a machine gun to the aircraft engine and prevented the gun from firing when a propeller blade was lined up with the gun's muzzle. This allowed the machine gun to be fired through the spinning propeller. For nearly a year, this invention gave the Germans almost total control of the air.

The Allies tried mounting their machine guns on top of the wing to fire over the propeller. This was not successful because it slowed the aircraft due to the increased drag.

In April 1916, a German aircraft equipped with this interrupting gear was captured and the Allies soon copied it. This was the start of the great "dog fight" era of air battles.

As aircraft engaged more and more in dog fighting, it became obvious that the fighter aircraft needed to be light, fast and very maneuverable. Some of the famous fighters developed during World War I included the Sopwith *Camel* and the *SE-5A* by the British, the *Spad* VII and *Nieuport* 28 by the French and the German *Fokker Dr*-I and *D*-VII.

One of the greatest technical accomplishments of World War I occurred too late to affect the outcome of the war. In May 1918, the German designer, Hugo Junkers, built the world's first all-metal, low-wing monoplane fighter called the *Junkers D*1. Only 45 were manufactured before the war ended. Few people realized they were seeing the fighter of the future.

The Sopwith *Triplane* could "turn on a dime." *(EAA)*

Fighter Aces

As aerial combat increased, the French developed a method of recognizing pilots who shot down many enemy aircraft. They coined the term "ace" for a pilot who shot down five enemy aircraft. This same number was adopted by the British and Americans. The Germans, however, required 10 enemy aircraft be downed before recognizing the pilot as an ace.

The term "ace of aces" was a designation given to the pilot from each nation with the most "kills." Included as ace of aces during World War I were Edward V. Rickenbacker, American (26 victories); René Fonck, French (75 victories); Edward Mannock, British (73 victories); and Baron Manfred von Richthofen, German (80 victories).

French "ace," René Fonck, shot down 75 enemy aircraft during WWI.

Captain "Eddie" Rickenbacker, America's Ace of Aces

The United States in World War I

World War I began in Europe in 1914, but the United States did not enter the war until 1917. Quite a few American pilots did not wait for their own country to declare war. Instead, they found ways to get into the flying services of other nations already engaged in combat. Most nations had some legal

difficulties in accepting the services of these American "foreigners," but France did not. The famous French Foreign Legion was willing and able to accept volunteers from other nations.

When the war broke out, seven wealthy young Americans living in Paris volunteered to fly for France. These Americans worked as a group and named themselves the Lafayette Escadrille, in honor of the French nobleman who lent his services to the Americans during the Revolutionary War.

By March 1917, the month before the United States formally entered World War I, only one of the original members of the Lafayette Escadrille was still living. By the time the war ended, 40 of the gallant Americans responsible for the Escadrille's fighting fame had given their lives for the French and Allied cause. Six of these Americans achieved "ace" status while flying for the French Air Service.

At first, the Lafayette Escadrille was viewed by the French largely as a propaganda device for winning American support for the war effort. The brave Americans, however, proved their value as fighting men. Before their unit was incorporated into the United States Army Air Service in February 1918, the Escadrille scored 199 confirmed victories.

One of the most widely known and most popular of the American flyers was Raoul Lufberry, a native Frenchman who had become an American citizen. He was one of several American citizens serving with the French Air Service who later joined the all-American Lafayette Escadrille.

Lufberry scored 17 victories during the war. He always advised his pilots to stay with their planes, even if they began to burn, which was one of the most dangerous possibilities. In those days, the fabric-covered aircraft burned very easily. On May 19, 1918, however, he ignored his own advice and paid the full price. Lufberry's aircraft was hit by enemy bullets and began to burn. Two hundred feet above the ground, he jumped, apparently aiming at a nearby stream. Instead, he landed on a picket fence and was killed.

Raoul Lufberry, was a French-born, American citizen who flew with the Lafayette Escadrille.

Eddie Rickenbacker, a former racing car driver, learned from Lufberry the value of watching the sky all around for enemy planes. He also learned that a flight patrol leader's main duty is to take care of his men.

The American 94th and 95th Squadrons were flying unarmed planes. When the French authorities learned that the Americans were flying unarmed aircraft, they quickly supplied them with machine guns.

The Americans began shooting down German airplanes, and Rickenbacker quickly accumulated five victories. After his fourth victory, Rickenbacker was named Commander of the 94th Squadron. He equipped his men with parachutes, solved a troublesome problem of jamming guns, and then kept his squadron atop the list of effectiveness against the enemy.

His 26 kills came in only 5 months of flying. Rickenbacker mastered aerial combat tactics just as he had mastered automobile driving tactics on dirt tracks and, later, on the speedway at Indianapolis.

If Rickenbacker and Lufberry knew the value of discipline and planning, Frank Luke was their opposite. Luke has been described as "an undisciplined, carefree maverick, . . . absolutely impervious to any squadron regulations." However, he was extremely confident of his abilities. He accomplished one of the most amazing feats of the war by destroying 15 enemy balloons and 3 planes within 17 days. German planes and their antiaircraft guns heavily guarded the balloons. These balloons were regarded by pilots as the most dangerous and difficult targets of all.

Luke was a loner. After one last spree in which he downed three balloons and two planes on the same raid, he did not return to his base. Luke had been wounded and went off by himself. He ran into enemy soldiers and strafed and killed six Germans on the ground, and wounded an equal number.

He then landed his plane and went to a stream to get

Many German pilots saw the French *Nieuport* 17 when they looked over their shoulders in air combat. *(EAA)*

a drink of water. He was discovered by a German foot patrol. He drew his revolver to defend himself, but was killed by the soldiers.

Many aviators earned fame through combat in World War I. One man who was very influential in aviation in that war, and who made a giant contribution to aviation tactics later, was not a famous fighter pilot at all, but a student of air power and its use. His name was Billy Mitchell.

Mitchell, son of a United States senator, grew up in Milwaukee, Wisconsin. One of his boyhood friends was Douglas MacArthur who, during World War II and the Korean War, won worldwide fame for outstanding service in the United States Army. By applying his considerable intelligence and abilities, Mitchell started breaking records at an early age.

He was the youngest student ever to enter George Washington University when he enrolled in 1895. He became a second lieutenant

Air Force General, Billy Mitchell, got his start in air combat during WWI.

in the Wisconsin Volunteers at age 18 and was promoted to first lieutenant a year later. By 1903, at the age of 23, he had become the youngest captain in the Army.

In 1909, he completed the Army Staff College and was a distinguished graduate. When he was 32 years old, he was ordered to Washington to serve on the War Department's general staff. Once again, he was the youngest officer ever given this assignment.

Mitchell's interest in aviation started after the beginning of World War I in 1914. He spent much of his time on the general staff in Washington urging for a separate and independent air service. On his own time, he studied flying at the Curtiss Company's School at Newport News, Virginia. He became a pilot at the age of 36. In those days, 36 was considered quite old for flying.

As the war progressed in Europe, Mitchell steadily climbed in rank and responsibilities, finally becoming Chief of the Air Service for the American forces in Europe. He did his best to get first-rate aircraft and mechanics for American pilots.

As a trained pilot himself, he tested British and French planes before he would accept them for his fliers. He rejected the Sopwith *Camel* because its rotary engine gave the plane a tendency to whip into a right-hand spin, and his pilots were not sufficiently experienced to control it. Later, United States pilots flew *Camels*.

Mitchell studied air power enthusiastically and met the leading theorists personally. From his friend, General Hugh Trenchard, Commander of the British Royal Flying Corps, Mitchell learned to think of the airplane as an offensive weapon, best used in giant fleets of bombers striking against the enemy's homeland.

Mitchell's Air Power Theory

Mitchell held the title of Chief of the Air Service, but control of the air wing was still totally in the hands of the Army. Mitchell saw aviation as a military effort to help the ground forces. He did not think that this could best be achieved by being subservient to them.

Most ground officers, however, thought of the Air Service as an auxiliary to the land troops. Airplanes were thought to be useful for keeping an eye on enemy infantry movements, and for keeping enemy airplanes away from friendly troops. Army officers of that time, of course, had been trained for ground warfare. So, it was often difficult to make a case for a strong and independent air service.

Billy Mitchell slowly gained favor with certain folks, but his outspokenness made him some enemies, too. He thought the air service should be separate from the Army so that it could "command the sky." Once his airplanes had command of the sky, they could be used offensively against the enemy's troops.

His influence was great on the American flying squadrons, some of whose members were to rise to later prominence. Those men carried Mitchell's teachings forward and made a great impact on the conduct of air warfare in World War II.

In September 1918, Mitchell commanded the first mass use of aircraft for bombing attacks on enemy supply routes and for supporting the ground troops. This attack involved nearly 1500 allied airplanes and was important in deciding the outcome of the war. However, it was not until after the war that Mitchell was able to demonstrate the effectiveness of the air weapon against naval vessels. Although Mitchell was forced to sacrifice his military career for his beliefs, he unquestionably had a large influence on aviation's golden age.

Because World War I was fought in Europe, the American public was isolated from the actual battlefield. Except for the American troops serving in Europe, Americans were unaware of the increasing importance of air power during World War I. Therefore, when the war ended, the United States was the only nation involved in the war that had not learned the most important lesson taught by World War I—*If you control the air, you cannot be beaten; if you lose the air, you cannot win.*

Key Terms and Concepts

- early pioneers of flight
- Signal Corps Aeronautical Division
- Aerial Experiment Association
- aviation development in the United States
- aviation development in Europe
- development of helicopters
- development of commercial aviation
- military role of the airplane in WWI
- fighter aircraft development during the WWI era
- legacy of Billy Mitchell

? Test Your Knowledge ?

SELECT THE CORRECT ANSWER

1. **(Robert Esnault-Pelterie / Matthew P.W. Boulton)** *built a Wright-style glider in 1904 and used ailerons to replace the wing-warping technique.*
2. **(Henri Farman / Alberto Santos-Dumont)** *flew the first powered aircraft in Europe.*
3. *Louis Bleriot was the first person to fly across the* **(English Channel / Atlantic Ocean).**
4. *The first international air meet was held at* **(Kitty Hawk, NC / Rheims, France).**
5. *The first four engine aircraft was built and flown by* **(Igor Sikorsky / Louis Bleriot).**
6. *One problem with early aircraft engines was that they were too* **(heavy / light).**

MATCHING

7. *French "ace of aces."*
8. *Former race car driver.*
9. *Dutch airplane designer.*
10. *British "ace of aces."*
11. *Commanded first mass-air bombing attack.*
12. *Member of the Lafayette Escadrille.*

   a. **Anthony Fokker**
   b. **Edward Mannock**
   c. **Raoul Lufberry**
   d. **Eddie Rickenbacker**
   e. **René Fonck**
   f. **Billy Mitchell**

TRUE OR FALSE

13. *The War Department was enthusiastic with the Wright brothers' offer to build airplanes for the government.*
14. *Before Glenn Curtiss became interested in aviation, he was a motorcycle racer.*
15. *Eugene Ely made the first flight from the deck of a ship.*
16. *Calbraith Perry Rodgers was the first person to fly nonstop across the United States.*
17. *The first woman to fly solo across the English Channel was Mathilde Moisant.*
18. *Helicopters are called rotary-wing aircraft because the wings (blades) rotate.*
19. *The first helicopter to lift a man into the air was built and flown by Henry Berliner.*
20. *The Soviet Union began regularly scheduled airline service on January 1, 1914.*
21. *By 1914, the United States had the most powerful flying service in the world.*
22. *The United States produced several American-designed combat aircraft during World War I.*
23. *At the beginning of World War I, the airplane was used primarily for observation.*
24. *The first bombing raids carried out by the Germans in World War I were done with the* Gotha *IV.*

25. *In World War I, fighter aircraft were used to drive off attacking bombers.*
26. *Eddie Rickenbacker was America's "ace of aces" in World War I.*
27. *The Lafayette Escadrille was composed of France's greatest aces.*
28. *A lesson learned in World War I was — If you control the air, you can not be beaten; if you lose the air, you cannot win.*

The 20-year period between the end of World War I and the beginning of World War II has been called the "Golden Age of Aviation." During this period, there were many exciting and dramatic exploits by daring aviators from many lands.New speed and altitude records were set, broken and reset, over and over again. There were oceans and continents to cross, and each accomplishment led to someone who wanted to do it better and faster. The airplane changed from a slow, wood-framed, fabric-covered biplane to a fast, sleek, all-metal monoplane.

bjectives

Describe the problems associated with the first attempts to cross the Atlantic Ocean.

Discuss the successful crossings of the Atlantic Ocean in 1919.

Recall how the United States cut back on investing in air power after World War I.

Describe the impact that barnstorming had on the development of air power.

Recognize the advantage air power has over ships.

Describe the military's attempt to fly across the American continent.

Describe the impact that the around-the-world flight had on the development of air power.

Identify what led the Navy to develop the aircraft carrier.

Recall the impact the National Air Races had on the development of air power.

Recall the impact of airmail delivery on the development of commercial aviation.

Discuss the importance of the Air Mail Act of 1925, the Air Commerce Act of 1926, the Air Mail Act of 1934, and the Air Mail Act of 1938.

Recognize the importance Charles Lindbergh's historic flight had on the development of civil aviation.

Identify the achievements of Amelia Earhart.

Explain the importance of Jimmy Doolittle's blind takeoff and landing.

Discuss the contributions Dr. Goddard made to the advancement of air and space power.

Discuss the impact of the McNary-Watres Act on the development of commercial aviation.

Identify the standard commercial airliner in 1938.

Identify the aircraft that flew across the Atlantic with no fatal accidents in 1938.

Discuss the most famous dirigible of all.

The Curtiss JN 4 *Jenny* (EAA)

Flying the Atlantic

The first natural barrier to be challenged was the Atlantic Ocean, and it was conquered in 1919. The first attempt to cross the Atlantic was made by the United States Navy flying three new Curtiss flying boats. The flight was to be made in four stages: from Rockaway, New York, to Trepassey, Newfoundland; to the Azores; to Lisbon, Portugal; to Plymouth, England.

The NC-1, NC-3 and NC-4, commanded by Lieutenant Commander R. Bellinger, Commander J. Towers, and Lieutenant Commander Albert Read, respectively, left Rockaway on May 8, 1919, and all arrived safely at Trepassey. The next stage was the critical one. It was the long flight to the Azores. They had to cross 1,200 miles over water. As a safeguard, naval vessels stretched 50 miles apart along the proposed route. If the planes remained on their course, an emergency landing would find them no more than 25 miles from help.

On May 16, 1919, the three planes took off from Trepassey. Over the Atlantic that night, they occasionally saw each other's lights and checked their courses by radio or by the rockets and searchlights of the destroyers marking the way. The next day, a thick fog settled in. Both Commander Bellinger in the NC-1 and Commander Towers in the NC-3 landed on the water to check their navigation.

In waves as much as 12 feet high, Commander Towers was able to land without serious damage to his craft. The plane was off course, southwest of its destination. The crew found that they could not takeoff in the heavy seas, and they were barely able to keep the plane afloat. They finally "taxied" the plane to Horta, Azores, which took 3 days on rough seas. The plane was so badly damaged that it was not able to continue the flight.

The NC-1 came down after flying 850 miles. It was badly damaged in the landing and began to break up in the water. A steamship rescued the crew. A naval destroyer tried to take the plane in tow, but it sank.

Commander Read, in the NC-4, kept to the air and came roaring down into the harbor of Horta, Azores, 15 hours and 18 minutes after leaving Trepassey.

On May 20, 1919, Commander Read and his crew flew on to Ponta Delgada, a 1-hour and 44-minute flight. On May 27, they flew on to Lisbon, Portugal, reaching there in 9 hours and 43 minutes. The total flying time for the Atlantic crossing Newfoundland to Portugal, was 26 hours and 45 minutes.

Sikorsky S-38C *Flying Boat. (EAA)*

On May 30, the NC-4 proceeded up the coast with stops at the Mondego River and at Ferrol, Spain. The next morning they landed at Plymouth near the spot where the *Mayflower* had moored 300 years before. The total airline distance from Rockaway was 3,936 miles. The total flying time was 52 hours and 31 minutes. This was the first transatlantic crossing. Amazingly, just 2 weeks later, the first nonstop crossing of the Atlantic was made.

In 1913, the *London Daily Mail* made a standing offer of $50,000 to the crew of the first airplane that could make a nonstop crossing of the Atlantic, starting from either side, and lasting no longer than 72 hours. Because of the war, no one attempted to win the prize until the spring of 1919. The first team to make the attempt was Harry Hawker, an Austrian war hero, and his navigator, Lieutenant Commander Kenneth McKenzie-Grieve of the Royal Navy. Their attempt ended in failure.

The second pair of hopefuls was Captain John Alcock and Lieutenant Arthur Whitten Brown. While Hawker and McKenzie were leaving Trepassey, John Alcock and Arthur Whitten Brown, with their Vickers-Vimy converted bomber, were on a steamship headed for Newfoundland. Brown, who was born in America, was a veteran of the Royal Air Force, as was Captain John Alcock. Both had outstanding war records. They reached St. John's, Newfoundland, on May 24.

This was the day before it became known that Hawker and McKenzie-Grieve had been rescued, and 3 days before the NC-4 reached Lisbon. It looked as if they still had a chance to win the *London Daily Mail* prize and also be the first to cross the Atlantic, but they were grounded for several days. The first delay was caused by bad weather and the second by needed radio repairs.

They took off at 4:28 p.m. on June 14, 1919, with 856 gallons of gasoline aboard. Their plane weighed 13,500 pounds; and the two 350-horsepower Rolls Royce engines were barely able to lift it over a fence at the end of the runway. With the help of a 30-mph tail wind, the plane was soon headed for Ireland at a speed of 120 mph.

When the aviators were scarcely out of sight of land, they ran into heavy fog. During the first 7 hours, they had only occasional glimpses of sea or sky. Later, the visibility became even worse. Once, at 4,000 feet, the plane went into a spin, and Alcock had difficulty pulling it out in time to prevent a crash.

As they flew on, the weather seemed to get worse. Snow and sleet clogged the radiator, and ice threatened to overload the plane. The radio quit early in the flight. This made it impossible for them to get bearings from ships and navigate as they had planned. When Brown was finally able to determine their position, he was delighted to find out that they were extremely lucky. They were on course and nearing Ireland. Soon they saw the islands of Turbot and Eashal, off the Irish coast. Next, they recognized the masts of the radio station at Clifden. They circled over the station, but no one appeared to see them.

Soon they discovered what appeared to be a meadow suitable for a landing place. It turned out to be a bog. When they landed, the front wheels disappeared and the nose of the plane plowed into the ground. Fortunately, neither Alcock nor Brown was injured, and they managed to get themselves out from the muck without too much difficulty.

It was then 8:40 a.m. on June 15. This was 16 hours and 12 minutes since they had left St. John's. They had traveled 1,880 miles at an average speed of almost 2 miles a minute to make the first nonstop crossing of the Atlantic and win the $50,000. This accomplishment of 1919 was a remarkable advance over the achievements of 1903.

Investing In Air Power

All of the nations involved in World War I built great aviation industries. During the war, France built 67,987 aircraft, Britain 58,144, Germany 48,537 and Italy about 20,000. Even the United States built 15,000, Austria-Hungary 5,431 and Russia 4,700 airplanes during the 21 months it was involved in the war. The British production had increased from an average of about 20 per month at the beginning of the war, to 3,500 per month when the war ended.

When World War I ended on November 11, 1918, there were over 177,000 aircraft in service in Europe. Despite our slow start, America's front-line strength consisted of 750 combat aircraft and 800 pilots. There were an additional 3,000 training aircraft and a total of about 9,500 men in the Air Service. This changed almost overnight after the war ended.

On November 14, 1918, 3 days after the war ended, the United States Government canceled $100 million in airplane contracts. Within 3 months, 175,000 factory workers were laid off and aircraft production dropped by 85 percent. The government's surplus warplanes were dumped on the market causing the aviation industries to lose what small market they did have. These industries, which had built up slowly during the war, now closed at an alarming rate. They could not afford to stay open.

Military aviation was cut back by 95 percent. The pilots and other aviation personnel who had taken so long to train were now unemployed. Military airfields were closed. This created a shortage of landing fields for those airplanes that were still flying. In fact, aviation in the United States almost died. If it had not been for two groups of people, the "barnstormers" and the Army aviators led by the outspoken General "Billy" Mitchell, it certainly would have.

The "Barnstormers"

After WWI, the Curtiss JN 4 *Jenny* became available to the general public as Army surplus and was used by many of the early barnstormers. *(EAA)*

The barnstormers were, for the most part, ex-military aviators who flew war-surplus aircraft such as the Curtiss JN-4 *Jenny*. They flew around the country, circling over a village or small town to attract attention, and landed on a nearby farm. When curious townspeople began to gather to get a good look at the plane, the pilot would offer rides to individuals. They usually charged people $3.00 to $5.00 per ride.

The barnstormers also put on flying exhibitions at county fairs, carnivals and anywhere else crowds gathered. Sometimes several of the pilots worked together as a team, calling themselves a "flying circus."

Those who did not work as part of a large group learned that they could offer the crowds more thrills if they teamed up with a stuntman. "Wing walking" was one of the tricks that always pleased the crowds. While the pilot flew the biplane in a circle, the stunt person would leave the cockpit and walk out on the edge of the lower wing. Then they would climb to the upper wing and walk back toward the cockpit. Some of the wing walkers would give the viewers an extra thrill by standing on their heads.

Besides ex-military aviators, there were a number of women aviators who attracted the public's attention during this barnstorming period. Less famous than Lindbergh, but a pioneer in her own right, was a female barnstormer named Phoebe Fairgrave Omlie. She not only ran her own "flying circus" but went on to become the first female licensed transport pilot in the United States.

Another stunt pilot was the first licensed black female pilot, Bessie Coleman. Coleman, who had to go to France to get her license, represented the first breakthrough for black women in aviation. She served as a model for other black women to enter aviation. Unfortunately Bessie Coleman, died in an airplane accident. She was a passenger in a plane piloted by someone else. She was thrown from the plane when it went out of control and died from the fall. Bessie Coleman died at age 34 (1892-1926).

When World War I ended, most people in the United States had never seen an airplane. If they thought of airplanes at all, it was probably with fear. Then came the barnstormers with air shows that may not have done away with the fears, but certainly created interest in fliers and flying.

Some say that if it were not for the "barnstormers," aviation may have died all together in the United States. These colorful daredevils ushered in two decades of people who were to see improvement in aircraft design and achievement by the people who took to the air.

Bessie Coleman, America's first licensed African-American pilot, flew a Jenny at air shows during the twenties.

Army Air Power Develops

While the "barnstormers" were encouraging interest in aviation among the citizens of the United States, General William "Billy" Mitchell was trying to encourage investment in military aviation. After he returned home from World War I, he was convinced that air power would decide the winner of the next Great War.

General Mitchell thought the airplane could be used to bomb military and industrial targets deep inside an enemy's homeland. He thought that after the United States achieved air superiority over the enemy, air power could then attack the enemy's ground troops and supply line. He thought this would be a better form of war because it might save lives.

General Mitchell had seen the bloody battles of World War I firsthand. Thousands of lives were lost when armies dug in deep and slugged it out. Air power, General Mitchell thought, could fly over that battlefield, attack the enemy's supplies, thus, shorten the war and save lives.

In order to achieve his vision of air power, General Mitchell was a very vocal advocate of an air service separate from, but equal to, the Army and Navy. The first problem he faced was to convince the Army he was right, then he had to convince Congress. He decided that the only way to overcome the indifference toward aviation, both within the Army and the Congress, was to demonstrate the capability of the airplane as a superior military weapon.

Since it was widely agreed that America's first line of defense was the Navy battleships, Mitchell chose to prove that an airplane could sink a battleship. With a successful test, Mitchell hoped to

Only a few of the WWI aircraft remain. This spectacular SPAD was restored by the San Diego Aerospace Museum and is currently on display.

The SPAD in it's finished form

Mitchell's bombers sinking the *Ostfriesland* battleship.

convince the military and Congress that they needed to shift the foundation of national defense from the battleship to the bomber.

By 1921, Mitchell had created such an uproar that the Navy agreed to allow him to perform his demonstration. Confident that he could not succeed, the Navy provided several captured German ships as targets, including the battleship *Ostfriesland*. The *Ostfriesland* was a huge ship that had been called "unsinkable" by naval experts. Using light bombs, Mitchell's pilots did little damage to the giant battleship.

The next day the Army fliers returned carrying 1,000-pound bombs, and again the battleship survived. On the afternoon of July 21, 1921, the Army pilots carried 2,000-pound bombs. Eight of these bombs were dropped and 25 minutes later, the "unsinkable" pride of the German Navy slipped beneath the waves.

The lesson to be learned from this demonstration, unfortunately, was lost on the Army generals. Congress, which controlled the purse strings, also rejected Mitchell. So, Mitchell did not get additional money for aircraft. Several Navy admirals, however, did learn the lesson. They could see that the airplane would play a dominant role in future naval warfare. Within 8 months, the Navy had its first aircraft carrier.

Since Mitchell was unable to convince Congress or the Army leaders to invest in air power, he decided to reach Congress through the voters that elected them. To do this, he decided to do some "barnstorming" of his own and planned some spectacular demonstrations of air power.

First thing he did was plan for flight over the American continent. In 1922, he had Lieutenant Oakley Kelly and Lieutenant John Macready of the United States Army Air Service attempt to fly nonstop from San Diego to New York. The first flight had to turn back because of bad weather. The second time, a leaky radiator forced them down at Indianapolis, Indiana, after flying almost three-fourths of the way across the United States.

After these two attempts failed, they decided to reverse their direction and fly from New York to San Diego. They believed the advantage of a light gas tank when crossing the Rocky Mountains would outweigh the advantage of the tail wind they would probably have traveling east.

At 12:30 p.m. on May 2, 1923, they took off from Roosevelt Field, New York, on their third attempt. Their plane was a Fokker *T*-2 with a 400-horsepower Liberty engine. The heavily loaded plane barely cleared obstacles at the end of the runway.

Kelly and Macready flew over Indianapolis after nightfall and entered the mountains near Tucumcari, New Mexico, early the next morning. Fortunately, they had a tailwind most of the way. In spite of their heavy fuel load, they flew much of the way at 100 mph. Shortly after noon on May 3, they landed at San Diego after flying 2,520 miles in 26 hours and 50 minutes.

The most spectacular flight demonstration organized by General Mitchell was the first round-the-world flight. The Army performed this amazing flight in 1924 using aircraft built by Douglas Aircraft. The four airplanes—the *Boston*, *Chicago*, *Seattle*, and *New*

Many WWI aircraft, such as this Nieuport 28, have either been restored or replicated by aviation enthusiasts. To see one flying today is a spectacular sight. *(EAA)*

Orleans—were named for the cities that sponsored each of them.

The flight started in Seattle, Washington, and went to Alaska, Japan, China, Indochina, Burma, India, Syria, Austria, France, England, Iceland, Greenland, Labrador, Newfoundland, Nova Scotia and across the entire United States back to Seattle.

The entire flight took 175 days, and only two of the

The Douglas DWC/DOS that flew around the world.

aircraft (the *Chicago* and the *New Orleans*) completed the entire flight. The *Seattle* crashed in Alaska soon after the journey began, and the *Boston* was forced down in the Atlantic between England and Iceland.

A replacement aircraft called the *Boston* II was taken to Nova Scotia, and the crew of the *Boston* flew it on to Seattle. The total distance flown around the world was 26,345 miles, and the actual flying time was 363 hours and 7 minutes.

In August 1923, the Army performed the first refueling of an airplane while in flight. Lieutenants Lowell Smith and J. P. Richter remained airborne for 37 hours and 15 minutes by refueling their aircraft through a 50-foot hose from another airplane. The refueling operation was done 16 times with about 50 gallons of fuel being transferred each time.

In 1929, Elinor Smith and Bobbi Trout, in an attempt at an endurance record, became the first women pilots to refuel thier plane in the air.

On June 23, 1924, Army Lieutenant Russell Maughan flew a Curtiss PW-8 pursuit aircraft from coast-to-coast in a dawn-to-dusk flight. The 2,670-mile trip was completed in 21 hours and 48 minutes at an average speed of 122 mph. Although he had to land five times to refuel, Lt. Maughan left New York at dawn and landed in San Francisco before dark.

Early attempts at air-to-air refueling were quite dangerous.

This flight demonstrated that Army aircraft located anywhere in the United States could be flown to any other location in the country in less than 1 day.

The Army also showed air power's ability to move troops quickly. The first demonstration of using paratroops (troops who use parachutes) was in September of 1929 at Brooks Field in Texas. Sergeant Erwin H. Nichols and a squad of 17 men jumped from nine DH-4s and landed safely on the ground 3,000 feet below. At the same time, three bundles of machine guns and ammunition were dropped from three Douglas transports, and within 4 minutes after the jump, the machine guns were in action.

All of General Mitchell's efforts gained wide national and world acclaim, but still did not result in the outcome Mitchell sought, a separate Air Service and more money for military aviation.

Following a world tour of foreign military aviation, Mitchell criticized the defenses of the United States, particularly at the Navy base in Pearl Harbor, Hawaii. He stated that a surprise air attack on Pearl Harbor would destroy the Navy's Pacific Fleet. No one would listen, and he was told to stop his attacks on the Navy.

General Mitchell's continued criticism of the military hierarchy eventually led to his court-martial and subsequent retirement. However, his court-martial led to some of the things he sought. Air power received more attention. The Army Air Service was changed to the Army Air Corps, and the post of Assistant Secretary of War for Aeronautics was created. This led to additional funds and more emphasis on research and development of military aviation.

Less than 15 years later, on December 7, 1941, the Japanese bombed Pearl Harbor. Mitchell's critics saw that he was right about the importance of aviation in the military, but it was a very costly lesson.

Early Parachute Jump Test

National Air Races

Air racing also had an impact on the development of air power. A newspaperman, Ralph Pulitzer, offered a trophy to promote high-speed flight. He did this when he saw that American aircraft were making such a poor showing in the European air races.

The first Pulitzer Trophy Race was held in New York at Mitchel Field on Long Island. On November 27, 1920, 37 entrants flew four laps around a 29-mile course. The winner was United States Army Lieutenant Corliss Moseley, flying a Verville-Packard aircraft at an average speed of 156.5 and top speed of 178 mph.

By 1924, the Pulitzer Trophy Race had grown into 10 separate events. Six were limited to civilian aircraft and four restricted to military aircraft. Because the air races had grown so large, the name was changed to the National Air Races.

In 1926, the military withdrew from competition for the Pulitzer Trophy. The Pulitzer Trophy was awarded for the last time at the 1925 National Air Races. It was won by United States Army Lieutenant

The original *Gee Bee* Racer was flown by one of America's great aviation pioneers, James "Jimmy" Doolittle. This replica, built and flown by Delmar Benjamin, puts on a spectacular show at events like the EAA's Annual Fly-In at Oshkosh, Wisconsin. (*EAA*)

Cy Bellis in a Curtiss R3C-1 racer at 248 mph. Although the Pulitzer Trophy Race was conducted for only 6 years, American air racing improved. The winning speed had increased by nearly 100 mph.

In 1930, Charles E. Thompson, president of Thompson Products, Inc., established a trophy to encourage faster land-based aircraft. The Thompson Trophy Race was the feature event of the National Air Races. It was an open event with no limit on fuel, or number or type of engines. It was open to civilian and military aircraft.

Like the Pulitzer Trophy Race, this was a pylon race, meaning that it was flown around a circuit marked by towers (pylons). The Thompson Trophy was awarded annually until the outbreak of World War II.

In 1931, the Bendix Trophy Race, a transcontinental speed race, was added to the National Air Races. Rather than fly around a closed course, the Bendix Race was flown from the West Coast to Cleveland, Ohio. Jimmy Doolittle was a winner of the Bendix Trophy. Both the Bendix and Thompson Races were resumed after World War II ended, but neither regained the glory of the prewar years.

Another air race, although not a part of the National Air Races, was the Schneider

The Curtiss Army R3C-2 Racing Biplane

Trophy Race. Jacques Schneider, a French aviation enthusiast, started this race in 1913. Schneider felt that water aircraft were not developing fast enough, so he offered a trophy for an annual race over open water by seaplanes. The 1913 race had four entries and only one finished. The average speed was 45.8 mph.

By 1931, when the Schneider Trophy was retired, the speed had increased to over 340 mph. The Schneider Trophy Races led to the development of seaplanes like the English Supermarine S.6B and the Italian Macchi MC-72. Both of these aircraft were faster than any land aircraft of the 1930s. In October 1934, the MC-72 established a world record for seaplanes of 440.68 mph. This speed is still a record for propeller-driven seaplanes and will probably never be beaten.

Women's Air Derby

In 1929, the National Air Races were opened to women for the first time. The Women's Air Derby, the first cross-country competition for women, was the major opening event of the 1929 races and signaled the start of women competing in air races. The first race went from Santa Monica, California, to Cleveland, Ohio. Louise Thaden won the race flying a Travel Air J-5. Second place went to Gladys O'Donnell, and Amelia Earhart finished third.

In 1930, a pylon race was added for women. Gladys O'Donnell won both the Derby and the pylon race. In 1931, the Bendix Trophy Race was opened to women for the first time, but no woman entered this race until 1933. Amelia Earhart finished fifth in the 1935 Bendix Trophy Race. In 1936, women finished first and second in this formerly male-dominated event. Louise Thaden and Blanche Noyes won the race in a Beech *Staggerwing* while Laura Ingalls finished second in a Lockheed *Orion*.

The only other woman to win the Bendix Trophy Race was Jacqueline Cochran in 1938. She flew a modified Seversky P-35. For Jacqueline Cochran, this was just a beginning of a career that would eventually lead to "Jackie" being called the "Greatest Woman Aviator of All Time."

The Women's Air Derby led to the formation of an association of women fliers called the "Ninety-Nines" (named after the 99 original charter members). Amelia Earhart was the first president. This organization, dedicated to the improvement of women's opportunities in aviation, included the leading female pilots from all nations. This organization still exists today.

Serversky P-35 like the one flown by Jackie Cochran in the Bendix Trophy air races.

Air Mail Speeds Up Delivery

While General Billy Mitchell was creating such controversy in military aviation, progress was being made in commercial aviation in the United States. The Post Office Department started air mail service in the United States on May 15, 1918, using aircraft and pilots borrowed from the United States Army. Three months later, the Post Office Department took over the operation completely, hiring its own pilots and buying its own airplanes.

The first air mail route was between Washington, D.C., and New York City. In 1919, air mail service was extended from New York to Chicago via Cleveland and, in 1920, from Chicago to San Francisco. However, true air mail service on a regular basis did not begin until July 1, 1924.

Many were opposed to the development of an air mail service, especially the railroads. They viewed the government subsidizing mail service as unfair competition. The Post Office Department justified the air mail service as experimental in nature, therefore, requiring federal funds. By 1925, the air mail service had developed to the point that it was no longer considered experimental, and the Post Office was ready to turn it over to private enterprise.

The legislation which made possible the private carrying of mail was the Air Mail Act of 1925, a law which essentially dealt with the economic regulation of the federal air system. This act authorized the Post Office Department to contract for air mail service. Among other provisions in the act was one that allowed the contractor to be paid 80 percent of the air mail profits for carrying it.

This was the incentive needed to get big business into the aviation field and really marked the beginning of commercial aviation in America. This was also a "shot in the arm" for the aviation industries, since the awarding of these air mail contracts created a demand for newer and larger aircraft.

As the air mail contracts were made, and as air mail service spread out across the country, a few commercial passengers were carried by the mail planes. However, it was much more profitable to carry mail than passengers. Except for the Ford *Tri-motor*, most mail planes were small and could carry only two or three passengers.

The first attempt to standardize and regulate commercial aviation was made on May 20, 1926, when Congress passed the Air Commerce Act. This act established the Aeronautics Branch within the Department of Commerce. It provided for the first federal safety regulation of aviation for both pilots and aircraft. The Aeronautics Branch was authorized to license all planes and pilots, establish and enforce air traffic rules, develop navigational facilities, map airways, furnish flight information, investigate accidents, and provide aviation safety through assistance and guidance to civil aviation.

Ford Tri-Motor carried the mail and passengers. *(EAA)*

The act was significant because it aided in the continuing development of the commercial airlines. At this point in time, civil aviation was regulated in the safety area by the Aeronautics Branch and in the economic area by the United States Post Office Department. This arrangement lasted for 8 years. It was then changed by a new air mail act.

On June 12, 1934, Congress passed a new air mail act that changed the economic and safety regulation

arrangement of commercial air transportation. Commercial air carriers became responsible to three United States Government agencies.

First, the Post Office Department awarded air mail contracts and determined routes and structures. Second, the Aeronautics Branch of the Department of Commerce (renamed the Bureau of Air Commerce) was responsible for operating airways and regulating the licensing of aircraft and pilots. Lastly, the Interstate Commerce Commission's (ICC) Bureau of Air Mail fixed rates of air mail payments to the commercial air carriers.

This act was significant because it separated the air transport companies from the aircraft manufacturers. It also developed a sound and well-organized air transport system through the use of governmental payments for carrying air mail. In addition, a thorough study of commercial aviation was conducted, which led to the establishment of the Civil Aeronautics Authority, Civil Aeronautics Board and Civil Aeronautics Administration.

Established air carriers felt threatened by the 1934 Air Mail Act, not only because of the subsidized competition of new independent carriers, but also by the prospect of losing business to the independents. They appealed to Congress for help, and on June 23, 1938, President Roosevelt signed into law the Civil Aeronautics Act of 1938. This law combined both economic and safety regulations into one independent agency called the Civil Aeronautics Authority (CAA).

The new law did keep competition within bounds and protected the routes of the established carriers. More importantly, it unified the economic and safety regulations of the entire field of aviation, independently of the Department of Commerce and increased government oversight of aviation activities and operations.

Early air transportation took on a new style in the 1930s. Stewardesses, dressed in nurse-like uniforms, were hired to serve passengers.

PIONEERS CONTRIBUTE TO THE
DEVELOPMENT OF AIR POWER

Progress in aviation in America was being made, but very slowly. Something was needed that would excite the American people and unite them in support of aviation. Many accomplishments in aviation were made because people offered prizes or money as incentives. These accomplishments included most of the long-range flights, flights over the North and South Poles, and many of the flights leading to speed and altitude records.

By 1927, only one of these prizes was left unclaimed. It was the $25,000 prize offered in 1919 by Raymond Orteig to the "first aviator to cross the Atlantic nonstop from New York to Paris." To this point many famous pilots had attempted this crossing, but all had failed.

In 1927, a 25-year-old ex-barnstormer, air mail pilot and captain in the Missouri National Guard, Charles A. Lindbergh, approached a group of businessmen in St. Louis seeking sponsorship for an attempt at flying the Atlantic. With the $13,000 that the sponsors provided and $2,000 of

Charles A. Lindbergh was the first person to fly the Atlantic solo. He convinced the world that air travel was possible and credible.

This is a flying replica of the *Spirit of St. Louis*, Charles A. Lindbergh's "New York to Paris" airplane. The original NYP aircraft can be seen at the National Air And Space Museum in Washington, D.C. This replica is in the EAA Air Museum in Oshkosh, Wisconsin.
(EAA)

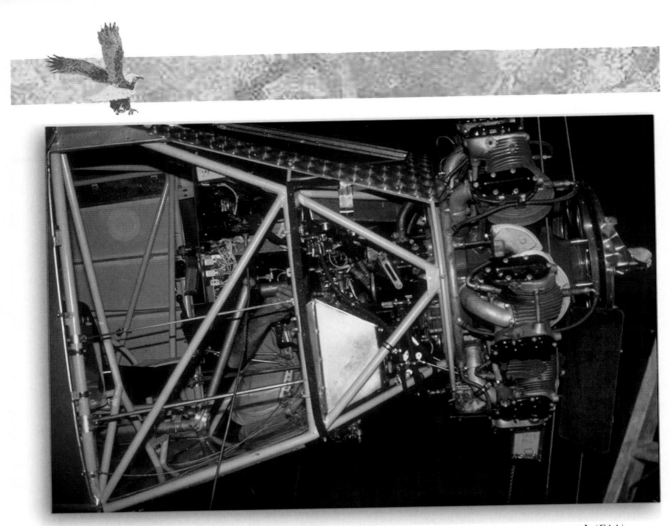

The engine compartment of EAA's *Spirit of St. Louis* replica is revealed with its cowling cover removed. *(EAA)*

his own money, Lindbergh asked Ryan Aircraft, Inc., in San Diego, to build him an aircraft to cross the Atlantic. Lindbergh wanted a high-wing monoplane powered by a single 220-horsepower, air-cooled, Wright Whirlwind engine.

Just 60 days after signing the contract, Ryan delivered the aircraft that Lindbergh named the *Spirit of St. Louis*. One month later, on May 20, 1927, Lindbergh took off from Roosevelt Field in New York and headed east. Flying alone through bad weather, with no radio and only a simple compass to guide him, Lindbergh crossed the Atlantic. Thirty-three and one-half hours after takeoff, he landed at Le Bourget Airport in Paris and instantly became a world hero. Never before had so many people throughout the world given so much admiration and affection to a single individual.

The response from the American public was explosive! Here was a symbol the public could identify with and respond to, and Lindbergh was equal to the role.

Following his return to the United States, the nation's new hero became a promoter of civil aviation, traveling to every state in the Union. He, more than any other individual, was responsible for thousands of people entering pilot training and for hundreds of airports being built.

Another individual who would rival the fame of Lindbergh was Amelia Earhart. She earned her pilot's license in 1923, and on June 17, 1928, she became the first woman passenger to fly across the Atlantic. She gained fame as the world's greatest woman flier before her disappearance in 1937.

Amelia Earhart. This Kansas-born flier was the first woman to cross the Atlantic Ocean both as a passenger and as a solo pilot.

In May 1932, she was the first woman to make a solo transatlantic flight. In her *Vega* monoplane, she landed near Londonderry, Ireland, instead of at Paris, her planned destination. The flight took 20 hours and 40 minutes. It promoted women's interests in flight and served as a mark for other women to beat. In August of the same year, she set a new long-distance record for women. She was also active in the women's Air Derby and was the first president of the "Ninety-Nines," the international organization of women pilots.

Earhart would probably have been the most outstanding woman in aviation, but she disappeared at the peak of her aviation career.

On March 17, 1937, Earhart and her crew, Fred Noonan, Paul Mantz and Captain Harry Manning, took off from Oakland, California, in her Lockheed *Electra* for the first leg of an around-the-world flight. Unfortunately, her plane ground-looped in Honolulu and had to be returned to Lockheed in California for repair. This delayed the flight until June 1, 1937.

This flight was her last. Earhart and Fred Noonan climbed aboard the *Electra* at the municipal airport in Miami, Florida. They were going east to west rather than west to east as originally planned. All went well, but as she approached her scheduled stop at Howland Island in the Pacific, she had trouble getting her bearing (direction). She could not hear the signals being sent to her by the Coast Guard Cutter, *Itasca*. Apparently, the plane went down somewhere in the Pacific, never to be seen or heard from again. Women's aviation lost its greatest advocate.

Aviation Grows

In the 1920s, small companies were formed to build private aircraft for a growing market of pilots. Among the earliest of these was a company called Travel Air Manufacturing Company, which was formed in 1925 in Wichita, Kansas. This company was formed by Lloyd Stearman, Clyde Cessna and Walter Beech. They were to become giants in the manufacture of small aircraft. They built small bi-wing sport planes that were very successful.

Later, Clyde Cessna was convinced that a small private monoplane would be even more successful. His two partners did not agree. So in 1927, Cessna

The Lockheed *Vega* was flown by such aviation pioneers as Amelia Earhart and Wiley Post.

The great airplane designer, Lloyd Stearman, was the "father" of the classic Stearman PT-17 trainer. *(EAA)*

left Travel Air Manufacturing Company and started his own company: The Cessna Aircraft Company. Eventually, the other two partners also broke away from Travel Air and formed their own companies. Beech Aircraft Company was started in 1932, and Stearman Aircraft Company started in 1926. All three remained in Wichita, and today, this city is the light aircraft capital of the world.

In 1929, another partnership was formed. The two men were G. C. Taylor and William Piper. Mr. Taylor was building aircraft on a very small scale in Bradford, Pennsylvania. In 1929, the stock market crash bankrupted him, and Piper, a wealthy oil man, bought the company for $761.

Piper reorganized the Taylor Aircraft Company, and kept Taylor as President. In 1935, he bought out Taylor's share of the company and renamed it Piper Aircraft Corporation. Taylor moved to Ohio and started the Taylor Aircraft Company. Both companies would produce fine aircraft, but none more famous than the Piper J-3 *Cub*.

The late 1920s also saw the science of aeronautics (aviation) take its place as a true and recognized science. In 1915, President Woodrow Wilson formed an organization called the National Advisory Committee for Aeronautics (NACA). Its purpose was to "supervise and direct the scientific study of the problems of flight, with a view of their practical solutions." During the 1920s, this federal agency performed valuable basic research in aeronautics and solved many of the problems that plagued early aircraft.

The Piper J-3 *Cub* was a classic pre-war fighter built by the Boeing Company. *(EAA)*

In 1926, Daniel Guggenheim, an air-minded New York philanthropist, founded the School of Aeronautics at New York University. He also established a $2.5 million "Daniel Guggenheim Fund For the Promotion of Aeronautics." Grants from this fund spread a program of aviation education across the country and provided many colleges and universities with money for private flying clubs. This ensured a supply of trained people in the aeronautical field.

The Beechcraft Staggerwing is considered to be the forerunner of today's corporate aircraft. *(EAA)*

The results were many improvements and changes in the aircraft built during the late 1920s and the 1930s. One advancement resulted in the bi-winged aircraft finally giving way to the more efficient monoplane.

Scientists developed more efficient wing shapes and cowlings (covers) to enclose the engines. Retractable landing gear was also developed. Pressurized cabins permitted higher altitude flights and air-cooled radial engines replaced heavier water-cooled ones.

Other refinements included the development of wing flaps to increase lift and allow slower takeoff and landing speeds, and the development of de-icing equipment made all-weather flying safer.

James H. Doolittle, a young Army lieutenant, did a lot of research on aircraft instruments to make flying at night and in bad weather safer. On September 24, 1929, Doolittle made the first successful "blind" takeoff and landing. He took off, flew five miles, made a 180° turn and then came down for a safe landing — all without looking outside the airplane. As a result of this research, instruments for flight and navigation and two-way radios were installed in aircraft.

With the development of an all-metal aircraft by Hugo Junkers, a German aircraft builder, and the stressed-skin principle by another German, Adolph Rohrbach, the airplane began to resemble modern aircraft.

Helicopters also became a successful aircraft during this period. Little progress had been made during World War I, and it wasn't until 1923 that significant rotary-wing advances were achieved. In that year, Juan de la Cierva (Spanish) built the first successful autogiro.

One of the great early general aviation companies was Stinson. They produced this classic *SM2A A* monoplane. *(EAA)*

The autogiro produced lift with rotor blades that turned independently in flight. A regular engine and propeller propelled the craft. However, the craft had some drawbacks. It could not move in every direction as the helicopter would. During the 1920s and 1930s, many autogiros were made, which eventually led to the helicopter design of today.

Progress in rotary-wing aircraft was also made in Spain, France and Germany during the 1930s. Cierva's earlier work on the autogiro (hinged rotor-blade and autorotation feature) contributed to the first helicopter with complete controllability. It was the Focke-Achgelis (FA-61) built in Germany in 1937 by Dr. Heinrich Focke. It had two rotors mounted side by side on outriggers that extended from the fuselage.

The world's first woman helicopter pilot, Hanna Reitsch, demonstrated the FA-61 inside the Sportzplatz in Berlin in 1938. She "hovered" and performed 360° turns as well as backward, sideward and forward flight.

The Russian-born American, Igor Sikorsky, developed the first practical helicopter. This aircraft, called the VS-300, accomplished vertical takeoffs and landings (tethered flight) in September of 1939. It could carry a useful load, perform productive work, and be controlled in flight. Its first free flight was May 13, 1940. (The *VS*-300 led to the R-4, the first military helicopter in the world which was used in World War II.) From this small 1,150 pound, 50-mph craft, the helicopter has grown to the successful workhorse we know today. The name of Sikorsky still stands for excellence in helicopters throughout the world.

Commercial Aviation Matures

All of the technology was present in the 1930s to develop "modern" commercial airliners. What was needed was a reason. This was provided by President Herbert Hoover's new Postmaster General, Walter F. Brown. In 1930, at Brown's urging, Congress passed the McNary-Watres Act as an amendment to the Air Mail Act of 1925.

Under the Air Mail Act of 1925, airmail carriers were paid according to the weight of the mail carried. The new law changed this so contractors could be paid according to the available cargo space (using a space-mile formula). In addition, a bonus would be paid to operators flying multi-engine aircraft equipped with the latest instruments. This was clearly an incentive for the operators to fly larger aircraft. It was also an attempt to provide aid to the airlines for carrying passengers as well as mail.

The McNary-Watres Act also authorized the postmaster general to extend or combine air mail routes. When Brown entered office, all transcontinental airmail was carried by United Airlines on the northern route (New York-Chicago-San Francisco). Brown opened two additional transcontinental routes. One was called the central route (New York-Kansas City-Los Angeles) and the other was the southern route (Atlanta-Los Angeles). Transcontinental and Western Airlines (TWA) were given the central route, and American Airways had the southern route.

The effect of the McNary-Watres Act on aviation wasn't long in coming. United Airlines contracted with Boeing Aircraft in Seattle to build a "modern" two-engine aircraft. In February 1933, Boeing brought out the 247, a twin-engine, all-metal, low-wing monoplane. It was constructed with stressed skin and retractable landing gear and could carry 10 passengers and 400 pounds of mail. The Boeing 247 had a cruising speed of 189 mph and made possible the first "same-day service" between New York and San Francisco.

Boeing 247, the first all-metal airliner. *(EAA)*

Transcontinental and Western Airlines (TWA) soon responded by contracting with Douglas Aircraft of Santa Monica, California, (September 1932) to build an airplane better than the *Boeing* 247. In July 1933, Douglas began testing the new aircraft, which they called the Douglas Commercial One (DC-1). Only one DC-1 was built for test flights and was delivered to TWA in September. When the production aircraft came out in May 1934, it was called the DC-2. It had a cruising speed of 192 mph and carried 14 passengers and several thousand pounds of mail. Douglas built and sold about 156 of these DC-2s, including many in Europe.

While United Airlines was flying its Boeing 247s and TWA its DC-2s, American Airways was losing money flying foreign-built aircraft. Douglas Aircraft was approached to build an aircraft bigger than its own DC-2. Douglas already had more orders for DC-2s than it could handle; but American Airways agreed to buy 20 of the new aircraft, with an option for 20 more. Douglas agreed to build it. In December 1935, the first of these new aircraft (called the DC-3) was finished. American Airways was first to put the DC-3 into service (June 1936). The DC-3 was larger than the DC-2, carrying 24 passengers or 5,000 pounds of cargo a distance of 1,200 miles.

The DC-3 soon became the standard commercial airliner for all commercial airlines. It was one of the most successful aircraft ever built. By 1938, DC-3s carried 95 percent of all commercial traffic in the United States, and by 1939, they were carrying 90 percent of the commercial traffic worldwide. Between 1935 and 1942, 800 DC-3s were built for commercial airlines, and more than 10,000 were built for the Army Air Corps. The Army called it the C-47.

The DC-3 was developed during the mid thirties and went on to serve in WWII as the C-47. It was officially known as the *Skytrain*, but pilots affectionately called her "Gooney Bird." *(EAA)*

Seaplanes Carry the Mail

A discussion about commercial aviation would be incomplete without mentioning the Pan American *Clippers*. In 1927, Pan American Airways was formed to fly the first air mail route between Key West, Florida, and Havana, Cuba. This route was extended from island to island throughout the Caribbean. It was eventually extended into Central America and down the Atlantic coast of South America.

Since most of this route was over water, and because seaplane bases were easier to build in remote areas than airports, Pan American Airways wanted a large advanced seaplane. Igor Sikorsky built a large, four-engine flying boat called the S-40. It could fly at 125 mph and carry 40 passengers. Sikorsky also developed a larger flying boat, the S-42, which had a range of 1,200 miles. This airplane became known as the Pan American *Clipper* and made the first airline crossing of both the Pacific and Atlantic Oceans.

In 1934, Pan American took delivery of an even larger flying boat called the *Martin* 130. Pan American dubbed it the *China Clipper*. On November 22, 1935, the *China Clipper* took off from California for the first transpacific flight. After stops in Hawaii, Wake Island and Guam, the *Clipper* arrived in the Philippines. By 1937, this route was extended to Hong Kong and Pan American Airways was making one round-trip flight across the Pacific every 7 days.

In 1936, Pan American contacted with Boeing to purchase six Boeing 314s to replace the Martin 130. The Boeing 314 was the ultimate flying boat and was luxury air travel. It opened to passenger service in 1939. Pan American ordered six more 314 Clippers with increased engine power and capacity for 77 passengers.

Pan American's *China Clipper*

Meanwhile, What About the Dirigibles?

During the time between World War I and World War II, people saw rigid airships (large balloons) rise to the peak of their success and then completely disappear from the field of aviation.

Following World War I, the Germans were forced to surrender all of their Zeppelins (dirigibles) to the Allies as part of war reparations, Germany built the LZ-126 and gave it to the United States. It was named the *Los Angeles*, and it served for eight years with the United States Navy. Then it was retired and scrapped.

In 1926, the Treaty of Versailles allowed the Germans to construct Zeppelins again and they built three giant rigid airships. These new Zeppelins were the LZ-127 *Graf Zeppelin*, the LZ-129 *Hindenburg* and the LZ-130 *Graf Zeppelin* II.

The *Graf Zeppelin* was very successful. It was launched in 1928, and the following year, it made a successful round-the-world flight. During the 10 years it flew, the *Graf Zeppelin* made 590 flights, including 144 ocean crossings. It flew more than 1,000,000 miles and carried 13,110 passengers. The *Graf Zeppelin* was retired in 1939.

The *Hindenburg* became the most famous of all Zeppelins, not because of its success but because of its failure. The *Hindenburg* was launched in 1936 and made 10 successful round trips between Germany and the United States. On May 6, 1937, as the *Hindenburg* was preparing for landing at Lakehurst, New Jersey, it exploded, crashed to the ground and burned. The *Hindenburg* had left Germany with 36 passengers and 61 crewmembers. Thirty-five crewmembers and passengers died along with one ground crewmember. These were the first fatalities in the history of scheduled airship operations.

The *Graf Zeppelin* II was commissioned in 1938. Before it could go into commercial service, World War II began and it was scrapped during the war.

The United States also had problems with rigid airships. In 1923, the United States Navy built a large airship, the ZR-l *Shenandoah*. On September 3, 1925, the *Shenandoah* broke up during a storm over Ohio. Fourteen of the 43-man crew were killed.

*The Hindenburg exploded during its landing at Lakehurst, N.J., in 1937.
The inset shows the Hindenburg during its glory days.*

In 1924, the Goodyear Tire and Rubber Company was granted patent rights by Germany to build Zeppelins in the United States. They built two airships for the Navy and both met with disaster. In 1931, the *Akron* went into service flying out of Lakehurst, New Jersey. On April 4, 1933, after only 1,200 hours of flying service for the Navy, the *Akron* crashed in a storm off the New Jersey coast. Seventy-three crew men were killed.

The other Navy airship, the *Macon*, was built in 1933. It flew out of Moffet Field, California, and patrolled the Pacific coast.

On February 12, 1935, the *Macon* suffered a structural failure of the upper fin. Gas leakage and structural collapse caused the *Macon* to crash into the sea off the California coast. Two crewmembers were killed.

Investigations by both the Navy and Congress endorsed the continued use of dirigibles for the Navy. However, due to the outbreak of World War II, attention was diverted elsewhere and construction was never started.

Military Air Power Developments
During the Interwar Years

The developments made in commercial aviation during the 1930s provided the business necessary to maintain a healthy aviation industry in the United States. These same industries were also helping develop military aircraft, although not as much as in the commercial field. Despite what General Billy Mitchell had done to champion the cause of air power, our national policy regarding military aviation was that the airplane was primarily a defensive weapon used to protect our homeland.

Many of our Army Air Corps officers understood the offensive potential of the airplane. It was only because of their efforts that some progress was made in the development of fighters and bombers during the 1930s. A prime example of this was the development of the B-17. This bomber gained fame during World War II.

When Douglas Aircraft built the DC-2 and DC-3 commercial airliners, the 247 that Boeing had built became obsolete. This was a blessing in disguise for the Boeing Company because it allowed them to

respond to an Army design competition for a new multi-engine bomber for use in coastal patrol.

The term "multi-engine" had always meant two engines, but several Air Corps officers encouraged Boeing to enter the competition with a four-engine aircraft. These officers were dedicated to Mitchell's doctrine of air power. They envisioned a large four-engine bomber that could be used not only for defensive coastal patrol, but also for long-range bombing.

On July 28, 1935, the four-engine giant, designated the Boeing 299, made

The Curtiss *P-6E Hawk* is a classic example of a military fighter in the early thirties. This aircraft has been totally restored and is on display at the U.S. Air Force Museum, Wright-Patterson Air Force Base, Ohio.

its first flight test. The 299 was flown to Wright Field in Dayton, Ohio, for competition against two competitors, both twin-engine aircraft. Not only did the 299 (Army designation X1B-17) win the competition, but it could outfly any pursuit (fighter) airplane flying at the time. The Army Air Corps made an initial order for 13 of these B-17s and, soon after, they ordered 39 more.

The evolution of the Boeing B-17 started with the 299 in 1935. This airplane was considered one of the greatest bombers of all time.

The Army Air Corps now possessed its first long-range bomber, but during its trials, the X1B-17 proved that we were lacking in fighter aircraft. Contracts were let for the Seversky P-35 and the Curtiss P-36, both "modern," low-wing monoplanes.

Army Air Corps leaders believed these aircraft to be equal to any fighter in the world. However, as the United States made these small advances in military aviation, other countries of the world were testing their aircraft in combat and developing better aircraft that they would use during World War II.

Meanwhile, the military was woefully behind in producing pilots to fly the new aircraft in the event of war. By the time Germany invaded Austria in 1938 and Czechoslovakia and Poland in 1939, some military planners could see that the Army Air Corps alone would not be able to train enough pilots to engage in combat should the United States enter the European war.

The Possibility of War

The Presidential message given to Congress on January 12, 1939, marked the beginning of Army Air Corps' expansion before World War II. The President called for a buildup of our existing forces, which he described as "utterly inadequate." Within 3 months of this address, the United States Congress would pass a bill authorizing an increase to 3,203 officers from the prior limit of 1,200 officers.

Under the impact of even more threats from abroad, the military planners could foresee that this officer strength would not be enough. Even if Congress were to appropriate money for more men and aircraft, the military establishment would be pressed for time to train pilots to be ready for our possible entry into the war in Europe.

Despite the lack of military training capability, war planners increased pilot training goals. These goals also called for the training of a proportionate number of other types of aircrew members such as bombardiers, navigators and ground technicians. The problem was that the Air Corps had neither the instructors nor the facilities to train men and women in such numbers. It also did not have the experience.

To fix this problem, the Army Air Corps turned to civilian flying schools. The civilian schools also had a limited supply of instructors, aircraft, flying fields, trained maintenance personnel and experienced administrative officials. There were only 23 privately owned flying schools that held an approved rating from the Civil Aeronautics Authority (CAA). The Air Corps still had a problem and needed someone to fix it.

General "Hap" Arnold was such a person. He had sized up the situation early in 1939. He said "to build another Randolph Field (the Air Corps' only pilot training base) to handle 500 pilots a year would take another 5 years." In a statement to the House Military Affairs Committee, and making no secret of his intentions, on January 18, 1939 (4 months before he would call eight private flying school operators to his office), Arnold said:

General Harry H. "Hap" Arnold.
The first general of the Air Force with
a five-star rank. *(DoD Media)*

> Our present system is training all our military pilots at our training center at San Antonio. The capacity is somewhere around 550 a year. That is approximately what we are turning out now. That is not sufficient. The output of pilots must be materially increased. If we are to continue our present policy, it means that we have to increase the facilities at San Antonio. I think the War Department decided that is not the proper way to do it. We should buildup a war reserve for pilots. The War Department policy contemplates the utilization of civilian schools for all our dual instruction.

Arnold then explained his plan for civilian-operated, Army-supervised flight schools. The Army would give volunteers for the Army Air Corps physical and mental examinations. Those who were

qualified would be sent to designated civilian schools in their immediate area to receive instruction. Regular Army fliers would examine graduates and give them "check rides." Cadets would then go to Army bases for basic and advanced training. General Arnold also required civilian instructors to get standard training at Randolph Field so all instructors would "speak the same language."

Congress did not think very much of Arnold's plan at that time. So Arnold went outside the Army for help. He asked eight World War I pilots and nonmilitary aviators who ran private flying schools to help train combat pilots for the Army, with or without pay. Fortunately for Arnold and the Air Corps, all agreed to his request.

With CAA approval in May 1939, preparations were made for nine of the schools (through eight contractors) to give primary flying training for the Army Air Corps. Although no contracts could be offered until Arnold finally got support in July 1939, the program got started.

Following Arnold's original blueprint, the Army sent flying cadets to the "contract" schools beginning July 1, 1939. Fifty cadets went to school first, then they went by the thousands. That first blueprint would be revised and refined as experience revealed its many flaws.

Also, the program, which looked so simple on paper, would be full of headaches and near-heartbreaks. In a short time, these "civilian bases" mushroomed throughout the nation doing for the Army Air Corps what it could not do for itself: produce combat pilots ready to go to war.

The Piper J-3 *Cub* was used to train thousands of pilots during WWII. The CPTP used this aircraft in large numbers to introduce civilians to aviation. The nickname of the CPTP was the "Putt-Putt Air Force!" *(EAA)*

Other civilian pilot training programs also served as a source of potential pilots. The Civilian Pilot Training Program (CPTP) was authorized in mid-1939 by the CAA. This program created a great reserve supply of pilots that could be used in a serious national emergency. President Roosevelt signed the Civilian Pilot Training Act of 1939 into law. The act authorized the CAA to conduct a program for training civilian pilots through existing educational institutions and to prescribe pertinent regulations. The objective was to provide sufficient training to prepare a student for a private-pilot certificate of competence.

The act authorized $5,675,000 for the program during fiscal years 1939 and 1940, and specified that, thereafter, the appropriations should not exceed $7 million for any one fiscal year. The act was to expire on July 1, 1944. The program called for the training of 11,000 civilian pilots. Considerably fewer were actually trained the first year.

The name of the program was changed to the CAA War Training Service (WTS) in 1942. Training was limited to inactive reserve personnel. The WTS eventually trained 300,000 pilots by 1944.

The CPTPs were setup in educational institutions throughout the country. They offered an extensive program of flight training. Many of these schools were segregated. For African-Americans,

The Tuskegee Airmen

the CPTP marked the beginning of the second era of black aviation progress. It dispelled doubts as to the black man's ability to perform in all areas of aviation. CPTP produced many famous African-American airmen.

One of the segregated schools was West Virginia Institute. Another, the Coffey School of Aeronautics in Chicago, operated by Willa Beatrice Brown, became the hub of African-American Civil Air Patrol (CAP) activity in 1941. Instructors at Coffey included famous aviators such as Henri Fletcher, Charles Smallwood, and Edward Gibbs who founded Negro Airman International.

The real start of African-American participation in the CPTP, and in the Army Air Corps, came as a result of a chance meeting. On May 9, 1939, Dale White and Chauncey Spencer set out on a 3,000 mile round-trip demonstration cross-country flight to promote African-American aviation to the public, and to urge Congress to allow more opportunities for African-Americans in the field of aviation.

On a stopover in Washington, D.C., the two men accidentally met Senator Harry Truman. The Senator was unaware that not only were African-Americans excluded from the Air Corps, but also did not figure in the proposed CPTP. This chance meeting led to the intervention of Congress on behalf of African-Americans regarding aviation opportunities.

From it came the activation of the famous 99th Pursuit Squadron, an all black unit, on March 22, 1941, at Tuskegee Sub Depot, Tuskegee, Alabama. This was the first CPTP for African-Americans, and was also the most well-known. The First Lady, Eleanor Roosevelt, did a lot to promote equal opportunity for African-Americans in aviation and worked to help make the Tuskegee program a success.

The Tuskegee program was run by Major James Ellison, base commander, and Charles Alfred "Chief'" Anderson, who was the principal flight instructor. A famous airman from Tuskegee was Benjamin O. Davis, Jr., whose father was an Army general. Benjamin O. Davis, Jr., earned the Distinguished Flying Cross and the Silver Star in World War II. He also commanded the all-black 99th Pursuit Squadron in March 1941 and served in combat in North Africa in 1943. He became commander of the 332nd Fighter Group ("Red Tails"), and was the first African-American to be promoted to Brigadier General in the United States Air Force.

The 332nd Fighter Group flew more than 15,000 combat sorties and destroyed 260 enemy aircraft. After his retirement from the United States Air Force, Davis became the Assistant Secretary of Transportation for Environment, Safety and Commerce.

Members of the 332nd Fighter Group
stationed in Italy during WWII.

Top right: Brigadier General Benjamin O. Davis, Sr., August 8, 1944, in France. The first African-American promoted to General Officer in the Army.

Bottom Right: Lieutenant General Benjamin O. Davis, Jr., in his earlier flying days. He was the first African-American to be promoted to General Officer in the United States Air Force.

Key Terms and Concepts

- investments in post-WWI aviation
- barnstormers
- Army Air Corps
- Billy Mitchell's push for an independent Air Force
- aerial refueling
- first parachute jumps
- air races
- evolution of air mail
- legacy of Amelia Earhart
- technical improvements in aviation in the 20s and 30s

- development of the helicopter
- development of rockets
- McNary-Watres Act
- seaplanes
- re-emergence of the dirigible
- Civil Aeronautics Authority (CAA)
- creation of civilian flying schools prior to WWII
- Civilian Pilot Training Program (CPTP)
- Tuskegee Institute

? Test Your Knowledge ?

SELECT THE CORRECT ANSWER

1. *The* (**Pulitzer Trophy Race / Schneider Trophy Race**) *began in America when Ralph Pulitzer offered a trophy to promote high-speed flight.*
2. *The National Air Races were a result of the* (**Pulitzer Trophy Race / Thompson Race**).
3. *The* (**Bendix Race / Thompson Race**) *was a transcontinental speed race.*
4. *The Woman's Air Derby led the formation of an association of women fliers called the* (**Powder Puffs / Ninety-Nines**).
5. *In 1915,* (**Woodrow Wilson / Daniel Guggenheim**) *formed an organization called the National Advisory Committee for Aeronautics.*
6. *More efficient wing shapes were developed by* (**NACA / School of Aeronautics at New York University**) *scientists.*
7. (**Dr. Heinrich Focke / Igor Sikorsky**) *developed the first practical helicopter.*
8. (**Charles Lindbergh / Amelia Earhart**) *was the first person to cross the Atlantic Ocean solo.*
9. *One decline in the use of dirigibles during the 1930s can be traced to* (**many disasters / lack of landing sites**).
10. *The* (**Treaty of Versailles / Treaty of Paris**) *allowed the Germans to build Zeppelins again after their defeat in World War I.*

MATCHING

11. *First attempt to standardize and regulate commercial aviation.*
12. *Authorized a thorough study of commercial aviation.*
13. *Unified the economic and safety regulations of the entire field of aviation.*
14. *Allowed the contractor to be paid 80 percent of the air mail revenue.*

a. Air Mail Act of 1925
b. Air Commerce Act of 1926
c. Air Mail Act of 1934
d. Air Mail Act of 1938

TRUE OR FALSE

15. *Three Navy Curtiss flying boats successfully crossed the Atlantic Ocean on May 30, 1919.*
16. *On June 15, 1919, Henry Hawer and Kenneth McKenzie Grieve completed the first nonstop Atlantic crossing.*
17. *The United States built 15,000 airplanes during the 21 months it was involved in World War I.*
18. *At the end of World War I, airplane production dropped by 85 percent.*
19. *Aviation in America might have died down after World War I except for two groups of people — the barnstormers and the Army aviators.*
20. *Barnstormers put on flying exhibitions at county fairs, carnivals and anywhere else crowds gathered.*
21. *The main contribution barnstormers made to aviation was that they publicized aviation.*
22. *After General Mitchell's sinking of the* Ostfriesland, *both the Army and Congress were impressed with the military power of the airplane over the battleship.*
23. *The first successful transcontinental flight was completed on May 2, 1923, by two Navy fliers.*
24. *The first round-the-world flight was completed on May 30, 1919, by the Boeing aircraft* Seattle.
25. *The Army first tested the feasibility of using paratroops in September 1929.*
26. *Mitchell's verbal attacks on America's defense systems lead to his being relieved of command and reduced in rank to colonel.*
27. *Beginning on May 15, 1918, the Army flew air mail until stopped by the Air Mail Act of 1920.*
28. *The railroads welcomed the development of air mail service.*
29. *Charles Lindbergh was the first person to fly solo across the Atlantic Ocean in his airplane,* Spirit of St. Louis.
30. *Charles Lindbergh was responsible for thousands of people entering pilot training.*
31. *Amelia Earhart was the first woman to fly around the world.*
32. *Amelia Earhart was the first president of an international organization of women pilots known as the "Ninety-Nines."*
33. *In 1925, one of the earliest aircraft companies built in the United States was Travel Air Manufacturing Company.*
34. *Travel Air was formed by Lloyd Stearman, Walter Beech and Clyde V. Cessna.*

35. *Under the Kelley Act, the air mail carriers were paid according to the weight of the mail carried.*

36. *The McNary-Watres Act provided an incentive for air mail carriers to fly larger aircraft.*

37. *The first "modern" aircraft built in 1933 was the DC-2.*

38. *TWA was the first airline to use the* Clipper *seaplanes.*

39. *The* Clipper *flying boats were replaced by large 4-engine land planes after World War II.*

40. *The Boeing 299 was later known to the Army as the B-17.*

41. *The Presidential message of January 12, 1939, to Congress described America's military's forces as entirely adequate to meet any threats in Europe.*

Chapter 4 AIR POWER GOES TO WAR

Some have called World War II the "Air War" because, for the United States, it started with an air attack at Pearl Harbor and ended with the aerial bombing of Japan 5 years later. During these 5 years, many lessons were learned about the use of air power. Moreover, during this one 5-year period, the airplane developed faster than during any other five-year period in its history.

 bjectives

Discuss German, Japanese and Italian air power preparations for World War II.

Discuss US and British air power preparations for World War II.

Recognize the German combined arms approach to warfare.

Recognize the impact technology had on the Battle of Britain.

Describe the lessons learned from the outcome of the Battle of Britain.

Describe how the Germans used air power when they opened up a second front against the Russians.

Identify the only country using women to fly combat sorties in 1941.

Discuss why the Japanese plan for the attack on Pearl Harbor attacked American air power first.

Discuss the impact the North African air campaign had on military air power.

Identify the theories of the early air power theorists.

Describe the early Royal Air Force bombing experience before the start of the Combined Bombing Offensive.

Describe the effectiveness of the Army Air Corps bombing strategy at the beginning of World War II.

Discuss what changes in strategy and tactics led to the Allies gaining air superiority over Europe.

Discuss the impact air superiority had on the European campaign.

Identify the first objective planned for by the Japanese during their advance through the Pacific.

Describe how Allied air power stopped the Japanese advance.

Identify the reasons the Japanese-held islands located in the southwest Pacific had to be captured by the Allies.

Identify the most destructive air raid in history.

Identify why the atom bomb was used against Japan.

Discuss air power's role in war.

Discuss the lessons learned in the European Air Campaign.

Discuss the lessons learned in the Pacific Air Campaign.

World War II

The Treaty of Versailles, which ended World War I, restricted Germany from developing any type of military aircraft. The treaty did not, however, except for a brief 6-month period, prohibit German manufacture of commercial aircraft. The German aircraft industry started its revival in the early 1920s, building aircraft that could be very quickly converted from civilian to military use.

Many German aircraft builders also established manufacturing agreements in such foreign countries as Russia, Sweden, Denmark, Italy and Switzerland. At the time, many German pilots were trained in foreign countries, especially in South America. It is important to note the facilities in Germany and in many of these foreign countries were small. The factories, nor the industrial base, were large enough to produce the required numbers of aircraft and engines.

During the '30s, Germany started building its air power. The Stuka dive-bomber was an important part of Hitler's "Lightning War," or Blitzkrieg.

It was, therefore, under the disguise of commercial aviation that the German Air Force was built. By 1932, the German Air Force (officially nonexistent) consisted of three bomber squadrons, four fighter squadrons and eight observation squadrons. There were also 1,500 trained pilots and another 3,000 in training in 1932. When Adolf Hitler assumed power in 1933, the buildup became more obvious. By 1935 all pretense ended, and the Luftwaffe, the German Air Force, was officially formed.

In July of 1936, the Spanish Nationalists, led by General Francisco Franco, launched a revolution against the Spanish Loyalist government. Both Germany and Italy provided aid to the Nationalists and used this Civil War to test their armies and military tactics. This provided a proving ground for the pilots of the Luftwaffe, and tested many of the German aircraft that were used in World War II.

In Italy, the Italian Air Force had become obsolete following World War I. When Mussolini came into power in 1922, he started to rebuild it. They started with about 100 aircraft and built it up to about 2,600 by the time they entered World War II. The Italians not only fought in the Spanish Civil War, mentioned previously, but also against Ethiopia in 1935 - 1936. The Italians were battle tested and ready for World War II.

On the other side of the world, the Japanese Air Force was growing as well. They received training from a group of 60 French airmen who arrived in 1919 to provide assistance to the Japanese Army. The Japanese actually had two separate air arms, the Army Air Force and the Navy Air Force. Each had a separate mission. The Army Air Force was designed solely to support the Japanese Army, and the Navy Air Force was responsible for convoy protection, coastal patrol and submarine patrol.

The Japanese built a strong Navy. This included carrier-based aircraft like this Aichi Val. *(EAA)*

In 1920, the Japanese Navy built its first aircraft carrier. In 1921, a group of retired Royal Air Force officers from Britain trained the Japanese in carrier operations.

When Japan invaded Manchuria in 1931 and then drove into China in 1937, the Japanese Air Force performed well. They became combat tested and very experienced fighter pilots. The Japanese pilots were also tested against Russia during the Russian-Japanese border clashes from 1936 to 1939.

Allied Preparedness

At the end of World War I, the Allied Nations (England, France and the United States) had the most powerful air forces in the world. However, as mentioned earlier, without exception, each country made a mistake. Once the war was over, they all began cutting back. By the early 1920s, their air forces were very weak. This was occurring while the Germans, Italians and Japanese were expanding their air forces.

England emerged from World War I with an independent air force, the Royal Air Force (RAF). Between the world wars, they emphasized an offensive doctrine and planned for a large fleet of bombers rather than smaller pursuit aircraft (fighters) to defend their shores from enemy bombers. Their pilot training was excellent, and they stressed quality rather than quantity. When the British saw that the German Luftwaffe was building up and had the capability to attack England, they changed their offensive doctrine. Instead of building bombers for offensive purposes, the RAF turned to a defensive doctrine and began concentrating on building smaller fighter aircraft. The aviation industry began increasing its production, and money was provided to expand and enlarge the RAF.

When England entered World War II, she had a small well-trained Air Force and an industry that was capable of producing large numbers of aircraft. The first task of the RAF, therefore, was to defend England and hold off the German Luftwaffe. The famous aerial defense of England was called the Battle of Britain. Meanwhile, France, the nation that best understood the important lessons of air power taught by World War I, found itself completely unprepared for World War II.

After World War I, the French spent their money on the development of a ground defense. It was called the Maginot Line, and it was intended to keep the Germans from invading France. The French believed this new wall of well armed forts would turn back any invading army.

This is why the French Air Force was not born until 1933. The results were a small, poorly trained Air Force and an aviation industry, that because of labor disputes and low morale, produced very few first-line aircraft. When World War II began, the French had about 400 first-line fighters, fewer than 100 modern observation aircraft and 400 obsolete bombers.

Following World War I, the United States' Army Air Corps was almost completely disarmed. Congress and the Army leadership failed to listen to General William "Billy" Mitchell's plea for separate, but equal Air Force. So, the Army Air Service received last priority for budgets enlarging and modernizing the nation's air arm. The mood of the United States was one of isolationism and this, coupled with the severe depression of the 1930s, resulted in very little money available for the military.

After World War II started, the United States began to see that it could not isolate itself from events taking place in the rest of the world. Even when France fell in 1940, a majority of Americans still believed that the United States should not become directly involved in the war. Many thought we should only provide additional assistance to Britain. The President and Congress did, however, begin to listen to the Army and Navy about improving defense, and did provide money for strengthening it.

In 1940 and 1941, great strides were made building up American industry for war. Orders from Britain and France, and from the American military, began pouring into American aircraft companies. In 1939, the aviation manufacturers in the United States produced only 2,100 military aircraft for the entire year. By July 1940, production increased to 570 planes per month, and 1,900 aircraft were produced in September 1941.

Despite the improvements, when Pearl Harbor was bombed on December 7, 1941, the United States military still used mostly obsolete equipment and had a shortage of military pilots ready for combat.

A New Type of War

Learning from Germany's terrible losses as a result of the trench warfare of World War I, German generals came up with a new type of warfare. It was called "Blitzkrieg" (lightning war). Blitzkrieg is also known as combined arms operations because the army and the air forces are used in combination with each other.

During World War I, armies lined up against each other and slugged it out. Terrible losses resulted for both sides. Thousands and thousands of men lost their lives and hardly gained an inch of ground.

At the end of that war, new inventions were used to break the stalemate. The tank was invented to safely move troops through enemy lines, and the airplane was used to drop bombs behind enemy lines. The result was that these new inventions changed warfare. Instead of lining up armies to slug it out on the battlefield, a new type of warfare emerged.

The new type of warfare, called combined arms, surprised almost everyone. The new tactics allowed territory to be gained quickly. Armed forts were by-passed, encircled, and cut off from supplies and reinforcements. Tanks and cannons with wheels, known as mobile artillery, allowed the army to run right through the enemy's lines. Combined with the airplane, this new doctrine of combining the firepower of the tank and the airplane worked well.

Airplanes allowed the army to spot enemy strongholds and by-pass them. Airplanes equipped with machine guns and bombs could easily "rain" bullets and bombs on top of the enemy. Warfare changed. The first to use it, the Germans, had the advantage until a strategy could be found to defeat this new type of war.

The backbone of the German Air Force was the Messerschmitt bf-109 similar to this Spanish version of the 109. *(EAA)*

The aircraft the Germans developed worked well for combined arms operations. Some, particularly the ME-109, FW-190, and ME-262, possessed outstanding qualities. The Messerschmitt 109 was the backbone fighter of the German Air Force and was produced more than any other fighter aircraft in World War II.

Turning to bomber aircraft, Germany's bombers did not compare to the American B-17 or the British Sterling. This was by design, since the German doctrine of combined arms did not emphasize long-range bombing. All the Germans needed for combined arms operations were short-and medium-range bombers. It was the British and the Americans who needed long-range bombers because they were located far away from the fight in continental Europe.

The German bombers were two-engine mediums, chiefly the Heinkel III and the Dornier 17. They also had the Junkers 87, the Stuka. The Stuka was perfectly designed for German Blitzkrieg, combined arms operations, and became a very highly publicized dive-bomber during the war.

War!

Austria was the first victim of German aggression. However, the Germans did not use warfare. Instead, they used propaganda and assassination. German troops marched into Austria and occupied it on March 11, 1938. On March 14, 1939, Germany took over Czechoslovakia in much the same manner.

Hitler tried the same tactics on Poland that had worked on Austria and Czechoslovakia. Poland, however, had a fairly strong modern army, and also had a formal treaty with England and France that promised armed support if attacked. Hitler was convinced that England and France would not intervene. When Poland refused to surrender, Germany invaded. The date was September 1, 1939, and this date marks the beginning of the fighting in World War II.

The German invasion of Poland was the first use of the German doctrine of combined arms operations, and it surprised almost everyone. The closely coordinated effort between the Luftwaffe and the German Army crushed all opposition.

The Luftwaffe first destroyed any opposing air force, generally by catching them on the ground with a surprise strike. Once this was done, the German Air Force hit railroads, ammunition dumps and troop concentrations without a fight. The German Army used their tanks and mobile artillery, called armored divisions, to strike rapidly through enemy defensive lines. Any attempt to reinforce the defenders or to retreat was immediately crushed by the Luftwaffe from the air. A new type of warfare had begun, and it was highly successful. Poland's Army, which was the fifth largest in Europe, was defeated in about one month.

The Germans used air power to machine-gun (strafe) and bomb enemy troops and supplies, and to transport aircraft. They moved infantry quickly to the battlefield, evacuated wounded soldiers and carried supplies to units moving speedily into new bases that were being setup as fast as they conquered new territory.

When Germany invaded Poland, Britain and France declared war on the Axis Powers (Germany, Italy and Japan), but were unable to provide any relief for Poland. Neither England nor France had sufficient military strength because they reduced the size of the armies after their tremendous victory in World War I. As a result of their lack of preparedness, the only thing they could do was initiate a defensive war.

America started building a larger Air Force during the '30s. Although it resembled airplanes of WWI, the Stearman was an excellent trainer for combat pilots. *(EAA)*

France began by calling up its force to mobilize behind the Maginot Line, and England sent a small expeditionary force to take up defensive positions in France. They established a naval blockade of Germany, and ordered an increase in the production of planes and tanks to fight Hitler wherever he attacked next.

Germany Takes Europe

To break the naval blockade in April of 1940, Hitler decided to acquire new ports. So, he decided to invade Norway and Denmark. This time the Germans used a new tactic. They parachuted in airborne infantry. This was the first time airborne troops were parachuted into enemy territory.

Like the invasion of Poland, the new German strategy worked well. Denmark was overrun in 1 day, and the Norwegian Army never really mobilized. The German airborne infantry landed at the Oslo Airfield and soon captured the Norwegian capital.

In 1 day, Germany had captured Norway's capital and its principal harbors. Although British troops landed to reinforce the Norwegians, they lacked the air power necessary to beat back the German Luftwaffe. The German Air Force controlled the air and the British were defeated. Norway surrendered in June 1940. All that remained free from German occupation was the Netherlands, Belgium and France.

While the Germans were taking Norway, the French continued to build up forces behind the wall of forts called the Maginot Line. German Blitzkrieg strategy called for bypassing strongholds and cutting them off from behind. This is what happened to France's infamous Maginot Line. Instead of running head-on into France's strong defensive fortress, the Germans simply went around it. They struck from the north through the Netherlands and Belgium.

Lacking the defensive air force to stop German air power, and with no air support for their Army, France fell in only 6 weeks. When France surrendered on June 22, 1940, only Britain's RAF stood between Hitler, England and the total conquest of Europe.

The Battle of Britain

The Hawker *Hurricane* was an outstanding British fighter. It was one of the "heroes" of the Battle of Britain. *(EAA)*

After their successes in France, the German Luftwaffe commanders urged an immediate invasion of England. The German Navy, however, was no match for the British Royal Navy and could not guarantee the security of the supply line across the English Channel.

In addition, the German Army needed time to secure the landing sites when they arrived. The best the German Army and Navy could hope for was a stalemate. What they needed was complete command of the air.

This is why Hitler decided not to invade England immediately, but to wait until the Luftwaffe could win the war in the air. Germany needed to defeat the Royal Air Force first. Then they could concentrate on defending their supply lines and beachheads without being vulnerable to air attacks.

The problem with the German plan was that they didn't design the Luftwaffe to be a long-range bombing force. Remember, previously we mentioned that combined arms operations required short- and medium-range bombers to support the infantry. The Luftwaffe was not designed to do long-range bombing.

Also, the German aircraft industry did not have the capability to build the larger aircraft with bigger engines, fuel tanks and longer range. These facts played a large role in determining the winner of the Battle of Britain.

The air war started during the first week of August 1940. The Germans began with sporadic air raids. They tried to feel out British defenses. To do this, the Germans had four types of primary bombers: the Junkers 87, Junkers 88, several models of the Heinkel III, and the Dornier 17 (sometimes known as the Dornier 215). They also had fighter escort to defend against the RAF fighter aircraft. The Messerschmitt 109s and 110s provided the escort.

The entire strength of the Luftwaffe was not thrown into the campaign at once. The attacks began on a moderate scale. During the next 10 days, mass formations of German bombers, along with their fighter escorts, made daylight raids on shipping and southern ports.

The RAF put up a heroic defense. The RAF fighters, like the Hurricane and the Spitfire, assisted by ground defenses, caused the Germans to call a brief halt to operations after August 18. On that day, they had lost 71 planes and had another 23 damaged. The RAF was getting the best of the Luftwaffe.

From August 8-23, the Luftwaffe lost 403 planes and had another 127 damaged. In contrast, the RAF announced that they had only lost 153 planes. The world had never seen such an aerial display.

British radio broadcast the battles live. Britons huddled around their radios and cheered the RAF on to victory.

The Luftwaffe had a problem. Their short-and medium-range aircraft could not fly from their bases in France, over the 22 mile English Channel, and then fight the RAF and still have enough fuel to reach their targets successfully. Two things that were mentioned earlier were now beginning to hurt the Luftwaffe.

First, they could not produce larger aircraft in the 1920s and early 1930s because the industrial base was not there. Secondly, when the Germans could have changed their production efforts, they chose not to because their new Blitzkrieg, and tactics called for short-and medium-range aircraft only.

At this point, the Luftwaffe decided to revise their tactics in order to concentrate on defeating the RAF. In the second phase of the campaign, from August 24 through September 6, the Luftwaffe reduced its bomber formations in size, and increased the number of fighter escorts. Targets were changed as well. The attacks were now directed mainly against air force bases and aircraft factories instead of shipping and harbors.

This campaign was designed to knock out the RAF. More escorts were added to fight as many RAF fighter aircraft as possible. The German's changed targets so if RAF pilots survived the fight, they wouldn't have air bases to which they could return and land.

In addition, if their aircraft were damaged, no replacements would be available. The fight for command of the air over the English Channel was on.

Once again the RAF successfully defended England, but it was not an easy fight. The Luftwaffe relentlessly attacked British defenses. The British leaned on new technology to help defend England. They built a warning system that relied on visual observation, telephones, and something new, radar.

Radar helped the British see the Luftwaffe when they were on their way across the English Channel. When radar first spotted the Luftwaffe, a telephone call was made to alert the nearest air base. While the pilots were getting ready, observers on the coast of England called in updates on the latest location of the Luftwaffe. This allowed RAF pilots to conserve fuel as they could takeoff and go directly to the fight. It also allowed the RAF to mass as many fighters as possible, and hopefully outnumber the Luftwaffe during the fight.

The Luftwaffe reacted to the RAF's tactics by attacking British radar sites. Fortunately, the bombing was not very effective because the British used decoys to distract the Luftwaffe, and after the Germans attacked the sites, they did not attack them again for a very long time. This allowed the British the opportunity to repair the radars.

One of the great legends of WWII, the Supermarine Spitfire. *(EAA)*

The Spitfire is a prized collector's airplane today. *(EAA)*

Nonetheless, repeated Luftwaffe attacks on RAF bases, factories and radar sites did take their toll. In fact, the Luftwaffe had the RAF on the ropes, and was about to win the battle for the skies over Britain.

However, the RAF's Bomber Command was not standing idly by while the Fighter Command bore the brunt of the German assault on Britain. Bomber Command was also launching bombing raids across the English Channel. One attack, although minor because it inflicted little damage, had a very large impact on the Battle of Britain. In fact, many argue that it was the turning point in the war because it infuriated Hitler.

Hitler was very angry when RAF bombers made it through German defenses and bombed Berlin. He, therefore, ordered the Luftwaffe to stop their attacks on RAF bases and aircraft factories. Then he directed a retaliatory attack on London.

Hitler did not realize that he had let the RAF off the hook. The RAF had been hurt, and hurt badly. They needed time to recover, but the Germans did not know this. Thus, Hitler inadvertently, gave the RAF time to recover.

This new phase and third phase (from September 7 to October 1) of the battle, was the peak of the German air effort. The Luftwaffe now directed their new effort toward industrial areas and London, in particular.

Meanwhile, Fighter Command repaired its runways, fuel supply areas, maintenance facilities and radar sites. This allowed the RAF to recover and reenergize their efforts. They needed time and they used it wisely.

By the end of September, the RAF turned the corner and began to assert control of the air over the British Isles. The long flights to London gave the RAF more opportunity to attack Luftwaffe aircraft. The British destroyed 435 planes and damaged 161. Total German losses from July 10 now amounted to 1,408 planes destroyed. Unable to sustain such losses, the Germans decided to change tactics even further.

This time, nearly all their so-called "long-range" bombers were withdrawn, while fighters and fighter-bombers continued the campaign with a decreasing number of daylight attacks and an increasing number of attacks at night. They did not change targets, however, and this was key.

London was still the principal target. During the Battle of Britain, the Luftwaffe dropped 190,000 tons of bombs on Britain, killing more than 43,000 civilians and seriously wounding another 56,000. Although the British suffered heavy casualties and extensive materiel damage, they did not lose control of the skies over the English Channel. This was the initial German objective of the Battle of Britain. They wanted to control the skies so they could invade, but they failed.

The Luftwaffe's aerial blitz was gradually reduced to intermittent attacks that continued throughout the spring of 1941. The Luftwaffe had sustained its first major defeat, and Britain had been saved.

In retrospect, there were many lessons to be learned from what has been called the finest defensive air battle ever fought in the history of air power.

First and foremost, it must be recognized that the Battle of Britain was a defensive battle for the RAF. Britain's decision to emphasize a defensive mind set was a key to the RAF's victory. The RAF started building fighter aircraft instead of offensive bombers, and concentrated on a defensive strategy centered on the Royal Observer Corps and the new radar.

So, the RAF had the right aircraft for the battle, while the Luftwaffe did not. The Germans had short-and

Ryan, the company that built Lindbergh's *Spirit of St. Louis*, later manufactured thousands of military training planes.

medium-range aircraft designed to support their Blitzkrieg doctrine of combined arms operations. They did not have the aircraft to conduct long-range strategic bombing.

Second, the RAF's use of radar cannot be understated. Without the radar, the RAF's Fighter Command would not have been able to mass their aircraft and take the fight to the Luftwaffe.

Third, Germany's lack of determination and persistence was another key to victory. If the Luftwaffe had started out by attacking the RAF and had not given up, they may have won. Instead, they started out attacking shipping, then finally London. The lesson here is that if you want to obtain command of the air, you must concentrate your offensive efforts on defeating the enemy's air force.

War on Two Fronts

When France surrendered to Germany in 1940, Italy joined with Germany and declared war on Great Britain. The immediate goals of the Italians were to capture the oil-rich Middle East and the Suez Canal. They also invaded Greece to secure their invasion of Egypt.

In January 1941, the German Luftwaffe moved approximately 330 aircraft into Italy and Sicily to support the Italians. On January 18, the Germans inaugurated the first of a long series of heavy air attacks on the island of Malta. Malta was a strategically located base for British operations in the Mediterranean and, therefore, a key target.

Before the end of 1941, the island experienced its one-thousandth air attack, but the British continued to withstand the pounding from the Italians and the Luftwaffe. By using advanced bases in North Africa, the Luftwaffe also began to strike at British forces in the Suez Canal area and to participate more actively in the African Western Desert Campaign.

USAAF personnel are shown here plotting an 8th Air Force bombing mission.

Similarly, during the Battle of Britain, pilots were directed to incoming German attackers by ground-based controllers using radar.

Meanwhile in Eastern Europe, by April 1941, German bombers moved into the Balkans in preparation for the next Blitzkrieg operation. From bases in Hungary, Bulgaria and southern Germany, the Luftwaffe began extensive operations in support of German ground forces against Yugoslavia and Greece.

The British expeditionary forces, though fully occupied in North Africa, came to the aid of Greece. But this time, the German onslaught overpowered all opposition, and German and Italian victories followed in rapid-fire succession. By the end of April, most of the British forces had been evacuated from Greece, and the Germans had entered Athens.

The next big activity for the Luftwaffe was to prepare for an airborne attack against the island of Crete, Greece. This attack was a spectacular and successful demonstration of glider-borne and parachute troop operations. After seizing key air bases, advanced German forces were supplied and reinforced by Junkers 52 troop carriers, while Luftwaffe bombers attacked the British who were attempting to evacuate the island.

By June, the British had been forced to yield Crete to the invaders. With new bases in Greece and Crete, the German Air Force was able to bring more strength to bear against British forces in the African Western Desert. The Luftwaffe, for a brief period, increased its support of German ground forces in the Northern Africa campaign.

Germany now occupied all of south and southeastern Europe and was moving through Africa against heavy British resistance. The Germans were also successfully blockading the British Isles through a combined submarine and Luftwaffe effort. However, Hitler made another big mistake. On June 22, 1941, Germany invaded Russia and created a second front.

The Russian Front

Because Hitler was convinced the Russian campaign would be concluded within a very short time, he was opposed to the destruction of Russian factories by bombing. Upon his insistence, the Luftwaffe was used primarily as an extended form of artillery in support of ground forces.

In its initial assault against Russia, 3,300 aircraft out of a total strength of approximately 5,900 operational and non-operational aircraft supported the German Army. In the drive toward Moscow, in the autumn

The Russian Stormavik Fighter

of 1941, the Luftwaffe deployed almost 60 percent of its strength along the eastern front and suffered extremely heavy losses.

Russia met the Luftwaffe with everything it had, including women pilots. Russian women flew combat missions almost from the beginning of the war. At this time, they were the only country among the major powers to use women in combat sorties.

In 1941, Major Marina Raskova formed three regiments of women fliers who flew fighters and bombers. These were all-female squadrons, but women also flew in male squadrons. Lilya Litvyak was a top woman ace who destroyed 12 German planes. In 1943, at age 22, she was shot down and received the Soviet Union's highest award for aviators.

Multiple Fronts Spread Them Thin

The Russian operations caused no immediate increase in German aircraft production. The German high command, apparently still convinced that the hostilities could be concluded in short order, seemed to feel that the impact of fighting on three major fronts was small. The Luftwaffe was fighting in Eastern Europe, the Mediterranean, and North Africa. As a result, German air strength was spread too thin and air attacks on England and British shipping could not continue at their previous pace. They eventually dwindled almost to the point of cessation.

During the last 6 months of 1941, no night attack against Britain exceeded 15 percent of the maximum scale of effort made during the autumn of 1940. The Luftwaffe assumed a defensive attitude in the west.

Hitler supposedly promised Luftwaffe leaders that the air offensive against Britain would be resumed after the defeat of Russia, but the opportunity had come and gone in 1940, and the future for the Luftwaffe in the west was only a defensive mission.

Hitler had hoped for a short-duration war, but was now settling down for a long struggle of large land armies. In this type of a struggle, Germany was bound to lose, especially when she was committed to fighting on three different fronts—British, Russian and African.

The Heinkel HE III bomber was used extensively in the Battle of Britain.

As the year 1941 drew to a close, Germany was still a powerful nation and the Allies (British and Russians) were still on the defensive. It was at this point that two new nations entered the war: one on the side of the aggressors and one on the side of the British and the Russians. The war, which had been limited to Europe and the Middle East, became a true world war. On December 7, 1941, the Japanese bombed Pearl Harbor and the United States entered World War II.

The United States Enters the War

Strategy

Even before the United States entered World War II, there were several conferences between Allied leaders (Britain, United States and Russia) to discuss the conduct of the war. The overall strategy decided on by the leaders gave priority to the war in Europe and defeating Germany first.

Since the Allies believed that Japan might also go to war against them, the Allies needed to contain Japan until Germany was defeated. There were several reasons for this. First, Germany was viewed as a more immediate threat and her industrial ability was more feared than Japan's. Second, the Allies in Europe had already been involved in the war for over 2 years and they needed more immediate relief. Third, the Allies did not believe their capacity, even including the United States, would be sufficient to allow a maximum effort in both Europe and the Pacific.

Japanese Territorial Strategy

The Japanese attack on Pearl Harbor was not a sudden irrational act. It actually began as early as 1931. The island nation of Japan had always depended on imports for her survival. As Japan's population increased in the early 1930s, she began to develop plans to expand her territory into China and Indochina to gain the raw materials she needed to become an industrial nation.

Japan moved into Manchuria and China in 1939 and expanded into French Indochina after the French surrender in 1940. Alarmed by these movements, the United States and Britain embargoed all trade with Japan. This embargo forced Japan to either give up her thoughts of expansion or to resort to war. Japan chose the latter.

The Japanese strategy called for striking swiftly in several directions, capturing the East Indies, Philippines, New Guinea, and the Marshall, Caroline and Mariana Islands. Japan would then use these as a defense perimeter by fortifying them and building air bases.

There were two weaknesses in the Japanese strategy, and they were both centered on her Navy and Merchant Marine. First, Japan needed to import large quantities of raw materials to manufacture the war goods necessary to sustain military operations. So she needed to ensure that her Merchant Marine could safely cross the Pacific.

Second, Japan's naval fleet was spread across more than 6,000,000 square miles of the Pacific. Japan realized this and, in order to succeed, planned to destroy the United States Pacific naval fleet at Pearl Harbor.

Pearl Harbor

The Japanese attack on Pearl Harbor early in the morning of December 7, 1941, was a well-planned and skillfully executed air attack. The Japanese task force of six aircraft carriers and 25 support vessels left Japan on November 28. They were directed to a spot 200 miles north of Hawaii before dawn on December 7th.

At 5:00 am on December 7th, two Japanese Zero reconnaissance planes surveyed Pearl Harbor and reported that the fleet was there. One hour later, takeoff orders were issued and soon 50 fighters, 50 horizontal bombers, 40 torpedo bombers, and 50 dive-bombers were in the air. Forty-five minutes later, a second wave composed of 50 horizontal bombers, 80 dive-bombers, and 40 fighters followed.

The primary purpose of the Japanese attack was to cripple the American fleet at Pearl Harbor. To do this, the Japanese decided to first achieve temporary air superiority over Hawaii. After achieving command of the skies, they could then concentrate their attack on the American naval fleet with little to no interference. Therefore, they planned to eliminate American air power on the

Mitsubishi A6M2 Zero Fighter

Japanese Attack on Pearl Harbor

ground with a surprise attack. At 7:55 am, the Japanese began bombing and strafing American airfields on the island of Oahu.

As planned, every advantage lay with the Japanese because they had achieved complete surprise. One Japanese advantage arose from America's fear of sabotage. On November 27, 1941, American Air Force and Navy airplanes had been taken out of their hangars and parked closely together on runways as a precautionary measure. They wanted to make sure no one on foot could get to their aircraft. So they put all of the planes in one place under armed guard.

The problem, of course, was that this made them vulnerable to an air attack. The Japanese destroyed 96 Army and 92 Navy planes and damaged 159 more. During the attack, only 6 Army fighters and 36 Navy aircraft were able to get into the air.

Meanwhile, as the Japanese were wiping out American air power on Oahu, other Japanese pilots were taking advantage of their air superiority. The Japanese attacked Pearl Harbor where 8 battleships, 7 cruisers, 28 destroyers, 5 submarines and 32 other ships sat vulnerable to the surprise attack.

For 30 minutes, starting at 8:00 am, the helpless fleet, moored and wholly unprepared, was pounded by wave after wave of dive-, torpedo and horizontal bombers. After a 15-minute lull, the Japanese renewed the attack with vigor.

In total, the Navy suffered a staggering blow. The battleships *Arizona*, *California* and *West Virginia* were sunk, the battleship *Oklahoma* capsized; and the battleship *Nevada* and three other battleships were severely damaged. Three cruisers, three destroyers, and a seaplane were also damaged.

The Japanese delivered one of the worst defeats in American military history upon the United States Pacific fleet in Hawaii. In addition to heavy losses of airplanes and ships, the human cost was staggering. The Navy and Marine Corps totaled 2,117 killed, 960 missing and 876 wounded. Two hundred and twenty-six Army and Army Air Force personnel were killed and 396 wounded. The Japanese lost 28 planes and a total of 64 men in the entire operation.

The only bright spot for America, in the bombing of Pearl Harbor, was that the Japanese failed to destroy the four aircraft carriers of the Pacific fleet. Fortunately, they were on maneuvers and not present when the attack occurred.

Because of the treaties between Japan, Germany and Italy, the attacks against Pearl Harbor brought the United States into the war automatically against all three of the Axis Powers. On December 8th, the United States declared war on Japan; on December 11, the United States declared war on Germany and Italy. England and the other Allies followed suit and declared war on Japan. Now, all the major powers were engaged in a total world war.

US Air Power Spins Up

The aircraft production of 1940 and 1941 was increased drastically after the United States declared war on the Axis Powers. However, the Army Air Forces still had problems with pilot training and their total strength. After Pearl Harbor, the "contract" schools increased their production of pilots. Then, on December 7, 1942, the Civil Aeronautics Administration's (CAA) Civilian Pilot Training Program became the CAA War Training Service. This change in name gave official recognition to changes that had already occurred in the armed services.

Beginning July 1942, and lasting until the following December, training under this program was given only to members of the inactive reserve of either the Army Air Forces or the Naval Reserve. In December 1942, the Navy placed its trainees under the program on active duty. The Army took this step in the summer of 1943. In all, some 300,000 pilots were trained in the War Training Service Program which lasted until June 1944, for the Army and until August 1944, for the Navy.

In the autumn of 1942, the Women's Auxiliary Ferrying Squadron (WAFS) was

Female pilots, in front of the B-17E, ferried aircraft from factories and repair facilities.

established within the Army Air Forces Air Transport Command. The WAFS personnel were civil service employees, not military members of the Army Air Forces, and were not given the Army Air Corps uniform.

Nancy Love, the WAFS's first director, personally led the group ferrying aircraft. To prepare women for their ferrying duties, Jacqueline Cochran formed the Women's Flying Training Detachment (WFTD). These two organizations eventually merged and in August 1943, the WAFS and the WFTD formed the Women's Air Force Service Pilots (WASP). With Cochran as the first director, the group continued delivering planes to England and to other spread out locations.

European Campaign

Grand Strategy

Once the United States entered the war, the overall Allied strategy changed from defense to offense; recapture territory occupied by Germany; and then, finally, force Germany and then Japan to unconditionally surrender. The campaigns were divided in two. The first was the European campaign and it took precedence over the other in the Pacific.

To understand the role air power played in World War II, we must examine how the military leadership treated air power at the start of the war. First, the Army and the Air Corps leadership had different ideas on how to use air power.

The Army leaders envisioned a large invasion of France and then a fight across France and into Germany. The Allied Army would crush the Axis forces and force the enemy to surrender. So, they viewed air power as necessary to support their ground operations.

Air Corps leaders viewed the use of air power differently. There were two things air power could do. It could support army ground operations, and it could launch large-scale strategic bombing operations. Using large bombers under the control of air force commanders, long-range bombers could attack deep within an enemy's homeland and destroy his will and ability to fight the war.

Air power was not just for supporting ground operations. That is what the Germans were doing, and one of the reasons they lost the Battle of Britain.

An American B-17 Flying Fortress.
Note the guns in the nose, rear, sides and on top. *(EAA)*

They were not equipped for long-range bombing. The United States, on the other hand, had the B-17, a bomber which was as fast as any fighter and armed to defend itself.

Learning in North Africa

One of the first operations conducted by Army Air Corps aircraft occurred in North Africa. The Allies were fighting a determined German effort to push them out of Africa. The German Luftwaffe harassed and pounded Allied ground forces. Although each allied ground commander had some aircraft at his disposal, they were out numbered by the Luftwaffe and continually beaten.

The problem was first identified by the British and later by the Americans, who also had to learn the lesson the "hard way," before taking counsel. Like the British, the Americans parceled out their air assets to individual Army commanders who used them to protect their troops from continuous Luftwaffe assaults. Each time the Luftwaffe attacked one of the Army units, the units tried to defend themselves and received very little help from the rest of the units nearby. This resulted in the Army Air Corps being outnumbered and beaten by the Luftwaffe every time.

The Army soon followed the RAF's lead and centralized control of the air assets. This way, when the Luftwaffe attacked, they would not be met by just one Army commander's limited amount of airplanes. Instead, the Luftwaffe would meet a much larger number of aircraft.

The centralized control of aircraft worked so well President Roosevelt and Prime Minister Churchill decided to further centralize control of the air forces at the Allied level over the entire European Theater.

This lesson learned had a tremendous impact. Centralized control eventually led to the defeat of the Luftwaffe in North Africa. The German Afrika-Korps, led by Field Marshal Rommel, began to feel the effects immediately as supplies of food, water, fuel, ammunition and replacements ran short. In October 1942, Rommel began retreating, but the Ninth Air Force and the RAF harassed his retreat.

Once Allied air forces gained air superiority over North Africa, the war on the ground turned around. By May 1943, the Axis forces were defeated in Africa. The United States Army Air Force learned several important lessons that would be used during the rest of World War II and are even still used today.

The most important lesson revealed that centralized control of the air forces allowed the following priorities (decided on after the initial defeats in North Africa) to happen:

1. <u>Gain Air Superiority</u>: Attack enemy airfields, repair shops, fuel supplies, and aircraft. This ensures that air operations can be conducted without meeting enemy resistance.

2. <u>Interdiction</u>: Cripple enemy supply lines, railroads, bridges, highways, supply dumps, troop concentrations and communications to isolate the battle area and prevent the enemy from entering or leaving the battlefield.

3. <u>Close Ground Support</u>: Use air power to bomb and strafe enemy troops and gun positions, and provide air cover for Allied troop movements.

In fact, the lessons learned in North Africa are so important they are still used today in the United States Air Force. One of the key principles of air power today is the centralized control of air assets.

Developing a Strategy

At the beginning of World War II, there were several theories on how to use air power. Before the United States entered the war, planners thought about how to best use America's air power. One theory came from the book called *Command of the Air*, written by Italian Air Marshal Giulio Douhet. Another theory was that of Sir Hugh Trenchard from England. Other theories were advocated by General Billy Mitchell and Captain Claire Chennault, both Americans.

Air Marshal Douhet wrote about gaining air supremacy with a massive first strike. This strike was supposed to be a surprise attack on the enemy's aircraft that were still on the ground. With little to no enemy opposition, one could then fly over the enemy's fielded forces and attack their population

The Lancaster, one of England's greatest WWII bombers. *(EAA)*

at home. This would wear down the enemy's will to resist, and they would eventually give in. Douhet believed that the strength of air power was so great, a large ground war would not be necessary.

Trenchard, who is considered to be the "Father of the RAF," also believed in long-range bombing. He thought that a proper force mix was about two-thirds bomber aircraft and one-third fighter. He differed a little with Douhet in what targets to hit.

He thought that air power could paralyze the enemy by knocking out its key vital centers. Bombing attacks would destroy the enemy's factories. Afterwards, the workers would have nowhere to work and paralysis would set in and destroy the enemy's will to continue the war.

American Billy Mitchell also believed that air power could fly over the enemy's fielded forces and take the war to the enemy's cities, and destroy their will to resist. He thought that 20 percent of the aircraft should be bombers, 20 percent small attack aircraft, and 60 percent should be fighter aircraft. He also thought the Navy should have at least 20 aircraft carriers.

All three theorists believed in long-range bombing and, most importantly, believed that the bomber would get through enemy defenses to its target. American Claire Chennault, on the other hand, did not believe that the bomber would get through unmolested. In fact, he proved it during an air exercise at Fort Knox, Kentucky, where he intercepted the bombers a good distance from their targets.

With this data to work from, planners at the Air Corps Tactical School at Maxwell Field in Alabama went to work. In essence, the result looked a lot like Douhet, and little like Mitchell and Trenchard, and not at all like Chennault. The Air Corps Tactical School also believed that the bomber would be able to get through enemy defenses to its targets. They, therefore, developed a theory that called for unescorted

Long-range reconnaissance planes, like the PBY, patrolled the vast expanse of the ocean. *(EAA)*

high altitude, daylight, precision bombing. In other words, they ignored Chennault's warnings. They decided that a well-armed bomber could fly high over enemy guns and with a new secret bombsight, called the Norden Bombsight, place bombs accurately on target. With that decided, America went to war.

The Eighth Air Force was formed to perform the strategic bombing of Germany, and moved to England. When they got there, they found that the RAF did not agree with their strategy. They had already

tried daylight bombing and suffered many losses. The RAF claimed their losses from German fighters and antiaircraft fire were less at night, and that daylight bombing was not the way to go. The United States claimed better accuracy with their new secret bombsight and persisted for daytime bombing.

In theory, it did seem like a good plan. With the Americans bombing during the day, and the British bombing at night, the pressure on Germany would never let up. On August 17, 1942, the plan was enacted and the bombing of German forces started.

The Combined Bomber Offensive

Throughout the war, the RAF and the American Air Force continued using their own strategy, and they did prove to complement each other. At the beginning, first priority targets were submarine factories, docks and ports. The German submarines were doing tremendous damage to Allied naval convoys and had to be stopped. In order to carry the war into Germany, both in the air and on the ground, the supplies had to get through.

Second priority targets were aircraft factories and munitions plants, and third priority went to communications and transportation systems.

The immortal B-24 Liberator was used worldwide in WWII but is best known for its raids on the Romanian oil field, Ploesti. *(EAA)*

Throughout 1942 and 1943, the Eighth Air Force's B-17 Flying Fortresses and B-24 Liberators bombed targets located mostly in France. During this time, the Allies were still in a building phase, trying to get aircraft to England from the United States and training the crewmembers. Also, the Eighth Air Force was having trouble with their strategy of unescorted, high altitude, daylight, precision bombing. The bomber was not getting through German defenses without a fight that resulted in many losses.

During the late summer and early fall of 1943, the Eighth Air Force made its first big effort at bombing deep inside Germany. The results were disastrous. In six missions from July 24 to July 30, they lost 92 bombers. Considering that the B-17 carried a crew of 10, over 900 aircrew were shot down and many lost their lives.

On August 17, in a raid against Schweinfurt and Regensburg, 60 bombers were lost. During the second week in October, 148 bombers were lost. The Luftwaffe's FW-190 ME-109, ME-110, and ME-210 fighters simply chewed-up the American bombers. The heavy losses had to stop, and an order was

An American B-17 braving anti-aircraft fire on its way to Germany.

Damaged B-17 returns to base and unloads injured crew.

issued to stop the air raids into Germany. There was no way the Americans could continue to lose aircraft and personnel at this rate. They simply did not have enough resources to continue at such a horrific loss rate.

The Americans reconsidered their strategy of unescorted, high-altitude, daylight, precision bombing. It seemed that Chennault was right. The bomber would not "always get through." Escorts were needed and the P-51 Mustang was on the way.

The Americans also decided they needed to change their tactics. They gave strict instructions to the short-range escorts to stay with the bombers as far as they could. Instead, new instructions allowed the fighter pilots the freedom to chase enemy fighters and shoot them down.

When the Combined Bomber Offensive resumed, the fighter escorts were modified with extra fuel tanks that could drop off. The drop tanks gave them a longer range, and allowed the fighters to drop them whenever the enemy appeared. This way the tanks did not slow them down in combat.

By the spring of 1944, the drop tanks were working and the P-51 Mustang had arrived. The long-range fighter escorts now allowed bombing activities to resume deep into Germany.

It was the fastest fighter-bomber of WWII. It had two names, Mosquito and the Wooden Wonder. *(EAA)*

The P-51 Mustang helped turn the tide of WWII's air war. *(EAA)*

On March 4, 1944, American bomber crews flew their first missions over Berlin. The priority targets were now fighter-manufacturing facilities, as well as oil refineries that produced fuel for the Luftwaffe. Other targets included engine manufacturers and ball bearing manufacturers. The ball bearings were targeted because almost all of the enemy's war-fighting machines, including aircraft, needed ball bearings.

Results of the renewed offensive into Germany were very good. The most important product of the new offensive was air superiority. The new tactics, combined with the bombing of

The P-47 Thunderbolt was one of the great fighters of WWII.
(EAA)

the oil refineries, hurt the Luftwaffe. American fighter escorts were now aggressively hunting down the Luftwaffe.

Meanwhile, aviation fuel was becoming scarce, which reduced Luftwaffe pilot training activity. New pilots had less training and, as a result, less skill. The Americans slowly gained the upper hand and the Luftwaffe ruled the air over Europe no more.

The Normandy Invasion

On June 6, 1944, Allies invasion forces landed in Normandy, France. Both the tactical and strategic air arms of the US Army Air Forces and the Royal Air Force supported the invasion. The pre-invasion air strikes went on for 2 months before the landings. These strikes were made against the Luftwaffe, railroad centers, coastal batteries and all airfields within a 130-mile radius of the landing beaches.

With air superiority obtained, the Normandy Invasion was almost completely unopposed by the Luftwaffe. Air superiority saved countless lives and pieces of equipment and hastened the defeat of Germany.

The strategic bombing of Germany continued after the Normandy Invasion with priority given to aircraft factories, oil refineries and transportation facilities. By 1945, the Luftwaffe had been beaten and was no longer a serious threat to the British and American bombers.

The Eighth and Fifteenth Air Forces were now built up to the point that it was not unusual for 1,000 to 1,500 bombers to be in the air every day. On April 15, the strategic bombing of Germany ended because there were no targets left to bomb.

On May 7, 1945, Germany surrendered and the war in Europe ended. During the air war in Europe, British and American planes dropped nearly two and one-half million tons of bombs. The Army Air Forces and the RAF lost approximately 8,000 bombers and 7,000 fighters. Luftwaffe losses were nearly 33,000 aircraft destroyed.

B-17 aircrew praying prior to takeoff from England.

ACES IN EUROPE

The Luftwaffe produced the most prolific aces of the war. The top three German aces shot down a total of 928 Allied aircraft. The top three European Theater of Operations American aces shot down 86 Axis aircraft.

Maj. Erich Hartmann	Germany	352
Capt. Hans H. Wind	Finland	75
Maj. Gen. I.N. Kozhedub	Russia	62
Prince C. Cantacuzino	Romania	60
Gp. Capt. J. E. Johnson	England	38
Lt Cvitan Galic	Croatia	36
Lt P. Clostermann	France	33
Flt Lt G. F. Beurling	Canada	31
Col. Francis S. Gabreski	United States	31
Lt Dezso Szentgyorgyi	Hungary	30

The Pacific Campaign

One of the Navy's first fighters of WWII was the Grumman *Wildcat*. (EAA)

While the Allies were fighting the war in Europe, they were also fighting a holding action in the Pacific, and they were not winning. By the summer of 1942, the Allies had been pushed back all the way to Australia in a series of Japanese victories.

At the same time as the attack on Pearl Harbor, the Japanese launched an offensive against the American bases on Midway Island, Wake Island, Guam, Hong Kong, Thailand, Burma and the Dutch East Indies. By March of 1942, the Japanese occupied the entire area of the southwest/central Pacific, which was what they had outlined in their original war plan.

Japanese/Allied Strength

From a military standpoint, Japan was stronger than either the British or the Americans. The British were fully engaged with the Germans in Africa and in defense of their homeland, so they would not be an immediate threat to the Japanese in the Pacific.

At the time Japan entered the war, they had an army of 2,400,000 well-trained men and 3,000,000 reserves. The Japanese Air Force consisted of 7,500 aircraft, and they were making over 400 new aircraft per month.

Opposing the Japanese in the Far East, the Allies had a force of about 550,000 poorly equipped Army troops, less than 1,000 obsolete aircraft, and nearly 90 naval ships.

The Japanese objectives in all of these campaigns were the same. Their air power would first gain air superiority. Then they would follow with an invasion. The Japanese controlled the air. That made it impossible to resupply Allied troops. It was only a matter of a short time before defenders had to surrender. The Allies were losing and were gradually being forced back toward Australia. By March 1942, what remained of the Allied air forces and navies had been evacuated to Australia.

Air Power Stops the Japanese Advance

The advance of the Japanese in the Pacific was stopped in the spring and summer of 1942 by two battles that were fought entirely by air power. These were the Battle of the Coral Sea and the Battle of Midway. Both of these battles were naval battles, but for the first time in history, these battles were conducted without the surface ships ever seeing each other, or firing a shot. They were fought entirely by aircraft.

The P-40 was one of the first US warplanes to encounter the Japanese. *(EAA)*

These two battles established the strategy for all of the rest of the naval battles of the war. The aircraft carrier, rather than the battleship, became the primary weapon of the US Navy.

Task forces from the United States and Japan met in the Battle of the Coral Sea off the East Coast of Australia on May 7 and 8, 1942. After reconnaissance aircraft learned where the enemy was hiding, aircraft from the carriers were launched. Their primary targets were the enemy aircraft carriers.

After a 2-day battle involving hundreds of dive-bombers, torpedo bombers and fighters, the Japanese lost one aircraft carrier and 100 aircraft. The United States lost the carrier *Lexington*, one destroyer, one tanker and 50 aircraft.

Almost exactly 1 month later, the United States and Japanese navies met again in the Battle of Midway in the north central Pacific. Midway was the first defeat of the Japanese Imperial Fleet in over 300 years.

The Japanese objective at the Battle of Midway was to lure the Americans into a massive battle. Once defeated, the United States would ask for peace. To do this the Japanese wanted to pretend that they were going to attack Alaska. When the US naval fleet exposed their position, they would surprise them from a different direction and overwhelm them.

The key to the Japanese plan was secrecy. Like Pearl Harbor, this was supposed to be a surprise attack. But this time it was the Japanese who were surprised. US intelligence personnel broke the secret code of the Japanese and found out that Midway was the real target. Now, all the Navy had to do was to find out where the Japanese were located.

A combination of skill, luck and technology helped the Americans find the Japanese fleet. Radar at Midway Island detected the Japanese attack. Knowing this, the aircraft carrier commanders launched the US counterattack. Meanwhile, US reconnaissance aircraft located the rest of the fleet and more counterattacks were launched. When Navy dive-bombers from the carriers, and B-17s and B-26s launched from Midway arrived, they found the Japanese carriers vulnerable to attack.

Martin B-26 Marander

The Japanese were changing their aircraft's bomb loads from torpedoes to bombs. They, therefore, were caught with unprotected ammunition on the decks of their carriers. Once fires were started by US attacks, the ammunition blew huge holes in the Japanese ships.

When the battle was over, the Japanese lost four aircraft carriers, a heavy cruiser, 322 aircraft and over 3,500 personnel. The United States lost one aircraft carrier (*Yorktown*), one destroyer, 150 aircraft and 300 personnel.

More importantly, according to Admiral Chester W. Nimitz, Commander-in-Chief of

The Civil Air Patrol made a great contribution to the war effort. *(EAA)*

the Pacific Fleet, the biggest impact was Japan's loss of over 100 front line pilots. The loss of their best pilots was one of the keys to defeating Japan. They never recovered.

With the loss of their carriers, the Japanese felt it necessary to resort to drastic measures. In late 1944, the Japanese started using kamikazes. During the last 10 months of the war, more than 5,000 Japanese airmen gave their lives in these suicide attacks against US naval ships. The tactic called for crashing their aircraft loaded with bombs into a Navy ship. The kamikazes aimed to sink US aircraft carriers.

The kamikaze raids worked fairly well. They wreaked havoc on the US Navy, and produced heavy damage and many casualties. Fortunately, they did not achieve their goal of stopping the progress of the war.

On the Offensive: Island Hopping Through the Southwest Pacific

The war in the Pacific was an entirely different war from the European Campaign. While the entire war in Europe was fought on a single land mass about one-third the size of the United States, the Pacific Campaign involved hundreds of separate islands scattered over millions of square miles. Thus, the problem for the Allies was that none of the islands they controlled were close enough to launch continual air strikes on Japan. This is why the Pacific Campaign is best described as a relentless struggle for island air bases.

This island-hopping campaign required that each island be invaded, then continually be supported with supplies. The Pacific War, therefore, required much more Navy involvement than had the European War.

As each island or group of islands was conquered, the United States built new airfields. These airfields were then used as bases to fly close-air-support missions in support of the next landing. Some of these battles became legends, and names like Tarawa, Rabaul, Bougainville, Kwajalein, Iwo Jima and Okinawa became household words.

The ultimate goal was capture and control of Guam, Saipan, and Tinian in the Mariana group of islands. If the Allies controlled these islands, they could start the strategic bombing of the Japanese Islands. The Japanese realized the significance of the islands, so the fighting was intense. The fight for the Marianas Islands, was particularly fierce. The Japanese casualties in this battle totaled 40,000. The United States suffered as well with over 7,200 killed and 18,000 wounded.

The Flexibility of Air Power

In command of the island-hopping campaign was General MacArthur. Admiral Nimitz and General MacArthur split the Pacific Campaign in half. The dividing line was the 159th meridian just east of Australia. General MacArthur's plan had two goals. One was to regain control of the Philippines, and the other was to capture the islands necessary to launch a bombing campaign against the Japanese homeland.

While the European Campaign was on going, the Pacific Campaign was somewhat ignored. The European effort received first priority for supplies and first line equipment. As a result, when MacArthur assumed command of the Southwest Pacific he said, "None of the three elements of my command — naval, air or ground — was adequate."

The "home front" continued sending thousands of pilots trained in aircraft like the North American T-6.

Major General George Kenney was MacArthur's air commander and he had his work cut out for him. Although there were over 500 aircraft in theater, his air force consisted of only 150 American and 70 Australian aircraft that worked. On top of that, the aircraft were spread out from one end of the southwest Pacific to the other.

Moreover, the problem of replacements and supply was formidable, and morale was low. General Kenney needed to fix these problems quickly. The Japanese were just outside of Australia and if they attacked successfully, the southwest Pacific Campaign could be over before it even started.

General Kenney's solutions to the problems were far from conventional. The first thing he discarded was the bombing doctrine used in the European Campaign. High altitude, precision bombing did not work in this theater because there was no industry to target on these islands. More importantly, Japanese resupply shipping was the target, and they just moved out of the way when these bombers dropped their bombs.

Instead of bombing ships from high altitude, General Kenney decided to bomb from low attitude. He decided the bombers could let the bombs go right at the surface of the water. They would then skip right into the side of the ships, just like when you skip a rock across a pond.

B-25s strafe and drop "para-frags" on Japanese Ki-61 fighters.

He also came up with a new way to attack Japanese airfields. This idea called for small parachutes to be attached to fragmentation bombs. The parachutes were added so that the allied bombers could come in low over the airfield and drop their bombs. The parachutes slowed the bombs down so they wouldn't explode and hit the plane that just dropped the bomb. The new "para-frag" bombs tore Japanese planes into a thousand pieces.

Another new device was called the "Kenney Cocktail." This bomb was filled with white phosphorus. When it burst, streams of fire flew out for almost 150 feet. These bombs were perfect for the jungle environment since they caught enemy aircraft, supply buildings and troop shelters on fire and destroyed them.

The new weapons had two main purposes that were designed to support one main objective, and that was to gain air superiority. Attacking the shipping cut off the bases from supplies, and attacking the bases destroyed the aircraft and supplies the Japanese already had. In General Kenney's words, "clearing the air means more than air superiority; it means air control so supreme that the birds have to wear our Air Force insignia."

The Air Force spearheaded the attack. Its function was to clear the air, and destroy the enemy's bases, so that advancing Allied ground forces could take control of the islands.

However, first, the advancing Japanese had to be stopped before they reached Australia. General MacArthur decided to move the troops into Port Moresby, New Guinea, just north of Australia.

Normally, they would be transported by ship, but that would take at least 2 weeks. General Kenney suggested the Air Force could get them there in just a few days. Soon over 600 troops were landing each day into Port Moresby. General Kenney used all the Australian transports he could find and even ferried some troops in converted B-17s.

Moving troops around the theater and keeping them supplied was just one objective that General Kenney had to accomplish right away. He also had to stop Japanese shipping. Once that was done, the Japanese would be cut off from supply and reinforcements.

The battle that marked the beginning of the end for Japanese shipping was the Battle of Bismarck Sea, located north of New Guinea. General Kenney coordinated an attack with just about all the aircraft he had. First, P-38 Lightning fought the Japanese escorts for air superiority over the sea lanes.

While this battle was waged high over the Japanese ships, B-17s came in under the air battle to bomb the Japanese ships. Under them, B-25s and Australian Beauforts came in with torpedoes. A follow-up attack was then conducted by 12 more B-25s who skipped 500-pound bombs into the sides of the Japanese supply ships.

The P-38 Lightning battled the Japanese Zeros for air superiority. *(Lockheed)*

At a cost of 13 men killed, 12 wounded, and 6 aircraft, the Air Force sunk 12 of the 18-ship convoy. For the Japanese, it was as shocking a defeat at Midway for it meant the end of large-scale resupply and reinforcement. The Japanese were now forced to live on what they could get through on submarines and small craft.

Weakened by the lack of supplies, the Japanese were not able to hold off American forces. Air power's flexibility to get the job done directly contributed to the Allies' victories in the southwest Pacific. After the Allies pressed ahead with victories on Guam, Saipan and the Marinas Islands, long- range bombing of Japan could then take place.

The Bombing of Japan

The first positive note for the people back home was the first bombing of Japan. This took place on April 18, 1942. This was a significant event because it lifted people's spirits. The war was long and hard, and the people at home were making sacrifices too.

Back in Britain, the English were trying to recover from the terrible bombings of their cities. In the United States, rationing was taking place nationwide. Californian's worried about an invasion by Japan. The war effort was felt nationwide. The first bombing of mainland Japan showed that progress was being made, and that the Japanese were not invulnerable.

This first bombing raid was led by Lieutenant Colonel James H. Doolittle. It consisted of 16 B-25 bombers. The amazing thing about this operation was that the bombers tookoff from an aircraft carrier, and then flew 800 miles to Japan. This had never been tried before. The bombers were launched from the US Navy aircraft carrier *Hornet*. The targets were the cities of Tokyo, Yokohama, Yokosuka, Kobe, Osaka and Nagoya.

The surprise Allied attack was so successful, not a single B-25 was lost to the enemy. The bombers crossed the East China Sea and then crash-landed in China. One bomber flew across the Sea of Japan and landed 25 miles north of Vladivostok, Russia. Most of the aircrews survived, although two were captured and killed by the Japanese. Although little damage was done, the Japanese were alarmed that the skies over Japan were no longer safe from Allied attack.

The next bombing of Japan began on June 15, 1944. This started the air campaign against the Japanese homeland. The first raids were flown from air bases in China. The bombing of Japan was carried out using a new strategic bomber designated the B-29 Superfortress. By November 1944, the island campaign in the Southwest Pacific had captured new air bases on the Marianas Islands. They were quickly put into operation, and the bombing effort moved from China to the Marianas.

Once again, however, the doctrine of unescorted, high altitude, daylight, precision bombing did not work. The doctrine developed at the Air Corps

B-29 Superfortress *(EAA)*

Tactical School prior to the war needed adjustments. First, the same problem that happened to the bombing effort in Europe happened in the Pacific. The bases in the Marianas were about 1,500 miles from Japan. This meant that the B-29s had to fly without the protection of fighter escort. The results were the same as over Germany. Losses amounted to about 6 percent per mission.

The bombers needed fighter escort. This resulted in the invasion and capture of Iwo Jima. This island was only 750 miles from Japan and served two important roles. It served as a base for fighter escorts and an emergency landing field for damaged B-29s. By the end of the war, 2,400 B-29s made emergency landings on Iwo Jima.

Another problem that contributed to the high altitude bombing not working was the wind at 30,000 feet. The wind was over 100 mph and caused the bombs to go off course. A new strategy had to be worked out.

General Curtis E. LeMay decided to have the bombers go in at low level and at night. He also decided to use incendiary bombs, because precision attacks would be impossible at night. These firebombs also made sense because the targets were different in Japan than they were in Germany. The Japanese industries were scattered within the cities instead of being concentrated in industrialized areas, like

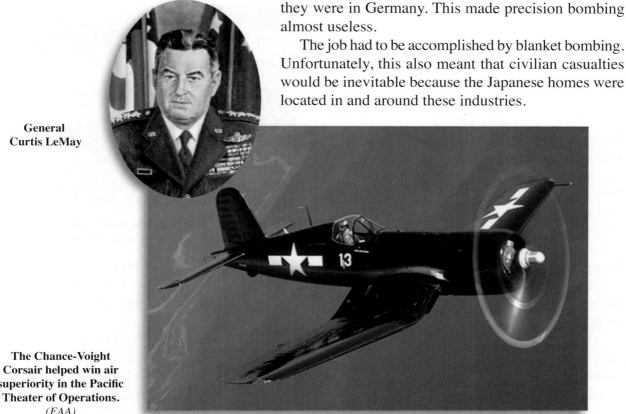

they were in Germany. This made precision bombing almost useless.

The job had to be accomplished by blanket bombing. Unfortunately, this also meant that civilian casualties would be inevitable because the Japanese homes were located in and around these industries.

General Curtis LeMay

The Chance-Voight Corsair helped win air superiority in the Pacific Theater of Operations.
(EAA)

On March 9-10, 1945, Tokyo was attacked. It was a night attack with 334 B-29s flying low at 7,000 feet with a total of 1,667 tons of bombs. The result was the most destructive air raid in history. Widespread fires created a firestorm that destroyed 15 square miles of the city. More than 83,000 people were killed and another 100,000 were injured.

The firebombs were very destructive. Since Japanese homes are traditionally made of wood with paper walls on the inside, they burned quickly. Many of Japan's larger cities were literally burned off the map. In total, 32 square miles of the most important industrial areas of Japan were destroyed.

The new strategy worked. Only 22 B-29s were lost during the raids. This meant that the loss rate dropped from 6 to less than 1.5 percent. The dramatic change was primarily due to the ineffectiveness of the Japanese fighters at night. Once again, flexibility was the key to air power's success. Low-level nighttime bombing successfully replaced high altitude daytime bombing. By mid-summer, the bombing of Japan had brought Japan on the verge of economic and moral collapse.

Atom Bomb Forces Surrender

In order to force the Japanese to surrender, plans called for an invasion of the Japanese Islands. However, the Japanese were tenacious fighters. They rarely surrendered, as the Allies found out during the island-hopping campaign in the Pacific. If every Japanese soldier were to fight to the death, there

would be terrible casualities.

In July 1945, there were still over 4 million Japanese soldiers fighting for Japan. President Truman feared that if fighting continued, hundreds of thousands of casualties would occur for both the Japanese and the Allies. For this reason, President Harry Truman made the decision to use the new "ultimate" weapon. He wanted to save lives.

On the 27th of July, at the final war meeting between the Allies, President Truman and Prime Minister Attlee of Great Britain issued an ultimatum to Japan. Japan was warned to surrender or face "inevitable and complete destruction of the Japanese armed forces and ... the utter devastation of the Japanese homeland."

If a crew named an airplane, it was usually adorned with "noseart." *(EAA)*

Japan replied through the Soviet Union, but for reasons that are still not clear today, the Soviets did not relay the message. Since Japan did not appear to be replying, President Truman ordered the dropping of the atomic bombs.

On August 6, 1945, a B-29, named the Enola Gay, dropped an atom bomb on the city of Hiroshima with a population of over 300,000. Two-thirds of the city was destroyed. Over 78,000 were killed and over 70,000 injured. Most of the remaining survivors suffered from the effects of the radiation for the rest of their lives. On August 9th, the Soviet Union declared war on a country nearly destroyed by war. Also on that date, the second atom bomb was dropped on Nagasaki, an industrial city of 230,000 people.

Luckily, hills protected portions of the city from the blast. Less than half of the city was destroyed. Over 40,000 were killed and 25,000 injured. The next day the Japanese communicated by radio that they were willing to surrender. On September 2, 1945, the Japanese officially surrendered on board the US battleship *Missouri* anchored in Tokyo Bay. World War II was officially over.

Lessons Learned

World War II ended the same way it began, with an awesome display of air power. The German Blitzkrieg in Poland was no less awesome a display of military air power to the people of Europe at that time than the atomic bombings were to the Japanese 6 years later.

During those 6 years, the entire nature of war, as practiced for over 6,000 years, changed. The

ACES IN THE PACIFIC

Although not as widely known as some of the German aces, Japan produced several outstanding aces during the war. The three leading Japanese aces shot down 248 allied aircraft. The three top-scoring American aces in the Pacific downed 112 aircraft.

Japanese
CWO Hiroyashi Nishizawa	104
CWO Shaichi Sugita	80
Lt Saburo Sakai	64
Lt Wataru Nakanichi	55

American
Maj Richard I. Bong, USAAF	40
Maj Thomas B. McGuire, USAAF	38
Capt David McCampbell, USN	34
Lt Col Gregory Boyington, USMC	28
Maj Joseph J. Foss, USMC	26
Lt Cecil E. Harris, USN	24

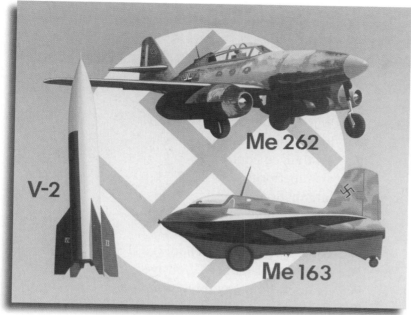

The German Luftwaffe developed both jet
and rocket weapons during World War II.

airplane became the dominant weapon of war, and the aircraft carrier became the primary naval weapon. While no claims are made that the war was won by air power alone, neither can it be argued that control of the air was not essential to the success of every major military operation of World War II.

Air power in the United States grew during World War II, and its leaders learned a great deal about how to use it effectively. First, in North Africa, the Allies learned that they needed to centralize the control of their air assets. This let them put all their assets together and overpower the Luftwaffe. Moreover, this provided the Allies with air superiority. Once that was achieved, the battle on the ground turned around. Air superiority became the number one priority of the air campaign.

Second, the American bombing doctrine that was initially developed to fight the war did not work. After terrible losses, the campaign was stopped and new technology and tactics were added in order to gain air superiority over Europe. The flexibility demonstrated by the Air Force leaders turned that losing situation into a winner.

The Pacific Campaign was very similar in that flexibility was again the key to air power's victories. General Kenney developed new tactics, procedures and weapon systems that were successful. Later, General LeMay did the same thing. He changed from high-altitude daylight bombing into low-altitude bombing at night. The changes were devastating for the Japanese and led to their defeat.

In the final analysis, the war was won by the technological and wartime production capabilities of the Allied Powers. Of all the Allied nations, it was the United States that combined the manpower and materiel into the greatest manufacturing effort in history.

The final lesson that World War II hopefully taught us was the utter futility of war in a modern society. Twenty million people were killed during the war. Four million of these were civilians. At least three times this many were injured, and many were severely and permanently disabled. Warfare had finally reached a point where no one could win or lose, and the only sensible solution was to prevent wars rather than to fight them.

Key Terms and Concepts

- combined arms operations
- Blitzkrieg
- Luftwaffe
- Royal Air Force (RAF)
- ME-109
- B-17
- B-25
- B-29
- Zero
- P-51
- P-38
- airborne
- Battle of Britain
- radar
- Pearl Harbor
- Allies
- Axis
- War Training Service (WTS)
- long-range bombing
- centralized control
- air superiority
- interdiction
- close ground support
- early air power theorists
- Air Corps Tactical School (ACTS)
- Combined Bomber Offensive
- strategic bombing: precision vs area bombing
- fighter escort
- Normandy Invasion
- air war in the Pacific
- kamikazes
- atomic bomb

? Test Your Knowledge ?

SELECT THE CORRECT ANSWER

1. The (**American / Japanese**) *strategy in the Pacific was to strike swiftly in several directions, capturing the East Indies, Philippines, New Guinea, and the Marshall, Caroline, and Mariana Islands.*
2. *The primary purpose of the Japanese attack on Pearl Harbor was to* (**destroy US ground forces in Hawaii / cripple the American fleet**).
3. *After Pearl Harbor, the "contract" schools* (**increased / decreased**) *their production of pilots.*
4. *The WAFS personnel were* (**military members / civil service employees**).

TRUE OR FALSE

5. *The major Allied Powers in World War II consisted of the United States, Britain, France, the USSR and Hungary.*

6. At the end of World War I, the United States, Britain, and France had the most powerful air forces in the world.
7. At the beginning of World War II, France had the best prepared air force in the world.
8. It was under the guise of commercial aviation that the German Air Force was revived after World War I.
9. For World War II, Germany's warfare strategy was a combined arms operations.
10. The tactic of Blitzkrieg was stopped by the French using the Maginot Line.
11. Hitler was surprised when Britain and France declared war on Germany.
12. The Battle of Britain began in August 1940 when German troops landed on the beaches of Dover.
13. Britain and Italy joined forces in 1940 to defeat the Germans in North Africa.
14. The Germans used glider-borne and parachute troops to capture Crete in 1941.
15. On June 22, 1941, Germany invaded Russia.
16. By the end of 1941, the short-duration war Hitler had asked for settled down to a long struggle of land armies.
17. Once the United States entered the war, the basic Allied strategy was to change from the defensive to the offensive.
18. At the beginning of the strategic bombing of Germany, the first priority targets were aircraft factories.
19. The first atomic bomb was dropped on Nagasaki.
20. The Allied invasion of Europe was savagely contested by the Luftwaffe.
21. The Japanese strategy during the early part of World War II was to gain air superiority followed by an invasion.
22. Two major defeats suffered by the United States in World War II were during the Battles of Midway and the Coral Sea.
23. Pinpoint strategic bombing was used against Japan's industry during World War II.
24. World War II was won by the technological and wartime production capabilities of the Allied powers.
25. The aircraft carrier became the dominant naval weapon of World War II.

AVIATION: FROM THE COLD WAR TO DESERT STORM

 bjectives

Discuss the political situation at the end of World War II.

Define the "Cold War."

Identify why the United States reduced its military forces after World War II.

Identify the date the United States Air Force was formed.

Discuss the first primary mission of the United States Air Force.

Identify several aviation advances that were made during World War II.

Identify the so-called German "vengeance" weapons that were used to terrorize Europe.

Discuss the use of helicopters during World War II.

Discuss air power's role in keeping Berlin from becoming a part of East Germany.

Discuss how ready the United States air power was for a war in Korea.

Discuss air power's role in stopping the North Korean army outside of Pusan.

Identify the reason American fighter pilots were able to defeat the MiG-15.

Discuss the air power's lessons learned from the Korean War.

Identify why the DC-4 was initially one of the most popular commercial airliners after WWII.

Identify the first "pure" jet commercial airliner.

Identify the "big three" in general aviation manufacturing.

Identify the problems encountered when attempting to break the sound barrier.

Define Mach 3.

Discuss the advantages of variable swept-back wings.

Discuss the potential impact new missile technology had on aircrews.

Identify the primary reason the B-52 bomber was built.

Discuss the impact television had on the Vietnam War.

Discuss the results of the Tet Offensive.

Discuss the impact technology has on air power, looking at the Thanh Hoa Bridge example.

Discuss the difference in how air power was applied during Operation ROLLING THUNDER and Operation LINEBACKER.

Identify aircraft built specifically for Strategic Air Command during the Cold War.

Discuss Strategic Air Command's mission during the Cold War.

Identify the contribution the Civil Reserve Air Fleet made to Operation Desert Shield.

Identify the "key" air power capability that allows US air power to be a "global striking force."

Identify several of the lessons learned from previous air wars that were used to help develop the Desert Storm air campaign plan.

Discuss why Iraq's command and control was attacked first during the war.

Discuss air power's contribution to the defeat of Iraq's counterattack into Saudi Arabia.

Discuss air power's contribution to the "100 Hour War."

Discuss the impact new technology had on the "War in the Desert."

Setting the Stage:
The Political Situation

The postwar years (after World War II) were called the "Cold War." The Soviet Union (Russia) tried to increase her influence in the world, and the United States tried to prevent the spread of the communist influence.

Although the Soviet Union and the United States were Allies during World War II, they did not share the same ideas on freedom, economics and government. The Soviet Union (Russia) had been hurt terribly by World War II and by previous wars. They wanted to ensure that never happened again. They also desired all the countries that were near them to be friendly towards them. So they directly influenced these nations' fate after World War II and beyond.

The countries the Soviet Union had liberated during World War II (Hungary, Czechoslovakia, Romania, Yugoslavia, Poland, East Germany, etc.) were shaped in the image of the Soviet Union. The Soviet Union installed governments that restricted people's freedoms, created socialist economies, and unrepresentative governments. All of these were exactly what the United States did not favor. The United States believed in freedom of speech, freedom to choose your religion, freedom to choose who represents you in government, and the freedom to choose what you want to do in life.

The United States and the Soviet Union clearly did not believe in the same things. This led to their antagonistic relationship. This relationship was known as the "Cold War" because their objective was not to get into a "hot" war. They both wanted to influence what happened in the world, but they didn't want to go to war. If they went to war, leaders feared it would be the last world war. The destruction would be too great. The two sides were clearly marked off. The Soviet Union and her new socialist friends, and the United States and her Allies.

Each side was trying to influence as many countries as possible into believing in its system of government and economics. The Cold War was so influential it shaped many of the developments in the world including the development of aviation.

The Douglas JD-1 served in WWII, then again during the Cold War.

Military Developments

Just like after World War I, the United States immediately rushed to "return to normal." The Army Air Forces had 2,125,000 men in uniform in September 1945, and by January 1946, there were less

than 900,000. By 1947, this figure was cut to 300,000. America was certain its monopoly on the atomic bomb provided all the security it needed. No one would dare attack the United States or her Allies for fear of massive strikes like the ones the Japanese experienced at Hiroshima and Nagasaki. Therefore, there was no need to maintain a large military force.

The RB-36D was one of the largest bombers ever built.
It was a mainstay of the Strategic Air Command in the 1950s.

A Separate Air Force: Designed to Defend the Nation

The lessons learned from World War II seemed to indicate that air power and the atom bomb could provide for the security of the United States. However, General Billy Mitchell was right, the United States needed a separate but equal Air Force. This would ensure a strong and powerful Air Force, like the Army and the Navy. If the Air Force was going to carry the bulk of the load for the defense of the United States, it had to be separated from the Army. This would allow the Air Force to grow without interference from the Army and, more importantly, give the Air Force its very own budget.

With the passage of the National Security Act, on July 26, 1947, the Army Air Forces of World War II became the United States Air Force (USAF). The first Secretary of the Air Force was Stuart Symington, and General Carl Spaatz became the first Chief of Staff of the United States Air Force.

This newly formed United States Air Force's primary mission was deterrence. The Air Force needed to be strong enough that no nation would dare attack the United States. The United States Air Force could destroy a nation with atomic bombs. This mission was given to the Strategic Air Command (SAC). At that time, SAC had nothing but a handful of B-29s, an improved offshoot called the B-50, and just a few atom bombs.

The new, giant B-36 started service in 1948. At this point in history, this bomber was the largest bomber ever built. It was designed in 1941 when it looked like England might lose the Battle of Britain to the Germans. If England had lost, bases would not have been available for the bombing of Germany. This is why the B-36 was designed to carry 10,000 pounds of bombs 10,000 miles. This huge plane weighed six times as much as the B-17 and was powered by six pusher propellers (later, four jet engines were added).

Wartime Advances

The huge B-36 bomber was just one of many developments during World War II. There were also advances in aircraft design, instrumentation, navigation, electronic systems, engines, and armor protection. Bombers grew in size, speed, and bomb load, showing little similarity to their prewar ancestors. The B-29 carried three times the bomb load and had three times the range of the B-17. In addition, the B-29 was the first bomber to have a pressurized crew compartment, which allowed it to fly at much higher altitudes. It also had a central fire control system for aiming and firing its guns by remote control.

The P-51 *Mustang* is often called the best fighter of World War II. A comparison of the P-51D and the Curtiss P-40C shows the advancements made in fighter aircraft during the war.

FIGHTER ADVANCEMENTS		
	P-51D	P-40C
Maximum weight	11,600 lb.	8,058 lb.
Maximum speed	437 mph	345 mph
Maximum range	2,300 mi	945 mi
Service ceiling	41,000 ft	29,500 ft
Rate of climb (ft/min)	3,500	2,690

War seems to bring out the survival instinct in many of us, and this instinct has led to many revolutionary developments that completely replaced previous technology. One case in particular is the jet aircraft, which rapidly made the piston-engine aircraft obsolete. Advances like these paved the way for even more development after the war.

Jet Propulsion

Before the war, Frank Whittle, an Englishman, designed the world's first turbojet engine for use in an airplane. He tested the engine for the first time in April of 1937. It was not until May 15, 1941, however, that England flew her first jet aircraft. By this time, Germany had already flown several jet aircraft. The first jet in the world to fly was Germany's Heinkel HE-178, which was first flown on August 22, 1939.

The United States flew its first jet aircraft, the Bell XP-59 *Airacomet,* on October 1, 1942. The P-59, however, was not much better than the piston engine P-51 *Mustang* and was never put into production. The first U.S.-produced jet fighter was the Lockheed F-80 (originally designated the P-80A) *Shooting Star*, which flew for the first time in January 1944. The *Shooting Star* was far superior to any fighter aircraft in the world (jet- or propeller-driven), but it came too late to be used in World War II.

The Bell Aircraft Company produced America's first jet fighter, the P-59A.

Both the British and the Germans produced jets that saw combat in World War II. In fact, before World War II ended, Germany had produced 22 different models of jet aircraft, including some with sweptback wings, delta wings, afterburners, ramjets, and even variable-swept wings. England produced two aircraft, the Gloster Meteor I and the DeHavilland Vampire, which were operational before the war ended.

The most famous jet of World War II was the Messerschmitt ME-262A. It could have possibly changed the outcome of the war if it had come a little earlier and in greater numbers. Fourteen hundred of these twin-engine German jets were produced during the war, but only about 100 ever saw operation as fighters. An additional 200 were used as tactical fighter bombers. The ME-262 was a very good aircraft. It carried four 30-mm cannons and was capable of a speed of 550 mph. Unfortunately for the Germans, it came too late.

"Vengeance" Weapons

The Messerschmitt ME-262 was the first, fully operational jet fighter.

During the World War II European Campaign, two new German "vengeance" weapons were used. The first was a small, 26-foot-long unmanned flying bomb called the V-1. The V-1 weighed 3,000 pounds and carried 1,800 pounds of high explosives. Powered by a pulsejet engine mounted in a "stovepipe" above the fuselage, this type of engine produced a unique sound, giving the V-1 its nickname, the "buzz bomb." Between June 1944 and March 1945, over 10,500 "buzz bombs" were launched against England, and 12,000 more against targets in Europe. Most of the V-ls were launched from ground ramps, but about 1,100-1,200 of those launched against England were air-launched from HE-111 bombers.

Flying at about 400 mph, the V-1 had a range of about 200 miles. It was not very accurate but served its purpose of terrorizing the enemy. Since the rockets were so large and noisy, they were fairly easy to locate. This made the V-1 vulnerable to fighter aircraft and ground fire. As a result, nearly 4,000 were shot down over England.

The other "vengeance" weapon was the rocket-propelled V-2 ballistic missile. It was the forerunner of the space age. It was the product of a brilliant rocket scientist named Wernher von Braun and was the first liquid-fuel missile ever built. Unlike the V-1, it was impossible to defend

The German V-1 "buzz bomb" terrorized Europe.
It is shown with American markings.

The Messerschmitt ME-163 Rocket Interceptor

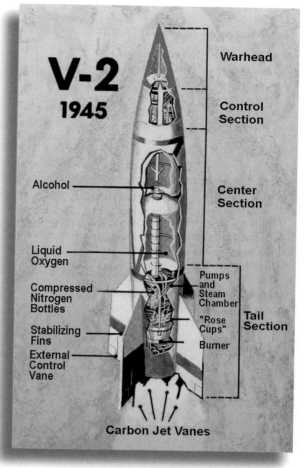

The German V-2 ballistic missile
started the race to space.

against the V-2. It carried a 2,000-pound warhead at speeds of about 3,600 mph and had a range of about 220 miles. The high, arching flight of the V-2 carried it to an altitude of about 100 miles from which it fell at speeds faster than the speed of sound, landing before any warning could be given. Altogether, about 4,300 V-2s were launched between September 1944 and March 1945.

Records show that approximately 1,050 actually fell on England. Again, it was fortunate for the Allies that this effort occurred late in the war. If Germany had been able to develop and launch great numbers of V-2s, the tide of the war might have been changed.

Helicopters

Another World War II aviation development was the Sikorsky R-4. It was the first successful military helicopter. In 1942, the R-4 went into service with the Army Air Forces. Before the war ended, 400 of them were used in Europe, the Pacific and in the United States.

Most importantly, on April 23, 1944, the R-4 was used to rescue a downed pilot from behind enemy lines for the first time. This event developed a role for the helicopter that still exists today. Helicopters are extremely good tools for search and rescue. After this first rescue, the helicopter became an integral part of the Army Air Forces, but it was not until the Korean War, some 5 years later, that the helicopter really demonstrated its value.

The Sikorsky R-4 was the first successful military rescue helicopter.

The "Cold War" Heats Up

The Berlin Airlift

The peace treaty ending World War II divided Berlin into four sectors, each controlled by one of the Allied Nations (United States, Britain, France and the Soviet Union). Additionally, Germany was divided into two parts – West Germany, controlled by Britain, France and the United States; and East Germany, controlled by the Soviet Union.

In June 1948, the Soviet Union decided to test the will of the other three Allied Nations by initiating the Berlin blockade. The blockade prevented any surface transportation into or out of Berlin.

Berlin was located in East Germany. This meant that all supplies for the sectors of Berlin controlled by Britain, France, and the United States had to travel through East Germany, which was controlled by the Soviet Union.

The Soviet Union decided to block the supplies going into Berlin so that the Allies would leave Berlin. Russia wanted to take over all of Berlin and, unless the blockade could be broken, the strategy would work. The answer to the blockade was the Berlin Airlift. Air power would be used to fly over the roadblocks and into the city of Berlin.

This was a massive undertaking. It was estimated that Berlin required 4,500 tons of supplies a day just to survive. Not only were there not be enough aircraft, but also the effort had to overcome the poor weather and other problems. At the start, there were only 105 C-47 aircraft for the effort. Each C-47 was capable of carrying three and one-half tons of cargo. There

The C-54 was the most widely used transport during the Berlin Airlift.

were also 54 C-54 aircraft that were able to carry 10 tons of cargo.

Within five months, the effort had grown to 319 C-54 aircraft (the C-47s had been phased out) and 150 British planes of various sizes. During the winter, the problem got worse. The airlift now had to include heating fuel (mostly coal) as well as other cold weather supplies. Amazingly, the Berliners made it through the winter with the supplies.

By April 1949, life was a little better as the airlift had grown to the point that 12,940 tons were delivered by 1,398 flights in one day. This record-setting effort was nearly three times what was estimated for Berlin's daily survival. The Berlin Airlift had clearly come a long way.

In May 1949, almost 1 year after they began, the Russians conceded that they could not isolate Berlin. They lifted the blockade. With great effort, the United States and her Allies had supplied a city for almost an entire year. In all, 2,330,000 tons of supplies were carried in the world's greatest demonstration of carrying cargo by air. Air power, once again, had won a big victory.

The Korean War

On June 25, 1950, shortly after the Berlin Airlift, North Korea, an Ally of the Soviet Union, invaded South Korea. Like Germany, after WWII, Korea was divided into two parts. When the Japanese surrendered, the Soviet Union was in North Korea and the United States in South Korea. North Korea, like the Soviet Union, became a communist country, and South Korea, like the United States, became a republic.

Once again, in the context of the Cold War, the United States and the Soviet Union were at war. They did not actually fight each other, they fought with each other's Allies. This became a favorite tactic of the Soviet Union. The Soviets would supply and support a communist nation in the takeover of another nation. They would do this without becoming directly involved in the fighting themselves. This time, the United States and her Allies fought a Soviet supplied communist North Korean Army for control of the Korean peninsula.

North Korea's invasion forced the United Nations to act. This was the first test of the United Nations (UN), which was formed after World War II to ensure world peace. On June 27, 1950, the United Nations resolved (the Soviet Union was absent on the day of the vote) that its members would provide assistance to South Korea. Sixteen nations provided armed forces, and five more provided medical assistance. The United States, with its powerful armed forces, took the lead.

Shortly after the United Nations' resolution was passed, President Truman authorized the use of United States armed forces. On June 30, he ordered General Douglas MacArthur to command the US effort. He subsequently became the UN forces commander as well.

The Lockheed F-80 *Shooting Star* became America's first operational jet fighter.

The first priority was to stop the advance of the much stronger North Korean Army. In little over a month, the communist forces had driven the United Nations' forces almost off of the Korean peninsula. The UN forces occupied only a very small perimeter around the port city of Pusan at the far Southeastern edge of Korea.

Like World War II, the Korean War was an air war. All of Korea was within range of naval aircraft operating off the US naval aircraft carriers of the Seventh Fleet, or US Air Force aircraft operating from bases in Japan and South Korea.

Since there were very few industrial targets in Korea for the B-29s based in Japan, they were used to bomb bridges, roads and supply areas. Most of the targets during the Korean War were really tactical in nature. This means that most of the air war consisted of UN fighter aircraft bombing and strafing enemy troops, supply lines, transportation systems and communications.

This is exactly what happened at Pusan. US tactical aircraft were able to bomb and strafe North Korean troops, and more importantly, cut their supply and transportation lines. This slowed down the

North Korean advance just enough so that the UN forces could be resupplied and hold their defensive positions. To accomplish this, the Air Force used the F-80 *Shooting Star*, the F-51 and the F-84 *Thunderjet*. The Navy carriers were equipped with the F-9F *Pantherjet* fighters, AD *Skyraiders* and F-4U Corsair propeller-driven attack aircraft. Soon thereafter, the UN forces had achieved air superiority over a small North Korean Air Force that consisted of about 120 obsolete Russian aircraft.

The F-84 was one of America's first jet aircraft to see combat in the skies over Korea.

In September 1950, the UN forces landed at Inchon. This amphibious operation placed the UN forces behind the enemy lines and was timed to coincide with the Eighth Army breakout at Pusan. The plan was so successful that within 10 days the North Koreans had been pushed back nearly 200 miles to the former South Korean capital of Seoul. During the push north, UN air power provided close air support to the forces engaged in the fighting and hammered North Korean supply routes.

South Korea's territory had been recaptured in a rout of North Korean forces. With the North Korean Army on the run, General MacArthur calculated the entire Korean peninsula could be swept clean of communist forces with a simple mopping-up operation. The UN and President Truman agreed that the original objectives of the Korean War allowed for the elimination of the communist force that would hinder a completely reunified Korean peninsula.

The communist Chinese, who had

The Chinese MiG-15 proved to be a formidable opponent in the Korean War. *(EAA)*

been supporting the North Korean war effort, did not take General MacArthur's threats lightly. They threatened that if UN forces moved past Seoul and the original border of North and South Korea (the 38th parallel), they would attack.

On November 25, 1950, after moving all the way up to the Chinese border with little North Korean resistance, the war changed completely around. The communist Chinese entered the war with 850,000 troops and the best fighter aircraft in the world. The Chinese were using the Russian-built MiG-15 fighter jet.

A new air war had started in the skies over Korea, and part of this air war was very new and different. It was an all-jet battle. The best Russian built jets versus the best that the Americans could build. The first all-jet air battle in history was won by an American F-80 piloted by Lieutenant Russell J. Brown against a Chinese piloted, Russian-built MiG-15. Meanwhile, the Chinese pushed the UN troops back across the 38th parallel and captured the South Korean capital of Seoul again.

The Chinese had about 1,000 MiG-15s when they entered the Korean War. The Russian built aircraft were smaller, faster and more maneuverable. They could climb faster and higher, and they possessed more firepower than the F-80 and the Navy F-9F fighters. In fact, the MiG-15 even had the edge, at high altitude, over the F-86 *Sabrejets*, which were the best aircraft the United States had during the Korean War.

The F-86 *Sabrejet* proved to be one of America's greatest jet fighters.
(EAA)

Although the Russian-built MiGs outperformed the American made jets, more MiGs were shot down than American jets. The biggest reason for this was that the United States had better trained pilots. The result was nine MiGs shot down for every one United States aircraft lost during the war.

When the Chinese invaded in November, the United Nations' aircraft provided air cover for the retreat and kept the UN forces from being completely overwhelmed. They used two weapons that proved to be the best weapons used in Korea. One was a new weapon, and the other was very similar to what was used on Japan during World War II. The new weapon was rockets delivered by airplanes. The rockets carried the destructive force of a 105-mm cannon shell and could be delivered with great accuracy by the fighter-bombers. The other weapon was a bomb just like what General Kenney used during World War II, a firebomb. These new bombs were called Napalm bombs, and were made of 110-gallon tanks of jelled gasoline, which when dropped, would explode and burn an area some 250 feet long and 80 feet wide. Postwar interviews showed that Korean and Chinese troops greatly feared these weapons.

Once the Chinese advance was stopped, UN troops recaptured Seoul and advanced as far as the 38th parallel.

KOREAN WAR AMERICAN ACES	
The top five American aces of the Korean War were:	
Captain Joseph McConnell, Jr.	16
Major James Jabara	15
Captain Manuel J. Fernandez	14.5
Major George A. Davis, Jr.	14
Colonel Royal N. Baker	13

From this point, the war neutralized into a stalemate. By the middle of 1953, United States' close air support for the ground troops developed into a very precise art. Just like the end of World War II, the Air Force had become very good at supporting the fight on the ground. It became clear, however, that the enemy could not win the war, and neither could we.

On July 27, 1953, a cease-fire treaty was signed, the fighting stopped, and Korea was almost precisely where it had been in 1950. Although neither side finished the war as an outright victor, the original objectives of the United Nations were accomplished. South Korea was once again an independent nation.

In retrospect, the Korean War was a limited or political war; the first of several for the United States. The overall controlling strategy of the war was to ensure that it did not enlarge into World War III. This meant the war had to be limited, and political leaders, rather than military leaders, were in charge of the strategy. This restricted the military leadership. Certain targets were placed off-limits. For example, the Chinese airfields that were located north of the Korean border in Manchuria were off-limits. American planes were not allowed to bomb targets north of the Yalu River, which marked the Korean-Manchurian border. In fact, US aircraft could not even pursue communist aircraft across the border. This meant that the communists could take off from their safe air bases in China, cross the Yalu River to fight, and then return back across the Yalu to safety. This type of fighting was like boxing with one hand tied behind your back.

Lessons Learned

Looking back, there were quite a few lessons to be learned by the Korean War. One was that US atomic arsenal alone is not enough to prevent involvement in war. Another was that the United States was not prepared for the Korean War. After World War II, the United States drew down its forces and invested in an Air Force focused on delivering the atom bomb.

This meant that the Air Force organized, trained and equipped to fight a war with atom bombs. To do

The McDonnell F-101 B Voodoo was developed as an interceptor during the '50s and later served in a reconnaissance role in Vietnam.

this, they created a large Strategic Air Command with plenty of bombers and atom bombs. They did not invest in fighter aircraft, fighter tactics or fighter personnel. As a result, the US Air Force was not prepared to support a ground war, and the United States paid for that mistake by giving up ground, and losing men and equipment to the enemy.

Lastly, the military leaders forgot the lesson they had learned during the North African Air Campaign during World War II. They forgot the benefits of having centralized control and decentralized execution. They forgot the benefits of having one person in charge of the air effort. During the Korean War, air assets were again divided with the Navy working in one area and the Air Force in the other. As a result, coordination and timely execution were poor.

Despite all the problems experienced during the Korean War, the United States still felt that the atom bomb could deter war. A comment by the Secretary of the Air Force, 1950 - 1953, Thomas K. Finletter, summarizes the philosophy at this time, "The Korean War was a special case and air power can learn little from there about its future role in the US foreign policy in the East." Put simply, they thought there was nothing to learn from the Korean War. Military strategy was going to continue to be based on the United States' ability to use the atom bomb.

Aviation Continues to Develop: An Ongoing Process

Meanwhile, interest in aviation continued to grow and there were many developments in the expanding world of aviation. Air power's huge contribution to World War II had made the world aviation-conscious.

Civil Aviation Developments

Another reason for aviation's expanding popularity rested on the more than 2 million Americans involved in building aircraft in World War II. In addition, more than 16 million Americans served in uniform and witnessed air power first hand. Hundreds of thousands of servicemen and service women flew for the first time during the war, either as a crew member or as a passenger. Millions of people had been exposed to aviation and were now aviation enthusiasts.

Many of the military veterans knew what aviation could do, and many that played important roles in the war continued to publicize the merits of aviation. Some wrote or lectured, and some continued flying. They all recognized the importance of aviation as a transportation system and this created an immediate demand for commercial airline travel.

They also recognized that this demand would create the possibility to make money. Commercial aviation companies set out to take advantage of this opportunity and started competing for the potential profits of the commercial aviation travel industry.

Commercial Airlines

There were remarkable developments in aircraft design during the war. This led to better instrumentation, better navigation and increased safety. There were also larger and better airports available because of wartime requirements. Radar, which improved navigation and safety, had been developed. There were more and better pilots available than prior to World War II. Weather forecasting and the ability to fly through weather had improved. In addition, there were a large number of surplus airplanes available at a very good price.

DC-4

Immediately after the war, the most widely used aircraft was the Douglas DC-3. More than 10,000 of these were built during World War II for the Army who designated them the C-47. The C-47s were modified for commercial use to carry 21 passengers, and they worked fine for short flights.

For longer routes where traffic was heavier, two other aircraft developed for the Army Air Forces were available. These were the four-engine Douglas DC-4 and the Lockheed *Constellation*. The *DC*-4 had been built for the military as the C-54 and the *Constellation* as the C-69. The *Constellation* had two advantages over the DC-4. One was that it was pressurized, which allowed passengers to be taken comfortably higher in the air, and it was about 100 mph faster.

The DC-4, however, won the first round against the Constellation as a commercial airliner because there were many more DC-4s available to use. There were about 1,100 DC-4s built during the war whereas only a few hundred C-69s were built.

Eventually, the DC-4 was used by nearly every large airline, including foreign carriers. When the supply of "cheap" surplus DC-4s ran out and the airlines had to start buying new airplanes, the Constellation became the top-selling airliner. This resulted in both Douglas and Lockheed developing several versions of their aircraft, each bigger and better than the last. The DC-4 was followed by the DC-6, DC-6B, DC-7, DC-7B and DC-7C. Meanwhile, Lockheed countered with the *Super Constellation* and the *Starliner*.

During the competition, the Douglas aircraft grew from 44 seats (DC-4) to 105 seats (DC-7C),

and the *Constellation* grew from 44 seats to 99 seats *(Starliner)*. Both the DC-7 and the *Starliner* were fast (300 mph) and long-range carriers. Both aircraft offered nonstop transcontinental service in about 8 to 9 hours and transatlantic service (New York to London). In all, about 800 DC-6s and DC-7s were built and about 650 *Constellations*. They were the airliners of the 1940s and 1950s and were the biggest, fastest, safest and most comfortable piston-engine airliners ever built.

The Lockheed *Constellation* was a "flying work of art." *(EAA)*

Another result of the increase in speed and range of the DC-7s and *Super Constellations* was the death of flying boats. The large clippers had been developed in the 1930s when nonstop flight across the oceans was impossible. The flying boats were used briefly after the war, but they were made obsolete by the much faster Douglas and Lockheed aircraft.

In the short- and medium-length route market, the DC-3 was challenged by the Martin 2-O-2 and the Convair 240 in 1947-48. Both were faster, pressurized and offered the same comfort to the short-haul passenger that the DC-6s and *Constellations* offered the long-haul passenger. The 40-passenger Convair 240 was enlarged to become the 44-seat Convair 340 in 1952, and in 1956, it grew into the 56 seat Convair 440. There were more than 1,000 of these Convair aircraft built for civilian and military use, and later more than 200 were equipped with turboprop engines.

It was right after the war that the first all-cargo airlines came into existence. They were also used in World War II C-47s and C-69s, but they carried air cargo rather than passengers. There were many of these all-cargo airlines (such as Riddle, Resort, Slick, Flying Tiger, etc.) formed, but of this list only Flying Tiger survives today.

The Boeing Stratocruiser *(EAA)*

Commercial Airlines Adopt Jet Engines

With the military converting to jet fighters and bombers, it was inevitable that jet aircraft would also be developed for airline use. When this did occur, the first jets were British-built, not American, which is rather surprising since United States aircraft had dominated the airlines since World War II.

There are two types of jet propulsion: turboprop and "pure" jet. Both types use a gas turbine engine, the difference being that in a turboprop the gas turbine is fastened to a propeller that is used to propel the aircraft. There is some thrust provided by the jet exhaust, but the propeller provides most of the power. In a "pure" jet, all of the thrust is provided by the jet exhaust.

The British developed both the first turboprop and the first turbojet airliners. The Vickers *Viscount*, powered by four Rolls-Royce Dart turboprop engines, was the world's first turboprop airliner. The *Viscount* first flew in July 1948 and went into commercial service in 1953. There was a total of 444 *Viscounts* produced in three series. The first series carried 47 passengers. This was increased to 75 in later models. The *Viscount* had a cruising speed of about 350 mph and a range of about 1,700 miles.

The DeHavilland *Comet* 1 was the world's first "pure" jet airliner and entered service in May 1952. The *Comet* revolutionized commercial travel by increasing air speed to 500 mph. Also, it flew at a higher altitude (25,000 - 30,000 feet), which put it above most of the weather and made for a much smoother ride.

In 1954, two *Comets* had fatal accidents caused by structural failure. Flying at extremely high altitudes, a pressurized aircraft has a tremendous amount of pressure on the inside. In the case of the *Comet*, the aircraft could not withstand the pressure difference and explosive decompression occurred. This caused the aircraft to disintegrate in flight. This was a serious setback to the British aviation industry, but as a result, all later jets were safer because of the knowledge gained from the *Comet* 1 disasters.

In 1940, the year before we entered World War II, our nation's airlines carried about 3 million passengers. By the end of the war in 1945, this figure was about the same due to wartime travel

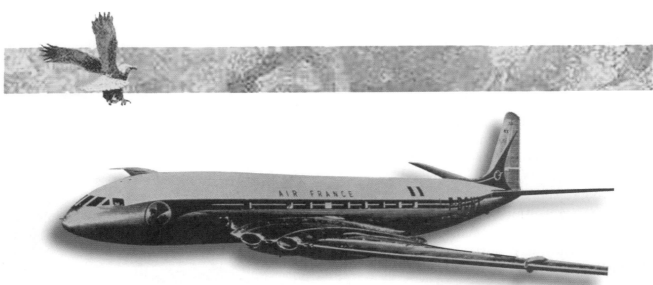

The DeHavilland *Comet* 1

restrictions. By 1950, however, it had increased 600 percent to 17 million. By 1958, the year the first commercial jets were introduced, this figure had grown to about 30 million.

Thousands of military veterans found work in the commercial airline industry and many did very well in their new line of work. Discrimination, however, held many of the black aviators back. The established airlines did not hire any blacks, despite the fact that hundreds of ex-World War II military black pilots were very good pilots and eager to fly commercial planes. Refused employment in the airlines, these black pilots had to turn to other occupations and fly in their spare time.

In 1948, however, James O. Plinton broke the trend and established an inter-island air service, flying the Boeing 247-Ds. This air service linked the islands of Jamaica, Port-au-Prince (Haiti), Grand Turk and Caicos. It was probably the first commercial air service begun and operated by a black pilot.

In summary, the commercial aviation business boomed after World War II and did not decrease during the Korean War as it had during World War II. This occurred because the national war effort was not as intense during the Korean War, and because we had enough large transport planes to serve both the military and civilian needs. This was true worldwide as well. Airline traffic increased from 3 million in 1938 to 18 million in 1946, and then to 24 million in 1948. The "Aviation Age" had arrived.

The Boeing 707 was America's first operational jet airliner. *(Boeing photo)*

General Aviation

Meanwhile, general aviation also fared well after World War II. There were thousands of pilots in America who had flown during World War II. Thousands more earned their pilot licenses using the GI Bill after the war. The Civil Aeronautics Administration (forerunner of FAA) predicted there would be 500,000 aircraft in service by 1950. This prediction failed to materialize, but there was a great demand for general aviation aircraft after the war. Surplus airplanes

Taylorcraft BC-12D

filled some of this demand, but the manufacturers also began building new civilian airplanes immediately after the war.

In 1946, Cessna Aircraft brought out its first postwar aircraft called the C-120 and the C-140. Both of them were all-metal, high-wing monoplanes. The 120 and the 140 were two-seaters. Prior to World War II, all Cessna aircraft were wood and fabric, but the new technology that developed during the war killed fabric aircraft. Both of these aircraft were very successful. The 120 led directly to the Cessna 150/152 while the 140 was the direct ancestor of the Cessna 172. By the end of the 1950s, Cessna had grown to the number one general aviation manufacturer.

Piper Aircraft also resumed production of general aviation aircraft right after the war. Here, too, they initiated a change that has become a Piper trademark through the years. Their first new postwar aircraft was called the *Skysedan*. It was a four-place, all-metal, low-wing monoplane. Prior to World War II, all Piper aircraft were high-wing, fabric-and-wood aircraft. The *Skysedan* can be considered the direct ancestor of the *Cherokee* series of Piper aircraft.

Of course, Piper also left World War II with the most famous light aircraft of all time. The J-3 *Cub* was the traditional high-wing, fabric-covered aircraft. After the war, Piper continued production of the *Cub*, producing the Piper PA-28 *Super Cub* that had a high wing and was fabric-covered.

During the war, the general aviation manufacturers had been involved in building training, observation and liaison aircraft for the military. After World War II, they began immediately to convert over to building aircraft for civilian use. Generally, the initial aircraft they built were the same types they had been manufacturing for the military with whatever changes were required to get them licenses for civil use.

On December 7, 1945, just 16 weeks after the war ended, Beech Aircraft received a certificate for their Beech 18 executive aircraft. Beech had produced more than 5,000 Model 18s during the war and now began delivering the civilian model at the rate of two airplanes per day.

In 1947, Beech first offered an airplane that would become a classic. The Model 35 Bonanza was an all-metal, low-wing

Cessna 140 *(EAA)*

retractable-gear aircraft that could fly at almost 200 mph. It was equipped with a two-way radio and all navigational gear required to fly at night and in all types of weather. This was the closest thing the public could get to a "fighter" and was so attractive that they had 500 on order before it made its first flight.

Cessna, Piper and Beech made themselves into the "big three" of general aviation manufacturers. Others,

Piper *Cherokee* **140** *(EAA)*

such as Mooney, Rockwell, Maule, also made very good names for themselves in general aviation manufacturing. General aviation aircraft were clearly popular and there were profits to be made in the business.

Aviation Research and Development

Much of the post World War II progress in aviation is directly related to the research and development done for the war. During the war, large-scale advances in research and development (R&D) occurred.

During the war, the National Advisory Committee on Aeronautics (NACA), which was founded in 1915 to do government-funded research in aeronautics, opened two more research centers. One was the Ames Research Center at Moffett Field, California, and the other was the Lewis Research Center in Cleveland, Ohio.

The aviation manufacturers also did a great deal of their own research, and many, such as Boeing and Lockheed, developed research facilities. They rivaled those of NACA, but most often industry research was done in support of the war. Generally, they contracted on a particular aircraft and not on researching basic questions about flight.

The research was mostly done by NACA or by a college or university under government contract. Many colleges and universities had departments of aeronautics and possessed wind tunnels to do research to support their graduate programs. Universities such as Purdue, Miami of Ohio, and Auburn are examples of schools involved in basic research in aeronautics.

During the war, a team effort between the NACA scientists and engineers, and their counterparts in industry and the universities led to some great developments. One example was the P-51 *Mustang*. A need existed for a fast, long-range fighter escort in Europe. The requirements were known, so a team from North American Aviation, the Royal Air Force (RAF), and the Ames Research Center went to work. The result was the P-51, which was designed, built and flown in only 120 days. This aircraft was equipped with a revolutionary new wing design called the laminar-flow wing.

After the war, there was a need to continue this type of aviation R&D. Many problems needed solving and questions needed answering. This was particularly true in the realm of high-speed flight. The new jet fighters, and some of the most modern propeller-driven ones, began to approach the speed of sound. They encountered many strange things. When approaching the "sound barrier," they would experience severe vibrations, or control reversal where the controls of the aircraft would function opposite to how they should function. In some cases, the aircraft did not make it through the experience and broke apart.

Research and development was so important that the Air Force formed a new command in 1950 called the Air Research and Development Command (ARDC) to lead the Air Force research effort. Part of the mission of ARDC was to do laboratory research and flight-testing. R&D is still very important and represents a massive on-going effort in the United States Air Force.

Airborne Research and Development

While some questions can be solved in the laboratory, eventually research aircraft must be built to test the laboratory theories. A number of experimental research aircraft were built and tested to solve complex aeronautical problems. Research findings from these aircraft have led to many supersonic and innovative aircraft.

Some of the post World War II efforts include Republic company's XF-91 two turbojet rocket engine in 1946, and the French ramjet aircraft called the *Leduc* 0.10. It was carried aloft by a Languedoc 161 transport and then released for its test flight.

Besides conventional airplanes, vertical-takeoff-and-landing (VTOL) aircraft also got their start during the 1950s. These experiments were attempts to lift off straight up as soon as the power to weight ratio of the turbojet was sufficient to lift an aircraft vertically on the jet thrust alone. One of these experiments was conducted by Rolls Royce in 1954. Their craft, called the *Flying Bedstead* was successfully flown straight up into the air. Also in the same year, the Convair XFY-1 *Tailsitter* took off vertically by means of a propeller mounted at the tail.

Breaking the Sound Barrier

One of the most famous tales today is the story of breaking the sound barrier. Several books and movies describe the events in some detail. The effort started in February 1945; the Army Air Forces and NACA decided to jointly develop a research aircraft to fly faster than the speed of sound. First, a contract was let to the Bell Aircraft Company to build a research aircraft to explore the problems of high-speed flight. This aircraft, called the X-1, made its first flight in January 1946.

There were actually six X-1 aircraft built for the flight tests. They were shaped like bullets, with short, very thin, nonswept wings, and were propelled by a rocket engine. Because their rocket engines consumed fuel at an extremely high rate, they could not take off from the ground. They would have

The specially designed B-29 carried aloft the Bell X-1 in which Captain Charles E. "Chuck" Yeager, left, first broke the sound barrier. Congratulating him is Major Arthur Murray who broke the altitude record of 90,000 feet in the Bell X-1A.

run out of fuel before they ever reached their operating altitude. The X-1 was carried to an altitude of 25,000 feet by a specially designed B-29 aircraft. The first flight tests were not powered and were designed to test its handling characteristics. They tested the X-1 by letting it glide to a landing on the dry lakebeds at Edwards Air Force Base, California.

Powered flights began on December 9, 1946, with the aircraft being flown a little faster on each flight. They experienced several problems as they approached the speed of sound. The aircraft would vibrate and become hard to control. Previous tests that tried to break the sound barrier had resulted in the aircraft breaking apart. Undaunted, the experiments pressed on, and on October 14, 1947, with Air Force Captain Charles "Chuck" Yeager at the controls, the X-1 penetrated the "sound barrier" and man first flew faster than the speed of sound. The speed the X-1 reached on that historic day was 670 mph at 42,000 feet.

Some of the other test pilots working with NACA were: Scott Crossfield, Pete Everest, Marion Carl, Bill Bridgeman, Kit Murray, Ivan Kincheloe and Mel Apt.

Flight tests continued with the X-1 and other aircraft too. These aircraft were pushed to higher and higher speeds. One of the most amazing discoveries was that once the aircraft passed the speed of sound, flight smoothed out and no further vibration problems existed.

In November 1953, Scott Crossfield reached the aviation milestone of Mach 2 (twice the speed of sound) or more than 1,320 mph. Although Crossfield had several hours in the X-1, he accomplished Mach 2 in the D-558-II *Skyrocket*.

In June of 1954, Yeager pushed the X-1A to a speed of 2.42 times the speed of sound (1,650 mph). Testing with the X-1 aircraft continued until 1956.

One test included having the X-1B outfitted specifically to test the effects of frictional heating on an airplane at very high speeds. This led to more tests with another experimental aircraft called the X-2.

This X-2 was designed to study heating in flight at three times the speed of sound. It was similar to the X-1, but had swept-back wings and a stainless steel airframe. Two of these aircraft were produced and, unfortunately, both were destroyed in accidents during the test program.

During its final flight on September 27, 1956, the X-2 flew three times the speed of sound. It had reached its design goal of Mach 3, but shortly thereafter, the X-2 disintegrated in flight killing the test pilot, Captain Mel Apt. Captain Apt's speed record of 2,094 mph, was not again approached until 1961.

The X-1 and X-2 series of aircraft were rocket powered. The next tests were done with the X-3, which was a jet powered aircraft designed to break Mach 3, three times the speed of sound. The X-3 was built of titanium alloy to protect it from frictional heating. Originally, there were three prototypes ordered from Douglas Aircraft, but only one was completed. The X-3 flew for the first time on October 20, 1952. It made more than 20 experimental flights. Unfortunately, however, the X-3 never flew Mach 3 because the jet engine did not have enough power.

The Douglas X-3 *Stiletto* was designed for aerodynamics, structural and other flight research in the Mach 2 range.

At the end of World War II, the United States captured the plans for the German Messerschmitt P-1101. The Bell X-5 was based on these designs and was the world's first aircraft with variable-angle wings.

Swept-back wings of a jet aircraft are very important. They are more efficient at high speeds and, in fact, are almost a requirement for supersonic flight. They do have one problem, however. The swept-back wings do not produce enough lift at low speeds to keep the aircraft flying. This means that the takeoff and landing speeds of the swept-wing jet are much higher than ones with straight wings. One solution to this problem is to be able to change the wing of the aircraft from straight wings for takeoff and landing to swept-back wings for high-speed flight. The X-5 was built to test this theory and provide the answers necessary to build variable-wing aircraft.

Two models of the X-5 were built, and the first flight was on June 20, 1951. The first prototype crashed in 1953, killing the test pilot Major Raymond Y. Popson. The second aircraft flew for several years and provided the knowledge necessary to build swept-wing aircraft like the F-111, F-14, and the B-1.

In summary, research and development made some outstanding contributions to air power and continues to do so today. The testing conducted in the 1950s led to many superior aircraft that eventually became operational aircraft that met the ultimate test, combat.

One example is the F-100 series of aircraft. In 1953, the F-100 *Super Sabre* flew for the first time at Edwards Air Force Base, California. This aircraft was the first in a line of superior aircraft, and was the world's first production supersonic fighter.

F-100 SERIES OF SUPERSONIC FIGHTERS	
Name	**Date**
F-100 *Super Sabre*	1953
F-101 *Voodoo*	1953
F-102 *Delta Dagger*	1953
F-104 *Starfighter*	1954
F-105 *Thunderchief*	1955
F-106 *Delta Dart*	1956

F-106 *Delta Dart*

Lockheed F-104 *Starfighter*

Bomber Developments

Manufacturing companies also worked on developing better bombers for the military. President Truman and then President Eisenhower decided that US foreign policy would be backed by the strength of the atom bomb. So, America needed the best bombers to deliver the atom bomb.

In theory, no country would challenge the United States' powerful atomic threat. So, the United States Air Force needed more bombers and requested bids from the manufacturers for a high-performance, all-jet bomber.

As a result, the aircraft companies built three prototypes: the North American XB-45, the Convair XB-46 and the Boeing XB-47. All three had straight wings. The Boeing engineers, however, were not satisfied with their initial creation.

They studied the captured German reports on sweptback wings and decided to try them on their aircraft. The result was the XB-47, and it became the United States Air Force's first all-jet bomber. The XB-47 flew for the first time on December 17, 1947, and more than 1,600 of these aircraft eventually entered service with the Strategic Air Command.

The B-47 had one shortcoming and that was its range. Unrefueled, its range was only about 3,000 miles. Because of this, the Air Force decided it needed another bomber; larger with longer range than the B-47. The result was another Boeing aircraft, the B-52. It flew for the first time on April 15, 1952. The B-52 is twice the size of the B-47 and has an unrefueled range of 10,000 miles.

During this time, the first supersonic strategic bomber, the B-58, was designed and built. It was a remarkable technical accomplishment, but very expensive to operate. Although the B-58 was faster than most fighter aircraft of its time, it was not that much better than the B-52. After a few years, the B-58 was retired.

**The B-47 *Stratojet* was introduced in 1951.
It was faster than many fighters during its time.**

Smart Bombs: Advances in Guided Missile Research

During this same period, research on missiles also progressed, leading to some remarkable results in the 1950s. One of the first developments was a drone called the Northrup SM62 *Snark*. It was a jet-propelled, tailless, pilotless airplane that flew 6,300 miles at Mach 0.94. It was small and hard to shoot down. The *Snark* had inertial and stellar guidance systems. So, it could guide itself much better than a pure dumb bomb that fell like a rock. Inertial and stellar guidance gave it some navigational capability and it was therefore smart.

As technology got better, systems got smaller. This allowed the developers to put the technology they used in the *Snark* drone, into a smaller missile. Whereas the *Snark* was a pilotless airplane, the next system, the GAM-63 *Rascal,* was a small, rocket-propelled, supersonic winged bomb. In 1957, B-47 bomber squadrons carried it and launched it 100 miles away from the target. Once launched, the bomber crew guided it by radar to the target.

These changes in technology were significant. These new rocket systems allowed the bomber aircrews to stay farther and farther away from the target. By keeping their distance from the target, enemy fire would be less effective. In the long run, these new weapons would save lives.

The B-58 *Hustler* was America's first operational supersonic bomber.

The Vietnam Conflict

While all these advances were happening in the world of aviation, the United States became more and more involved in Vietnam. America's involvement in Vietnam can be broken down into four fairly distinct phases that cover a period of about 25 years.

Phase I, July 1950 - July 1954

In February 1950, France requested military and economic aid from the United States for its war with communist separatists in Vietnam. At the time, Vietnam was a French colony. President Truman responded by granting $15 million in assistance in July 1950. He did so because he wanted to help the French stop the spread of communism in Vietnam.

To do this he established a US Military Assistance Advisor Group (MAAG). This unit initially consisted of 342 military advisors who advised the French Expeditionary Corps in its war against the communists. This 4-year period was really a normal operation for the United States. As a part of US foreign policy, military advisors are often stationed in many countries around the world to help them set up their own defense forces, and also to help with other civil and humanitarian efforts.

Phase II, July 1954 - August 1964

During the next 10 years, US involvement grew from helping the French and the South Vietnamese, to fighting along side the South Vietnamese. It all started with the defeat of the French at Dien Bein Phu by General Giap and his Viet Minh forces. The Viet Minh were Vietnamese communist separatists who started the separatist movement.

Shortly after this defeat, the French agreed to pull out of their colonies in Southeast Asia. Vietnam, Cambodia and Laos were then recognized as independent countries at an international conference held in Geneva, Switzerland, in July 1954.

One of the agreements signed at the conference was an agreement for French forces to withdraw slowly and be completely out by 1957. At this point Vietnam was temporarily divided, at the 17th parallel, into two parts. This would continue until elections could be held to let the people elect their choice of governments.

The two choices were the communists who dominated the north and wanted to control all of Vietnam and a western representative type of government who dominated the South. No Vietnamese wanted to see a permanently divided Vietnam, and an election was scheduled to take place in July 1956. Unfortunately, it never happened, as both sides feared that they would lose. The result was exactly what the people of Vietnam did not want, and that was a divided nation. The stage was set for a civil war.

After the division of Vietnam, the newly formed government of South Vietnam requested assistance

MiG-17

from the United States. President Eisenhower authorized a military training mission to help reorganize the South Vietnamese military into a strong fighting force. At this point, US troops were not fighting in the civil war, they were helping South Vietnam organize, train and equip themselves.

The South Vietnamese struggled with the Civil War and by 1961 President Kennedy expanded the commitment of the United States. The goal was to prop-up the South Vietnamese military until they were able to conduct the war by themselves. To do this, President Kennedy sent in US Special Forces, Air Force T-28s and B-26 bombers. By February 1962, over 11,000 US forces were in Vietnam and participating in actual combat.

Despite US participation, the civil war continued to go poorly for the South Vietnamese. Although several advisors to President Kennedy agreed that success in Vietnam was not likely, he decided to

increase US involvement. By the end of the Kennedy Administration, the U.S. had over 17,000 troops in Southeast Asia, and over 100 killed in a war not yet authorized by the Congress of the United States (only Congress can declare war).

Phase III, August 1964 - June 1969

On August 2, 1964, the destroyer USS *Maddox* was patrolling in international waters off the coast of North Vietnam and was attacked by North Vietnamese torpedo boats. President Johnson then ordered retaliatory naval air strikes against North Vietnamese coastal torpedo boat bases and an oil storage depot on August 5th. On August 7th, Congress passed the Tonkin Gulf Resolution, which allowed President Johnson to "take all necessary measures to repel an armed attack against the forces of the United States and to prevent further aggression." This was the beginning of what was to become known as the "Vietnam War." Although war was never declared by Congress, President Johnson used the Tonkin Gulf Resolution to justify the start of the "Vietnam War."

In October and December of 1964 and in February 1965, the North Vietnamese launched several attacks, one against the US support base at Bien Hoa and another against Pleiku Air Base. Four Americans and two Vietnamese were killed and over 15 others were wounded. Several American and Vietnamese aircraft and helicopters were also destroyed.

The North Vietnamese were not giving in to continued American pressure. In response, President Johnson ordered systematic air strikes on selected targets in the southern panhandle of North Vietnam. In response, the communists increased their terrorist activity and sabotage of US bases. In March 1965, President Johnson called in the US Marines to protect US air bases, and thus slowly escalated US involvement in Vietnam's Civil War.

By mid-1965 and despite President Johnson's addition of 7 more US Army ground battalions, the war was still not going well for the South Vietnamese. In order to prevent a South Vietnamese defeat, President Johnson ordered B-52 bomber strikes on known communist bases.

One of the greatest bombers of all time is the Boeing B-52.

Operation Rolling Thunder: 1965-1968

The "tit-for-tat" air strikes were intended to warn of heavier punishment to come if the communists continued with the war. Unfortunately, President Johnson did not trust his military advisors, so he and his Secretary of Defense personally ran the Vietnam conflict. Unlike World War II where the objective was unconditional surrender of Germany, Italy and Japan, the objective of the Vietnam conflict was not so clear. In World War II, the military experts developed a strategy, ran it by the President for his approval and then conducted the war. In Vietnam, President Johnson called all the shots. He even picked out targets for the air strikes.

President Johnson's objective was to raise the morale of the nearly defeated South Vietnamese Army, and to demonstrate to North Vietnam that if they did not start negotiations for peace, the bombings would continue. In the background, there was also another objective.

President Johnson did not want either the Soviet Union or the Chinese to enter the conflict and thus start a world war. This is why Operation ROLLING THUNDER was another gradual escalation of the conflict. This is also why President Johnson and Secretary of Defense MacNamara ignored the advice of their military experts, and

F-100F *Wild Weasel* **Also Known as the** *Super Sabre*

personally went through the maps of Vietnam and selected targets to be hit. This way they ensured the targets that were sensitive to either the Soviet Union or the Chinese were not hit. For example, surface-to-air missile sites were not targeted because there might be Soviet advisors at the sites. These kinds of rules made it seem like America was fighting with one hand tied behind its back.

The conduct of the war so frustrated the Army Chief of Staff, General Harold K. Johnson, that he later said, "I remember the day I was ready to go over to the Oval Office and give my four stars to the President and tell him, 'You have refused to tell the country they cannot fight a war without mobilization; you have required me to send men into battle with little hope of their ultimate victory; and you have forced us in the military to violate almost every one of the principles of war in Vietnam. Therefore, I resign and will hold a press conference after I walk out your door.'"

The war continued. Operation ROLLING THUNDER lasted for 3 years and is the longest operation of its kind in history. It severely disrupted North Vietnam's war effort and severely destroyed many ammunition depots, oil storage facilities, power plants and railroad yards. But, it did not destroy North Vietnam's will to resist. The piecemeal attacks allowed the enemy to repair vital needs. Every time President Johnson ordered a stop in the bombing to see if North Vietnam would negotiate, the communists repaired and resupplied.

Success was hard to measure and it was being assessed every night during the five o'clock news. Television was now an affordable luxury for almost every American family and, as a result, families

nationwide saw the ugliness of war. President Johnson now had over 300,000 American soldiers in the area, and many were not coming home. As a result, the war became the most unpopular war in American history. Americans did not understand why Vietnam was worth the terrible cost in American lives, and they began to protest in mass.

AMERICAN TROOPS IN VIETNAM	
31 Dec 65	184,000
31 Dec 66	385,300
31 Dec 67	485,600
31 Dec 68	536,100
30 Apr 69	543,400

The bombing during Operation Rolling Thunder was carried out by US Air Force B-52s and F-105s, while F-4s beat back North Vietnamese MiG-15, MiG-17 and MiG-21 fighters. The F-105 had a tough time because it was originally designed to deliver tactical atom bombs on large targets in a World War III-like scenario against the Soviet Union. It was not an all-weather, nighttime fighter-bomber. American airmen, however, made it work.

One technological advantage was putting "eyes into the skies." The Air Force put an early warning radar on top of a cargo plane to look for enemy MiG fighters taking off from their airfields. As soon as they were spotted, the Air Force EC-121 directed Air Force and Navy aircraft where to engage the enemy.

The UH-1 *Huey* Helicopter became a *symbol* of the Vietnam War.
(EAA)

The North Vietnamese countered this with Soviet-built technology called surface-to-air missiles (SAMs). Combined with anti-aircraft artillery (AAA) fire, the SAMs and the AAA created a good defensive curtain against US air power. It was not undefeatable however. Tactics were developed to counter the threat.

One such tactic was to use the EB-66 aircraft to confuse enemy radar. This was a large cargo aircraft equipped with high technology equipment. The EB-66 sent out electronic signals that confused the enemy's radar so that they could not see US aircraft coming towards them.

Placing radar-detecting equipment on board a fighter aircraft created another tactic. The first of these aircraft were F-100Fs, called *Wild Weasels*. The *Wild Weasels* could find enemy radar and then use a new radar homing missile to destroy them. The new missile called the AGM-45 *Shrike* had a radar receiver in it. The AGM-45 *Shrike* used the receiver to find the enemy's radar. When the enemy had their radar on, the receiver would find it and then follow it all the way to it. Then it exploded and destroyed the enemy's radar.

Another development was the US Navy's A-6 bomber. Launched from the Navy's aircraft carriers off the coast of Vietnam, these small fighter-bombers were all-weather capable because of the sophisticated radar that they used to distinguish large targets, such as an airfield, from the surrounding area.

The Navy also used a television-guided glide bomb. This bomb was called the Walleye. This was another step toward "smart" weapons. "Smart" weapons were preferred because pilots could launch them far away from the targets and thus stay away from enemy defensive weapons.

Meanwhile, the war progressed and US involvement increased. In mid-1966, US troops launched their first prolonged offensive aimed at destroying communist units and bases. Reports coming back to the United States via television sounded good as President Johnson trumpeted the news.

Unfortunately, what was really happening was that the enemy was running from the conventional fight and resorting to guerrilla warfare. This way they did not have to fight a superior US force head-on. Instead they used hit-and-run tactics, then disappeared into the dark jungle to hide. This worked until 1968.

The Deadly MiG-21

The Tet Offensive

In January 1968, the communists launched a large-scale surprise conventional attack on US and South Vietnamese forces. Abandoning small guerrilla warfare attacks, the North Vietnamese attacked during a holiday cease-fire. Simultaneous attacks were carried out all over South Vietnam. Hoping that the South Vietnamese would give-in, the North Vietnamese attacked 36 of the 44 provincial capitals in South Vietnam. They attacked 23 airfields and five of the six principle cities, including the capital of South Vietnam, Saigon. Fighting went block to block in the cities. Enemy soldiers even entered the American Embassy in Saigon. Americans watching on television were shocked.

Air power did everything expected of it during the attacks. In fact, with the enemy now out in the open and not hiding in the jungles, air power worked even better. Close air support missions leveled enemy troops engaged with US and South Vietnamese forces. Enemy supply lines were cut and, probably the worst thing for the enemy, US troops were airlifted quickly thereby reinforcing, then

The F-105F, *Thunderchief*, was used extensively during the Vietnam War.

overwhelming communist forces.

At one point, more than 12,000 troops were moved within hours from southern military regions to northern areas under attack. US C-130s moved men, ammunition and supplies quickly and effectively. Meanwhile, 6,000 US Marines needed help as they were barely hanging on at Khe Sanh. Unlike when the communists defeated the French by surrounding them at Dien Bien Phu, the US Marines were going to win because of air power.

The battle for the Marine base at Khe Sanh lasted over 2 months. More than 20,000 air attacks destroyed over 3,000 communist trucks that were supplying North Vietnamese forces. Another 25,000 sorties dropped over 110,000 tons of bombs on the enemy. Air Force cargo planes air-dropped over 12,000 tons of supplies into Khe Sanh while under constant enemy

The incredible A-1H *Skyraider* was capable of carrying a bomb load with as much destructive power as a WWII bomber.

fire. In the end, some 6,000 US Marines, previously surrounded at Khe Sanh, won the battle, and over 10,000 communist troops were killed.

All total, the North Vietnamese communists lost over 50,000 in the Tet Offensive battles. They were turned back and out of South Vietnam. But the battle changed the political and social climate in the United States. The Tet offensive was brought into America's living rooms every night. There were now over 500,000 American forces fighting an undeclared war in Vietnam. American soldiers were dying in a war they were told that we were winning. The American public did not understand what was going on or why.

Shortly after the Tet offensive, President Johnson surrendered to the public's protests about the war and decided not to run for a second term. The next President would win the presidential race by calling for a US withdrawal from Vietnam.

Phase IV, June 1969 - April 1975

On January 22, 1969, Richard Nixon replaced Lyndon Johnson as President of the United States. Nixon campaigned on the promise to "end the war and win the peace."

The plan to end America's involvement in the war was called Vietnamization. The basic idea was to gradually turn the fighting over to the South Vietnamese after building up their supplies and fighting abilities. The plan was implemented and, by the end of 1971, it appeared that South Vietnam might be able to win the war.

As President Nixon had promised, American forces began to leave Vietnam. Nearly 545,000 troops were there in 1969, and President Nixon's goal was for that number to be down to less than 70,000 by May 1972. While the Americans were leaving, however, the North Vietnamese were building up along the demilitarized zone between North and South Vietnam. The US Air Force responded with over 1,000 sorties bombing SAM and AAA sites.

Unfortunately, the attacks only delayed the impending North Vietnamese attack. While the United States was withdrawing troops from Vietnam, the Soviet Union was arming the North Vietnamese with new guns, SAMs, tanks, and MiG-15, MiG-17, MiG-19 and MiG-21 fighter aircraft.

On Good Friday, March 30, 1972, 120,000 North Vietnamese Army troops invaded South Vietnam again. President Nixon reacted with B-52 strikes, the first since 1968. This campaign, named Operation LINEBACKER, was different from President Johnson's Operation ROLLING THUNDER. President Nixon trusted his military advisors and let them run the campaign. Unlike President Johnson, who selected targets while having lunch on Tuesday afternoons, President Nixon let the military experts run the campaign. At the same time, Henry Kissinger, the President's National Security Advisor, talked to the Chinese and the Soviets about the war. Even with the Soviet's help, North Vietnam did not want to negotiate.

With US troops still leaving Vietnam as scheduled, the South Vietnamese troops fought hard to defend their country. Support came from the US Air Force, Navy, and the relatively new Royal Vietnam Air Force. Together they prevented the North Vietnamese from overrunning the country. The war was now in the hands of the South Vietnamese Army and they had stopped the invasion with the help of US air power.

F-4 *Phantom* was the workhorse of the Vietnam War.

Since the North Vietnamese still did not want to negotiate, President Nixon launched massive air attacks. Operation LINEBACKER was designed to not only bomb the Vietnamese to the negotiating table, it was designed to cut off North Vietnam from Chinese and Soviet supplies, and destroy their ability to make war.

Operation LINEBACKER was conducted without as much worry about Chinese and Soviet reactions to the war.

North Vietnam's harbors were mined so that Soviet supplies could not enter the country, and railroad lines heading from China into Vietnam were destroyed. In addition, SAM sites were no longer off limits.

The result was an all out air war between Soviet built MiG fighters and the US F-4s, and between American bombers and Soviet built SAMs and AAA. The fighting was intense. Each side gained a short-lived advantage over the other by changing tactics and procedures, or by developing a technological counter to the threat.

The Versatile F-4 Was a Workhorse During Vietnam

One such example was the continuing development of precision guided munitions or smart bombs. The Thanh Hoa Bridge survived hundreds of missions by Air Force and Navy bombers. It seemed like nothing could destroy that bridge. After losing dozens of pilots and planes to that bridge, one mission consisting of 14 F-4s, armed with new laser guided bombs, destroyed the bridge. Technology had found a way to get the job done, and more importantly to save lives in the process.

By October of 1972, US ground forces had withdrawn from Vietnam and the bombing of North Vietnam had resulted in negotiations. The negotiations did not proceed well, however, and President Nixon ordered more bombing on December 18th. This operation, dubbed LINEBACKER II, was aimed at driving the North Vietnamese back to the negotiating table.

US Air Force B-52 bombers were lined up in long waves. It was reminiscent of World War II. It looked like the waves of B-17 and B-24 bombing attacks on Germany during World War II. For 11 days, B-52 bombers attacked 34 targets in North Vietnam dropping over 15,000 tons of bombs.

It was a very large team effort. Escort duties were handled by Air Force F-4s. Meanwhile, Navy EA-6 and EA-3 aircraft jammed North Vietnamese radar, and Air Force F-105s and Navy A-7Es attacked SAMs. Even though the enemy was able to get off over 900 SAMs at the B-52s, only 15 bombers were lost.

The A7D Corsair II saw duty in Vietnam and later in many Air National Guard units.

Air Power in Vietnam

In summary, the United States used air power as a foreign policy tool during the Vietnam War. President Johnson's initial objective for air power was to raise the morale of the South Vietnamese Armed Forces and to contain the military advances of the communists.

As America became more deeply involved in the conflict, the doctrine of gradualism restricted the use of air power. President Johnson did not really want to get involved in an all out war. He therefore decided to use small portions of military power to influence enemies. This is why he did not set forth on an all out war against North Vietnam. Air power was used to support ground troops, deny the communists areas of sanctuary, punish the North Vietnamese, limit the flow of enemy troops and supplies, and coerce the communists to negotiate.

Comparative American War Costs

The President's gradualism policy and his personal hands-on day-to-day control of its use restricted air power's proper use in Vietnam. These policies took away many fundamental principles of success in war. Under this policy, the politicians committed American air assets piecemeal, restricted certain targets from attack, dictated the frequency and level of attacks, and even limited certain types of tactics. As a result, this allowed North Vietnam

COSTS		
	Battle Death	**(In Billion $)**
World War I	53,500	$ 22.6
World War II	292,100	$ 310.4
Korea	33,600	$ 18.0
Vietnam	47,200	$ 138.9

to study American strategy, weapons and tactics. The government in Hanoi was able to build up its air defenses and disperse its people, supplies and industries, and force the United States to lose billions of dollars and thousands of lives.

In contrast, the employment of air power changed drastically under President Nixon. Gradualism was discarded and military leaders were allowed to plan and execute what they believed were the best plans to obtain the President's objectives. President Nixon authorized senior field commanders to make day-to-day decisions, and he lifted restrictions on many targets that had been off-limits. This time when the North Vietnamese invaded, President Nixon's reaction, Operation Linebacker, cut off North Vietnam from external supply sources, and stopped the communist advance.

In mid-December 1972, when peace talks in Paris broke down, President Nixon decided to punish North Vietnam and drive them back to the negotiating table. Operation LINEBACKER II was the only true strategic bombing campaign of the war, and 12 days after its start, North Vietnam was negotiating a cease-fire. This time air power was swiftly and massively applied to the heart of North Vietnam. Although it is not known for sure, this proper application of air power may have shortened the war.

Meanwhile: The Cold War Continues

The F-14 *Tomcat* was a frontline fighter for the US Navy used at the end of the Vietnam War.

It is debatable whether both the Korean War and the Vietnam War could have been avoided if the end of World War II had been handled better. At the end of World War II, the Japanese were defeated and a power vacuum was created. In the case of both Korea and Vietnam, the communists filled that vacuum and the countries were split in two. Conflict was nearly inevitable.

The Soviet Union was pushing the spread of Communism while the United States tried to contain it. Both had the capability to use the atom bomb and were, therefore, feared by many. However, most of all, the world feared a war between the two.

As a result, both countries created large defenses designed to deter the other from attacking with atomic weapons. The large defenses consisted of early warning systems and interceptor type aircraft. Unfortunately, as defensive systems got better, offensive systems were developed to overcome them. The result was an arms race.

Research and development expanded as both nations strived to develop the ultimate weapon. In charge of most of this effort in the United States was the Air Force's Strategic Air Command (SAC). SAC grew into a very large command whose primary mission was to defend the United States from atomic (later called nuclear) attack.

To perform their mission, SAC bought hundreds of B-52 bombers and KC-135 tankers. The tankers refueled the bombers in the air, thereby allowing the bombers to fly farther. The bombers and tankers were stationed throughout the United States and in some overseas areas as well.

As the arms race continued, some analysts feared that the only way to win a war would be to preempt the enemy from using his bombs. In other words, if you launched a surprise attack, you could destroy most of the enemy's weapons before he had a chance to use them. This way you could win and, hopefully, only endure a little damage. As this thinking spread, reconnaissance, surveillance and command and control became more important.

Reconnaissance aircraft, like the U-2, flew over the Soviet Union to locate where the Soviets were hiding their missiles. As missile technology and space power improved, both the Soviet Union and the United States created missiles that could fly across the world and deliver a nuclear weapon. Missile fields soon spread across the United States and the Soviet Union.

This placed an even greater emphasis on space power. Satellites were needed to constantly watch over the enemy's missile fields so that they could not launch a surprise attack. The information from the satellites had to be monitored constantly. This resulted in the creation of hardened underground command posts; hardened to withstand a nuclear attack. Once the command post survived the initial attack, they could launch a retaliatory strike.

As the arms race continued, missiles could go farther and became more accurate. Command posts were, therefore, vulnerable and a new system had to be developed. The new system was a mobile airborne command post designed to mirror the capabilities of the now vulnerable underground command post. SAC called their airborne command post "Looking Glass" for this very reason. It could do everything the underground post could do, including launching the nuclear missiles. To do their mission, Looking Glass aircraft flew constantly to ensure that no one could launch a surprise attack and destroy US command and control capability. In fact, for over 29 years SAC had at least one Looking Glass aircraft airborne over the United States every minute of the day.

The arms race produced faster and better aircraft, missiles, radar and satellites. Some weapons became smarter as precision guided munitions developed further, and some weapons even appeared to

AWACS—the Air Forces' *Eyes in the Sky*

get smaller. Becoming smaller was important because radar had become better. Radar could detect and identify aircraft miles away, which therefore made them vulnerable to attack. What was needed was a way to hide from radar. This new dramatic development was not a function of speed, nor was it really about size. It was radar cross section.

Earlier, this text discussed the Battle of Britain and the British use of radar. They used the radar to see when the Germans were coming across the English Channel. This gave them increased warning time and allowed them to get their fighters in the air and defend England from attack. The radar worked by sending out an electronic pulse. When the pulses bounced back, there was something there. Large targets bounced back pulses that could be seen by radar very easily. This was because they had a large radar cross section.

B-2 *Spirit* (*Boeing photo*)

What was needed was a way to avoid detection, and the experts in research and development did it. They did it by making an aircraft from material that absorbs some of the electronic pulse and deflects the rest of it. This way only a small portion of the radar's electronic pulse is bounced back. The blip on the radar screen is so small, and the radar cross section is so small, it can not be distinguished as a plane. This is what led to the development of the B-2 Bomber: a stealth (hard to see by radar) bomber designed to fly through Soviet air defense systems.

End of the Cold War

The Cold War and the arms race that came with it started right after World War II and ended in 1989 with the fall of the Berlin Wall and the collapse of the Soviet Union. Many conflicts were fought and billions of dollars were spent. In the final analysis, the lack of dollars may be why the Soviet Union collapsed.

Between World War II and 1989, the Soviet Union faced off against the United States and its Allies over a dozen times. Wars in Korea and Vietnam were fought between the United States and enemies backed by the communist Chinese and the Soviet Union. Middle Eastern conflicts between Israel and her Arab neighbors were also backed by both the Soviet Union and the United States. Almost every continent in the world was affected by the Cold War.

Every US president since the end of World War II had to deal with the Soviet Union, and all of them share in the ultimate US victory. President Eisenhower fought the communist expansion in Korea. President Kennedy stood fast when the Soviets tried to place medium-range missiles in Cuba. President Carter objected to Soviet expansion into Afghanistan, and President Reagan outspent them.

The best aspect of the Cold War is that an all-out war between the Soviet Union and the United States never occurred. Great restraint was exercised many times by many leaders and many soldiers, sailors and airmen. Although dozens of soldiers, sailors and airmen lost their lives on spying missions, an all-out war never happened.

Although there is some debate, most agree that the key element of the Cold War was economics. The United States simply outspent the Soviets. When President Reagan decided to build a strong military to counter the Soviet threat, the Soviet Union reacted. Bigger tanks led to more tanks, better airplanes led to even better airplanes, and better missiles led to better missile defense. Missile defense was probably the straw that broke the camel's back. President Reagan's missile defense system, called "Star Wars" by some and the Strategic Defense Initiative officially, was a huge undertaking and a great expense.

The Soviet Union's economy simply could not sustain the pace. The communist central planning system was plagued with problems that resulted in labor and food shortages and, in turn, hurt industrial productivity. With the economic problems at home and the constant military struggles overseas, the Soviet Union was overextended.

The wall that separated East and West Berlin came down, and the Soviet Union separated into independent states.

The Lockheed TR-1A spy plane could operate at altitudes well above 90,000 feet.

War in the Desert

With the end of the Cold War, the stage was set for the most dominating display of air power the world had ever seen. On August 2, 1990, Iraq invaded Kuwait over a dispute concerning oil and outstanding Iraqi loans. The Emir of Kuwait fled and the Iraqis were in complete control by August 4th.

The F-117 Nighthawk has the radar signature of an insect.

F-15E Strike Eagle is considered by many aviation authorities to be the finest jet fighter in the world. *(Boeing)*

Operation Desert Shield

Fearing an advance into the Kingdom of Saudi Arabia, King Fahd asked the Kingdom's allies for defensive assistance on August 6th. The United Nations immediately passed Resolution 660 demanding an Iraqi withdrawal, and President Bush ordered an immediate military deployment to defend Saudi Arabia from Iraq. By August 8th, Tactical Air Command's 71st Fighter Squadron was in Saudi Arabia and ready to defend. Operation DESERT SHIELD had officially started.

Within 5 days, more fighter squadrons arrived, and soldiers of the 82nd Airborne Division arrived via airlift. Egyptian and Moroccan forces arrived on August 11th, and American B-52s arrived in Diego Garcia, poised and ready to strike. By August 21st, American F-16, F-15E, F-4G, F-117, A-10, E-3B, RC-135, KC-135, KC-10, and C-130 aircraft had arrived.

That day, Secretary of Defense, Dick Cheney, declared that the threat of an Iraqi invasion had ended. Air power had already achieved its first victory in the desert.

The UN passed a resolution calling on the Coalition Forces to use "all means necessary" to compel the immediate and unconditional withdrawal from Kuwait all Iraqi forces, if Iraq did not comply by 15 January 1991. They did not. US, French and British troops arrived in Saudi Arabia, followed by forces from Saudi Arabia, Italy, Canada, Egypt, Syria, Qatar, Bahrain, Pakistan, Czechoslovakia, United Arab Emirates, Morocco, Bangladesh, Senegal, Niger, Germany and Belgium. DESERT SHIELD soon became the most massive airlift in the history of air power. Six weeks into the airlift operation, DESERT SHIELD had already flown more ton-miles than during the entire Berlin Airlift, and the Berlin Airlift took 10 times longer. The huge airlift operation was truly a team effort, composed of US Air Force active duty, Reserve, Air National Guard, and US commercial airliners. For the first time in history, the Civil Reserve Air Fleet (CRAF) was activated. Thirty-eight commercial airliners contributed cargo and passenger aircraft to the airlift effort. By the end of the operation, a total of 158 CRAF had been called to active duty.

War planners adopted the lessons of Vietnam into their preparations. Unlike Vietnam, President Bush let the military war planners develop and use their plans with little interference. As Commander-in-Chief, President Bush also set clear and measurable objectives for the military to accomplish. These were to first deter further Iraqi aggression and defend Saudi Arabia. This new initiative was called Operation DESERT STORM. The next objective came from the United Nations calling on the troops to expel Iraq from Kuwait. Again, these objectives were clear and measurable. The whole world understood that the objective was to restore the country of Kuwait, and that would be done when the Iraqis were completely out of Kuwait.

Previous air campaigns, like the Combined Bomber Offensive during World War II, had attacked

C-130 H Hercules is the workhorse of several air forces.

targets one at a time. When attention was focused on the next target, the enemy repaired the previous target. This time air campaign planners directed that targets would be attacked at the same time and keep the pressure on so they couldn't be repaired. In addition, they planned that all forces would work together. In Vietnam and Korea, the air campaign was divided up. The Navy would work one area and the Air Force worked in another. This time everyone worked as an integrated part of one team.

The plan was called an Air Tasking Order (ATO), and every day a new ATO was issued to all nine of the different air forces in the UN coalition.

This enhanced the effort of the entire coalition. The lessons learned during the World War II North African Air Campaign did not go unnoticed. Air Forces work better when there is one person directing the effort. This allows one person to mass and concentrate the air force effort where it is needed the most. It cuts down on wasted or duplicate effort, and allows for the different units to work off of each other's strengths.

The final coalition air campaign plan called for four phases: (1) target Iraq's command and control sites, air bases, surface-to-air missiles (SCUD) sites, Iraq's nuclear, biological and chemical facilities, and Iraq's war making industry, (2) target enemy air defenses to ensure unhindered flying over Kuwait, (3) cut supply lines and target the enemy's main troops in Kuwait, and (4) close air support of friendly troops as they conduct the ground campaign.

After several attempts were made to allow Iraq to leave Kuwait, and after the January 15th UN deadline for Iraq to leave had passed, the war started. Early on the morning of January 17, 1991, Special Operations Forces headed towards one enemy radar site. The idea was to open a small window in the enemy's defensive curtain; then fly through it, turn around and destroy the rest. While US helicopters attacked the radar site, low observable F-117 Stealth Fighters flew into Iraq and went all the way to downtown Baghdad. US naval ships launched Tomahawk Land Attack Cruise Missiles (TLAMs) and another 400 other fighter and bomber aircraft entered Iraq.

Just as the air campaign plan called for, the first day of the war saw a parallel attack. Air attacks were conducted on the largest number of separate targets in the shortest period of time in the history of war. Indeed, the major damage occurred in the first 10 minutes. Within that timeframe, the lights went out in Baghdad, microwave towers, telephone relay stations, cables and land lines were destroyed; thus destroying Saddam Hussein's ability to communicate. During the next hour, Iraq's integrated air defense system had collapsed. Hussein could not communicate, and his defense systems were being destroyed. Surface to air missile (SAM)

The FB-111A is a potent weapon system. Because of its unusual shape, it has been named the Aardvark!

The A-10 Warthog was designed to be a tank killer.
It proved itself in combat during the Gulf War in 1991.

and fighter air bases were attacked, radar was destroyed and command centers were reduced to rubble. Within several hours, attacks left key Iraqi airfields full of craters and known nuclear, biological and chemical weapon storage sites were rendered unusable. With no command and control system, the Iraqi Air Force ceased flying or risked being shot down. Air superiority had been won and now the battlefield was prepared for the ground campaign.

In a desperate move to inflict US casualties and thereby erode American support at home, Iraq launched an attack into Saudi Arabia on January 29th. The plan called for a two-pronged strike that would go through the Kuwait Wafra Forest and other would be through the small Saudi Arabian border town of Khafji. However, the element of surprise was taken away from the Iraqis as US Air Force E-8 JSTARS aircraft spotted the Iraqi tanks moving toward the border, as well as US Marine Corps personnel spotted their nighttime move, three miles away. While the bulk of the Marines pulled back, some of them hid on top of a building in the outskirts of Khafji and called in air strikes. The Iraqis tried to move forward, but their reserves were cut off by coalition air strikes once the main movement was spotted. Attacked by F/A-18s from the USS *Saratoga,* and USAF A-10s, B-52s, and Special Operations AC-130 H Gunships for the next three days, the Iraqis only held Khafji for a day and were driven back into Kuwait. While the USAF lost one AC-130 gunship and its crew of 14, the Iraqis suffered 2,000 casualties and lost over 300 tanks.

On the 22nd of February, President Bush demanded Iraq's withdrawal form Kuwait or they would be forced out. Iraq again refused. The next day the ground war started at 4:00 am local time. Lacking the same big picture that the United States received from its satellites in space, Iraq had no idea that coalition forces had moved and were attacking from the west.

The left hook maneuver was made possible by cutting off Iraq's ability to communicate, and by keeping our own plans secret. The surprise attack from the west was accompanied by a straightforward push north into Kuwait, then another northeastern push through southwestern Kuwait. UN forces reached Kuwait City on the 25th of February. The vaunted Iraqi Republican Guard, elite units of the Iraqi Army, was no match for US and British armor.

UN casualties were extraordinarily low with 95 killed, 368 wounded, and about 20 missing during the 100-hour war. The Iraqis mostly abandoned their positions before UN forces arrived. Escaping forces were caught by coalition air power and pummeled. Iraq's losses were difficult to assess, but at least 60,000 Iraqis were captured, while another 30,000 and 60,000 were killed and at least 50,000 were wounded.

The poor Iraqi performance can be attributed to three factors. Frist, coalition air power completely dominated the Iraqi forces. They were denied aerial intelligence and coalition bombing destroyed their ability to communicate. Further strikes severely weakened their forces and ability to resupply. Second, Iraqi morale and the will to fight was devastated by continued coalition air strikes. Widespread desertions seriously weakened combat units.

The state of the art C-17 jet transport now serves the USAF around the world. *(Boeing photo)*

Only a few Iraqi units held together for the fight and they were surprised by the coalition left hook and their lack of knowledge of the coalition's advance. Lastly, Saddam Hussein made the mistake of letting UN forces build up. If Iraq had attacked Saudi Arabia and taken the ports, it would have been extremely hard and potentially very costly to land forces in Saudi Arabia.

The victory in the Gulf did exactly what UN Resolution 670 called for—the expelling of Iraqis from Kuwait and the Kuwaiti's return to their homeland. President Bush perhaps summed up the victory best in his commencement address at the United States Air Force Academy in Colorado Springs, May 29, 1991: "Gulf lesson number one," he emphatically stated, "is the value of air power."

Operation Allied Force

The breakup of Yugoslavia proved to be the North Atlantic Treaty Organization's (NATO) greatest challenge in the 1990s. Militant Serbian nationalism and policy of "ethnic cleansing" promoted by Yugoslavian President Slobodan Milosevic created a crisis in Kosovo in 1999. Meanwhile, Albanian separatists in the Kosovo Liberation Army (KLA) fanned the flames of violence. After diplomatic talks broke down, NATO worried about potential genocidal civil war and destabilization throughout the Balkans. As NATO debated intervention in early 1999, President Milosevic unleashed a ruthless offensive designed to crush the KLA and drive ethnic Albanians out of Kosovo. Faced with a massive humanitarian crisis, NATO turned to airpower.

In early 1992, General Merrill McPeak, Chief of Staff of the Air Force, revised the mission of the Air force: "to defend the United States through control and exploitation of air and space." Resultant organizational changes permitted the Air Force to attain an unprecedented level of integration between air and space capabilities by the time the Air War over Serbia (AWOS) commenced in 1999. On 24 March 1999, President Bill Clinton commenced Operation ALLIED FORCE (OAF), announcing three objectives: demonstrate NATO's opposition to aggression; deter Milosevic from escalating attacks on civilians; and damage Serbia's capability to wage war against Kosovo. Milosevic and Serbian forces presented US and NATO forces with an opponent with a capacity for skilled propaganda and utter ruthlessness. The ensuing 78-day battle would be directed against both the Serbian military and Milosevic's propaganda efforts.

From 24 March through 9 June 1999, NATO air forces flew over 38,000 sorties, with 13 of NATO's 19 nations pressuring Milosevic, destroying Serbian fielded forces engaged in Kosovo, and maintaining popular support for intervention. Initially, 214 strike aircraft followed a limited air campaign against approximately 50 targets. The Northrop Grumman B-2 Spirit flew its first combat missions, delivering 650 Joint Direct Attack Munitions (JDAMs) in forty-nine 30-hour sorties from Whiteman AFB, Missouri. On 27 March 1999, Serb air defenses shot down an Air Force F-117, but Combat Search and Rescue personnel recovered the pilot. After weeks of caution and frustration, NATO expanded the scale of the air campaign. The USAF sent 563 aircraft and 13,850 American Airmen to 24 deployed locations.

By June 1999, NATO airpower accomplished its objectives. However, despite a concerted effort to avoid civilian casualties, at least 20 major incidents occurred, including the accidental bombing of the Chinese embassy on 7 May 1999.

The 1999 air campaign against Serbia proved precise, effective, and rapid airpower represented the only means available to coerce an implacable foe. Assessments of Operation ALLIED FORCE concluded that air and ground commanders must agree on the enemy's centers of gravity (those characteristics, capabilities, or sources of power from which a military force derives its freedom of action, physical strength, or will to fight) and that micromanagement of the targeting process limits military effectiveness.

The McDonnell Douglas AV-6B Harrier II was originally developed by the British and is currently in use by the US Marine Corps. It can hover like a helicopter, yet fly an attack mission at speeds in excess of 500 mph.

The KC 135R Stratotanker and their crews are the unsung heroes of many air campaigns.

The Global War on Terrorism

Operation NOBLE EAGLE

On 11 September 2001, 19 terrorists from Al Qaeda, an Islamic extremist group, highjacked four airliners and crashed them into New York City's World Trade Center, the Pentagon, and a remote field in Pennsylvania, killing about 3,000 people in all. In response, President George W. Bush declared a global war on terrorism. Operation NOBLE EAGLE immediately focused on protecting the US homeland from both internal and external air attacks of the nature used on 9-11. US Air Force fighter, tanker and surveillance air assets provided up to 24-hour intercept response coverage for virtually the entire US in the form of ground alert and airborne combat air patrols over designated locations. Civil Air Patrol was also called upon to conduct reconnaissance flights over the devastation for accurate assessment by government agencies.

Operation Enduring Freedom

Operation Enduring Freedom (OEF) focused an international coalition, with forces from the United Kingdom, Australia, Canada, the Czech Republic, Denmark, France, Germany, Italy, Japan, Jordan, the Netherlands, New Zealand, Norway, Pakistan, Poland, Russia, Spain and Turkey. As of our final revision of this publication, Operation Enduring Freedom continues in hopes that a new democratic government can be established and the troops can return from the conflict in Iraq.

The F-16 Fighting Falcon is one of the greatest fighters of the 20th century.

The Future

There have been many remarkable accomplishments in the short time since the Wright brothers flew for the first time. The history of flight is filled with these remarkable stories and this text has tried to explore several of them. As each unsolvable problem is miraculously accomplished, new doors open and more unsolvable problems need to be solved.

Are these problems unsolvable or will new developments and accomplishments solve them just as they have all others? Only time will tell, but, without a doubt, there will be even more amazing developments in the future. Part One of this book has dealt with many of them, but there are more to come.

Key Terms and Concepts

- Cold War
- National Security Act of 1947
- Strategic Air Command (SAC)
- B-36
- P-51
- HE-178
- F-80
- ME-262
- vengeance weapons
- V-1 and V-2
- R-4
- Berlin Airlift
- C-47
- Korean War
- 38th Parallel
- radar
- DC-4 and the Constellation
- Convair series airliners
- turboprops and pure jets
- Vickers Viscount
- DeHavilland Comet 1
- Cessna, Piper, and Beech
- National Advisory Committee on Aeronautics (NACA)
- sound barrier
- X-1 and X-2
- swept-back wings
- century series fighters
- B-47, B-52, B-58
- smart bombs and precision guided munitions
- Vietnam War
- ROLLING THUNDER
- LINEBACKER I and II
- Tet offensive
- F-4, A-6, A-7
- MiG-15, 17, 21
- EC-121
- SAM and AAA
- guerilla warfare
- DESERT SHIELD and DESERT STORM
- satellites
- F-15, F-16, F-117, A-10
- KC-135, KC-10
- AWACS, JSTARS
- C-141, C-5, C-130
- Civil Reserve Air fleet (CRAF)
- Tomahawk Land Attack Cruise Missiles (TLAMS)

? Test Your Knowledge ?

TRUE OR FALSE

1. *At the end of World War II, the world was left with two major political forces — Soviet communism and Western democracy.*
2. *In the years immediately following World War II, Hungry, Poland, Romania, and East Germany belonged to the North Atlantic Treaty Organization (NATO)?*

3   During World War II, the United States led the world in jet propulsion development.

4.   The two German "vengeance" weapons were the V-2 and R-4.

5.   The helicopter became part of the Army Air Forces during World War II, but it was the Korean War that really demonstrated its value.

6.   The expected great demand for general aviation aircraft after World War II failed to materialize.

7.   Initially, the DC-4 was more popular than the Constellation because the Army built more of them.

8.   The Constellation had two advantages over the DC-4 — it was pressurized and it was 100 mph faster.

9.   The French developed the first turboprop and the first turbojet airliners.

10.   In the late 1940s, the "big three" in general aviation manufacturing were Lockheed, Cessna and Piper.

SELECT THE CORRECT ANSWER

11.   The United States reduced the size of its military forces after World War II because (**the United Nations outlawed war / it was the only country possessing the atomic bomb, and it felt secure with that weapon**).

12.   In 1947, after the United States Air Force became a separate service, its primary mission was (**continental air defense / nuclear deterrence**).

13.   The Berlin Airlift resulted (**from a massive earthquake / when the Soviet Union prevented any surface transportation in or out of the city**).

14.   The Korean War began when (**North Korean / communist Chinese**) troops invaded South Korea.

15.   The Korean War taught America a lesson: (**the atomic arsenal alone was not enough to prevent involvement in war / the United States must maintain an enormous standing Army**).

16.   The (*B-52 / B-58*) is still in use today.

17.   The world's first production supersonic fighter was the (*F-100 / F-101*).

18.   The first "pure" jet commercial airliner was the (***Vickers Viscount / DeHavilland Comet 1***).

19.   The term "Mach 3" means (**three times the speed of sound / 30,000 feet above sea level**).

MATCHING

20.   Built to supercede the B-47 because it had more range.   **a. *X-1***

21.   Broke Mach 3, but came apart due to frictional heating.   **b. *B-52***

22.   First VTOL aircraft.   **c. *P-51***

23.   Had a revolutionary new wing design called the laminar-flow wing.   **d. *X-2***

24.   First aircraft to break the "sound barrier."   **e. *Flying Bedstead***

FILL IN THE BLANKS

25.   In 1950, Vietnam was a _____ colony.

26.   The South Vietnamese struggled with their civil war against the North Vietnamese and by 1961, President _____ expanded the commitment of the United States.

27. On August 7, 1964, Congress passed the _____ which allowed President _____ to "take all necessary measures to repel an armed attack against the force of the United States and to prevent further aggression [in Vietnam]."

28. _____ helped to "unpopularize" the Vietnam War.

29. The _____ marked the beginning of the end of the war in Vietnam.

30. _____ or _____ enabled US pilots to finally destroy the Thanh Hoa Bridge — a long-standing and critical North Vietnamese target.

31. As opposed to Operation _____, Operation _____ was conducted without as much worry about Chinese and Soviet reaction to the war in Vietnam.

32. During the Cold War, the Air Force's _____ primary mission was to defend the United States from nuclear attack.

33. During Operation DESERT STORM, and for the first time in US history, the _____ was activated to provide logistical support.

34. Two aircraft were key links to moving troops, cargo and fighters into Southwest Asia during Operation DESERT SHIELD/STORM: _____ and _____.

35. The US/Coalition Air Forces quickly gained air superiority in Operation DESERT STORM by first attacking Iraq's _____ and _____ systems with precision guided munitions.

SHORT ANSWER

36. Briefly define the "Cold War."

37. How did air power achieve "victory" in the Berlin Airlift?

38. What roles did air power play in the Korean War?

39. Why were American pilots able to defeat the technologically superior Russian-built MiGs during the Korean War?

40. What aviation improvements developed as a result of World War II?

41. Early attempts to break the sound barrier resulted in what kinds of problems?

42. Name one advantage and one disadvantage to swept-back wings.

43. Why was new missile technology of the mid-1950s important?

44. Name three aircraft, along with their roles, that were built for the Strategic Air Command during the Cold War.

45. What lessons from previous air wars were used to develop the Desert Storm air campaign plan?

46. What impact did air power have on Iraq's counterattack into Saudi Arabia?

6 ADVANCES IN AERONAUTICS

The aeronautics research flights so important in the early 1950s continued into the early 1960s. From the latter part of the 1960s up to the present, flight-testing has been primarily of prototypes of various operational aircraft rather than of research aircraft.

Objectives

Discuss the flights of the X-15.
Discuss the XB-70.
Discuss the importance of composite materials.
Discuss solar aircraft.
Discuss the advancements in military aerospace.
Discuss the advancements in civil aviation and general aviation.

Aeronautical Research

The X-15

The two *X*-series aircraft, which were flown during the 1950s and 1960s, were the *X*-15 and the *XB*-70.

The X-15 project was a joint Air Force, Navy and NACA project aimed at building an airplane that could fly at a speed of 4,500 mph and reach an altitude of 250,000 feet. At this speed and altitude, the temperature of the aircraft would reach 1,200° F. To withstand this temperature, the X-15 was constructed of a nickel-steel alloy called Inconel X.

The X-15 was 50 feet long and had a 22-foot wingspan. It weighed about 33,000 pounds, of which over 18,000 pounds was fuel. The X-15 was rocket powered and was launched by dropping it from a specially modified B-52. The first powered flight took place in September 1959, and the aircraft reached a speed of almost 1,400 mph. The first eight flights of the X-15 were piloted by North American Aviation test pilot Scott Crossfield. The first government flight was performed in March 1960, by NASA test pilot Joe Walker.

Flight testing continued through 1967 with the three X-15s performing over 200 flights. In the end, the X-15 exceeded both of its design goals. It reached a speed of 4,534 mph (Mach 6.72), which is twice as fast as a rifle bullet, and it reached an altitude of 314,750 feet, which is 59.6 miles straight up. The pilots on these record-setting flights were Major Robert White, USAF, for the speed record, and NASA test pilot Joe Walker for the altitude record.

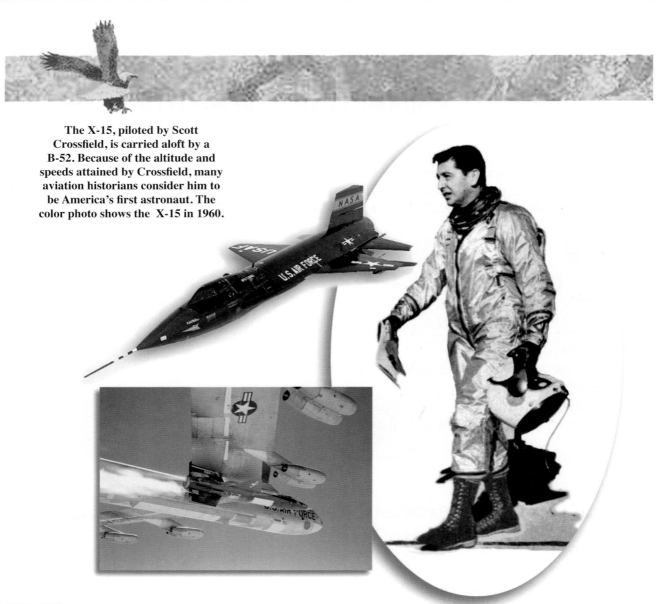

The X-15, piloted by Scott Crossfield, is carried aloft by a B-52. Because of the altitude and speeds attained by Crossfield, many aviation historians consider him to be America's first astronaut. The color photo shows the X-15 in 1960.

XB-70

In 1954, the United States Air Force requested bids on a contract to build a supersonic replacement for the B-52. This aircraft would have to fly three times the speed of sound and at an altitude of 70,000 feet. North American Aviation won the competition and received a contract to build two prototypes. The result was the XB-70, one of the largest, fastest and most controversial aircraft ever built. The first XB-70's initial flight was September 1964, and the second one first flew in July 1965.

In 1964, Congress decided the Air Force did not need a supersonic bomber and canceled the program. The Air Force and NASA used the two prototypes for supersonic research. In October 1964, the XB-70 reached its design speed (2,000 mph) and altitude (70,000 feet) requirements. In June 1966, the second XB-70 prototype was destroyed in a mid-air collision. The first is now at the United States Air Force Museum at Wright-Patterson Air Force Base, OH.

Since the Wright Flyer, aircraft research and design have been continually changing as aircraft designers determined which configuration produced the best performance characteristics—especially at high speeds. While performance has always been the major design factor in the past, today other factors are also important.

The XB-70

Other Research

For the military, changing air tactics, advanced weapons systems and new technology advantages in aerodynamics, structures and propulsion have entered the design picture. Beginning in the mid-1970s, fuel efficiency and environmental considerations became driving forces in commercial aviation, as well as in military aviation.

Research in the past was always limited by weight and stress limitations. Many designs looked good on paper, but could not be tested because the aircraft would be too heavy and/or unable to withstand the in-flight stresses. However, advances in construction materials in the 1970s overcame some of these limitations.

Super-strong, but lightweight, nonmetallic, epoxy graphite composite materials were developed that were stronger than many common metals used in aircraft construction. These composites were tested in every major structural component of an aircraft—from the wings and fuselage to helicopter rotor blades. Research tests demonstrated their strength and opened new doors either to go back to old designs that were more efficient or to advance to new, previously untested designs.

One such advance came in 1988 when the FAA certified Beech Aircraft Corporation's all composite Model 2000 Starship I. The business airplane's fuselage and wing structure use epoxy graphite and honeycomb sandwich panels made of epoxy resin.

Other research was conducted on airfoil design, which produced some revolutionary concepts. The list contains forward-swept wings (FSW), oblique wings, joined wings, mission-adaptive wings, supercritical wings, winglets and canards.

Sweeping the wings forward goes back more than 100 years to pre-Wright experiments of the 1870s. The concept was flight tested earlier in this century and has theoretical advantages. Its use had

been overshadowed by rearward-swept wings, since forward-swept wings needed to be structurally stronger in high-speed flight.

In the past, this meant making the wing heavier using conventional metal alloys. Composite-material technology made the FSW practical. This technology enables the wings to be made lighter, smaller and less costly than equivalent performance planes with rearward-swept metal wings. The FSW design also reduces weight cost and drag.

Test data showed that this technology provided an aircraft that can weigh less, fly longer and turn very tight at supersonic speeds. The X-29A was built in the early 1980s to demonstrate the capabilities of forward-swept wings.

The forward-swept wings of the X-29A

Another research project was on oblique-winged aircraft. This type of aircraft is also known as adaptive-wing, skewed-wing or pivoting-wing aircraft. The oblique-wing aircraft (OWA) changes form during flight for optimum lift under different circumstances and can be rotated to different positions for the best aerodynamic characteristics.

The ability to change the wing angle provides efficiency at both low and high speeds. For takeoff, landing and low-speed cruise, the wing is perpendicular to the fuselage; at high speeds, the wing is pivoted to different oblique angles.

NASA flight-tested an oblique-wing aircraft in 1982 and called the aircraft the AD-1 *Scissors*. In this aircraft, the wing rotates around its vertical axis with one end pointing forward and the other end rearward. This design explored the feasibility of using an adaptive wing as a low-drag, supersonic airfoil for future transport airplanes.

Another project explored winglets. An airfoil produces lift by creating pressure differences on its upper and lower surfaces. At the wingtips, this difference in pressure produces wingtip vortices. This swirling air increases drag, decreases lift and can produce potentially dangerous air turbulence around airports. The winglets, placed in a vertical position at the end of the wings, eliminates the vortices and improves the efficiency of the wing.

Two other projects explored canards and mission adaptive wings. Canards are horizontal surfaces forward of the main wings and are used for trim and control. The use of canards increases maneuverability and can allow the main wings of an aircraft to be smaller and lighter. The picture of the *X-29A* shows an excellent view of the canards forward of the wings.

Mission adaptive wings are now used on several different aircraft. This type of wing is similar to the one used on the B-1B bomber. This wing maintains its best efficiency under most flying conditions by moving forward for slow speed flight and folding to the rear for supersonic flight.

The research and development benefited military, as well as commercial aircraft. Both military and commercial aviation wanted aircraft to be faster, with higher performance. Two of these advanced aircraft were developed to fly over enemy territory at high altitude. They were the U-2 and SR-71.

The B-1B Lancer is affectionately known as the "*Bone*."

**Faster Than a Bullet -
The SR-71 Blackbird High-
Altitude Reconnaissance Aircraft**

**The U-2 High-Altitude
Reconnaissance Aircraft**

The X-33 Advanced
Technology Demonstrator
is an unmanned vehicle,
launched vertically like a
rocket and lands horizontally
like an airplane.

The X-43A, shown below, is part of NASAs experimental hypersonic flight research program that seeks to demonstrate airframe-integrated, "air-breathing" engine technologies that promise to increase payload capacity for future vehicles including faster than Mach 5 and reusable space launchers.

The Convair XF2Y-1 Sea Dart was an experimental jet-powered sea plane.
It is on permanent display at the San Diego Aerospace Museum.

Significant developments in new materials and designs allowed the construction of stealthy aircraft, which were almost invisible to radar. The B-1B grew out of studies beginning in 1962. Unlike America's past bomber designs, which emphasized high-altitude capabilities, the B-1 was designed to be a low-altitude penetration bomber. To defeat Soviet defenses, the bomber was designed with low-observable technology, which produces a radar cross section 1 percent that of the older B-52.

Two other aircraft, the B-2 bomber and the F-117A, are true "stealth" aircraft designed to be invisible to enemy radar. The B-2 bombers have a unique flying-wing design and can only be described as a radical departure from conventional aircraft designs.

Research and Development and Civil Aviation

Armed with the experience of building large jet aircraft for the military, the Boeing Company unveiled the 707-120 in 1954. The 707 outclassed every airliner in use at that time in all aspects... size, speed, range and capacity. It was the 707 that revolutionized the commercial aviation industry and went on to become the standard long-range jet of the 1960s. The 707 also found service with the

Air Force as the C-135. It was followed shortly by other similar long-haul jets—the Douglas DC-8 and the Convair 880 and 990.

So immediate was the success of the 707 and DC-8 airliners that both Boeing and Douglas began working on smaller, short-haul jets. The first short-haul jet was the French Caravelle I which first flew in 1955 and went into service with Air France in 1959. More than 200 Caravelles in four models were manufactured. This aircraft had a jet engine attached to either side of the rear fuselage and carried between 65 and 90 passengers. United Airlines was the only US carrier to fly the Caravelle I.

In February 1963, Boeing unveiled a new short- and medium-haul trijet called the 727. The 727s have been produced in five models and is the most successful jet ever built. Over 1,700 of these aircraft have been manufactured. The other short-haul Boeing aircraft, the 737, is a twinjet airliner. It went into service in 1968 and carries 80 to 113 passengers. More than 800 of the 737s have been built.

Douglas entered the short-haul market in 1962 with the announcement of their twinjet DC-9. The DC-9 flew for the first time in February 1965. The DC-9 resembles the Caravelle in the placement of the engines, but is a larger aircraft that carries from 80 to 115 passengers. More than 1,000 of these aircraft have been sold.

By the mid-1960s, jet airline travel had reached a peak. In April 1966, Boeing announced they would begin production of the Boeing 747. This jumbo jet was huge even when compared to the 707. It had a wingspan 65 feet longer than the 707, and its fuselage was nearly 90 feet longer and almost twice the diameter. The 747 offered a new standard of luxury that included seating for 385 passengers and an upstairs cocktail lounge.

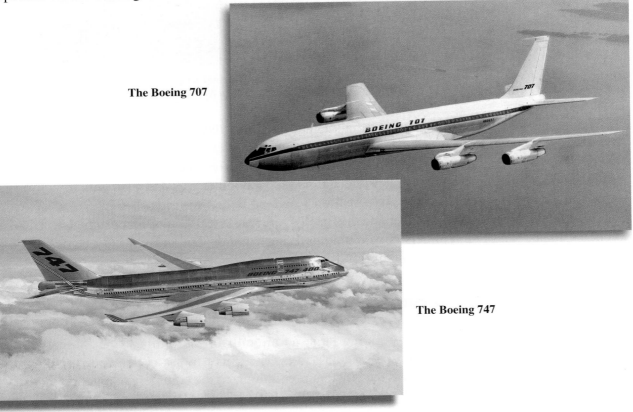

The Boeing 707

The Boeing 747

The Boeing 757 and 767 *(Boeing photo)*

Both Lockheed and Douglas entered the jumbo-jet field in 1966 with announcements of intent to build a medium-haul jumbo jet. The Douglas DC-10 flew first in August 1970, while the Lockheed L-1011 flew in November 1970. In addition to following a very similar timetable, the two aircraft are very similar both in appearance and in performance. They are both trijets with one engine under each wing and the third on the tail. In the DC-10, the rear engine is mounted above the fuselage, while in the L-1011, it is mounted inside the rear fuselage. They both carry about 350 passengers for distances up to 4,000 miles. Both aircraft have been very successful. Over the years, improvements to the basic models of the 747, DC-10 and L-101 have continued to keep these aircraft in the marketplace.

Before 1978, the Americans had the technological edge over foreign aircraft manufacturers, with 85 percent of all world airliners being US manufactured and designed. By 1978, the technology gap had narrowed to the point that US aircraft manufacturers began to feel a technological threat from abroad, especially from the A-310 advanced-technology transport. This threat gave rise to the introduction of a new family of advanced-technology jetliners for the 1980s. The DC-9 Super 80, the Boeing 767 and the Boeing 757 are three aircraft that were developed to improve efficiency using advanced technology.

Airbus Industry continues to put the pressure on American aircraft manufacturers with the introduction of the Airbus A-320 in late 1988. This commercial transport is designed for short and medium ranges powered by twin turbofans. It also incorporated several technological firsts. It was the first subsonic commercial aircraft to have control by fly-by-wire throughout normal flight. It also has a centralized maintenance system, side stick controls in the cockpit in place of control columns, and has composite materials that makeup the major elements of the airplane's primary structures.

In the early 1960s, the Bristol Aeroplane Company (which later became part of the British Aircraft

The Boeing 777's "Glass Cockpit"

Corporation (BAC)) in England and Sud-Aviation (which later became Aerospatiale) in France were both working on designs for a supersonic passenger airliner. They both came up with very similar designs for a delta-wing aircraft, which could carry about 100 passengers and fly at about Mach 2.2 (1,400 mph). They also both discovered that the development costs of such an aircraft would be so high that neither nation could afford to build it.

In November 1962, an international agreement was signed which would allow BAC and Sud-Aviation to jointly build the aircraft, and the governments of Britain and France would share the development costs. Thus, the Concorde was born.

At that time, unknown to anyone in the Western World, the Soviet Union was also working on a supersonic transport (SST) known as the TU-144. The TU-144 was very similar to the Concorde in size and shape, but was designed to fly a little faster at Mach 2.35 (1,500 mph).

The United States, not to be outdone, decided to enter the SST competition. However, the Concorde and the TU-144 already had a head start because the United States did not start its SST program until 1965. The American SST contract was awarded to Boeing. They called their SST the Model 2707. Due to its late start, it was evident that the 2707 could not beat either the British or the Russian SST into service and lost both public and government support. The project was eventually canceled

The Concorde *(EAA)*

before the 2707 ever flew.

The TU-144 won the race into the air, but a disastrous crash allowed the Concorde to beat the Russian SST into commercial service. On May 24, 1976, the Concorde began flying from London and Paris to Washington, DC. The flight took less than 4 hours.

General Aviation

From 1958 to 1982, general aviation in the United States grew at a faster rate than military or commercial aviation. This is not generally true in other nations of the world (with the exception of Canada). There are three main reasons for this: (1) geography, (2) expense and (3) freedom to fly.

The United States is a very large nation, while some European countries are smaller than most of our states. To fly from Amsterdam to Rome would require crossing through four independent nations and asking permission of each to enter its airspace. This trip is shorter than the trip from San Francisco to San Diego in California. Because of the short distances and excellent ground transportation, there is no real reason to fly within any of the European countries.

Also, the expense of owning and operating a general aviation aircraft is very high, and the United States is one of the few nations in the world with a standard of living that will permit the average person to own an airplane. Most nations of the world do not have a developed aviation manufacturing industry, so if a citizen of one of these nations wants to own an airplane, he or she would have to import one from the United States. In addition, the cost of fuel in most foreign countries is almost twice as high as in the United States. Finally, many nations of the world are ruled by a government that does not want its citizens to have the right to fly whenever and wherever they want.

As mentioned previously in this text, immediately following World War II, Beech, Cessna and Piper began to build all metal, single-engine monoplanes. These aircraft evolved through the years to become more and more sophisticated. The pilots wanted them to fly higher, faster and further, so many became turbocharged and were equipped with retractable landing gear. More instruments and electronic aids were added, all of which led to the general aviation aircraft of today.

Navajo

In the 1950s, the manufacturers began adding twin-engine aircraft to their inventories. This was an answer to the need for business and executive aircraft. The first of these twin-engine aircraft was the Beechcraft Twin Bonanza in 1951, followed by the Aero Commander in 1952, and the Cessna 310 and Piper Apache in 1953. During the 1960s, more and more innovations were added to these twins,

The Beechcraft King Air

and by the end of that decade, most manufacturers had twin-engine aircraft as fancy as the commercial airliners.

It was also during the 1960s that the first turbojet business and executive aircraft were built. The first was the British Hawker Siddeley 125, a twinjet that entered service in 1963. American business jets included the Learjet (1964), the North American Sabreliner (1966) and the Grumman Gulfstream II (1967).

During the 1980s, aircraft such as the Gulfstream IV (1986), Learjet 55 (1981) and Beechcraft Starship I (1988) were built using the newest technologies in composites, airfoils and engines to increase performance, while making the aircraft economical to operate.

As research and development continues, military, commercial and general aviation aircraft will continue to benefit. Aviation will continue to get better, faster and less expensive.

The Joint Strike Fighter

The Lockheed Martin F-35 Joint Strike Fighter.
(Courtesy of Lockheed Martin)

The Lockheed Martin F-35 Lightning II, is the next generation of stealthy, supersonic, multi-role aircraft. It is part of a family known as a Joint Strike Fighters. It will be built in three versions: the F35A, which will be a conventional take-off and landing (CTOL) aircraft for the USAF. The F-35B is a short take-off and vertical landing (STOVL)vehicle for the Army and Marine Corp, and the F-35C (CV for carrier version) is specifically designed for the Naval operations.

The USAF F-35A is primarily an

air-to-ground strike aircraft used as a complement to the F-22. The USMC F-35B is slated to replace the F/A -18B/C and the AV-88. Orders from the United Kingdom are scheduled to replace the Sea Harriers. The C model is also designed to replace the F/A -18B and C models as well as the A-6 while complementing the F/A -18 E and F models.

In order to minimize weight, the aircraft is made of an approximate 40% carbon fiber composite construction. In order to minimize the structural weight and complexity of assembly, the wingbox section integrates the wing and fuselage section into one piece. To minimize radar signatures, sweep angles are identical for the leading and trailing edges of the wing and empennage. The fuselage and canopy also have sloping sides. The seam of the canopy and the weapons bay doors are sawtoothed and the vertical fins are canted at an angle.

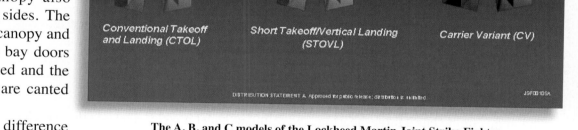

The A, B, and C models of the Lockheed Martin Joint Strike Fighter.
(Illustration Courtesy of Lockheed Martin Communications)

The main difference between the naval and other JSF versions is related to carrier operations. The internal structure of the naval version is stronger due to the high loading of catapult launches and tail hook landings.

The CV aircraft has larger wing and tail control surfaces giving more control authority during low-speed carrier landing operations. A larger wing area provides for an increased payload and higher fuel capacity giving the aircraft an extended range.

Weapons are located within two parallel bays located forward of the landing gear. The "A" version has an internally-mounted gun while the Navy/Marine can be fitted with an external gun pod.

For targeting, Lockheed Martin's Missile & Fire Control and Northrop Grumman Electronic Sensors and Systems are jointly integrated in the JSF's electro-optical system. The LM Electro-optical Targeting System provides long-range detection and precision targeting capability. As a stealth design, the F-35 has the radar signature of a golf ball!

Power is provided by Pratt & Whitney's afterburning turbofan F-135 engine. This is a derivative of the F-119 fitted to the F-22 Raptor. On the F-35B version, the engine is coupled with a shaft-driven "lift fan" system for STOVL propulsion. The counter-rotating lift fans, developed by Rolls-Royce, can

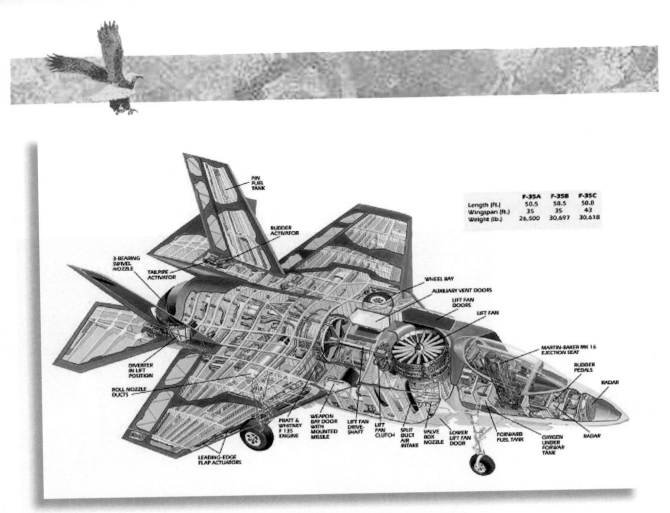

Cutaway Illustration Courtesy of Lockheed Martin

generate more than 20,000 pounds of thrust.

The main engine has a three-bearing, swiveling exhaust nozzle. The nozzle, which is supplemented by roll control ducts on the inboard section of the wing, together with the vertical lift fan, provides the required STOVL capability.

The aircraft is a joint effort of Lockheed Martin, Northrop-Grumman, BAE Systems, Pratt & Whitney, and Rolls Royce. Final assembly of the aircraft will take place at Lockheed Martin's plant in Fort Worth, Texas. Major subassemblies will be produced by Northrup Grumman Integrated Systems at El Segundo, California and BAE Systems at Samiesbury, Lancashire, England. BAE Systems is responsible for the design and integration of the aft fuselage, horizontal/vertical empennage and the folding-wing mechanism of the CV variant.

Micro Air Vehicles

A whole new generation of Micro Air Vehicles (MAV) has been developed since the turn of the century. Most of these "micros" are battery-powered and made of lightweight composite compounds. Some of the MAVs currently under development are as small as 6 inches in height and even smaller "insect-sized" craft are in the experimental stages. Military MAVs have already been used for flight into buildings during terrorist surveillance.

All of the current MAVs carry on-board cameras and can be operated by one soldier in or near a battlefield environment. These have the capability of gathering real-time information that can, through a field-operated lap-top computer, be relayed a command post for planning and attack decisions.

The Honeywell MAV is currently the front runner in what is known as the UAVs, or Unmanned Aerial Vehicles. The *Micro Air Vehicle,* shown here, has flown hundreds of successful flights between ground level and 500 feet AGL. Honeywell says it will function as high as 10,500' if required. As a recon vehicle, it allows soldiers, police officers, and other combatants, to see over a hill, in or around buildings and into other non-secured areas.

These are all part of a new technology that falls into a category called "FCS," or Future Combat Systems. They are small, lightweight, and affordable, man-portable, backpackable UAVs that can be used by dismounted

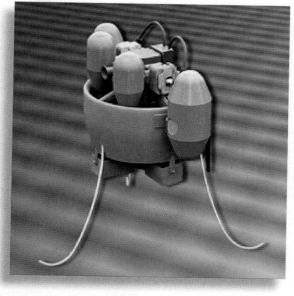

Micro Air Vehicle
(*Image Courtesy of Honeywell Aerospace*)

infantry, Marines, and Special Operations personnel can use the UAVs for reconnaissance, security, and target acquisition operations in open, rolling, mountain, desert, and urban warfare. The small airborne vehicles have the capability to loiter either in the air or on the ground. While on task, they can "hover and stare," and "perch and stare." The vehicle can then transmit real-time data back to an individual or a command post.

Personal Air Vehicles

Currently under development is an aircraft that has revolutionary possibilities. This is called the ***Personal Air Vehicle*** and one company, Carter Aviation Technologies, has created and flown a rotor-craft that has an unpowered rotor above and a pusher propulsion system at the rear of the fuselage. A four-place model is in the final stages of development and will have the capability of flying forward at a top speed of 270 mph and slow to a speed which allows it to land vertically. It is fully pressurized allowing it to fly comfortably at 35,000 feet. Carter Aviation Technologies has

Carter Aviation Technologies PAV in flight.
Photo by Jason Bynum /Courtesy of Carter Aviation Technologies

developed a method of automatically controlling the collective pitch of the rotor that is independent of any electronics. This will provide the proper pitch from a jump takeoff, transitioning to high speed cruise and then back to a hovercraft type of landing.

Their "slowed-rotor" compound design allows this aircraft to have a vertical takeoff & landing and a highly efficient small wing

CarterCopter in Flight. (*Courtesy of Carter Aviation Technologies*)

for horizontal speeds up to 500 miles per hour.

On June 17, 2005, test pilot Larry Neal, achieved a milestone for rotorcraft while flying the CarterCopter. It reached what is known as Mu-1. This is the first time in history that any rotorcraft has reached this mathematical point. The condition was achieved during normal flight-testing while collecting data on a newly developed speed controller for the rotor. It was not planned, but evolved because the rotor remained very stable as the rpm was decreased. Neal decreased the rotor rpm in small increments when he was near Mu-1.

With all systems stable the decision was made to proceed. Data from the flight shows that the airspeed was 170 mph and the rotor was slowed to 107 rpm. Previously, the lowest rotor speed every achieved was 115 rpm. The Mu-1 flight time was just 1.5 seconds before Neal reduced the throttle to slow the aircraft, but it was operated continuously above 0.9 Mu for over over 20 seconds.

The CarterCopter has the potential of becoming an aircraft that any qualified operator can land and takeoff from a non-dedicated airfield location, such as a driveway or street near one's home. With wings folded and rotor stowed, the aircraft can safely land near and taxi to a gas station for re-fueling. In various other configurations, this aircraft has the capability of operating from a carrier, or a standard Naval vessel, yet achieve forward speeds in the subsonic range. Because of its simplicity, the CarterCopter can provide a very effective service in many aerospace applications with a very low production cost.

Aging Airliners get a new life as firefighters

Several aging airliners are now being used as high-capacity slurry bombers in the fight against America's forest fires. The featured image shows a DC-10 that has been converted to carry 3 tanks each with 12,000 gallons of water, or fire-retardant. The engines of the former passenger liner have been up-graded to 42,000 pounds of thrust and in its fully operational state, can drop a layer of retardant 50 feet wide and ¾ of a mile long! This kind of power can bring an enormous amount of life-saving liquid to the fire-line.

DC10 dropping a payload water.
(*Photo courtesy of Omni Air International and Cargo Conversions LLC.*)

Key Terms and Concepts

- X-15 and XB-70
- composites
- forward-swept wings
- oblique-wing aircraft
- winglets
- canards
- mission-adaptive wings
- joined wings

- supercritical wings
- solar powered aircraft
- stealth technology
- B-1B, B-2, F-117
- long-haul jets vs short-haul jets
- jumbo jets
- advanced technology jets
- supersonic transports

? Test Your Knowledge ?

TRUE OR FALSE

1. *Epoxy graphite composite materials have been developed that are stronger than many common metals used in aircraft construction.*
2. *The Boeing 747-600 is the world's first airliner to be built totally out of composite materials.*
3. *The first twin-engine General Aviation aircraft was the Beechcraft Twin Bonanza.*
4. *The U-2 and the SR-71 were developed to fly over enemy territory.*
5. *The B-52 is a "stealth" aircraft.*
6. *The first turbojet business land executive aircraft was the British Hawker Siddeley 125.*
7. *The Boeing 727 was the most successful jet ever built.*
8. *The DC-4 was the Douglas entry into the jet-powered, short-haul market.*
9. *Douglas built the first jumbo jet, the DC-10.*
10. *The A-320 is an advanced-technology airliner using composite materials for the majority of the aircraft's primary structures.*
11. *The TU-144 is the US equivalent to the Concorde supersonic transport.*
12. *Between 1922 and 1928, general aviation aircraft sales reached an all-time high.*

SELECT THE CORRECT ANSWER

13. *The (XB-15 / XB-70) was designed as a bomber.*
14. *The (XB-15 / XB-70) was rocket-powered.*
15. *The (XB-15 / XB-70) was constructed of a nickel-steel alloy called* Inconel X.

MATCHING

16. *X-29A*
17. *AD-1 Scissors*
18. *Eliminates wingtip vortices*
19. *B-1B*

a. **Oblique wings**
b. **Winglets**
c. **Forward-swept wings**
d. **Mission-adaptive wings**

PART TWO

Principles of Flight and Navigation

Chapter

7 BASIC AERONAUTICS AND AERODYNAMICS

Objectives

Explain the difference between aeronautics and aerodynamics.
Understand the properties of air that are important to flight.
Understand why scientists use simplifying assumptions during study.
Define airfoil.
Know the parts of an airfoil.
Describe the concepts of relative wind, angle of attack and streamlines.
Describe Bernoulli's principle.
Describe the four forces of flight.
Give examples of aircraft characteristics that can improve each force.
Explain how the loss of one force affects the other three forces.
Describe the real world effects of viscosity and compressible airflow.
Name two effects wings have on airflow not accounted for by airfoils.

The Realm of Flight

The science and art of flight through the atmosphere is known as aeronautics. Aerodynamics, on the other hand, is the science relating to the energy of gases in motion.

To understand the science of aeronautics and aerodynamics, you must study the air and the machine that operates in it. Once you gain an understanding of the machine and its environment, you can appreciate the technological marvel of flight. One has only to watch a bird in flight for a short while and it becomes obvious that this living machine is capable of using the energy of the atmosphere to defy gravity.

The science of aerodynamics involves many investigations. Besides the study of airflow around an aircraft, it also includes the passage of air through a jet engine and even the expulsion of energy from a rocket motor. The common denominator of each of these examples is fluids in motion.

The Composition and Properties of Air

The atmosphere is a mixture of several gases. For practical purposes, in the region where most flight occurs, it is a homogeneous mixture of one-fifth oxygen and four-fifths nitrogen. The atmosphere extends upwards to about 100 miles and can be compared to a pile of blankets.

The Great Lakes biplane typifies the wonderful airplanes built in aviation's Golden Era.

Pressure

Air at the higher altitudes is like the top blanket of the pile; it is under much less pressure than the air at lower altitudes. At the bottom of the atmosphere, say sea-level, the weight of all the layers of air above it press the bottom layer down at a pressure of 0.07651 lb/ft^3 (for dry air at 59°F, 40° latitude). That gives you a standard day pressure of 14.7 psi, or 29.92 on a mercury barometer.

Temperature

Temperature is a measure of the energy within a gas. The hotter the air, the more energy it has internally, and the faster its molecules move around.

The temperature of the atmosphere decreases at a rate of about 3.5° Fahrenheit, per 1,000 feet increase in altitude. This decrease in temperature continues up to about 38,000 ft MSL. You should remember, however, that the temperature of the air is under no contract to actually follow the standard. Sometimes, the temperature actually increases with altitude for a short distance.

Density

The density of air is essentially how many molecules are squeezed into a given volume. Higher density air is squeezed together more tightly than lower density air. From this, it can be assumed that air is compressible.

Because the air at higher altitudes has less pressure, it is also less dense. At sea level, on a cool day, the air is dense and airplanes perform very well.

Density is also related to temperature. As the air is heated, the molecules move farther apart and this means there is a decrease in density. On a hot day at a high elevation such as the airport in Leadville, CO (over 9000 ft MSL), some airplanes have difficulty taking off because the air is too thin.

Viscosity

Viscosity is defined as a fluid's resistance to flow. An easy comparison would be water and honey. Honey is more viscous.

Since air is a fluid, it also has a resistance to flow. This is because of (1) the attraction between the molecules of the air and (2) the attraction between the air and the molecules of whatever it touches. If a force is applied to air, its molecules resist a tendency to flow. The greater the density of the air, the greater the resistance.

A phenomenon known as viscous drag occurs when an object is placed in the path of moving air. The mutual attraction of molecules slows the rate of flow. This form of drag is transmitted to other air molecules that are not actually touching the surface over which they are flowing.

This transmission of drag is the result of a mutual attraction between molecules within the airstream, but it is not transmitted to all the air molecules. At some point away from the surface, the effect of viscous drag is lost.

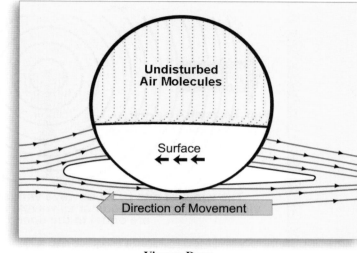

Viscous Drag

Laminar Flow

As an object moves through the air, there is a flow pattern around it. This flow pattern is either smooth or turbulent. The smooth, and more desirable flow, is known as laminar.

In actual flight, an airfoil may experience both laminar and turbulent flow patterns. Aeronautical engineers are, therefore, constantly searching for ways to improve performance and laminar flow is given careful consideration in the design of new aircraft.

The P-51D Mustang shown here had a very efficient laminar flow wing.

The Speed of Sound in Air

If a pebble were dropped in a lake, ripples would spread out from the point where it impacts the water. This is a visualization of how sound waves travel away from the source that is making the sound.

In this example, the rock had to push against some water molecules, and they in turn push against other molecules. If another rock were placed in exactly the same location as the first one, another wave would be created. The "sound source" of energy does this.

A disturbance with enough energy to produce a sound causes a reaction that is transmitted from

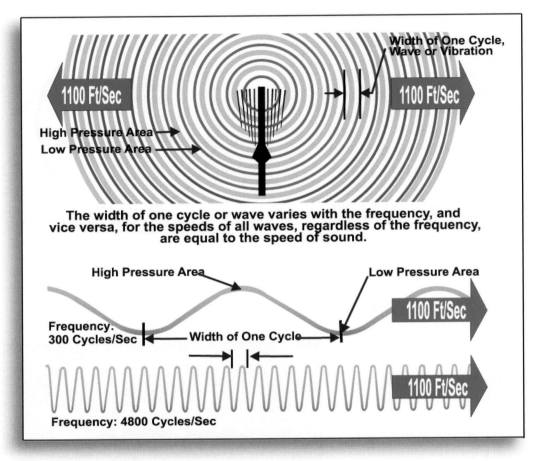

The width of one cycle or wave varies with the frequency, and vice versa, for the speeds of all waves, regardless of the frequency, are equal to the speed of sound.

Sound Wave Radiations

molecule to molecule in all directions. These collisions of molecules cause small, local pressure changes within the gas, and it appears to radiate outwardly in a series of waves from the source. The speed at which the disturbance travels is called the speed of sound.

The Austrian physicist Ernst Mach (1838-1916) is given credit for determining the correct mathematical value for the speed of sound. His last name and the number "one" after it represents the speed of sound through a fluid medium—as in "Mach One."

The speed of sound varies with altitude because temperature generally decreases with an increase in height. For example, the speed of sound in air is about 761 mph when the air temperature is 59° F. If the air temperature is lowered to -30°F, the speed of sound drops to approximately 692 miles per hour.

In the mid-40's, it was thought that the speed of sound couldn't be attained. It was called the "sound barrier." The Bell Aircraft Corporation built an airplane, called the X-1, to break this barrier. It was a known fact that a 50-caliber rifle bullet could exceed the speed of sound and the Bell engineers used this shape as the basis for the fuselage of the X-1. After extensive testing, it exceeded the speed of sound on October 14, 1947, with Air Force test pilot, Charles E. "Chuck" Yeager, at the controls.

Airfoil—Designs that Capture the Energy of the Wind

An airfoil is designed specifically to cause a dynamic reaction from the air through which it moves. Those parts of the airplane specifically designed to react with the air include the wing and tail surfaces. Likewise, propellers are airfoils by design and their rotation through the relative wind creates a "forward lift."

Airfoil Design

This illustration shows the cross-section of a wing, but it could be a tail surface or a propeller because they are all essentially the same.

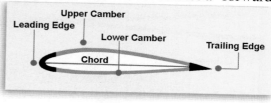

Airfoil Cross-section

Leading Edge. The leading edge of an airfoil meets relative wind first. The shape at this location depends upon the intended use of the airfoil. If the airfoil is designed to be flown at high speeds, its leading edge will be sharp such as those found on the wings of jet fighters. The leading edges of the wings on slower training and pleasure-type aircraft (such as the single-engine trainers and gliders) are more rounded and thicker.

Camber. Immediately behind the leading edge, there is the upper and lower camber. This curvature determines the airfoil's thickness. Camber can be either positive or negative. Positive camber curves away from the centerline while negative camber moves

Going Supersonic! F/A 18 breaks the sound barrier.

toward the centerline of the airfoil.

Early airfoils, such as the ones used on the Langley Aerodrome, were similar to the wings of birds. In aerodynamic terms, this means that the wing has a positive upper camber and negative lower camber.

A close examination of the Wright *Flyer* will show that it too has a positive-upper, negative-lower camber.

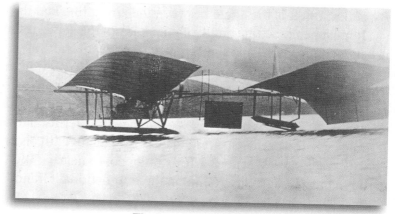

The Langley Aerodrome

The *Wright Flyer*

When the Wright brothers found that their calculations were not providing the expected lift for their gliders, they built a wind tunnel and experimented with small-scale airfoils. These experiments proved invaluable in achieving success on December 17, 1903. The airfoil that was eventually used on the *Flyer* was only a part of their successful design. The key ingredient to their achievement was control. Others had achieved varying degrees of success with lift from primitive designs; however, the Wrights were able to control their craft once it was aloft.

Trailing Edge. Whether the camber is pronounced or thin, positive or negative, the upper and lower surfaces must come together at the rear of the wing. This thin junction is called the trailing edge. The trailing edge area is where the air stream rejoins after having been separated at the leading edge and directed over, and under the airfoil surface.

Chord. A very important part of an airfoil is its chord. This imaginary line is shown in the illustration of the airfoil cross-section on page 177. It connects the leading with the trailing edge. It is used in the scientific explanation of several aerodynamic functions. One of the most important is the concept of angle of attack.

The Relative Wind is opposite the flight path and impacts the airfoil at any angle to the chord line. Even though the air at an airport may be calm, when the airplane moves down the runway for takeoff, a "relative wind" starts blowing over the wing. At some point in the takeoff roll, the pilot increases the angle between the chord line and the relative wind. At that moment, a substantial amount of lift is created and the airplane takes flight. Pilots call this rotation.

Angle of Attack. The angle created by the pilot during takeoff is known as the angle of attack. By definition, it is the angle between the chord line and the oncoming relative wind.

It must be noted that angle of attack is not the same as the Angle of Incidence. The incidence angle is between the chord and the centerline of the aircraft.

In the world of automobile racing, airfoils also play an important role. If a race car builder wants to improve traction, it is a common practice to mount an airfoil somewhere on the car. If properly designed and mounted, an airfoil can create a substantial amount of down force.

Angle of attack is also expressed in negative terms and when a car-mounted wing is angled with its leading edge lower than its trailing edge, a "negative lift" is created. An extreme example of this is found on oval track racers. Their airfoils often cover nearly 50% of the car! Some of the most sophisticated aerodynamic designs are found on the international Grand Prix and Indianapolis 500 race cars.

Who is Daniel Bernoulli?

In 1738, Daniel Bernoulli, a Dutch-born physicist, was given credit for developing the laws that explain how a wing lifts. What Bernoulli discovered was a relationship between the pressure and speed of a fluid in motion. More specifically, as the velocity of a fluid increases, the pressure decreases.

This illustration shows the flow of air, called streamlines, over an airfoil. They show air that is moving at the same velocity. Streamlines help visualize the fact that as the airfoil moves through the air, the air must go around the shape.

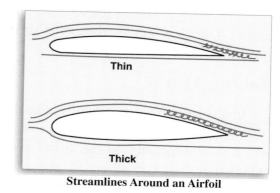

Streamlines Around an Airfoil

Because the air flow separation must have continuity, it splits at the leading edge and comes together once again at the trailing edge of the airfoil. The air that goes over the top of the airfoil must travel a greater distance than the air, which goes under the bottom; this is because the upper camber is designed to have a greater curvature.

Bernoulli's principle states, once again, "As a fluid's speed increases, the pressure within the fluid decreases." So the pressure of the air on top of the airfoil must be less than the pressure below. If the pressure above is less, and the pressure below is greater, the airfoil has no choice but to move upward, toward the lower pressure. It is literally a "suction" on top and "push" from underneath.

To a great extent, the camber determines the amount of lift that a wing will produce at a given speed. The thicker, or more pronounced, camber generally produces the most lift because it makes the airflow travel faster over the upper surface. This accelerated flow rate produces a much lower pressure. The more negative pressure induced to the upper camber, the more lift produced. At low speeds, it is desirable to have a high-lift airfoil. This is particularly evident in STOL, or short takeoff and landing, aircraft.

The Forces of Flight

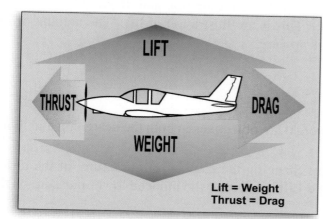

Lift = Weight
Thrust = Drag

The Four Forces of Flight in Balance

The four forces of flight represent centuries of study by many historic figures. Leonardo DaVinci's detailed notes of his nature observations lead to the idea that lift could be produced by flowing air. Sir Isaac Newton's study of classical mechanics led to the mathematical explanations of gravity. Octave Chanute and Otto Lilienthal developed mathematical equations for lift. These were used although later disproved by the Wright brothers.

These forces are *lift, drag, thrust,* and *weight.* By definition, the lift force acts perpendicular to the relative wind or the line of flight.

The drag force acts parallel to the relative wind. The thrust force usually acts parallel to the centerline of the fuselage and the weight always acts in the direction of gravity.

First, think about the forces that oppose one another: lift vs. weight, thrust vs. drag. If you can get more lift and less weight, then your air vehicle will be able to fly. More thrust and less drag would allow the airplane to move forward.

Taking Flight

In this section we are ready to take the next step in understanding how airplanes fly. First, we must introduce the rest of the aircraft surrounding the airfoil. Without getting too deep into parts, we can add a third dimension to the airfoil and get a wing.

In the photo here, the airplane is in straight-and-level, unaccelerated flight. That means nothing is changing. It does not accelerate, go up, down, or turn. This, of course, is another simplifying assumption.

In straight-and-level, unaccelerated flight the thrust force balances the drag force and the lift force balances the weight. More thrust than drag would make the airplane accelerate. More lift than weight would mean the aircraft would climb in altitude.

Early biplanes had a great deal of lift and a great deal of drag. *(EAA)*

Vectors

A vector is a graphic mathematical illustration showing both direction and magnitude. There is a force moving in a vertical direction from the wing. This is an illustration of lift. The amount of lift being produced is the magnitude and its direction is upward.

Lift Overcomes Weight

It is obvious that increased lift and decreased weight are objectives in both the designing and flying of aircraft.

Lift can be increased, as mentioned before, by changing the camber, or curvature, of the airfoil shape of the wing. This type of lift is called Induced Lift because of the induced lower pressure on the top of the wing due to the camber.

Also important is the angle of the wing as it encounters the relative wind. That, we learned earlier, was called angle of attack. Lift is increased as the angle of attack is increased for two reasons. First, as the

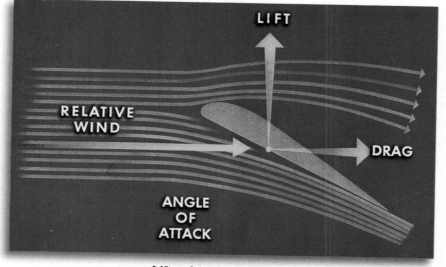

Lift and Angle of Attack

angle is increased relative to the wind, the air has to go a further distance over the top of the wing. That means a lower pressure above the wing and therefore, greater induced lift. Secondly, because there is more relative wind striking the wing's bottom surface at higher angles of attack, the pressure created on the wing's bottom surface is higher. This is the same feeling you get when you

NASA's Dryden Flight Research Center, Edwards, California, is using this modified F-18 aircraft to explore an area of flight called angle of attack. During maneuvers, pilots often fly at extreme angles of attack with the nose pitched up while the aircraft continues in the original direction. This can lead to conditions in which the airflow becomes separated from the airfoils, resulting in insufficient lift to maintain altitude or control. This project by NASA is creating a data base on aerodynamics at high angles of attack to help engineers and designers develop more maneuverable aircraft in the future. A thrust vectoring system has been installed on the F-18's two engine exhaust nozzles to redirect the exhaust flow to enhance control and maneuverability for this research project. The thrust vectoring system allows the research aircraft to fly at steep angles of attack for long periods of time to collect aerodynamic data. Future aircraft to benefit from this program are expected to be highly maneuverable fighters, hypersonic vehicles and high performance civilian aircraft.

put your hand out of the car window while driving. Because the dynamic pressure of the air on the lower hand surface causes it.

Notice that there is a large increase in lift as angle of attack is increased. This is because changing angle of attack gains you both induced and dynamic lift. It should come as no surprise to you that the lift produced by the wing also depends upon the air.

Remember the air's characteristics of pressure, temperature, density, and viscosity? Each can affect the ability of a wing to create lift. High-pressure air at sea level is more dense than at higher altitudes. Colder air is more dense than hotter air. Denser air flowing over the wing means more mass. More mass means more molecules and this translates to greater lift.

Weight

Since weight directly opposes lift in straight-and-level, unaccelerated flight, weight is a problem to be overcome. How is the problem of weight managed? First of all, the airplane must be constructed of the lightest-weight materials that can be used. Today, most airplanes are built of aluminum alloys. These are used extensively in aircraft construction because of their strength and light weight. The use of composite materials is making an impact too. Composites can be shaped easily and some have strength that exceed metals.

It's amazing how this much weight can fly! *(EAA)*

The weight of the airplane's cargo also receives very careful consideration. Each airplane has a total weight limitation called the maximum gross weight. Anything above this limit is considered unsafe for flight. It is possible to keep putting luggage or other cargo into an airplane until it is so heavy it will not fly. Since the pilot cannot put the airplane on a scale to make certain that the airplane is within its weight limits, another approach must be used. This approach is for the pilot to consult documents produced by the manufacturer of the airplane. These documents (which must remain in the airplane) will contain the maximum gross weight and the empty weight. All the pilot has to do is subtract the empty weight from the maximum allowable weight to find out how many pounds may be loaded into the airplane. This is called the Useful Load.

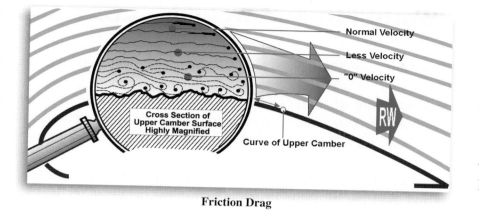

Normal Velocity

Less Velocity

"0" Velocity

Cross Section of
Upper Camber Surface
Highly Magnified

Curve of Upper Camber

RW

Friction Drag

Thrust and Drag

Thrust is the force that propels the aircraft forward. The ultimate goal is to design an engine that produces a lot of thrust on a machine that weighs very little. This gives the pilot more speed, more lift, and less weight.

Drag is the force that opposes all motion through the atmosphere and is parallel to the direction of the relative wind. Drag is created because of the airplane's motion through the air.

There are many components of drag. Part of the total drag is caused by the friction of air particles rubbing against the parts of the airplane. An illustration of Friction Drag is dragging your hand across a smooth surface and then a piece of sandpaper. The movement of your hand over the sandpaper simulates the effects of friction drag.

Another type is Form Drag. The very shape of something may create turbulence as the aircraft flies. In this turbulence are pockets of low- and high-pressure air leaving a wake behind the airplane. This turbulence disrupts the flow of air over the wing and reduces how well it creates lift. The smooth, low-pressure air over the top of the airfoil is pushed by the turbulence at the trailing edge. This pushing back upstream against the flow slows the airflow over the airfoil and causes the streamlines to separate away from the wing. As a result, a force vector trails the airplane and works against its forward motion. Streamlining the aircraft will reduce form drag. Parts of an aircraft which do not lend themselves to streamlining are enclosed in covers called fairings.

Drag is almost always detrimental to aircraft performance. Because it works to slow the airplane as it moves through the air, the engine must make more thrust to go faster. More thrust usually means a bigger engine and more weight.

Sometimes, however, drag is useful. When you want to slow down quickly you can deploy a speedbrake. This is usually a big plate that sticks out into the wind and creates an enormous amount of form drag. In a dogfight, the speedbrake can be used to quickly slow down and force your enemy to fly past you.

Airliners also use speed brakes to slow their airspeed in preparation for landing.

In the old days there were wires, wings, large front ends and the pilot's head sticking out in the wind. All of these created a great deal of drag.
(San Diego Aerospace Museum)

Real World Lift and Weight

The last few pages defined the four forces of flight. Now, let's talk about them in practical terms, in the real world.

If the atmosphere and its characteristics are what allow us to fly and we change those, then our forces of flight must be affected. Additionally, if we remove some of the simplifying assumptions and start looking at the whole airplane in flight, we will see that there is more to flying than we thought earlier.

Lift was broken down into induced and dynamic lift components. Induced lift came from the low-pressure air on the top of the wing and dynamic lift came from the high-pressure air on the bottom. Here are two examples of how the lift force works in the real world.

Turbulence. Air flowing over the surface of an airfoil is rarely very smooth. Streamlines do as the air separates around the wing, but those streamlines are not very smooth close to the surface of the aircraft. This is because air is not really viscous. As it flows over the wing's surface it scrapes against the rough metal and is slowed down and churned up. The churning of air is called turbulence and reduces the efficiency of the airfoil. Therefore, the lift created by the cambered wing is somewhat less than the ideal design prediction.

Stalls. There is a point where the streamlines, located in the boundary layer of air right next to the wing's surface, will separate from the airfoil. Once separation occurs, the air begins to flow more

There are 4 forces at work all the time in every airplane. *(EAA)*

form slowly and the lift producing low-pressure on the top of the wing is lost. The aircraft begins to sink and, if the stall becomes serious enough, departs controlled flight and plummets to the earth.

Aeronautical engineers try to design aircraft that stall predictably. They design the wings and fuselage so that the burbling of air shakes the aircraft and tells the pilot that a stall is imminent. When that cannot be done, they build mechanical and electronic devices that warn the pilot of the stall. And if all else fails, they try to make the stall easily recoverable so that the pilot can regain control of the aircraft.

You might wonder why the force of power from the engine couldn't take the place of the loss of lift from the airfoil. Very simply, there just isn't enough of this force available from a conventional aircraft's engine. Some of the more powerful jet fighter and aerobatic sport airplanes can, for a short time

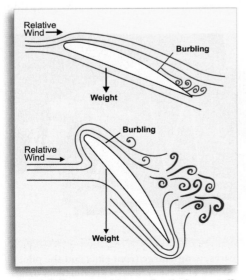

An airfoil approaching and entering a stall.

and distance, climb straight up without any significant help from their airfoils, but these airplanes will eventually stall and start to fall toward earth.

Weight Distribution. Gravity, or weight, always pulls the aircraft toward the earth, but its location in the air vehicle is extremely important. Here is an example of how the weight force can affect flight in the real world. Where the weight, or useful load, is placed in the airplane has a pronounced effect on how well an airplane will fly. Recall that a moment is created when you exert a force on a body at some distance from its center of gravity? For an airplane that means it would rotate around the center of gravity in the direction of the moment. The pilot would have to use the control stick to counter the rotation. The danger of poorly placed weight in the aircraft is that the control surfaces may eventually not be able to counter the rotation. This would cause the aircraft to fly out of control. Although flight out of control is sometimes fun in a stunt plane, airline passengers and attendants generally frown upon it.

Real World Thrust and Drag

If the ideal were possible, our air vehicles would have infinite thrust and negligent drag. You could go as fast as desired in any direction and never slow down if you did not want to. Of course, this is not the case in the real world. Thrust from an engine has some limitations and can be used to the aircraft's advantage as these examples show.

Thrust Vectoring. Thrust on an aircraft is normally used to generate forward motion through the air so that the airfoil-shaped wings can develop enough lift to counter the aircraft's weight. If the thrust force could be pointed in any direction then it could assist in maneuvering as well. That is what thrust vectoring allows.

Engines are designed so that their thrust forces can be pointed along a direction other than the aircraft's longitudinal axis. This is done by pointing the engine's exhaust using mechanically driven plates, or special exhaust ports, called directional nozzles.

Thrust vectoring can be used to assist lift, reduce the chance of a stall, or allow the aircraft to fly at extremely high angles of attack and

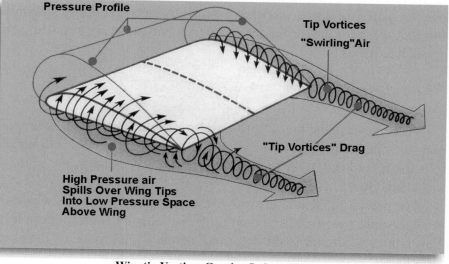

Wingtip Vortices Causing Induced Drag

very slowly. This might allow the use of very short runways or make a jet fighter very maneuverable. Like the other forces, drag becomes a greater problem as our assumptions are eliminated and we consider the whole aircraft. Here is an example of a real world drag effect.

Induced Drag. If lift always acted in an upward direction it would be ideal because it would always

help us get to a higher altitude.

The flow across a wing does not move only from the leading edge to the trailing edge. It also moves toward the wingtip and, sometimes, toward the fuselage. This spanwise flow on the top of the wing eventually must join the spanwise flow on the bottom of the wing. When they do, they form a swirling vortex. This vortex causes the lift vector of the wing to be slanted toward the rear of the aircraft. The slant results in a component of the lift vector pointing in the same direction as the drag vector. This component of lift adds to the drag and is called the induced drag.

The winglets on this Learjet help reduce induced drag.

Supersonic Aerodynamics

For flight at slow speeds, below about 260 knots, air was assumed to be an incompressible fluid. However, as speed increases, air at the leading edges of the vehicle can actually be compressed. Airflow over the surfaces is no longer represented by smooth orderly streamlines. The air is simply moving so fast that it cannot turn around edges very easily. Instead, at leading edges it compresses and at trailing edges it expands.

Supersonic Flow

When an airplane flies at subsonic speeds the air ahead is "warned" of the airplane's approach by a pressure change in front of the aircraft. Remember the pebble dropped in the pond creating a wave that tells the rest of the water to move out of the way? That wave in the air moves at the speed of sound, or "Mach One."

The pebble-pond analogy provides a very good picture of what is happening when an airplane flies at supersonic speeds. If a person drops pebbles into a smooth pond, each pebble will make a wave. This would be similar to the pattern of sound waves made by the aircraft's engine as it sits still on the airfield.

Now suppose we start dropping the pebbles one each second as we run along the bank. Each pebble still produces a circular wave, but the circles are crowded together on the side toward which we are moving. If we now move around the pond at a speed greater than the wave's speed, the pattern looks different than those previously formed. Smaller circles, or those made more recently, are no longer completely inside the next larger ones. Now all the circles are jammed into a wedge-shaped region.

This is similar to the sound-pressure wave pattern for an airplane flying at supersonic airspeeds. The leading edges of the airplane are a continuous disturbance in the air that leaves behind a wedge shaped wave.

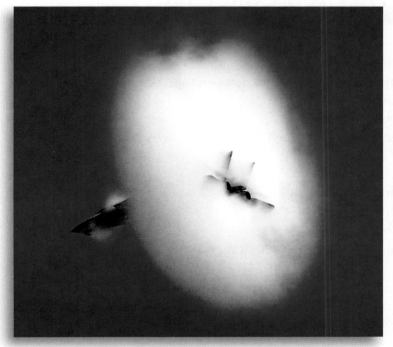

A ring of condensation occurs in the wave as this F-14 goes supersonic.
(US Navy)

This wave pattern would be similar to the pattern of engine sound as the airplane flies at subsonic airspeeds. It also is the pattern made by the pressure change at the aircraft's leading edges. At the leading edges the air is being pushed forward and this push is sent upstream of the airplane at the speed of sound, telling the rest of the air to get out of the way. The air ahead of the airplane is warned of the arrival, and the warning time is decreased as the airplane's speed approaches the speed of sound. The warning time is zero when the airplane flies at Mach One, and has a wave pattern.

If the airplane travels at supersonic speeds, the air ahead receives no warning of the airplane's approach because the airplane is outspeeding its own pressure wave. Because the air is unprepared for the airplane's arrival, it must move aside abruptly to let the airplane pass. This sudden displacement and resulting wedge shaped wave is called a shock wave.

There are two types of shock waves. Those formed when the air must move aside as a leading edge passes and those formed when the air must fill back in as the trailing edge passes. The first is called a compression wave and the second an expansion wave.

Supersonic aerodynamics requires different designs than those used on subsonic aircraft. This is a conflict with the fact that our aircraft still have to take off and land, and those are usually done subsonic.

Wave Drag. When air flows across a shock wave it undergoes a change in temperature, pressure, and velocity. These changes result in another component of drag called wave drag. Although the exact description of this drag is complex, it is really the result of lost energy.

The air that moves across the shock waves is being violently altered. These changes take some energy to produce, since you never get something for nothing. The loss in energy is depicted as additional drag on the air vehicle that would require more thrust (positive energy) to overcome.

The Concorde aircraft daily took passengers across the Atlantic Ocean at a speed of Mach 2. They sat enjoying the comfort of first class for a period of three hours. All this time, all the violent forces of supersonic flight were present, but the passengers were not aware of it. Isn't this wonderful technology?!!

Key Terms and Concepts

- aeronautics and aerodynamics
- properties and characteristics of gases: pressure, temperature, density, viscosity
- laminar vs turbulent air flow
- Mach number, speed of sound, supersonic
- airfoil design: leading edge, camber, trailing edge, chord
- relative wind and angle of attack
- Bernoulli's principle
- four forces of flight: lift, drag, thrust, weight
- induced lift and dynamic lift
- useful load and load distribution
- types of drag: friction drag, form drag, induced drag, wave drag
- turbulence
- stall
- thrust vectoring
- shock wave, compression wave, expansion wave

? Test Your Knowledge ?

MATCHING

1. *Movement of objects through the atmosphere*	a. **pressure**
2. *Science relating to the energy of gases in motion*	b. **temperature**
3. *Decreases with an increase in altitude*	c. **laminar or turbulent**
4. *Measure of how much energy the gas has*	**flow**
5. *The measure of how many molecules are squeezed into a defined space*	d. **viscosity**
	e. **aeronautics**
6. *Resistance to the flow of a liquid or gas*	f. **Mach number**
7. *The smooth or rough flow of air over an object*	g. **aerodynamics**
8. *The ratio of the speed of an object to the speed of sound in air*	h. **density**

FILL IN THE BLANKS

9. The part of the airfoil that meets the air first is the _____.
10. The area determining the airfoil's thickness and thus its lift is the _____.
11. The _____ is the rear junction where the upper and lower parts of the airfoil meet.
12. The _____ is the imaginary part of the airfoil that is the starting point for designing an airfoil in cross-section.
13. Ideally, when a plane is in smooth flight, the force of the total lift equals the force of the total _____ and the force of _____ equals the force of drag.
14. Lift and weight are in opposition to each other. Induced lift can be increased by changing the _____ of the _____.
15. A _____ occurs when lift is destroyed and the force of weight takes over.
16. The sudden displacement of air and the resulting wedge-shaped wave is called a _____ _____.
17. Each airplane has a total weight limitation called _____.
18. If a pilot subtracts the empty weight from the maximum gross weight the result is how many pounds can be loaded into the airplane. This is called the _____.

TRUE OR FALSE

19. Mach is the ratio of the speed of an object to the speed of sound in air.
20. All fluids possess viscosity, which is a resistance to flow, but air is not included here.
21. Slowing the flow rate is known as viscous drag.
22. On an in-flight aircraft, laminar and turbulent flow are found at the same locations.
23. The angle formed by the airfoil chord and the relative wind direction is the angle of attack.
24. Induced lift is caused by the angle of attack.
25. Dynamic lift is caused by camber.
26. Positive atmospheric pressure at the bottom of the wing only increases the induced lift.
27. Generally, the less dense the air, the less lift is available.

SHORT ANSWER

28. In one sentence, define relative wind, including the words speed, direction, and lift.
29. What's the difference between airspeed and ground speed?
30.. If drag is decreased, what happens to thrust?
31. Name two ways that drag can be decreased.
32. What is unique about supersonic aerodynamics?

Chapter
8
AIRCRAFT IN MOTION

Aircraft, spacecraft and even submarines (in a limited way) are capable of moving in all possible directions. That is, if one considers such craft to be suspended at the center of an imaginary sphere, the vehicles can move in any direction away from the center of the sphere, and aircraft and spacecraft can roll and spin toward any of the possible directions. This movement or motion is in three dimensions. Automobiles, trains and surface ships are restricted to two-dimensional movement because they move over the earth's surface only.

No matter how you paint it, it's still going to roll, pitch and yaw.
(EAA)

Everyone is familiar with control over the motion of an automobile. The driver can speed it up, slow it down or stop it. A car's direction of movement can be controlled by changing the direction toward which its wheels point, but it cannot go above or below the road. A train's movement is restricted by the rails over which it must travel, so its range of motion is either forward or backward. The airplane and the spacecraft are the only true three-dimensional machines because of their complete freedom of motion. They can move in any of three axes.

bjectives

Identify the basic parts of a conventional airplane.
Name the three axes of rotation.
Describe the locations of the three axes of rotation with regard to a conventional airplane.
Identify the three different types of fuselage classification.
Explain why box construction is better than wire support.
Describe how the use of aluminum and composites in aircraft construction improve each force of flight.
Identify the purpose of landing gear.
Describe the three types of landing gear arrangements.
Describe the typical functions of aircraft fuel systems.
Describe the typical functions of aircraft hydraulic systems.
Describe the typical functions of aircraft electrical systems.
Describe the earliest aircraft instruments.
Classify the three major groups of aircraft instruments by their uses.
Classify the three major groups of aircraft instruments by their principles of operation.
Describe any one new concept in aviation.

The Axes of an Aircraft

The airplane shown in the picture to the right demonstrates the typical parts of a fixed wing aircraft. There are many variations to the parts shown, and rotary wing aircraft have a design quite different from fixed wing aircraft.

The fuselage of the conventional airplane is the basic structure to which all the other parts are attached. Even the engine is attached to the fuselage, and this is true for most single-engine aircraft. The primary source of lift is the wing, and attached to the wing are its ailerons. The tail, or empennage, consists of the horizontal stabilizer with its attached elevators and the vertical stabilizer with its attached rudder. Often, the vertical stabilizer is referred to as the vertical fin.

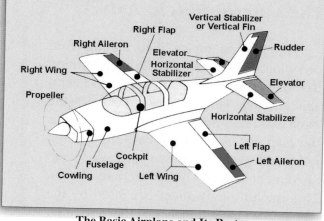

The Basic Airplane and Its Parts

The Longitudinal (Roll) Axis

Running from the tip of the nose to the tip of the tail is the longitudinal axis of a single-engine airplane. This axis can be thought of as a line running from the tail to the nose of the aircraft.

Aircraft roll is a motion about the longitudinal axis and is a result of aileron movement. The ailerons are attached to the wing and to the control column in a manner that ensures one aileron will deflect downward when the other is deflected upward.

When an aileron is not in perfect alignment with the total wing, it changes the wing's lift characteristics. This change in lift is due to a change in the wing camber. In the picture below, notice that the left wing aileron is deflected upward and the right downward. The lift on the right is increased

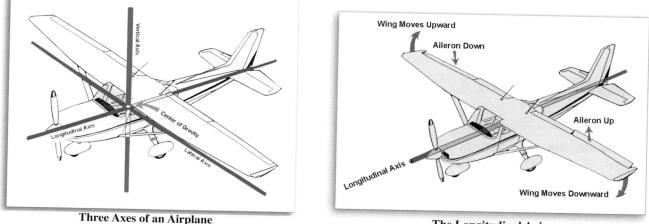

Three Axes of an Airplane

The Longitudinal Axis

because the camber is increased. More lift on the right and less on the left result in a rolling motion to the left around the longitudinal axis.

The Lateral (Pitch) Axis

Another imaginary line, running from one wingtip through the fuselage and exiting the other wingtip, forms an airplane's lateral axis. Another name for the lateral axis is the pitch axis. This name makes sense because the airplane is actually caused to pitch its nose upward or downward, and such movement is made about the lateral axis. This pitching movement is caused by the elevator, which is attached to the horizontal stabilizer. The elevator can be deflected up or down as the pilot moves the control column backward or forward.

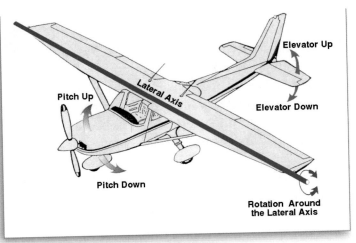

The Lateral Axis

Movement backward on the control column (or stick) moves the elevator upward. This changes the shape of the stabilizer airfoil so that the direction of lift on this particular tail surface is down. Thus, it pulls everything aft of the airplane's lateral axis down with it and causes everything forward of the lateral axis to pitch upward. This movement increases the wings' angle of attack creating more lift and causing the airplane to climb.

Deflection of the elevator downward increases the camber of the tail and increases lift at the tail. Before leaving the horizontal stabilizer, the term *stabilator* should be clarified. Some aircraft are no longer designed to use a stabilizer with an elevator arrangement. Instead, the entire horizontal tail surface is hinged so that the surface's angle of attack is changed as the pilot pulls or pushes on the control column. This type of design is doing the job of both a stabilizer and elevator so it is called a stabilator.

The stabilator design originated during the first supersonic flight testing of the Bell X-1 at Edwards Air Force Base in California. As the test aircraft approached supersonic speeds, the elevator became ineffective. The stabilator was found to be more effective as the shock waves passed over the aircraft.

The Vertical (Yaw) Axis

Another imaginary rod or axis, which passes vertically through the meeting point of the longitudinal and lateral axes, is called the vertical or yaw axis. Aircraft yaw is a motion of the longitudinal axis, either left or right, around the vertical axis. It would be like turning the nose left without banking the wings. The nose goes left, the tail goes right. This would be called a left yaw.

When the pilot moves the airplane's rudder, the aircraft yaws about this axis. When the pilot presses on the cockpit-located rudder pedals, the rudder is deflected from its neutral, or streamlined, position

with the vertical stabilizer. Like the elevator and stabilizer, the deflected rudder forms a curved or cambered airfoil surface, which on one side generates induced lift while on the other side dynamic lift results.

The rudder controls are rigged so that the rudder moves toward the direction of the rudder pedal that is pressed. This causes the airplane's nose to point toward the direction (left or right) of the rudder pedal being pressed.

The Vertical Axis

The *Proteus*, designed by Burt Rutan, has a front-mounted airfoil called a "canard." It provides lift and pitch control.
(EAA)

Aircraft Structures and Components

Engines

With the exception of an occasional feat like the human-powered airplane, all aircraft that can climb are propelled by some type of engine. The two types of common engines are the reciprocating engine and the turbine engine. Other types of engines include ramjets, scramjets and rockets.

Previous discussions about aeronautics, aerodynamics and aircraft control have considered only the effects of the aircraft's propulsion system. It is now time to discuss the types and general operating principles of various aircraft propulsion systems.

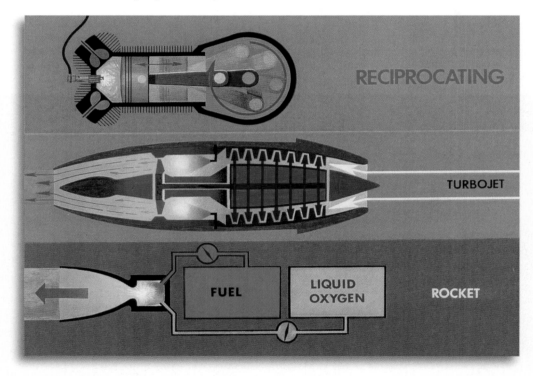

Aircraft Reciprocating Engines

Reciprocating engines power the conventional vehicles used for transportation, work and pleasure. Reciprocating engines provide power for automobiles, lawn mowers, tractors, motorcycles, boats, airplanes and many other devices used today.

All reciprocating engines are basically the same. The term reciprocating is the common factor, and it means that certain parts move back and forth in straight-line motion. This straight-line motion has to be changed to rotary motion in order to turn the wheels of automobiles and trains, and the propellers of boats and airplanes.

The reciprocating engine is also known as an internal-combustion engine. This name is used because a fuel-air mixture is burned within the engine. To understand how a reciprocating engine operates, a familiarity with its parts is essential. The most vital parts are (1) the cylinders, (2) the pistons, (3) the connecting rods, (4) the crankshaft, (5) the valves, (6) the spark plugs and (7) a valve-operating mechanism (cam).

Principle of Operation. The cylinder is the central area where fuel is converted into energy. It is closed on one end (the cylinder head), and the piston fits snugly in the cylinder.

As the engine runs, the cam also controls the opening and closing of the intake and exhaust valves.

Parts of a Reciprocating Engine

All of this motion happens in a regular cycle called the Otto Cycle for gas engines, after Nicholas A. Otto, who built the first successful engine in 1876.

Consider the movements of the piston (four strokes) and the five events of the Otto Cycle depicted in the picture below.

The Intake Stroke (1). The cycle begins with the piston at top center of the cylinder. As the crankshaft pulls the piston downward, a partial vacuum is created in the cylinder chamber. The cam arrangement has opened the intake valve and the vacuum causes a mixture of fuel and air to be drawn into the cylinder.

Compression Stroke (2). As the crankshaft drives the piston upward in the cylinder, the fuel and air mixture is compressed. The intake closes as this upward stroke begins.

Ignition and Power Stroke (3 & 4). As the compression stroke is completed and just before the piston reaches its top position, the compressed mixture is ignited by the spark plug.

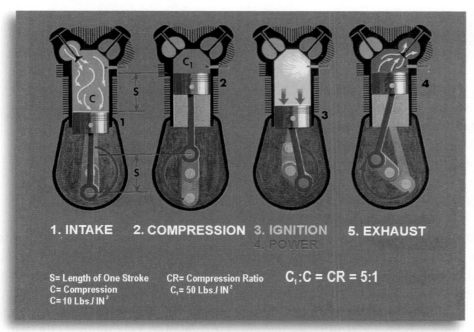

1. INTAKE   2. COMPRESSION   3. IGNITION   5. EXHAUST
4. POWER

S= Length of One Stroke   CR= Compression Ratio $C_1:C = CR = 5:1$
C= Compression $C_1= 50$ Lbs./ IN^2
C= 10 Lbs./ IN^2

The 4 Stroke, 5 Event Cycle

The very hot gases expand with tremendous force, driving the piston down and turning the crankshaft. The valves are closed during this stroke also.

Exhaust Stroke (5). On the second upward stroke, the exhaust valve is opened and the piston forces the burned gases out.

At the moment the piston completes the exhaust stroke, the cycle is started again by the intake stroke. Each piston within the engine must make four strokes to complete one cycle, and this complete cycle occurs hundreds of times per minute as the engine runs.

The up-and-down movement of the piston is converted to rotary motion. This turns the propeller. It is in this way that the power provided by the engine is turned into a thrust force.

Propeller. The propeller is the action end of an aircraft's reciprocating engine because it converts the useful energy of the engine into thrust as it spins around and around. The propeller has the general shape of a wing, but the camber and chord (curvature and cross-sectional length) of each section of the propeller are different. The wing has only one motion, which is forward, while the propeller has both forward and rotary motion. The path of these two motions is like a corkscrew as the propeller goes through the air.

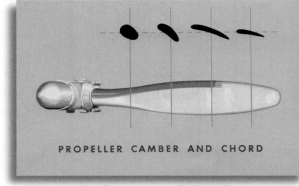

The Cross-section of a Propeller

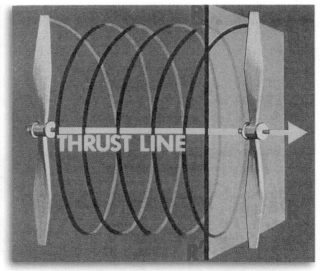

The Motion of a Propeller Through the Air

As the propeller turns, it generates "forward lift" in the direction of the nose of the aircraft. This force pulls the airplane forward through the air resulting in the corkscrew motion shown above. The pulling force of the propeller is the thrust force generated by this type of engine.

Aircraft Turbine Engines

Most powered airplanes that do not use reciprocating engines as their source of thrust use some type of turbine engine. The word turbine means "whirl" and refers to any type of wheel device that has vanes attached to it in a manner that will cause the wheel to turn as the vanes are struck by the force of a moving fluid. Remember that air is a fluid.

Turbine engines found in aircraft use the force of hot flowing gases striking a turbine. Some of these engines are geared to propellers, which are similar to the types of propellers used with reciprocating engines. The turbine engine has also found widespread use as the source of power for military and civilian helicopters. In helicopters, the turbine is linked by gears to the helicopter's rotor in a manner that can be compared to the turbine-driven propellers for airplanes.

Turbines are of four basic types. They may be classified as turbojet, turbofan, turboprop, and propfan. Improvements in each type help make them more efficient and capable of flying higher and faster.

As a group, the turbine engines have many advantages over reciprocating engines. They are capable of flying at higher altitudes and higher speeds. Engine vibration is less as a result of rotating parts rather than reciprocating parts. Cooling is less complicated because the engine "processes" a large amount of air. The most important advantage is the simplest to understand; they make more thrust per pound of engine weight...always back to the four forces of flight!

Some disadvantages are high fuel consumption and poor performance at low power settings, low speeds and low altitudes. However, engineers are continuing to find ways to reduce these disadvantages and make turbines more useful throughout a very large flight envelope.

Principle of Operation. Turbine engine operation is very simple. They take in a small amount of air at the intake and accelerate it to extremely high velocities through the exhaust nozzle. The high velocity air pushes the aircraft forward and is the thrust force generated by the engine.

Turbine engineering and materials are very complex. The rotating parts of a turbine spin at rates in the tens of thousands of revolutions per minute. The air temperatures inside the engine can be several thousand degrees Fahrenheit. As engineers become more inventive and tougher, and lighter materials are developed, the turbines will spin faster and get hotter.

There are five basic sections to a turbine engine (depicted below). These are the inlet, compressor, burner (combustor), turbine and exhaust (nozzle). As the different types of engines are presented, remember that all turbine engines operate according to the same principles.

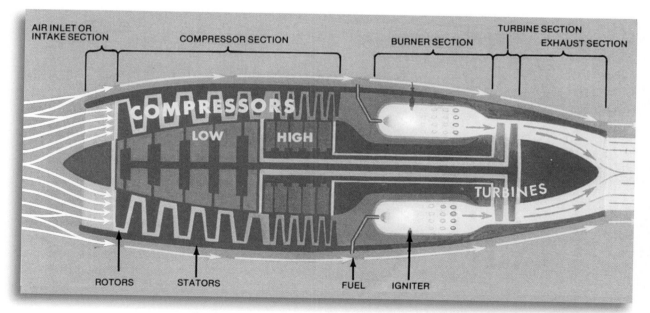

Sections and Parts of a Turbojet Engine Simplified

Turbojet Engines

The turbojet uses a series of fan-like compressor blades to bring air into the engine and compress it with a series of rotor and stator blades. Rotor blades perform somewhat like propellers in that they gather and push air backward into the engine. The stator blades serve to straighten the flow of this air as it passes from one set of rotor blades to the next.

As the air continues to be forced further into the engine, it travels from the low-compression set of rotors and stators to the high-compression set. This last set puts a final squeeze on the air.

The combustion chamber receives the high-pressure air, mixes fuel with it and burns the mixture. The hot, very high-velocity gases produced strike the blades of the turbine and cause it to spin rapidly. The turbine is mounted on a shaft connected to the compressor. Thus, the spinning turbine is what causes the compressor sections to turn. After passing the turbine blades, the hot, highly accelerated gases go into the engine's exhaust section.

The exhaust section of the jet engine is designed to give additional acceleration to the gases and increase thrust. The exhaust section also serves to straighten the flow of the gases as they come from the turbine.

With all the heat produced in the turbojet engine, how is it kept from overheating? Like most reciprocating aircraft engines, the jet is also air-cooled. Of all the air entering into the compressor section, about 75 percent passes around the combustion chamber and turbine area to serve as a coolant.

Turbojet engines used in certain military aircraft will have an afterburner attached to the exhaust section. The afterburner is used for short-term bursts of additional thrust, such as required in some takeoffs and in combat situations. Afterburners are an additional length of the engine's exhaust section. When needed, fuel is sprayed directly into the afterburner and ignited. This is really nothing more than a controlled explosion that accelerates the exhaust to higher velocities and adds thrust.

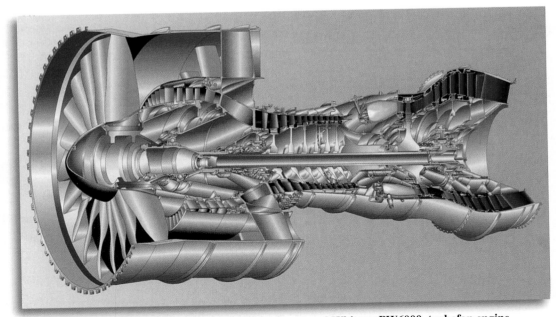

See if you can name the components of this Pratt and Whitney PW6000 turbofan engine.

Turbofan Engines

The turbofan engine has gained popularity for a variety of reasons. One or more rows of compressor blades extend beyond the normal compressor blades. The result is that much more air is pulled into the turbofan engine than is pulled into the simple turbojet.

Most of this excess air is ducted through bypasses around the power section and out the rear of the engine with the exhaust gases. This sounds like it is wasted airflow, but it is not. There are two ways to get high thrust. You can either take a small amount of air and accelerate it to very high speeds, or you can take a large amount of air and accelerate it a little. Turbofans use a turbine engine to help get a large amount of air moving faster, creating very high thrust.

Turbofans are much quieter than turbojets, which makes them more acceptable to people who live near airports. The turbofan engine is also more fuel-efficient than the turbojet. Using the same amount of fuel, a turbofan produces greater thrust for taking off, for climbing and for cruising flight. However, turbofans have speed limitations and poor low-altitude performance, which make them undesirable for some aircraft.

Turboprop Engines

The turboprop engine is the result of an effort to combine the best features of turbojet and propeller aircraft. The first is to be more efficient at high speeds and high altitudes; the latter are to be more efficient at speeds under 400 mph and below 30,000 feet.

The turboprop uses a gas turbine to turn a propeller. Its turbine uses almost all the engine's power to turn its compressor and propeller. It depends on the propeller for thrust rather than on the high-velocity gases going out of the exhaust. Study the figure below and particularly note how the turbine turns the compressors and the propeller.

The gas turbine can turn a propeller with twice the power of a reciprocating engine and is lighter in weight. Reduction gears slow the propeller below the turbine's high speed. This must be done because propellers do not operate efficiently as their tips approach supersonic speeds.

Just to prove that engineers dislike limits, newer prop designs have been developed that reduce this limitation and increase the flight envelope for prop aircraft. So, the turboprop engine receives fairly extensive use in military and civilian aviation circles.

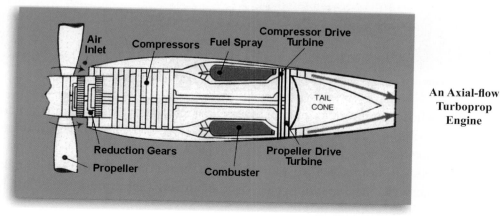

An Axial-flow Turboprop Engine

Propfan Systems

August 20, 1986, marked the first flight of an advanced-technology propfan engine. It replaced the regular turbofan of a Boeing 727-100. The thruster resembles a ship's screw more than it does an airplane propeller. The propfan system combines the air-moving efficiency of the turbofan engine with the thrusting efficiency of the propeller. What is achieved is a dramatic reduction (up to 30 percent) in fuel consumption while retaining the turbofan's high power and the speed it makes possible.

More specifically, the propfan system combines elements of the other three turbine systems. In this system, a turbojet serves as the gas generator to drive a large external fan, or propulsor. Sometimes the prop consists of two propulsors rotating in opposite directions.

The multi-bladed propulsors move large amounts of air at a relatively slow speed while a much smaller amount is burned and accelerated through the core of the engine at a higher velocity. Propulsion systems of this type have bypass ratios of 60 to 1 or greater. This means 60 times as much air flows around the turbine core as passes through it. High bypass engines are very efficient at subsonic speeds. For airliners, this is about Mach 0.8 or 525 mph.

Ramjet and Scramjet Engines

Frenchman Rene Lorin invented the ramjet in 1913. It is the simplest type of all-jet engines because it has no moving parts. The picture below shows a typical arrangement of the parts of a ramjet engine. The force of inertia "rams" air into a streamlined chamber of a fast-flying ramjet. Air flowing through the chamber is compressed, slowed down to subsonic speed, mixed with fuel, ignited, and released. The airflow will extinguish the flame, unless flame holders or slowly burning grain (a mixture of fuel, binder, and a small amount of oxidizer) is used. Scramjets work the same way, only the air is not slowed to subsonic speeds within the engine.

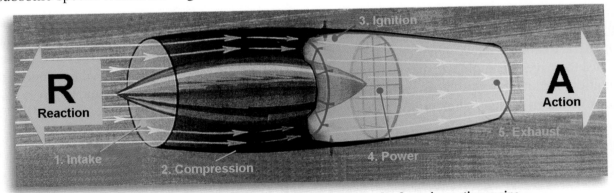

Functions of a ram jet engine compared to five-event cycle of a reciprocating engine.

A ramjet/scramjet whose intake does not change shape provides thrust within a narrow range of velocities, typically 1-2 km/s. A variable geometry ramjet provides thrust over a wider range of velocities, but is much heavier.

Ramjets and scramjets will not make thrust until enough air is coming through the intake to create a high-pressure flow. Otherwise, the expanding gases of the burning fuel-air mixture would be expelled from both ends of the engine.

The ramjet/scramjet has to be traveling through the air very fast before it is started. This means that it has to be boosted to the proper speed by some other type of engine or rocket propellant. Using two engines on a single-air vehicle may not always be practical, but may have some specific applications as the flight envelope is expanded for commercial and military aviation.

In theory, these engines have no maximum speed; they can keep accelerating indefinitely as long as it stays within the atmosphere. In practice, the engine is limited to low-hypersonic speeds (five times the speed of sound) because atmospheric friction will melt the materials used in its production. They also suffer from a high rate of fuel consumption.

In the early 1950s, a ramjet (on the blade tips) was used to power an experimental helicopter known as the *Hiller Hornet*. *(EAA)*

Flight Controls

Wilbur and Orville Wright were not the first people to fly. There were many inventors and aviation enthusiasts who developed gliders or built balloons long before their historic flight at Kitty Hawk. What they did contribute to the aviation field was the first sustained, controlled, powered flight of a heavier-than-air vehicle. The key word for this section is controlled, because flying at the whim of the air currents lends little to the practical use of flight.

Control of the aircraft is accomplished through the control surfaces. These include the ailerons for roll, elevators for pitch and rudder for yaw control. Combined use of these devices allows for pilot control of all motions through all three axes.

There are a wider variety of control surfaces developed every day. Wilbur and Orville used a technique called "wing warping" to reshape the wings of their aircraft and provide steerage. Eventually, separate surfaces were invented that were hinged to the wing and tail, and could be bent into the free flowing air to control the aircraft. Later, in the 20th century, NASA developed reactive wings that could reshape themselves to optimize the flow of air over the airfoil as the situation required.

The use of computer flight control systems have given engineers the opportunity to control aircraft in ways we could never have imagined only a few years ago. Aircraft can be built that defy every aeronautical engineering principle of controlled flight. They are controlled using programmed, high-speed computers that correct the flight path far faster than their human pilots could do by hand. For instance, the B-2 has no vertical fin or rudder for yaw control. It uses aileron-like control surfaces that are moved at different amounts on the left and right side of the airplane to control yaw.

By adding various structures to an airplane's airfoils, its aerodynamics can be changed significantly. Perhaps you have been aboard an airliner when the pilot prepares for landing. All kinds of devices start moving from the leading and trailing edge of the wing.

These devices are thrust into the airstream to increase the lift efficiency of the wing at low airspeeds. Other approaches for increasing lift are being developed and used every day.

Flaps

The flaps of an airplane are attached to the trailing edge of the wing. In cruising flight, the flaps simply continue the streamlined shape of the wing's airfoil.

When flaps are lowered either partially or fully, two things happen: lift is increased and so is drag. This is why pilots use flaps only during certain takeoff conditions and during most landing conditions.

The flap increases the camber of the wing airfoil for that portion of the wing to which it is attached. It does not affect the remainder of the wing. Looking at a wing cross-section with flaps lowered, air flowing over the top of the wing now has farther to travel. This causes the air to speed up, particularly over the wing section where the most lift is created. On the underside of the wing, dynamic lift is increased because there is now more surface area exposed to the impact of the relative wind.

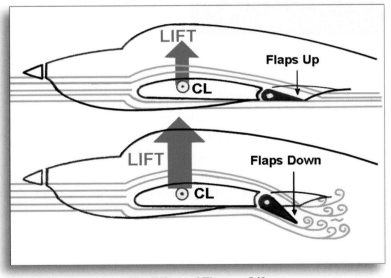

The Effects of Flaps on Lift

On the negative side of this situation is the drag produced by the flap. Anything that obstructs the airflow increases drag. So what is the total effect of this increased-lift/increased-drag situation when flaps are lowered? Without an increase in power to compensate for the additional drag, the airplane will descend much more steeply than possible without flaps and the increased lift will allow slower flight because the stall speed is decreased. The pilot can land more steeply and avoid the trees at the end of the runway. He can also stop on a shorter runway because he is going slower when he lands.

Using flaps when taking off helps the airplane get off the ground in a short distance. This might be desired when the runway is short and a short-distance takeoff is necessary. Using flaps when taking off from a soft or muddy field helps too by keeping weight off the wheels.

There are many different types of flaps. Some hinge, some slide, some open with slots and some help the flow of air over the wing remain smoother even though high angles of attack are flown during landing. Each has been given a unique name based upon its look or its inventor. Some are simple and some are mechanical miracles...but they all help do the same thing.

Slats

Slats are protrusions from the leading edge of a wing. They also add to the induced lift of a wing and can be found on the more sophisticated flap systems. The secret of the slat is the slot it produces. Particularly at a high angle of attack, the relative wind passing through the slot is speeded up, and this additional velocity helps keep the airflow smooth. This is how slats and flaps work together to maintain laminar flow over the top of the wing. The slat causes energy to be added at the front, while the flap causes energy to be added at the back. The combined actions of these devices result in a significant increase in lift.

Spoilers

Where flaps and slats work to increase lift and where ailerons, elevators and rudders work to change the direction of lift, spoilers work to destroy lift. This is the origin of the name spoiler—it spoils lift.

Spoilers are found on various aircraft from the jet airliner to the sailplane. The spoiler will be found somewhere along the top of the wing and it will be located along a line on the airfoil where its deployment will be the most effective. The term *deployment* is used because spoilers fit into or flush with the surface of the airfoil. The size of the spoiler will vary according to how much lift is to be "spoiled."

On faster aircraft, spoilers are hinged so that their aft portion is tilted upward into the laminar airflow. Many of the sailplane types are designed to thrust straight up from the wing's surface. Both arrangements of spoilers do the same thing. They destroy the laminar flow of air for a portion of the wing, thereby reducing a certain amount of induced lift. Their design is different because faster airspeeds tend to damage spoilers that stick out straight into the airflow.

This Air Force Academy TG-7A has spoilers above and below the wing.
They are located just inboard of the USAF insignia.

An airplane, such as an airliner, can fly at a safe airspeed while reducing some of the induced lift using a spoiler. The result is a steep descent for landing or quick change of altitude in a short distance. A most favorable feature about spoilers is that they can be deployed or retracted quickly. If, for instance, an airplane has them deployed and is descending toward the runway but suddenly has to "go around," the spoilers can be retracted and lift is restored.

The use of flaps lowers the stall speed so an airplane may fly again, if it bounces upon landing. When the airplane is equipped with spoilers, the pilot can keep this from happening. The next time you are on a jet airliner watch how the spoilers pop up when the craft lands. Quick spoiling of the lift prevents the airliner from flying back up into the air, even for a poor landing, but not the worst of poor landings.

Spoilers serve a similar purpose for sailplanes. The sailplane's wing is an especially high-lift device. If it were not for the effect of spoilers, it would be very difficult to get some models of sailplanes to land within the confines of the airport.

Spoilers can also be used like ailerons to roll the air vehicle. If the pilot moves the control wheel to the right, the right wing spoiler pops up and the right wing loses lift. The aircraft responds with a turn to the right. The General Dynamics F-111 used spoilers and differential stabilators to turn. It did not have ailerons because its wing was designed to sweep back for high-speed flight. Ailerons would have been ineffective for rolling the aircraft when the wings were swept back. Can you reason why this would be so?

An inventer by the name of Molt Taylor created a very successful car that flew!
(EAA)

Drag Devices

Some airplanes are equipped with special devices that produce drag only. These devices may be located at the trailing edges of the wings or they may protrude from the craft's fuselage upon activation by the pilot.

Ultralights are fun to fly even if they don't have much of a fuselage. *(EAA)*

These devices may be called speed brakes, air brakes, dive flaps or drag parachutes. Their purpose is to produce a significant amount of drag without affecting the airfoil's lift. Why would such devices be needed? Because they allow very steep descents and rapid changes in airspeed which can be stopped almost instantaneously by retracting the devices.

The devices discussed in this section are not all of the flight control surfaces that exist. We already mentioned that vectored thrust could allow for very slow flight and rapid changes to aircraft attitude. In a sense, vectored thrust acts like another flight control. When its use is programmed into a computer to respond to control stick and throttle positions, it is acting directly as a control surface. Engineers can be very inventive, and will continue to make new control surfaces and devices.

The Fuselage Structure

The word fuselage is based on the French word *fuseler*, which means "to shape like a spindle; to streamline." Since the normal fuselage contains the flight crew, passengers, and other cargo and must also withstand many of the forces created by the airfoils and landing gear, it must be strong in addition to being streamlined.

Fuselages are usually classified according to the design of their force-resisting structure. These classifications are known as the truss, the semimonocoque and the monocoque.

The truss-type structure for fuselages is made of

Fuselage Assembly at Boeing *(Boeing photo)*

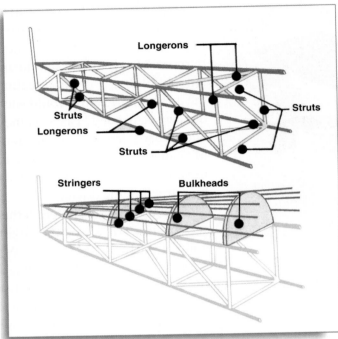

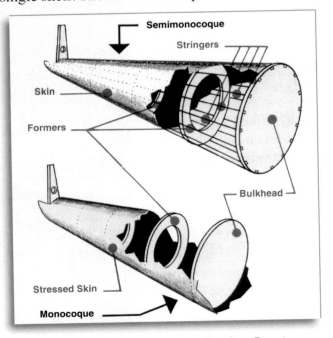

The Basic Truss-type Fuselage Structure

tubing welded in place to form a well-braced framework as shown. Long lengths of tubing called longerons characterize the basic form. Welded to these longerons are vertical and horizontal struts which give the structure a square or rectangular shape as viewed from one end; however, this isn't enough bracing. Other struts must be placed so that stresses coming from all directions are resisted. Thus, struts at various angles to the longerons and horizontal/vertical struts are necessary. Imagine how the truss structure could be twisted, bent, stretched, sheared and compressed. This is how the total structure performs its job.

The truss structure is not a streamlined shape. Before the skin is added, something must be done to make the structure a streamlined one or the aircraft will have a form drag problem. Additions to the basic truss structure can be added. The label "bulkhead" may also be known as a "former," but in either case, if the addition is to give shape to the fuselage, it will have stringers attached. The purpose of these stringers is to support the covering that will go over the fuselage.

Monocoque is a French word which means single shell. The true monocoque construction depends on the covering or skin to provide the required strength to resist the stresses of flight. True monocoque construction like that illustrated in the picture to the right is not common. The semimonocoque is the most often used approach for high-performance aircraft.

The semimonocoque construction uses internal braces to help the skin carry the forces generated. Semimonocoque literally means half a single shell. The internal braces include longitudinal stringers and vertical bulkheads or formers.

The semimonocoque structure is easier to streamline than the truss structure. Since the skin of the semimonocoque structure must carry much of the fuselage's strength, it will be thicker at those points where the stresses on it will be the greatest.

Semimonocoque and Monocoque Fuselage Structures

Why cover the fuselage anyway? It's not the airfoil, so should the engineer be concerned with airflow over the fuselage? Certainly, because everything in the flow of air affects the forces of flight.

An 1/8-inch strut or supporting wire, like those used on old biplanes to brace the wings, creates as much drag as a conventional cambered airfoil. If the fuselage remained open, the drag created from each strut would soon overcome the engine's ability to thrust the vehicle forward enough to generate more lift than weight. This would require either a more powerful engine or less weight. Aerodynamics always returns to the four forces of flight.

If we now understand that a covering for the fuselage is required, with what should it be covered? Something strong would make the vehicle more durable and capable of more dynamic maneuvers. But strength usually means more weight, and you know where that leads you. So the best choice is the strongest, lightest material that can be manufactured and fitted to the fuselage.

Aluminum sheeting is generally the cheapest and most effective choice for covering. Engineers hate doing anything the usual way, so they have continued to develop new materials that are stronger, lighter and more easily molded to a fuselage shape. Composite materials are one such invention.

Composites are many materials layered together in a strength-producing pattern, similar to a radial tire or woven fabric. Because many materials are used, designers can add materials that give the aircraft structure special characteristics – like radar stealth. The materials are very flexible when first constructed, much like fiberglass. They can be molded to almost any shape and allow for extremely useful designs that could not be cheaply constructed using aluminum and pop-rivets.

Landing Gear

The *Wright Flyer* used skids as its landing gear at first, but the inventors soon attached wheels to the skids. Since that time, various arrangements have been used for wheels and structures to connect the wheels to the airplane's fuselage and/or wings. Today, there are three types of landing gear arrangements in common use: the conventional, the tricycle and the tandem.

Conventional

The conventional landing gear consists of two wheels forward of the aircraft's center of gravity and a third, small wheel at the tail. All landing gear must be strong to withstand the extra load of the

The conventional landing gear is nicknamed "taildragger".

aircraft's weight plus the downward force of landing. To help absorb this additional force, some type of arrangement must be made to cushion or absorb some of the additional stresses encountered. The earlier conventional gear aircraft used a flexible material for the landing-gear struts (the part between the airframe and the wheels). This allowed the landing-gear assembly to flex outward upon landing.

The tailwheel, which evolved from the plain tailskid of the past, is castered - free to turn in any direction. How does a pilot maintain control while taxiing with the conventional landing gear system if the front wheels are not steerable? It is done with a combination of rudder movement and the careful application of brakes.

At taxi speed, the prop-wash from the propeller and relative wind striking the tail, coupled with the freewheeling tail wheel make rudder control possible. The rudder is deflected into the prop-wash and turns the tail of the aircraft just like it would in the air. The use of brakes is necessary only at a very low taxi speed when the rudder is ineffective.

Landing an airplane that has conventional gear is more difficult than the other types. At least, this is the claim made by pilots who are qualified to fly them. The claim seems reasonable in that the main landing gear provides a fulcrum about which the airplane can be pitched fairly easy. The application of brakes too soon and/or too much just after touchdown could cause this pitching action to take place, and the result could be a complete nose-over. Another possible cause of nose-over could be the tailwheel striking the ground first If this happens with enough force, the main landing wheels are slammed onto the surface and the entire airplane pitches over.

The tendency for conventional-gear airplanes to pivot about the vertical axis can be another problem during windy landing conditions. The main landing gear provides a pivot point about which the usually large rudder moves the airplane very easily and quickly when strong wind hits the rudder.

Tricycle

Tricycle landing gear make an airplane very easy to control on the ground. This is particularly true of the newer models because the nose gear is linked to the rudder pedals and is steerable.

Landing forces are absorbed through the use of a shock absorbing system called the oleo strut. The shock-absorbing strut cushions the landing and helps keep your dining tray in the up and stowed position.

Like the conventional gear,

This is an example of tricycle landing gear. *(EAA)*

the main landing gear on the tricycle types are fitted with brakes. These brakes also operate independently of each other so they can be used in steering the airplane if necessary.

Tandem

Tandem landing gear is an arrangement where the main gear consists of two sets of wheels which are located one behind the other on the fuselage (tandem may also be called bicycle). The B-52 bomber, AV-8 Harrier close air support aircraft and the U-2 reconnaissance/research aircraft have this type of landing gear. The tandem landing gear requires the use of outrigger wheels mounted on a highly flexible wing for lateral support.

The AV-8 Harrier has a tandem landing gear. *(EAA)*

Brakes

Although all aircraft landing gear are fitted with brakes, they must be used with caution. An airplane moves much faster than a car, so there is a great deal more stopping force required of the airplane's brakes. Too much sustained brake pressure upon landing can cause overheating, warping or even complete brake failure. Should a brake lock upon landing, the tire will wear through and fail rather quickly and this could cause an accident.

To prevent or help prevent this from happening, aircraft use what is called an antiskid system. This system actually keeps the brakes or wheels from locking by automatically releasing the brakes upon the first indication that the wheel isn't turning. This means that it also works if the wheels start sliding on a slippery surface, such as ice. If the pilot has applied brakes to slow the airplane and just one of the wheels hits a patch of ice, the brakes on that wheel will be released as soon as the wheel stops turning and starts skidding.

Fixed vs. Retractable

In addition to the arrangement of the landing gear—conventional, tricycle, or tandem—the gear can be either fixed or retractable. Generally speaking, the less expensive, smaller airplanes have fixed gears because it is much less costly to build and to maintain. The basic reason for making landing gear retractable is to get them out of the airstream and thereby reduce drag, which allows the airplane to fly faster. The reason why most small aircraft do not have retractable gear is that the additional expense and weight of a more complex system added to a slow moving aircraft is not justified.

The Aerosport II has fixed landing gear. *(EAA)*

An example of
retractable landing gear.

Systems

Every aircraft is made up of many parts. Some parts are structures, like the previous sections have detailed. Other parts are needed to manage the flow of fluids, control engine parameters, receive radio signals, and release weapons or cargo. These parts are called the aircraft's systems.

Each aircraft has a different set of systems that help it get the task of flying done correctly. The major systems of most aircraft include a method to handle fuel, hydraulics, and electrical power.

Fuel

Fuel Systems. The fuel system for an aircraft engine includes everything that involves delivery of fuel to the engine. The beginning of this delivery system is the fuel tanks, the middle is the fuel lines and the end is the engine's combustion chamber.

Fuel Tanks. Fuel tanks can be located anywhere in the aircraft. Some aircraft have fuel stored in tanks inside the wings, some in the fuselage and others in any place the fuel will fit. The need for fuel and the rate at which it is burned helps the aircraft designer decide how much fuel is to be available.

Fuel is forced from the tanks into the engine where it is mixed with air and drawn into the combustion chamber. To get the fuel from the tanks to the engine requires force. This force may be provided by one of two possible fuel-feed systems.

The simplest is known as gravity feed, and as the name implies, uses gravity to cause the fuel to flow from the tanks downward to the engine. The gravity-feed system will most likely be found in a high-wing airplane or as a backup to the next type of feed system.

Most airplanes use a pump to drive fuel from the tanks to the engine. The fuel pump usually is run from the electrical power system of the aircraft. It is a small motor that helps to keep a positive flow of fuel from the tanks to the engine so that it does not stall. In some high performance aircraft this is a difficult task. The F-15 Eagle in full afterburner consumes over 80,000 pounds of fuel per hour at sea level. That's over 200 gallons per minute!

All fuel tanks must have a place where fuel can enter for the filling process; this is known as the filler cap. In addition to this filler cap, all such tanks must have a vent pipe to the outside. The vent allows expansion of the fuel when it is heated by the sun and protects the tank from being broken open by the pressure of expanding fuel vapors. On a very hot day at an airport, you might see liquid fuel

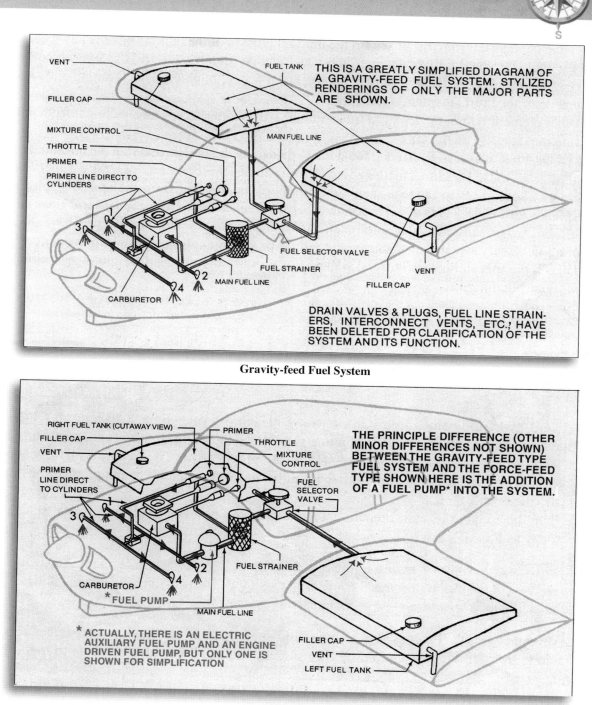

Gravity-feed Fuel System

Force-feed Fuel System

coming out of these vents on some airplanes.

Within the fuel tanks are some mechanisms that measure how much fuel there is in the tanks. These mechanisms might be simple floats or complicated rods that measure fuel electrical capacitance.

At the lowest point in each tank is a fuel-tank drain. These drains are designed to remove any water

that may have condensed from the air within the unfilled portion of the tank. If there is any water in the fuel and the fuel is drained into a container, the water can be seen because it is heavier than the fuel. The water will appear on the bottom of the container as a water "bubble." This draining and checking process can continue until all water is removed.

One other element within the tank is a fuel strainer. This strainer keeps any sediment from entering the fuel line that leads from the tank.

Fuel Lines. Fuel lines lead from each fuel tank to distribute the fuel throughout the aircraft. In some light civil aircraft, these fuel lines merge somewhere in the cockpit and are joined by a fuel selector. Fuel selectors allow pilots to manage their fuel supply by taking fuel from the tank of their choice. Some airplanes also have a "both" selection that permits fuel to flow from the left and right tanks at the same time. Larger aircraft have automated fuel control systems that are electrically controlled. This is often necessary when fuel management would be complex, time consuming or dangerous to do manually. If the fuel storage was miscalculated, the aircraft might exceed weight distribution limits and depart controlled flight.

Hydraulic and Electrical Systems

Hydraulic Systems

The word hydraulic comes from Greek words meaning "water tube." An aircraft's hydraulic system may operate the brakes, lower the landing gear, move the flight controls, and extend and lower the flaps. The mechanism that controls the pitch of the propeller may be hydraulically operated. In fact, any mechanism that can use a pressurized fluid to make parts move as the pilot desires can be hydraulically run.

More than three centuries ago, French mathematician and philosopher Blaise Pascal stated what we know today as **Pascal's law:**

> Pressure exerted anywhere on a liquid in a closed container is transmitted undiminished to all parts of the wall of the vessel containing the liquid. The pressure acts at right angles to all surfaces with an equal force on equal areas.

What does this mean? It means that when a fluid such as oil is confined in a container, the fluid can be made to transfer the pressure put on it to something else. It can also be made to multiply the original pressure.

In using a lever to pry up a rock, one can exert more force than if he or she tried to lift the rock directly. This is called mechanical advantage, which is the same principle used in hydraulics.

By using the mechanical advantage gained in the hydraulic system, the pilot can exert great pressure on the aircraft control systems or structures within his human strength limits. Aircraft have hydraulic pumps to generate the hydraulic pressure necessary to operate the various components of the aircraft. These pumps pressurize the system and allow the pilot to stop thousands of pounds of aircraft with the flex of his ankles on the brake pedals.

Hydraulic systems look a great deal like fuel systems. The fluid is stored in tanks called reservoirs. It is pressurized, strained and then distributed through hydraulic lines to the parts of the plane that need it. Once it has done its work, it is returned to the reservoir for later use.

Electrical Systems

The electrical system, like the hydraulic system, is important in operating an aircraft. A generator mechanically attached to an aircraft's engine provides the electricity required to charge the battery, start the engine, operate the radios, and operate navigation and landing lights. Any electrical device can be run from this system if the designer plans for the proper voltage and current.

On some aircraft, electricity may be used through electric motors to change the pitch of propellers, lower and raise flaps, and actuate portions of the hydraulic system. More modern aircraft are usually dependent on the electrical system to power critical parts of the vehicle. These parts might be as basic as the Liquid Crystal Displays (LCDs) used to fly in the weather or as complex as the digital flight control system used to point the aircraft where you would like it to go.

Without the assistance of hydraulic systems and electrical systems, pilots could not fly the larger, more sophisticated aircraft. Even the smallest aircraft powered by an engine must have an electrical system at least for ignition. Most require power to control and display the many aircraft instruments that help the pilot fly and navigate.

Aircraft Instruments

Instrument Panel of a Cessna 182

The size of an airplane and its tasks determine how many instruments there will be in the cockpit. The purpose of the instruments is to convey to the pilot some information. This might be attitude information, such as which way is up. It might be position information, such as miles from the airport. It might even be weapon information, such as lethal shot distances.

It is not absolutely necessary to have any instruments for the pilot to monitor. An airplane can be flown without instruments. Crop dusters and ultralights rely on the pilot's eyes and ears to provide enough environmental clues to remain aloft. However, as the mission becomes more complex, it is often necessary to give the pilot more than his eyes and ears can provide.

Early Aircraft Instruments

The first aviators had to rely on their senses, as there were no flight instruments. Instruments were then invented to help the pilot. Although they were very primitive by today's standards, many early instruments proved to be adequate for "low and slow" aircraft.

Airspeed was first judged by the force of the wind on the pilot's face and the whine of wind through the rigging. If the pitch of the wind whistling through the wires was "right," the airspeed was correct. Early airspeed indicators were merely wind gauges.

When pilots could see farther than they intended to fly, heading indicators and navigational instruments were unnecessary luxuries. Similarly, altimeters were not of much value when the aircraft could get only a few hundred feet off the ground. When they could climb higher, perhaps above an altitude where the air was thin enough to cause the pilot to pass out, altimeters became a safety necessity.

Cockpit and instrument panel of the immortal P-51 Mustang. *(EAA)*

In the early days, it was possible to estimate how long the fuel would last, but it was also easy for pilots to forget to check takeoff time and then to have to guess when the fuel would run out. The problem was solved by putting a stick with a cork on it in the fuel tank. By tying a piece of colored string near the top of the stick, another safety feature was added. When the string disappeared, it was time to land.

The attitude of the aircraft was extremely critical in the early days. Pilots solved this problem by tying a piece of heavy string to the aircraft. If the string was flying straight back, the pilot was doing fine. However, if the free end of the string was off to one side, the airplane was not flying directly into the wind. It was trying to fly sideways and this increased the aircraft drag. What type of drag would this be?

These early instruments were designed to give pilots specific information about the engine or the attitude of the aircraft. Even today, all aircraft instruments can be classified according to how they assist the pilot.

Instrument Classification

Aircraft instruments are classified either in terms of their use or in terms of the principle underlying their operation or construction. What the instruments tell the pilot is usually of more use to the aviator than how the instruments work, so we'll concentrate on that.

Classification by Principle of Operation. Instruments can be classified by their principle of operation. The three major groups are: mechanical (including gyroscopic) instruments, pressure instruments, and electrical instruments. A brief description of these operational groupings is useful because it helps to understand how an instrument works as well as what it tells the pilot.

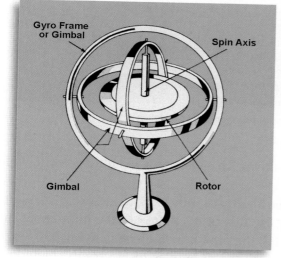

Parts of a Gyroscope

Mechanical Instruments. Some mechanical instruments work by means of direct mechanical linkage. For example, a gear may be attached directly to the engine of an aircraft in order to give a reading on a gauge of how fast the engine is operating. A float might rise and fall in a fuel cell and be linked to the fuel gauge by a cable.

Some mechanical instruments work on the principle of the gyroscope. Because the gyroscope is used so extensively in flight instruments, here is a brief review of its operation. A gyroscope consists of a heavy rotor wheel mounted so that it is free to rotate on its axis within a frame. This frame is designed so that the rotor can move any direction—pitch, roll, or yaw.

The principle that you should know about the operation of the gyroscope is gyroscopic stability. Gyroscopic stability means that a spinning flat weight tends to line up on one of its axis. That axis is the one perpendicular to the face of the weight. Once the weight is aligned on the axis, it will remain there, just like a top does.

For example, if you held the gyroscope by the base, you could move the base to any position but the rotor (spinning weight) and spin axis would still point in the original direction. Gyroscopic stability helps you ride a bicycle. As the wheels turn (spinning weight) they become stable around the axle's axis. It is then harder to lean left or right, or fall down, because the wheels stabilize the bike.

If a flying airplane can move around any of its three axes, then it might be useful to have something on board that does not move with the aircraft. Why, you might ask? Because at some point after we have pitched the airplane up, rolled it left and kicked the rudder to yaw, the pilot will want to know how to get back to straight and level flight. If, while on the level ground before takeoff, he aligned a

Instrument Panel of the *B-25 Mitchell* Bomber *(EAA)*

gyroscope with the ground he would always know up from down. The gyroscope would stay level while he moved the aircraft around it.

    Pressure Instruments. Pressure instruments work on the idea that a fluid, such as air, exerts pressure. Pressure decreases with height, and pressure instruments use this principle to tell the pilot about the performance of the aircraft. How could pressure changes tell the pilot how high he is flying?

    Electrical Instruments. Electrical instruments operate on the principles of electricity, including magnetism. Electrical instruments often take the place of mechanical and pressure instruments, and are being used more and more in modern aircraft. They are usually more accurate and give the aviator a way to precisely control his aircraft.

    By viewing the instruments in these ways, one can see that each has a separate functional purpose and means of operation. Even though the instrument panel of today's aircraft looks complicated and confusing, pilots need to know all of the information the instruments provide. If you had to know what every gauge or dial read at every moment, you would be overwhelmed. Engineers design warning systems that monitor critical instrument readings and alert the aviator of problems. This allows the pilot to focus on flying, monitor other indications and focus on problems when they happen.

    Classification by Use. Instruments classified by their use fall into two major groups: performance and control instruments. Performance instruments tell us how the aircraft has responded to our commands. Control instruments tell us the current state of some aircraft devices, so that we are aware of its condition.

It is a little easier, however, to discuss instruments as they are actually used. With that in mind, we'll look at instruments in three categories: engine, flight and navigation.

Engine instruments keep the pilot aware of how his thrust-producing device is operating. These instruments might tell him engine speed (rpm), oil temperature, oil pressure, fuel flow, etc. Flight instruments inform the pilot of the altitude, the airspeed, and the attitude of the aircraft. Navigation instruments help the pilot find the way from the point of departure to the destination. Such instruments include the clock, the compass, the directional gyro, the radio, radar, GPS, and radio direction finder.

Typical Instruments

Engine Instruments. One of the most important of the four basic engine instruments is called the tachometer. This instrument derives its name from the Greek word tachos, meaning speed, and the word meter, which means measure. Thus, tachometer means speed measure and that's what it shows—how fast the engine's crankshaft is turning.

This measure is expressed in revolutions per minute (rpm). On the smaller aircraft engines, these revolutions per minute are conveyed from the crankshaft to the cockpit tachometer by a flexible shaft, making it a mechanical instrument. If the engine placement or complexity makes this difficult to design, the flexible shaft linkage is replaced with

Tachometer

electrical tachometers. The electrical tachometer uses an electric generator that is geared to the engine's crankshaft. As the crankshaft turns, the generator makes electricity. The faster the crankshaft turns, the more electricity generated. The varying amount of generated electricity produces a varying RPM reading on the tachometer.

Whether the tachometer is mechanical or electrical, it will have a colored arc printed on the scale to show the normal operating range (green) and a red line for maximum allowable revolutions per minute. For safety and long engine life, engine operation should be kept within the green arc. The red line is definitely a danger point where the engine could fail, especially if the engine is run at that speed for more than a few seconds.

Another metering operation shown by the tachometer is time on the engine. This part of the tachometer records the total number of hours and tenths of hours that the engine has run since it was installed. The purpose of this information is to keep engine maintenance up to date.

Oil pressure and temperature gauges provide constant readings on the pressure and temperature of oil while the engine is operating. Both gauges have the standardized green markings for safe operating ranges and the red markings for maximums. If these gauges indicate anything but the green operating range, pilots know that they must take corrective action. This may be as simple as reducing engine speed or as drastic as preparing for an emergency landing.

Oil Temperature and Pressure Gauge in a Cessna 182

Aircraft engines have other gauges that are either necessary or helpful to the pilot. Depending on design these are mechanical, pressure, or electrical instruments. One safe bet is that every engine instrument is worth monitoring. Most pilots and passengers dislike the sudden silence that accompanies engine failure.

Flight Instruments. Flight instruments have two purposes. The first and most important purpose is that they allow for safe flight through clouds and at night. The second purpose is that the instruments show the pilot how well the airplane is being controlled.

Flight instruments are not absolutely necessary. After all, airplanes were flown before flight instruments were invented. Many pilots fly by "the seat of their pants." They reference outside-the-cockpit visual clues plus the sound of the engine, the feel of control pressure, and the feel of flight forces acting upon their bodies.

Seat-of-the-pants flying is not as effective when the earth's horizon and surface cannot be seen. Under these conditions, the pilot must rely on the airspeed indicator, the altimeter, the turn-and-slip indicator, the vertical speed indicator, and the attitude indicator. Human senses were not developed in the air, so they are unreliable if you take away the horizon, light and the solid feel of the ground under your feet.

The airspeed indicator informs the pilot of the speed through the air in terms of miles per hour and/or knots. It measures pressure of air rammed into a pitot tube at the front of the aircraft and translates it into aircraft speed.

Airspeed indicators are marked with colored areas to show maximum allowable speeds, normal speeds and approved flap-operating speeds. The range from stalling speed through normal operating speeds may be shown by a green arc; a yellow arc may show the speed from the maximum normal operating to the never exceed speed; and, a white arc may indicate flap operating speeds. These markings help keep the pilot from structurally damaging his aircraft from the dynamic pressure of the relative wind.

Airspeed Indicator

Aircraft altimeters are aneroid barometers that read in feet of altitude and are calibrated to atmospheric pressure in inches of mercury. Recall that pressure decreases with altitude, and the pressure change is shown on the altimeter reading. Even if the airplane is on the ground, a change in local air pressure will cause the altimeter to show an altitude change. Therefore, to get an accurate measurement, the pilot has to adjust the altimeter to show the atmospheric pressure for the flying area.

If the pilot sets the altimeter to zero while on the ground, it will then show actual height above the ground as he flies in the local area. This is only true if all of the ground in the area is the same height from

Altimeter

the center of the earth and the local pressure does not change. For most flying, height above sea level is more useful because the height of the ground changes as you fly over it. Local atmospheric pressure is updated as the pilot travels, but usually does not change very rapidly.

Pictured here is a typical altimeter, although the appearance may differ according to manufacturer. The long pointer shows changes of altitude in units of 20 and 100 feet. It can be read in units of 10 feet when the pointer is between two 20-foot units. The short pointer shows units of 200 and 1,000 feet.

This altimeter is of a dial-type style. Other styles exist which make quick recognition of altitude a little easier on the aviator. These styles include vertical tapes that go up as the aircraft altitude gets higher and those with digital readouts. Whatever style is employed, on any indicator, the goal should always be to let the pilot understand the reading as quickly as possible. It may be the difference between a nice landing and explaining why your Cessna is parked in someone's living room.

The turn-and-slip indicator is actually two instruments in one. The turn indicator, which is the needle, indicates the direction and rate of the turn. The ball in the glass tube, called the inclinometer, indicates the quality of the turn.

If the airplane is slipping toward the inside of the turn, the ball will be displaced in that direction or to the low side. That would mean that your tail is slipping down to the inside of the turn. This would create added drag and is referred to as *uncoordinated* flight. Can you reason why there would be more drag in a slip than coordinated flight?

If the airplane is skidding, displacement will be in the other direction. Skidding happens when the tail is being thrown toward the outside of the turn. This is also a type of uncoordinated flight.

The ball will stay in the middle if the turn is properly coordinated. The turn indicator is calibrated to show when the airplane is turning at the rate of 3° per second, or a full circle in 2 minutes. To fly wings-level in a constant direction, the pilot would keep the indicator centered.

Some aircraft are equipped with what is called a turn coordinator. The **turn coordinator** does the same things as the turn-and-slip indicator. However, a small aircraft silhouette (aft view) replaces the turn indicator or needle. As the aircraft banks, the silhouette banks. This view is easier for the pilot to visualize, so he gets an understanding of the instrument quicker.

The vertical velocity indicator (VVI) tells the pilot at what rate (in feet per minute) the airplane is climbing or descending. It is a pressure instrument much like the altimeter in that the reading is a reflection of atmospheric pressure changes. The more rapid the pressure change, the greater the rate of climb or descent. The needle rotates clockwise to indicate climb and counterclockwise to indicate descent. The vertical speed indicator may also be known as the **rate-of-climb indicator.**

Turn Coordinator

Vertical Velocity Indicator (VVI)

Attitude Indicator or Artificial Horizon

The attitude indicator is a gyroscopic instrument that provides an artificial horizon to the pilot. If the aircraft goes into the clouds and the pilot cannot see the real horizon, he can look at the attitude indicator and still fly level.

Usually, one will find that a small stationary aircraft symbol on the instrument case is the point of reference to the horizon. If you imagine that the symbol is the rear of your airplane and that you are looking from the tail to nose of your aircraft, you'll see that the attitude indicator is just a picture of how you are flying. If the little symbol is above the horizon, you are climbing. If the symbol is below, you are diving. Right turns look like a right bank as seen from the rear of the airplane. Get it?

Navigation Instruments are those that help the pilot find the way to the destination. One might reason that several of the flight instruments help toward accomplishing this goal. As a matter of fact, the airspeed indicator can be considered a navigation instrument. If the pilot did not know what the airspeed was, it would be difficult to determine how fast he was flying toward the destination.

In addition to the airspeed indicator, a clock is a very important navigation instrument. The airplane will have a built-in clock on its instrument panel, but the pilot will have a backup clock, usually in the form of a wristwatch.

The most basic and most important navigation instrument is the magnetic compass. Every airplane has a magnetic compass because it is a very reliable direction-sensing device in the airplane. It is usually the best backup means of telling what your heading is in the event of a primary system failure.

Most airplanes have what is known as a **heading indicator** for a primary heading instrument. This is a type of compass, and it looks like one. The heading indicator has all the directions printed on its compass card which the pilot sees, but behind this compass card is a gyroscopic device. When the aircraft is started, the gyroscope spins up and is stabilized. The pilot either sets his known heading on the compass card or it is set by some other computerized system like an inertial

Heading Indicator

navigation system (INS) or GPS. From then on, the compass card continues to tell the pilot which way he is flying. What Wrong-Way Corrigan wouldn't have given for one of these!

Aircraft designers have come up with some very useful heading indicators that give the aviator a lot of information quickly. A horizontal situation indicator (HSI) gives the pilot one instrument that tells him heading and navigation information quickly. A moving map display is a *God's-eye* view from above the aircraft and tells the pilot his position relative to ground references, like highways.

New Concepts

Cockpit of the Russian MiG-15 *(EAA)*

If you were an engineer or pilot, and maybe you are, what would you change to make air vehicles better? What is better? Is it cheaper? Greater cargo capacity? Faster? Each and every answer here is "yes." You, the aviation interested individual, will decide the course of aviation development. Just like

DaVinci envisioned a human-powered air vehicle, you might envision a hypersonic transport that can fly half way around the world and still not have to serve a single meal.

During the time this text was written, civil aviation was concerned with speeding up the overall aviation system. That is, how to make aircraft that help get the passenger and cargo to their destination the quickest and cheapest way.

One popular concept was the V/STOL aircraft. V/STOL stands for vertical/short takeoff and landing. The V/STOL aircraft could get into and out of small airports that were located close to the customer's destination. This concept would help reduce congestion at larger airports by getting people directly to their final destination. It also would reduce the size of airports and help lessen environmental impacts like noise.

Below is one of the popular designs based on a tilt-rotor concept. These aircraft turn their rotors up to takeoff and land like helicopters, and down to fly like fixed-wing vehicles.

The Bell/Augusta 609 is a commercial tiltrotor aircraft. *(Bell Helicopter Textron Photo)*

Hypersonic transports are those designed to travel at Mach 5 and greater. These vehicles would allow extremely fast trips over large distances. A corporate executive could fly from New York to Hong Kong, negotiate new contracts, fly back to New York, and still have time for dinner with a friend.

Such convenience comes with some very heavy design costs. These vehicles will require special construction materials to help keep the fuselage from melting, reduce wasted material weight and adjust to the changing environment from low to hypersonic speeds.

For Mach 4-7 flights, the waverider concept is a candidate for transportation. A waverider is a hypersonic or supersonic vehicle that has an attached shock wave along its leading fuselage edge. The vehicle appears to be riding its own shock wave – hence the name waverider. This type of vehicle has been considered as an option for interplanetary transportation as well.

Military emphasis at the time this text was written was on cost-savings and multi-role uses. If there is not a great deal of money to spend on defense, then what is spent needs to meet more needs.

One concept was the modular air vehicle. The idea is to build air vehicles from different sections that allow the airplane to do different missions. The designer just mixes and matches sections to meet the needs of country defense.

The Joint Strike Fighter was one such aircraft. Modules were put together to make the aircraft capable of vertical takeoffs for the Army so that it could support battles close to the war front. The Air Force version was put together with modules that made it better for deep strikes behind enemy lines.

LOFLYTE (Low-observable Flight Test Experiment) is used to explore new flight control techniques involving neutral networks, which allow the aircraft control system to learn by mimicking the pilot.

Boeing X-32A Joint Strike Fighter

The flight deck of the Boeing 767 shows state-of-the-art instrumentation. (Boeing Photo)

Key Terms and Concepts

- aircraft parts: fuselage, wing, tail or empennage, horizontal and vertical stabilizer
- major flight control surfaces: ailerons, elevator, rudder
- aircraft control axes: longitudinal (roll), lateral (pitch), vertical (yaw)
- typical engine types: reciprocating, turbine, turbojet, turbofan, turboprop
- propfan system
- ramjet and scramjet engines
- other flight control surfaces: flaps, slats, spoilers and drag devices
- fuselage structures: truss, semimonocoque, monocoque
- landing gear types: conventional, tricycle, tandem
- fixed landing gear vs. retractable gear
- major aircraft systems: fuel, hydraulic, electrical
- performance vs. control instruments
- mechanical vs. pressure vs. electrical instruments
- flight instruments, engine instruments, navigation instruments
- gyroscopic stability
- V/STOL, waverider, modular air vehicle

? Test Your Knowledge ?

PICTURE TEST _____

1. 3 = _____
2. 4 = _____
3. 8 = _____
4. 5 = _____
5. 2 = _____
6. 1 = _____
7. 7 = _____
8. 9 = _____
9. 6 = _____

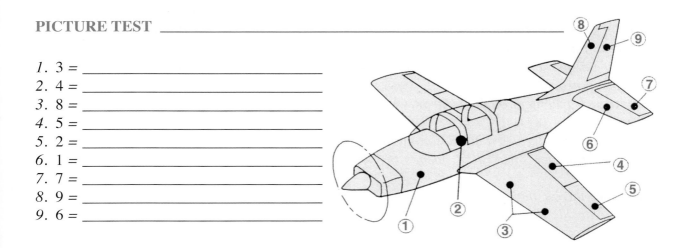

FILL IN THE BLANKS _____

10. The _____ axis of rotation runs from one wingtip, through the fuselage and to the other wingtip and is controlled by the _____.
11. The _____ axis of rotation runs from the tip of the airplane nose to the tip of the tail and is controlled by the _____.
12. The _____ axis of rotation runs from the bottom of the fuselage through the top of the fuselage and is controlled by the _____.
13. The flap _____ the camber of the wing airfoil for that portion of the wing to which it is attached.
14. Flaps are often used for both _____ and _____.
15. The slat is a _____ from the _____ edge of a wing that produces a _____.
16. The slat adds to the _____ lift of a wing.
17. Spoilers destroy the _____ flow and simultaneously reduce a certain amount of _____ lift.
18. Drag devices produce drag without affecting the _____.

MATCHING

19. *Air is accelerated and compressed by stator and rotor blades, then mixed with fuel and ignited in the combustion section, resulting in high-velocity gas or thrust.*
20. *Aircraft propellers turned by a turbine.*
21. *Crankshaft and pistons working together to convert straight-line motion to rotary motion in order to turn an aircraft propeller.*
22. *Have to be traveling through the air very fast in order to work.*
23. *Takes in air, accelerates it, pushes it out the exhaust nozzle to produce thrust that pushes the aircraft forward.*
24. *Combines the air-moving efficiency of the turbofan engine with the thrusting efficiency of a propeller.*
25. *Produce greater thrust and are more fuel efficient than standard turbojet engines.*

a. reciprocating engine
b. turbine engine
c. turbojet engine
d. turbofan engine
e. turboprop engine
f. propfan system
g. ramjet/scramjet engine

MATCHING

26. *Uses internal braces to help the skin carry the stresses generated in flight.*
27. *Utilizes longerons and struts welded together at various angles to form its basic shape.*
28. *Its covering provides the required strength to resist the stresses of flight.*

a. truss
b. monocoque
c. semimonocoque

SHORT ANSWER

29. *What name is given to the landing-gear arrangement that has two main front wheels and a small tailwheel?*
30. *If a plane has a nosewheel and two main wheels, what kind of landing gear does it have?*
31. *What type of landing gear has two sets of main wheels, one behind the other, located in tandem along the fuselage?*
32. *What is the purpose of anti-skid brakes?*
33. *Why do most small aircraft not have retractable landing gear?*
34. *What are the functions of these fuel system components: fuel pump, vent pipe, fuel tank drain, fuel strainer and cockpit fuel selector?*

TRUE OR FALSE

35. An hydraulic system is based on Pascal's law of pressure applied to a liquid in a closed container.
36. The hydraulic system of an aircraft may operate the brakes and control the flaps and propeller pitch, but is not used in lowering the landing gear.
37. A pilot can exert great pressure on control systems or structures by using the mechanical advantage gained in the hydraulic system.
38. A generator is a small electrical device used only to ignite the fuel-air mixture in the engine's cylinders.
39. Most electrical devices and controls on an aircraft receive their energy from the generator and battery system.

FILL IN THE BLANKS

40. One of aviation's first fuel gauges involved string, a stick and a _____.
41. Early _____ indicators were merely wind gauges.
42. String was also used on the first aircraft by helping the pilot determine _____.
43. Instruments classified by their use are in the major categories of _____, _____ and _____ instruments.
44. Instruments classified by their principles of operation include _____, _____ and _____ instruments.

MATCHING

45. Measures altitude and most often is an aneroid barometer.
46. Heavy roto wheel mounted so it is free to rotate.
47. A type of compass which makes use of a gyroscopic device and is affected by very little turbulence.
48. The most basic and important navigational instrument.
49. Measures how fast the engine's crankshaft is turning.
50. Measures the passage of time.
51. A gyroscope instrument which provides a horizon to show relationship to pitch and bank.
52. Measures rate of climb or decent.
53. A two-in-one instrument revealing direction, rate and quality of turn.
54. Informs the pilot of his or her speed through the air by use of a pitot tube.

a. gyroscope
b. tachometer
c. airspeed indicator
d. altimeter
e. turn-and-slip indicator
f. vertical velocity indicator
g. attitude indicator
h. clock
i. magnetic compass
j. heading indicator

TRUE OR FALSE

55. *The Wright brothers were the first to fly a sustained, controlled, powered flight of a heavier than air vehicle.*
56. *The Wright brothers used a technique called wing warping to reshape the wings of their aircraft.*
57. *The classifications of fuselages are slats, spoilers and truss.*
58. *The conventional landing gear has one wheel forward and two wheels in the back.*
59. *The fuel system for an aircraft engine includes everything that involves delivery of fuel to the engine.*

Spaceship Earth
(EAA)

"*Navigation is the science of getting ships, aircraft or spacecraft from place to place ...the method of determining position, course and distance traveled.*" This is what one dictionary says about navigation. For purposes here, the dictionary's definition will be simplified to say that navigation is knowing where you are, where you are going and how to get there.

We could say that each of us navigates in order to get from place to place during our daily activities. In familiar territory, we navigate without thinking by following the right streets and making proper changes in direction to get to our destinations. If time is a concern, we estimate how long it will take us to travel the required distance.

To assist navigational tasks, descriptive city and road maps are used when going into unfamiliar territory. Hunters, explorers and others going into unmarked territories use special types of maps (topographic) and direction-indicating instruments (compasses) to help them navigate through the territory.

Aviators and seafarers are even more concerned with maps and direction-indicating instruments because they may not be able to see the land for long periods of travel. The aviator cannot simply stop by the local convenience store and ask for directions.

Navigation principles are generally the same for any type navigation. They do, however, involve considerable detail when a navigation problem is complex. An examination of these basic principles is given in this chapter. However, remember that pilots must learn (and practice) much more than is discussed here.

bjectives

Explain how a grid is constructed to provide a system of coordinates for use on a map.

Identify the terms "small circle" and "great circle."

Describe how the coordinates of a location are written.

Describe which map projections are used for what purposes.

Define prime meridian, equator, hemisphere, parallels, meridians and graticule.

Describe the purposes served by sectional aeronautical charts.

Name methods of showing relief on a sectional aeronautical chart.

Identify symbols used to indicate cultural features on a sectional aeronautical chart.

Explain why hydrographic features are a valuable navigational aid.

Name the two broadest classifications of airports.

Describe an airport using the symbols and data printed on a sectional aeronautical chart.

Define joint-use airports.

Name the agency responsible for regulating planes, pilots and airspace.

Describe controlled airspace and its subdivisions.

Identify special-use airspace categories.

Describe the functions of specialized aeronautical charts.

Identify the major factors influencing air navigation.

State two causes of magnetic variation.

Explain why compass deviation occurs.

Describe the purpose of a wind triangle.

Define true airspeed and ground speed.

Explain pilotage navigation.

Describe dead-reckoning navigation.

Identify the basic steps involved in dead-reckoning navigation.

Describe the use of the aircraft radio as a navigational aid.

Explain the use of the VOR/TACAN receiver as a navigational aid.

Identify limitations of the automatic direction finder (ADF) as a navigational aid.

Describe the use of distance-measuring equipment (DME) as a navigational aid.

Name the parts of the VOR System for navigation.

Describe how to navigate using the VOR System

Describe how to plot a position on a LORAN chart.

Name the two types of GPS positioning systems and who might use each.

Describe why the Inertial Navigation System is different than the other systems.

Describe three types of landing systems.

Maps and Map Projections

The ability to navigate through the air is not much more difficult than following a road map. It is simply more important to know and record where you have started from, where you were heading and how long you have been flying at a certain speed. Without roads to follow, the pilot can become lost easily if he flies the wrong way. Without signs to read along the way, the pilot might miss a turn.

Understanding navigation is best accomplished by first understanding the maps used. Let's start with some aviation charts and then learn a little practical math.

Global Coordinate System. When navigating by using road and local topographic maps, you might not have noticed the vertical and horizontal lines that appear on almost every printed map. Some kind of system will allow the map reader to use coordinates for finding the street for which he or she is looking.

This system of coordinates may involve numbers across the top of the grid and letters down the left side. An alphabetical listing of the city's streets and their coordinates, such as J-9, will appear somewhere on the map. To find a certain street that has coordinates of J-9, locate the "J" column on the left and the "9" column at the top of the map. Following "J" from left to right and "9" from top to bottom. The block formed by the intersection of the two columns is the coordinates of the street.

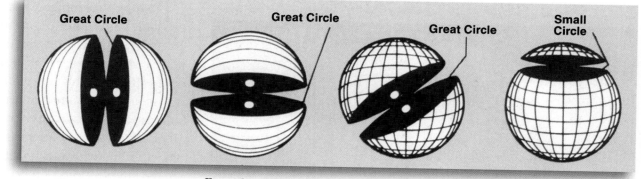

Examples of Great Circles and a Small Circle

A similar grid can be constructed for any type map, and locations on the map can be found by anyone who knows how to use the grid system. This grid system allows the identification of a position that has no nearby identifiable features.

This is exactly what has been done for locating any position on the earth. The global coordinate system is constructed as a sphere to match the surface of the earth. It consists of 360 great circles that intersect both the North Pole and the South Pole. A great circle is any circle on the earth's surface that is made by a plane passing through the earth's center. Any circle other than a great circle is a small circle. The difference between a great circle and a small circle is shown graphically in the figure above. Ninety degrees to the north-south great circles is the equator—also a great circle—and to the north and south of the equator are the small circles.

The basic grid system (graticule) for Earth uses 18 primary great circles going north-south. These lines are called lines of longitude. At 90 degrees to these lines of longitude are the planes of the equator,

the parallel small circles and the two poles. The parallels have 10 degrees spacing between them from the equator to the poles and are known as lines of latitude.

Latitude, as we said, is a series of lines parallel to the equator. These lines are based on the angular displacement of a small circle and the equator, a great circle. A latitude line (small circle) designated as 40 degrees, has an angular displacement of 40 degrees above or below the equator.

Just like on the road map discussed earlier, the grid system must be labeled. Instead of using A-B-C and 1-2-3 for the grid labels, the graticule uses degrees of a circle. This happens to be very convenient because the earth is pretty much a circular body.

Lines of longitude are divided into those on the west half of the world and those on the east half. The starting point, or zero degrees, is the great circle line that passes from the North Pole to the South Pole through Greenwich, England. This is known as the prime meridian. Meridian is another name for a north-south line that is a great circle or part of a great circle.

All longitude to the east of this meridian is designated east longitude and that to the west is west longitude. On the opposite side of the globe where east and west longitude meet is the 180 degrees meridian. 180 degrees east plus 180 degrees west add up to 360 degrees total, the same number of total degrees in a circle.

The picture below shows the basic scheme of longitude and latitude. Notice that the equator divides earth into the northern and southern hemispheres. By definition, hemisphere is half-sphere. The plane formed by the prime meridian divides earth into the eastern and western hemispheres.

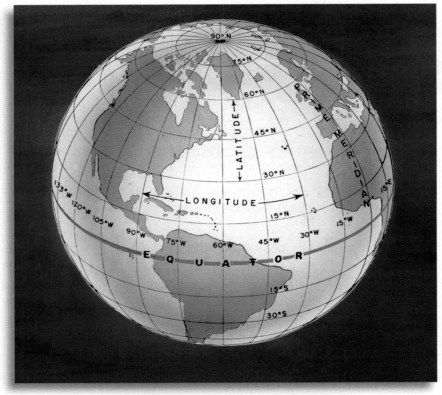

The Basic Schemes of Longitude and Latitude

Through reference to the graticule, any point on earth can be designated or identified. For example, it is not necessary to physically point out on a globe to another person the location of a city. The city, wherever it is on earth, has coordinates. Coordinates are the intersections of meridians and parallels. Continuing with the example, coordinates are read first according to latitude (north or south) and then according to longitude (east or west). To locate the eastern part of Knoxville, Tennessee, the coordinates would be designated: 36 degrees N 84 degrees W. For a city or location that does not lie at the intersection of a printed parallel and meridian, a further breakdown of degrees into minutes and seconds would be used. Just in case you did not know, here is a small table that shows the breakdown of degrees, minutes and seconds.

		Examples	
Degrees	360 per circle	23° N	
Minutes	60 per degree	23° 10' N	
Seconds	60 per minute	23° 10' 34" N	

Locations According to Coordinates

One more piece of information would be useful to us if we desire to navigate using maps with a graticule. We need to know how far it is between points on a map. Most maps have a scale shown that tells the user how many miles there are in one inch, measured on that particular map. As a bonus, the graticule we developed can also tell us distance – and it always stays the same no matter which map scale we use.

At the equator of the earth, one degree distance is equal to about 60 nautical miles or 69 statute miles. Since each degree is divided into 60 minutes, one minute of arc is equal to one nautical mile (6,076 feet). So if you want to know the distance between two points on a chart, you can take a piece of string and stretch it between the two locations. Then, holding the two endpoints, stretch it out along any great circle (longitude line) and count the number of minutes. That number of minutes is equal to the number of nautical miles between the points! Why could you not use any latitude line except the equator?

Mercator and Conic Projections. There is one challenge remaining to be solved. The maps we use for flying are not shaped like spheres. They are flattened out onto a piece of paper so that they can be easily carried. Some distortion occurs when a surface section of a sphere is flattened. You can prove this by trying to flatten a hemispheric orange peel. As the peel is flattened, it tears apart trying to conform to a flat surface. Even if the peel were elastic, like a balloon, stretching has to occur for the curvature to conform to the two-dimensional surface of a flat plane. Stretching means distortion, and distortion means what you are seeing is not what the world is really like. This could affect the accuracy of your navigation. Although it is sometimes nice to end up somewhere you did not expect, if you miss an island by 60 miles, you might get an unexpected swim to shore.

Map makers, or cartographers, use several techniques to draw the features of the spherical earth on a flat surface, complete with lines of longitude and latitude. Consider a clear globe of the earth marked with dark lines of latitude and longitude. If you put a bright light inside the globe and held a piece of paper near the surface, you would see the spherical surface and lines projected onto the flat paper. The pattern of this map projection would be different depending on where the light was placed and where the paper was held. For some maps, the paper is kept flat and held above one of the earth's poles. For others maps, the paper is rolled into a cone or cylinder around the globe.

Mercator projections are most useful when the map only shows a very small part of the earth's surface. The curvature of the earth is pretty small, so if you are very close to it the surface appears flat.

Each technique results in a different map projection. Notice the picture that shows the different projections and their names.

Lambert-Conformal maps are made by wrapping a flat map folded into a cone, around the globe. This makes a map that is more useful for longer distance travel near the middle parts of the earth. The distortions caused by projection are minimized and great circle lines appear very much like straight lines.

Look at the other types of projection maps. Where do you think they might be used? Why are they suited for that area or type of travel

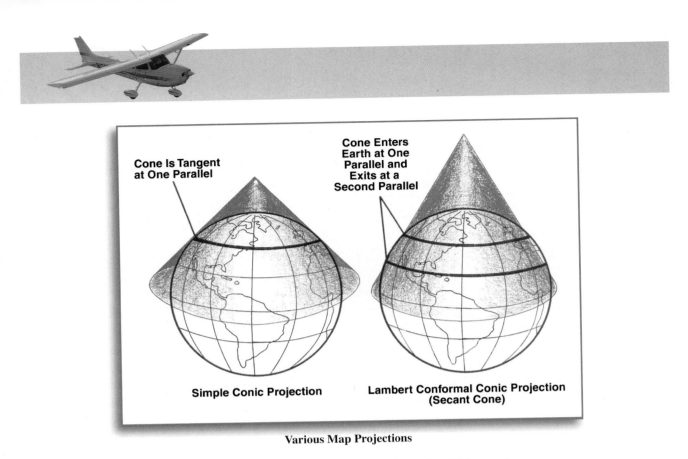

Cone Is Tangent
at One Parallel

Cone Enters
Earth at One
Parallel and
Exits at a
Second Parallel

Simple Conic Projection

Lambert Conformal Conic Projection
(Secant Cone)

Various Map Projections

Section Aeronautical Charts

The most commonly used aeronautical chart is called the sectional aeronautical chart. The primary reason for the popularity of this chart is that they are particularly useful to pilots who fly small aircraft over short distances. Such charts contain all kinds of information that the pilot-navigator can use to visually monitor the plane's rate of progress and its position over the ground. In addition, the sectional presents that information necessary to basic radio navigation, which is the pilot's electronic means of updating his position.

Sectionals are Lambert-conformal projections, and each one represents a relatively small portion of the earth's surface. All sectional charts begin as blank sheets of paper and upon these are printed the data, in different colors, that cartographers have prepared. The charts show many symbols and include a legend, which explains most of the symbols and colors.

A person using a sectional could glance back and forth between the actual chart area and the legend area and do a fair, though time-consuming, job of reading the sectional. However, this is not the best way. It is better to study the symbols and colors until there is a feeling of seeing the earth's surface in its real form. To help instill this feeling, cartographers try to make the basic chart look as much like the actual surface as possible. By necessity, they must superimpose other data. Some of these superimposed data are relief, hydrographic and cultural features.

Relief. Relief is the term used to describe elevations. Relief is depicted by color tints, contour lines, and shading. In the legend of each chart, a vertical, graduated scale shows different tints and the number of feet above sea level represented by each tint. Now, imagine that a green tint represents all the surface area that is between sea level and exactly 1,000 feet above sea level on the chart. This tint will follow the contour of the terrain; consequently, the border of the green tint will be very irregular, as if all the hills and mountains had been sliced through horizontally at the 1,000-foot level. Since different color tints normally represent 1,000-foot increments in elevation, the next color would represent a 1,000- to 2,000-foot-above-sea-level land elevation. Thus, the colors representing terrain elevation change for however many thousands of feet are depicted on the particular chart. The irregularity of their borders gives an indication of terrain roughness.

Contour lines are used to show changes in elevation smaller than the 1,000-foot color-tint scheme. These contour lines join points of equal elevation. Elevations represented are printed on certain ones. Spacing of the contour lines shows whether the rise in elevation is gradual or abrupt; that is, a hill with a gradual slope would have widely spaced contour lines. A steep hill, like a volcanic cone, would have closely spaced contour lines. If a hill or mountain has a vertical cliff, its contour lines would come together at the location of the cliff. The highest point on a hill and the highest points within a group of hills or mountains are pinpointed by black dots, which have the exact elevation printed beside the dots.

In the very hilly or mountainous areas, another technique is used to give the impression of relief. It is called pictorial presentation. With an airbrush, cartographic illustrators make the mountains look as if the sun were shining on them from an angle. The steeper the mountains, the darker the shadows will be on the opposite-the-sun sides.

With the exception of marsh grass, vegetation that covers the terrain is not shown. You can see why, if you think of the many other colors and tints that would be required. An already cluttered chart would become even more difficult to read. Big trees and small trees also look very much the same from an altitude of several thousand feet, so vegetation is of little or no value as a visual navigational aid.

Hydrographic Features. Water, on the other hand, is a very valuable navigational aid. Streams and lakes are depicted with the color blue. These water, or hydrographic, features are accurately drawn. As

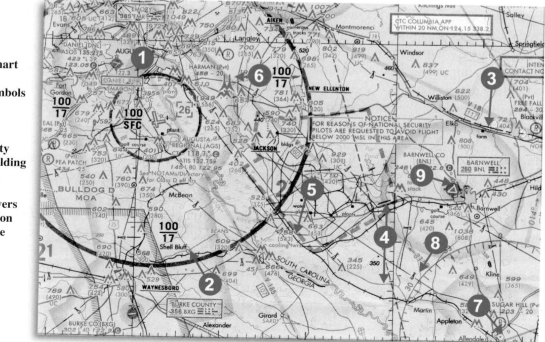

Portion of Sectional Chart with Key to Selected Symbols

1. City
2. Small Community
3. Single Building
4. Highways
5. Railroads
6. Radio Towers
7. VOR Station
8. Power Line
9. Airport

an example, every lake has a unique shape, and it is very easy to identify a lake by comparing its actual shape, as seen from the air, to the shape shown on the sectional chart on the previous page.

Cultural Features. The landscape has been marked by people. The pilot can easily see most of these changes from the air. These objects come under the general classification of cultural features. Where possible, cartographers duplicate the shapes of such cultural features.

If a city, or town, is large enough to have a distinguishable shape, it is printed in bright yellow with a thin, black-line border. Very small communities, consisting of a store or two and a few houses, are shown by a small black circle. In both cases, the name of the city, town or community is shown.

Significant cultural sites that would be visible from the air are usually indicated on sectionals. For instance, mines are charted as picks and sledgehammers. Highways are printed as black or magenta lines. Railroads look like lines with crossties and powerlines look like lines with towers. In any case, the location is on the map and is accurate and visible.

Each obstruction is clearly identified on the sectional. There may be altitudes listed next to the symbols, if they meet certain height criteria. If an obstruction is between you and your destination, then you should know its height.

Airports

Locations of airports and data about them are among the more prominent symbols printed on sectional and other types of aeronautical charts. Most airports within the area covered by the sectional are shown.

There are many kinds and sizes of airports. Some are so small that their use is, by aircraft performance, restricted to small aircraft. Others are so large and involve so much air traffic that they are restricted to serving only those aircraft that possess special electronic equipment.

There are several ways of classifying airports, but the broadest classification identifies them as either civil airports or military and joint-use airports.

Civil Airports. Since the majority of airports are civil, they are a good starting point for discussion. If the airport is unpaved, a prominent magenta circle will show its location on the sectional. This means that a landing area is available and that it may consist of either a sod or graded runway. Near the airport symbol will be printed the name of the airport, its height above sea level and the length (in hundreds of feet) of its longest runway.

If the airport has facilities, four small projections, or ticks, radiate outward from the circle: one projection toward each compass direction. What is meant by facilities? Very simply, this means that the airport has more than just a runway available. It may have only aviation fuel available or it may have all kinds of facilities, including food, lodging and hangar space. To find out exactly what facilities are available, the pilot has to refer to a special publication such as the *Airport/Facility Directory*.

Many civil airports are privately owned. To distinguish these, a large R is shown within the circle and the abbreviation (Pvt) follows its name. If verified information about an airport has not been received but it serves as a landmark, its circular symbol will contain a U to indicate that it is unverified. Some closed airports, which have paved runways, are also good landmarks. They are shown as a circle with an X across the circle to let you know the runway may no longer be suitable for landing.

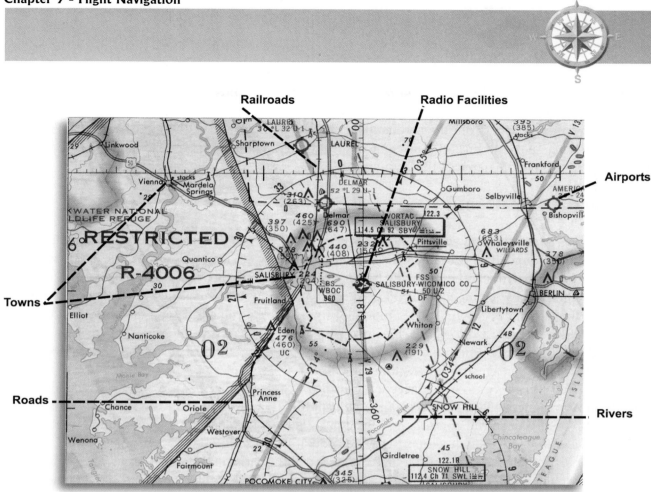

Airport Symbols on an Aeronautical Chart

Airports with paved runways 1,500 to 8,000 feet long are shown by either a magenta or blue disk. If the airport does not have an air traffic control tower, the disk is magenta. If it has a control tower, the disk is blue. The airport's runway layout appears within the disk.

Those airports with one or more runways longer than 8,000 feet are printed as heavily outlined runways. The color of this outline also indicates whether or not the airport has a control tower. Seldom seen airport symbols like heliports, unpaved military airports and seaplane bases are shown on most sectional aeronautical charts.

The basic information pilots need in order to land at an unfamiliar airport is printed near the airport symbol. First will be the airport's name, next will be the airport's surface elevation above mean sea level, and then the length of its longest runway shown in hundreds of feet. Additional information about airports is contained in several FAA publications to give the aviator sufficient details to fly into and out of the airport.

Military and Joint-use Airports. Military airports are depicted in the same manner as civil airports. The only distinguishing feature is in the airport's name: an abbreviation for the owning military service, such as AFB for Air Force Base, follows the name. Joint-use airports are found where civil aviation and military aviation share the runways. This does not mean that they will share the facilities. More

than likely, the civil aviation passenger terminal and other facilities will be distinctly separated from the military operations.

How do pilots know (from the aeronautical chart) that an airport is the joint-use type? They will know from the name of the airport. The name of the military installation, such as Sheppard AFB/Wichita Falls, appears above the name of the civil airport.

Airspace and Airways

Years ago, when aviation was just beginning to be recognized as a useful tool of society, not many airplanes were around. The people who were pilots could fly anytime and anywhere. There was little danger of colliding with another airplane because so few were in the sky.

Today, things have changed. There are hundreds of thousands of airplanes in the United States alone, and the number is growing. The amount of flying these airplanes do and the airports where they converge make it necessary to setup rules and restrictions that govern the planes, the pilots who fly them and the airspace in which they fly. The Federal Aviation Administration (FAA) establishes and enforces these rules and restrictions within the USA.

Controlled Airspace. This is a general term for airspace that has several subdivisions and is shown on aeronautical charts. When an airplane is flying in or through controlled airspace, it is subject to control by FAA air traffic controllers. This controlled airspace has dimensions; some of it starts at surface level while other subdivisions begin and end at various altitudes.

The largest area of controlled airspace is called the continental control area. This subdivision generally starts at 14,500 feet above mean sea level, extends upward into space and covers the United States (excluding Alaska and Hawaii) like a blanket.

Most pilots have to fly into control zones because these control zones are around many airports. They begin at surface level and end at the base of the continental control area.

If there is an operating control tower at an airport, there will be an airport traffic area within the control zone. This is a special controlled airspace area in which aircraft are directed during takeoff and landing operations.

In many parts of the country, there is uncontrolled airspace, which starts at the surface and extends upward to the continental control area. There are also rules and restrictions for flying in uncontrolled airspace, but not as many as there are for controlled airspace.

Airways. Airways are three-dimensional highways in the sky and are another subdivision of controlled airspace. There are low-altitude airways and high-altitude airways for use by all aviation traffic. Occasionally, special circumstances require the use of a specified airway. If this requirement is routine or known, then that information is provided in the supplemental FAA publications for the area.

Low-altitude airways are shown on the sectional chart. These are known as Victor airways and are based on the locations of radio navigation stations, which are called Very-High-Frequency Omnidirectional Radio Range (VOR). To follow these airways accurately requires the use of a special directional radio receiver.

Special-use Airspace. There are some special, but relatively small areas of the airspace that most pilots have to avoid. Therefore, it is part of the pilot's duty to make sure the flight doesn't include travel through such airspace. Prohibited airspace and restricted airspace are clearly marked on all types of aeronautical charts. The legends of the charts include details on the airspace. Prohibited airspace means that a pilot must avoid it. Restricted airspace actually means that at certain times all aircraft flight within the area is prohibited.

Warning and alert areas mean that pilots are expected to exercise extreme caution when flying through such areas. These areas are clearly marked on aeronautical charts as well.

A military operations area (MOA) is a special segment of the airspace where military flight-training activities are conducted. It is identified on aeronautical charts, but this does not necessarily prohibit other aircraft from using the same airspace. It is simply a notification to the civilian pilot that military aircraft may be in the area. These military aircraft usually fly very dynamic profiles, changing altitudes and airspeeds rapidly. This type of flying places the civilian aircraft in the MOA at a higher than normal risk for collisions.

A military training route (MTR) is a sometimes-flown, low-level training route appearing on sectional aeronautical charts. The aircraft on such routes are practicing low-altitude flying and may not be aware of your position. Civil pilots should be familiar with the MTRs and can find this information on the sectional chart.

Other Types of Aeronautical Charts

There are a host of additional chart types available to the pilot. Each chart has an intended use or shows important information in a unique way. Terminal Area Charts, for instance, show extreme detail around airfields so that the pilot can study the takeoff and landing areas closely. High-altitude en route charts show less terrain feature information and more electronic navigation aid information. When aircraft are flown at high altitude, terrain features are less important to the pilot than the airway information, so it is reduced to make the chart cleaner.

Finally, all aeronautical charts are updated rather frequently. Most of the sectionals are updated every 6 months, while others are updated once per year. The frequency of chart updates is controlled by pilot requirements and how often information changes. These updates help prevent accidents from happening, so they are very important to the FAA and the aviator.

Basic Navigation Principles

The aeronautical charts previously discussed influence navigation. An outdated chart, for example, certainly can influence navigation to the point of making it unsafe. Weather is also a major factor in navigation. The list could go on and on and would eventually pertain to everything involved with flight of the airplane. For this section, only the basic factors that must be considered by all pilots will be presented.

The True-course Line. It was mentioned earlier that a straight line drawn on a sectional aeronautical chart approximates a great-circle route. There are times, however, when the shortest distance is not the best. If the navigator intends to use radio navigation, it might be necessary to draw a series of straight lines between the origin airport, the radio navigation stations to be used and the destination airport. Another situation could involve flight around a high mountain or around prohibited airspace.

It doesn't matter whether there is a single line or a series of lines since the true course is what the navigator indicates as the course the airplane will follow. Why are such lines called true-course lines? It is because they are indications of direction with regard to true north.

True north is the location of earth's north geographic pole. All lines of longitude converge at the North Pole. Each line of longitude on the sectional shows the direction of true north with regard to any location on the chart because it is drawn through the pole.

Charts are printed so that the top is north. One can measure true direction from a line of longitude. Where a true-course line crosses a line of longitude, a point is formed. The direction in degrees is measured clockwise from the line of longitude to the true-course line. Of course, the navigator knows whether the direction of travel is east or west, but if it were west, the direction would continue clockwise until the second interception of the true-course line.

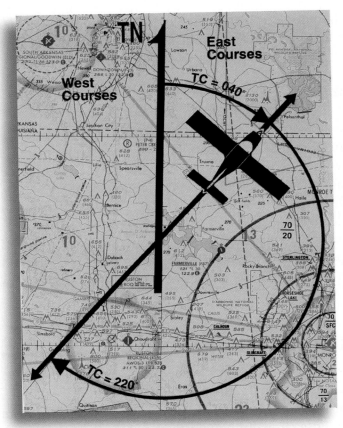

True Course as Measured from True North

Magnetic Courses. Generally, the direction of magnetic north is different from true north. This is because the magnetic poles, north and south, are not in the same place as the geographic poles. Also, the magnetic lines of force do not form straight north-south lines, as do the imaginary lines of longitude. The magnetic north-south lines of force weave back and forth a little much like lines of contour. They show where the earth's magnetic field is the same, not the direction to the magnetic pole.

These lines are shown on the sectional chart as rather dark dashed lines and are printed in a reddish color (magenta), usually running in a north-south direction. The lines are broken intermittently to show the number of degrees difference (east or west) between true north and magnetic north where the line is located. These lines are called isogonic lines because they connect the points where the angle between magnetic north and true north is equal. Across this sectional chart, for example, the difference in direction between magnetic north and true north from one side of the chart to the other is 9 degrees, 30 minutes. This was as of 1988. The next issue of this particular chart may show a greater or lesser variation because magnetic lines of force change periodically as the earth's surface shifts and the core moves around.

The magnetic compass points toward magnetic north; it has no idea of true north's location. The pilot, therefore, must steer according to the direction or heading shown by the magnetic compass. Since there almost always is a difference between magnetic north and true north, this difference (in degrees east or west) must be subtracted from or added to the true-course direction. Otherwise, the airplane will not follow the true course drawn on the chart.

Compass Deviation. Although the magnetic compass is the most reliable indicator of direction, it is a mechanical device and no mechanical device is perfect. The compass must be adjusted against a known standard that is correct.

Installing the magnetic compass in an airplane causes other influences to come into play. Most metals and electrical power will cause a compass needle to deviate from magnetic north. This means that the compass must again be adjusted once it is installed in the airplane. The deviations caused by electrical power and metal are entered on a compass correction card and kept in the aircraft for reference if the pilot chooses to fly by the magnetic compass.

Altimeter. The altimeter usually is thought of as a flight instrument; however, it is also a factor in navigation. The altimeter is the only non-electronic means the pilot has of determining the airplane's distance above the surface. Since heights of cultural and natural surface features are shown on aeronautical charts in feet above mean sea level, the correctly adjusted altimeter is the means of determining safe flight clearance above obstructions. The altimeter also plays a significant role in the determination of the next factor, true airspeed.

True Airspeed vs. Ground Speed. True airspeed is useful to the pilot because it is a measure of how fast the airplane is flying through the air. The air changes with altitude and temperature, right? Yes, it does. However, the instruments in the aircraft measure flight through air, not across the ground.

Ground speed is a measure of how fast your aircraft is going across the surface of the earth. If the relative wind were behind you, your ground speed would be higher than your true airspeed because you are getting a push along. Your true airspeed would not change because it measures what is happening to you in the air mass. The air mass is moving along with the wind, so you don't see it affect the true airspeed. Ground speed is important to the pilot because it determines how long it will take to get from a start point to the destination, not coincidentally, measured across the ground.

Wind and the Wind Triangle. The effect of wind upon an airplane in flight can either increase or decrease ground speed depending on whether the airplane is flying with or against the wind. This effect is rather easy to determine. All one needs to know is how fast the wind is blowing and whether the flight is with or against the wind. Flying with the wind requires adding the wind speed to the true airspeed, and flying against the wind requires subtracting the wind speed from the true airspeed.

The situation changes when the airplane's flight path is at an angle to the wind. What happens is that the airplane does not follow the course drawn on the aeronautical chart. This is because the wind tends to make the airplane travel along with it at the same direction and speed. This effect of the wind is called drift.

The only way to correct such a situation is for the pilot to fly a heading that will compensate for the amount of drift caused by the wind. In flight, this can be done by trial and error until a heading is arrived that will keep the airplane on the intended course line.

A better way to combat wind drift is to determine the heading that will be needed well before departure. In fact, this is a task of preflight navigational planning and it isn't difficult to do.

The figure on the next page shows a wind triangle, a tool used by the pilot to figure out where wind drift will cause the aircraft to fly over the ground. It can also be used to counter the effect of drift. The grid shown is oriented to true north. The line pointing off of the aircraft's nose is the true course from

A to B. The wind line blows the aircraft off course and results in an actual track across the ground labeled as the ground track.

So what would you do if you wanted to correct for the wind drift? Fly into the wind. Since we fly direction using aircraft heading, we need to know how many degrees to steer into the wind. This is found by measuring the number of degrees between the true course line and the ground track. Then, steer that many degrees into the wind. Simple!

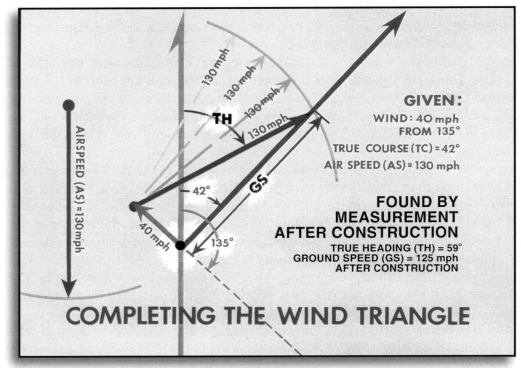

Using a Wind Triangle

There are several tools that help the pilot figure out drift corrections. Flight plotters are aviation-specific protractors that make determining angles and headings quick and painless. Flight computers come in many varieties. They may be little more than circular slide rules (find an old guy and ask him what a slide rule is) or as complex as hand-held computers that can rapidly calculate flight information.

Navigation Techniques

The two basic techniques of air navigation are pilotage and dead reckoning. One or the other of these has been used since cross-country flights were first possible.

Pilotage. Pilotage means navigating by reference to visible landmarks. It can be as basic as flying above and following a highway or railroad to the destination. If a pilot is totally familiar with the geographic area of the flight and has flown the route many times before, references to landmarks may not be necessary. On the other hand, it might be necessary to use a sectional chart as backup for an area that is not quite so familiar.

Use of the pilotage navigational technique in completely unfamiliar territory requires more caution and preparation. This preparation may involve the following steps:

(1) A true-course (TC) line is drawn on the aeronautical chart from the point of departure to the destination.

(2) Using the scale printed on the chart, or a flight plotter, the total distance to be flown is measured and the TC line marked off in segments of 10 miles each. These distance segments help the pilot or navigator locate landmarks and determine the progress of the flight over unfamiliar territory.

(3) Landmarks are selected along or very near to the TC. The landmarks along the TC are used as checkpoints, with the word checkpoint meaning the place over which the airplane should be at a certain predetermined time. It is also good practice to select a checkpoint at the end of the destination so that the pilot will know immediately if the airport has been overflown.

(4) "Brackets" on each side of the course should be selected. Brackets are easy-to-see surface features to either side of the TC; they are used between checkpoints to help maintain the proper course over the ground. If you are very unfamiliar with the area, choose easily recognized features like large cities or mountains.

Pilotage can involve extensive planning. It was presented earlier how wind affects the airplane's rate of progress and direction over the ground. With other navigational methods, this is considered and calculated prior to beginning the flight. Pilotage, on the other hand, involves observing how much drift to the right or left of the TC the wind is causing and compensating for the drift by changing the heading of the airplane. It is a basic, "eyeballs out" method of navigation that is an essential skill.

Navigation by pilotage, then, can vary from doing considerable planning to no planning. When flights are of short distances over familiar territory, most pilots simply preflight their airplanes and go.

Dead Reckoning. Dead reckoning is the basis for professional-level navigation. While pilotage is an "eyeballs out" form of flying from one place to another, the dead-reckoning technique involves the systematic consideration of all factors that will and could affect the flight. These factors are considered in the proper sequence, calculated, recorded or logged where appropriate, and

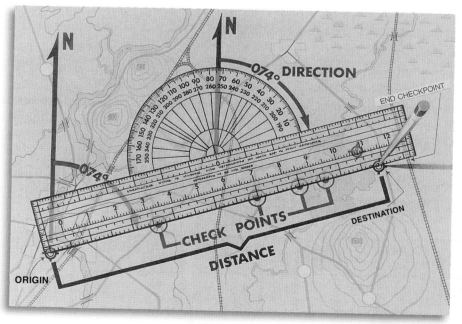

Flight Plotter

updated as the flight progresses.

The term dead reckoning originated with the mariners of long ago. These ship navigators deduced their positions at any given time by using distances and directions that their ships had sailed since passing or leaving a known position. Such positions were determined at frequent intervals and were entered in the ship's logbook under a column headed by the abbreviation "ded.pos." for deduced position. The reckoning (counting up or figuring) necessary to obtain these entries was known as "ded. reckoning," which later became dead reckoning. Since the task of the nautical navigator is to know the position of the ship at any given time, the air navigator using dead-reckoning navigation should know the position of the airplane at any given time.

By measuring and calculating, by keeping account of navigational factors, by using a flight plan and by properly using the basic navigational instruments, it is possible to fly directly to any place in the world. Essentially, this is what happens during present-day long-distance flights. However, dead reckoning today is backed up by various electronic aids.

Let us bring together the basic factors bearing upon air navigation. We will do this by constructing a cross-country flight plan according to dead-reckoning navigation. What we are about to do is no more difficult than knowing which direction to go to the grocery store, what turns to make and how long it takes between turns.

Our flight will be from Phillipsburg Airport at Phillipsburg, Kansas, to Oakley Airport at Oakley, Kansas. The distance is 78.5 nautical miles, which you could measure with a plotter or a string. A quick look at the "3⁹" near Oakley on the chart tells us in order to clear the highest known feature within the area of the intended flight path by 500 feet, we will need to fly at least 3,900 feet above mean sea level (MSL). However, we will use 6,500 feet MSL as our cruising altitude, so any unknown obstructions should be no problem.

To keep track of our calculations, we will use a pilot's planning chart like the one below. There are many types of planning charts. Some are standardized to provide aviators with a planning tool that is the same all across the United States. Some are customized to provide the pilot with quick look information first, then details as required.

Now we are ready to step through our basic planning process to make a dead reckoning flight plan. Work from the figure below as the steps are described.

Step 1. Draw the TC line and measure its direction and distance. The 100-degree meridian is nearest the midpoint of the TC line. Measurement with the protractor portion of a flight plotter shows the TC at this intersection to be 242 degrees and the distance is confirmed at 78.5 nm (nautical miles) from airport to airport. This data is entered on the pilot's planning chart.

Step 2. Estimate the true airspeed. We will cruise at an airspeed of 95 knots on the airspeed indicator. This airspeed is called the indicated airspeed, because it is indicated on the airspeed indicator. Get it?

TC	WIND		WCA R+ L-	TH	VAR W+ E-	MH	DEV CORR	CH	TOT MILES	GS	TOT TIME	FUEL RATE	TOT FUEL
	FROM	KTS											
242°	320°	20	+11	253°	-8°	245°	-4°	241°	78.5	102 KTS	46 MIN	8 GAL/HR	6.1 GALS

Pilot's Planning Chart

250

There is about a 2 percent increase in airspeed from indicated to true airspeed for each 1,000 feet of altitude. For 6,500 feet, this should be a 13 percent increase, which makes our estimated true airspeed 108 knots.

Step 3. Check the weather. The weather service reports the sky clear with visibility unlimited. The wind at cruising altitude will be from 320 degrees (true north) at 20 knots.

Step 4. Determine wind correction angle, true heading and ground speed. Using the wind face of a flight computer or a pilot's calculator, you would find that the wind correction angle is 11 degrees right. (Don't worry about figuring this out. The math is not important for this example.) Adding the 11 degrees wind correction angle to the TC gives a true heading of 253 degrees. The flight computer and calculator would also show that the ground speed is 102 knots instead of the 108 knots estimated for true airspeed. That should make sense. The wind is blowing in our face, so we should be slowed down a bit. The wind correction angle, true heading and ground speed are entered on the pilot's planning chart.

Step 5. Determine magnetic variation and magnetic heading. Looking at the isogonic lines on the chart reveals that magnetic variation is 8 degrees E near the middle of our route. We will consider this to be the average variation, so 8 degrees E must be subtracted from the true heading. This leaves a magnetic heading of 245 degrees.

Step 6. Determine the compass heading. It requires checking the compass deviation card in the airplane. Let's say that we find it to be -5 degrees. This leaves a compass heading of 240 degrees. Following this compass heading should keep the airplane's ground track on the planned TC.

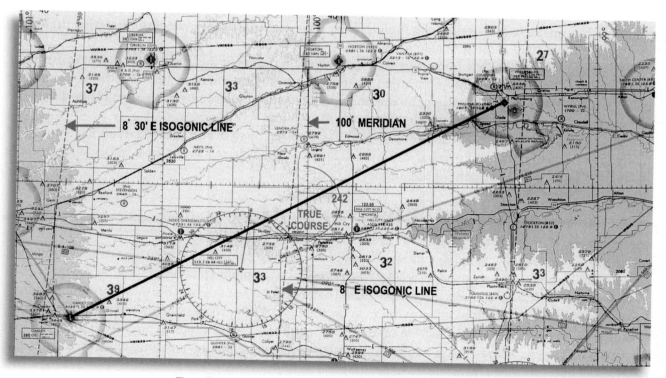

True Course from Phillipsburg Airport to Oakley Airport

Step 7. Determine the time en route. We know that the distance is 78.5 nm and that the ground speed should be 102 knots (nautical miles per hour). A little math magic would tell us:

$$\frac{78.5nm}{102nm/hr} = 0.77 \ hrs$$

That's about 46 minutes of flight time. Total time would take slightly longer because we have not counted the additional time required for takeoff and landing maneuvers.

Step 8. Determine fuel usage. This airplane burns 8 gallons of fuel per hour. A flight computer, or some more math magic, tells us that for 46 minutes of flight time, we will use 6.1 gallons of fuel.

Step 9. Select checkpoints. Checkpoints are selected according to the pilot's or navigator's choice. For example, the TC line crosses a distinct bend in the highway/railroad system that is 6.5 nm out from Phillipsburg Airport. Much farther along the TC there is another very good checkpoint east of Tasco — a lake, a highway, a railroad and a stream with a U bend in it. Again, the selection of checkpoints is an individual's choice, but make certain you choose something you'll be able to identify from the air.

Step 10. File a flight plan. It is always good sense to file a flight plan with the nearest FAA flight service station. This is done by telephone, computer or radio, and its primary purpose is to have a record of where the flight will be going and when it will be completed. If the flight isn't completed and the flight plan is still open with the FAA, a search for the missing craft can be started within a very short time. Think of it like leaving a note with your mother. Mother likes to know where you are.

As you probably have already concluded, the preparing of a dead-reckoning navigational flight plan can be approached in different ways, or it can be put together differently from the example we have given. The sequence of the steps isn't too important. The important thing is that all factors bearing on the flight be considered. So, filing the flight plan is always the last step in beginning such a flight, and closing the flight plan is the first step in concluding the flight.

The world of aviation has numerous aids to navigation. Some of these aids have become essential; that is, many flights into highly controlled airspace or through certain weather conditions would be either unlawful or impossible without modern navigational aids. Electronic developments or refinements are the basis for most of these in-flight aids to air navigation.

Electronics have also allowed the development or improvement of complete navigational systems. A navigational system, according to our definition, can provide accurate navigational information without depending on any other system or technique.

Electronic Aids

In this section, we will acquaint you with a number of navigational aids. From the coverage provided, you should be able to understand how and when such aids supplement dead-reckoning navigation.

The Aircraft Radio. The aircraft radio is an aid to navigation because it is the pilot's communication's link with FAA personnel and others who have an interest in the progress and termination of a cross-country navigational flight. The picture on the next page shows what a typical aircraft radio looks like. Its main working parts are encased behind the instrument panel, and the antenna, which transmits and receives signals protrudes from somewhere along the airframe, usually the fuselage or vertical stabilizer. The microphone contains a button that is depressed when transmitting and is popularly known as a

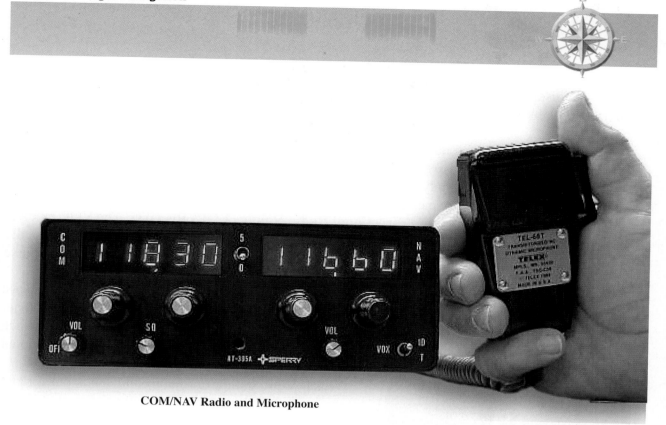

COM/NAV Radio and Microphone

push-to-talk button. In small airplanes, the radio speaker usually is located somewhere in the overhead roof of the cockpit, but it can be anywhere. Most aircraft also provide the aircrew a place to plug in headphones so that aircraft noise can be reduced while listening to the radio. Military fighter aircraft have the microphone and headset inside the pilot's helmet so that he can keep his hands free to employ weapon systems while talking to his wingmen.

Radios transmit voice communications over certain frequencies. These frequencies are assigned to different FAA regions and airfields, and allow you to talk specifically to a single controller. As you fly from one region to another, the controller has you change frequencies to talk to the next region. This organized way of handing you from one controller to the next allows the controller to concentrate on your safety while in his or her area.

Where do you find out which frequency to use? A current aeronautical chart will show some frequencies such as those to contact an FAA flight service station or an airport's control tower. Such frequencies are changed from time to time for one reason or another, so all that plan a navigational flight are cautioned to double-check the frequencies printed using other FAA publications.

Two other controls found on the aircraft radio are the volume and squelch. The volume control's purpose is obvious, but the squelch control serves to reduce background noise. This control decreases the sensitivity of the reception getting through to the radio's speaker. This allows only the stronger voice signal to come through. When the voice signal you want to listen to is weak, however, it might be necessary to put up with a certain amount of background noise to make sure you do not miss a radio call meant for you.

Aviation is very dependent on radio communications and such communications have to be as brief as possible. Airplanes taking off and landing at a busy airport leave little time for extended conversations between the aircraft controller and the pilots. It is the controller's job to space the airplanes so there

will be a safe distance between them. The controller, therefore, must give pilots clear instructions in the shortest possible time. The pilots must reply in the same manner when they give information to the controller.

Over a period of time, there has developed what we might call a spoken shorthand, that is used for aircraft radio communications. Key phrases are used to ensure that the pilot has understood directions from the controller and will comply with those directions. The shorthand communication helps keep the airwaves clear for emergency messages or critical commands.

The Very-High-Frequency Omnidirectional Radio Range (VOR) Receiver. The VOR receiver is the second half of the aircraft radio. The two are separate operating units, but electronic firms usually build a unit that contains both types of receivers. In addition to the receiver, there is a VOR course deviation indicator situated elsewhere on the aircraft's control panel.

A VOR Course Deviation Indicator (CDI)

To use the receiver, it must be tuned to the broadcast frequency of the VOR radio station in the same manner as the aircraft radio. The appropriate frequency for each station is printed beside the VOR symbol on the sectional aeronautical chart.

Each VOR station on the ground sends out a radio signal in a 360-degree circle around the station. Each degree line extending away from the site is called a radial and goes out for as far as the VOR signal can be received.

The pilot can set his indicator's selected course so that it matches one of the radials. Then the indicator will tell him if he is right, left, or on the selected radial. It will also tell him if he is heading toward or away from the VOR station.

You can probably see why the VOR is useful for navigation. It gives the pilot a way to tell where he is from a given ground point without actually seeing that point. With a VOR you could navigate without seeing the ground. When might that be useful?

The Automatic Direction Finder (ADF). This is another type radio receiver that is used to determine direction, but it does not provide as much information to the aviator as the VOR. The ADF station transmits a beacon signal that is the same for all directions around the transmitter. This means that radials are not selectable for precise navigation to and from the station by the pilot. A common term for a type of ADF station is Non-directional Beacon, or NDB. You might see several of those on an aeronautical chart.

The picture here shows an ADF navigational display. The needle on the ADF receiver's navigational display

An ADF Bearing Indicator

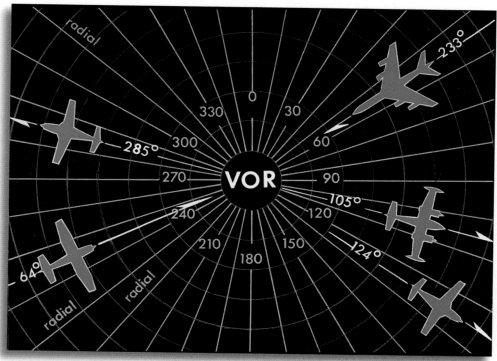

Radials Broadcast by a VOR Station

points toward the station to which the receiver is tuned. Therefore, all the pilot has to do is align the nose of the airplane with the needle and flight will then be toward the broadcasting station.

There are several problems with the use of the ADF as compared to the VOR. The ADF display does not compensate for the effect of wind. The airplane might follow a curved instead of a straight course to the station, if the pilot does not manually turn into the wind to avoid drift. Signals in the frequency range used by the ADF will give incorrect directional information to the ADF receiver occasionally because they bounce off of land features much like an echo.

With all of its drawbacks, the ADF system is a useful aid to navigation. It still provides some directional information to pilots, helping them if they cannot see the ground. It just requires more work by the pilot to fly precise routes between points.

Distance-Measuring Equipment (DME). Many of the VOR stations across the country have a special unit called tactical air navigation (TACAN). When this unit is installed with a VOR, the station is called a VORTAC.

The TACAN portion will respond with a broadcast signal when it receives a signal from the DME unit in the airplane. The DME sends a signal and measures the time it takes to go from the aircraft to the VORTAC and return. The DME unit converts the time to nautical miles distance between the airplane and the station.

The VOR receiver is tuned to the same VORTAC as the DME unit. The VOR shows which radial the airplane is on and whether the flight is to or from the station. The DME tells how far away the airplane is at any given moment. So now, the pilot not only knows which direction he is from a ground station, like an ADF, but can plan to fly on a particular radial and knows how far it is to the station.

This gives the aviator enough information to precisely define where he is, using only one electronic navigation aid.

There is one minor error associated with DME. It measures line-of-sight distance between the airplane and the VORTAC station. This means that it does not measure the horizontal distance between the airplane and the station because the airplane is at an altitude above the surface. This error is not of great significance, but you can see that the DME on an airplane flying at 30,000 feet and passing over a VORTAC station would show the airplane to be about 5 NM from the station, straight up.

Weather and Ground Radar. Radar, as you probably know, works on the principle of reflected radio energy. Its transmitter sends out a narrow beam of super-high-frequency radio energy. Some of this energy is bounced back to the radar unit's receiver and is shown as bright spots and areas on a cathode-ray tube. This tube is known as the radar scope.

This can be useful to the navigator because radar can see very far, through the darkness, and through some weather. Small, radar reflective points on the ground can be listed on an aeronautical chart and used to identify your position very accurately.

Weather radar shows areas of precipitation, but its most important function is to show storm cells (thunderstorms) ahead. This allows the pilot or navigator to change course and to avoid those places that might be dangerous to flight.

Radar units can be very simple or very complex. Simple units might just show what is ahead of the aircraft so that the pilot can adjust the flight route. Complex systems provide color displays that tell you the intensity of weather, allow pilot designation of ground targets and are integrated with other navigation systems and helps update errors in those devices.

Radar gives the aviator one more tool to navigate better. It helps the pilot see far away and plan for route changes. As en route navigation becomes more complex for the pilot, any and all tools are appreciated.

Navigation Systems

The VOR System. We have touched on the VOR system during previous discussions. Recall our mention of VOR stations in the description of airways. We also mentioned VOR and VORTAC stations in the descriptions of the VOR receiver and DME. The total VOR system includes the airplane receivers and the ground stations working together to help the pilot navigate.

A modern VOR or VORTAC station is easily identified visually from the air or the ground. Inside the station, two radio signals are created and broadcast. One is stationary and produces a constant, unchanging outpouring of signals in all (omni) directions. The other signal is broadcast by a directional antenna that rotates at 1,800 revolutions per minute.

When the VOR station is placed in operation, it is adjusted so that the stationary signal and rotational signal are lined up in the exact direction of magnetic north for the location. The aircraft receiver measures the difference that develops between the two signals as the rotational signal spins around. The difference is then converted to radial information so that the pilot can select a specific navigation route.

Although the signals from VOR and VORTAC systems are line-of-sight signals and can be stopped by the terrain (such as a mountain) that lies between the station and an airplane, it is difficult to be out of range of at least one station on any flight. Therefore, it is possible to pick out a line of VOR/VORTAC

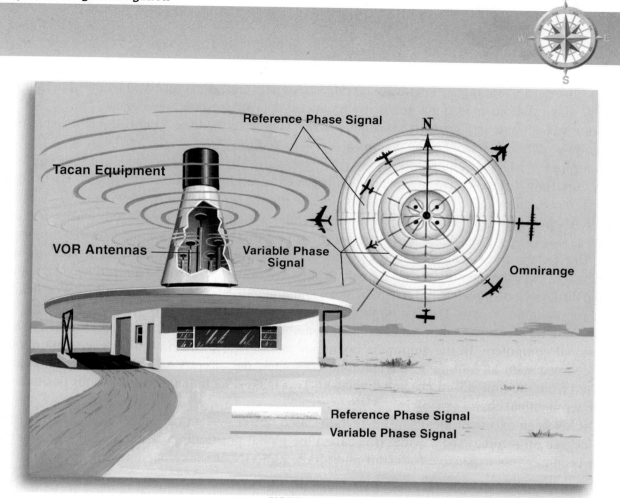

VORTAC Station

stations between an origin and a destination, and use them for a cross-country navigational flight. The pilot only has to tune in to one station and fly to and from the station, until within radio range of the next station. Within range of the next station, the to-from process is repeated, and so the flight proceeds.

Another very useful and important feature of the VOR system is that of providing a position fix. Obtaining a position fix is exceptionally easy when the airplane is equipped with two VOR receivers (as many are). The receivers are tuned to different stations and their course indicators are rotated until FROM readings are obtained and the CDI needles are centered. This procedure gives the radial from each station on which the airplane is located at the moment. Lines drawn on the sectional chart extending from the two VOR radials will cross. The point at which these lines cross shows the position of the airplane at the time the radials were taken.

Long-range Navigation (LORAN). LORAN is an acronym for long-range navigation. It is a complete navigational system, and its basic form has been in existence for many years. LORAN is used by large cargo ships and many small, privately owned seaworthy craft. It is also used by aircraft as a means of navigation.

Several modifications to improve LORAN have caused it to be identified as A, B, C and D. LORAN-C is what we might call the most popular model. The system uses, at any one time, at least three ground-based radio stations, a receiving unit aboard the aircraft and special LORAN navigational charts.

The ground-based radio stations are located many miles apart and are known as master and slave

stations. The master station automatically broadcasts signals that, when received by the slave stations, cause the slave stations to also automatically broadcast delayed, responding signals.

Radio waves travel at a virtually constant speed. Thus, from the time a radio signal takes to travel between two points, distance can be determined.

An airplane's LORAN unit receives the signal transmitted by the master and slave stations. It then displays the time difference (in microseconds) between receiving the different signals. By using the time differences shown, the airplane's position can be plotted on the LORAN navigational chart.

LORAN navigational charts show the time differences of signals received from master and slave stations as lines of position. These time differences appear on the chart as curved lines. By finding the curved line for the time difference received, the pilot or navigator knows that the aircraft's position is somewhere over the territory covered by that specific thin line. To find the aircraft's exact position, the time difference of signals from a second slave station is measured. Where the curved line from the second set of signals crosses the first on the LORAN chart is the aircraft's position.

The LORAN-C receiving unit can be set for automatic operation, and it can be coupled with automatic navigational computers. In the automatic operation mode, it displays time difference continuously. When coupled with an automatic navigational computer, the aircraft's geographic coordinates are converted from the time difference and displayed. This makes it a bit easier to plot your position on a regular aeronautical chart.

LORAN is an excellent means of navigation, but a newer system has been developed that offers a high degree of accuracy worldwide. It is called the global positioning system or GPS. As this new system becomes less expensive to install in aircraft, LORAN use may decrease and may even stop being used altogether.

The Global Positioning System (GPS). The GPS navigation system consists of roughly 30 satellites in orbit around the Earth, several ground tracking stations and a receiver in the aircraft. The total number of satellites varies as some are repaired and upgraded. The ground control sites watch where the satellites are in orbit and continually correct their reported location and time-of-day signals. This is done so that when the satellite communicates with your receiver, it gives the best possible position it can to help navigate.

The GPS receiver converts the signals coming from the satellites into position coordinates. It can give the pilot his latitude, longitude, elevation and current time, if the receiver can see any four of the 30 satellites.

GPS Receiver

The Segments of a Global Positioning System

GPS satellites were controlled by the US Department of Defense at the time of this writing. Because position accuracy is very important to military operations, GPS accuracy is very good. However, that "good" signal is encoded so that only US forces can use it, which helps keep the enemy from using it against the US military. The usefulness of GPS for the civilian community demanded that they have the ability to receive its position data as well. Therefore, the GPS satellites send out two signals for position data.

The **Precise Positioning System (PPS)** is the military's encoded signal. Its accuracy is classified, but public literature suggests position location within about 30 meters. The **Standard Positioning System (SPS)** is the civilian public's signal and its accuracy is controlled by a program called **Selective Availability (SA).** During times of peace, SA degradation of the SPS signal is not necessary and SPS accuracy is near that of PPS. However, in time of crisis, SA can be returned to service degrading, or even denying, SPS service to any region and even the entire globe, if necessary.

GPS accuracy can be greatly improved at a specific location using a technique called differential GPS. If a ground GPS station is setup and its latitude, longitude and elevation is very precisely measured,

it can send out a correction signal to nearby aircraft using GPS. This signal fixes the little errors in the satellite signal and makes the received position very accurate. Why might you need such an accurate signal?

Inertial Navigation. The inertial navigational system is a little different than the others we have discussed. It is a self-contained unit located within the aircraft that needs only to be programmed for a starting point and destination. The unit does, however, need electrical power to keep its parts functioning. An inertial navigational system does not measure airspeed or wind velocity. It does not actually measure anything except movement. This movement is translated into speed, direction and distance. Movement is detected with a very sensitive device called an accelerometer.

Accelerometers function somewhat like a pendulum. The amount a suspended pendulum will be moved depends upon the change in movement of the body to which it is attached. If a pendulum is attached to a string and suspended in an airplane that is maintaining a constant speed, the pendulum will remain motionless. Slow the airplane and the pendulum will swing forward; speed the airplane up and the pendulum will swing backward.

The real accelerometer could be a spring-loaded mass in a container that allows the mass to move in a single linear direction (forward and back). The springs serve to center the mass when an inertial force is not acting upon it.

Accelerometers mounted on a platform and set 90 degrees to each other could sense left-right, forward-backward and up-down motions. These motions are watched by an integrator and sent to a guidance system computer. Sounds futuristic, doesn't it? The computer really does no more than keep track of where the airplane is, based on where it started and what motions have happened since it was turned on.

INS accuracy does get worse over time. Most systems drift by about ½ NM per hour. The good news is that inertial systems are usually integrated with the other systems on the aircraft. These systems can update the INS with known ground point positions. For instance, the radar could pinpoint a landmark and tell the INS exactly where it is. GPS can also update the INS and keep it accurate to either the PPS or SPS limits. Finally, if you see a landmark and know its coordinates, you can fly over it and do a visual update to the INS.

The Area Navigation System (RNAV). We might say that the heart of the area navigation system (RNAV) is a computer. That's because RNAV is really more of a computer controlled navigation system than a set of stations and receivers. This system uses VOR-type radio stations or GPS as reference points, but allows the pilot or navigator to fly directly from the airport of origin to the destination airport without following the airways. It is possible to use this system and fly very long distances without passing over a single VOR station. This might be very useful if you desire to fly a long great circle course and save time and fuel en route.

The RNAV computer takes your desired straight path between start point and destination, then looks to see how that path flies past the VOR stations. It monitors your real flight path and tells you when you are getting off course by comparing its predicted position from the VOR and its actual position. GPS flown RNAV uses GPS position backed up by either INS or ground station signals. The FAA has some rules on when and how GPS can be used for RNAV and publishes them in their flying publications.

Landing Navigation Systems

The area navigation systems covered thus far are fine for getting around the countryside, but do not have the position accuracy necessary to get a pilot on to a 50-foot wide runway. That requires a special navigation system that is highly accurate within a limited range. These landing systems fall into two categories: precision and non-precision. Precision landing systems can get a pilot very close to the end of the runway, and in some cases even land the aircraft using its autopilot. Non-precision landing systems get the pilot very close to the runway so that when they get below the weather, they can easily see the airfield and land.

The Instrument Landing System. The Instrument Landing System (ILS) is used only within a short distance from the airport and only when the purpose is to land the airplane. During clear weather, it is not necessary to use an ILS because the pilot can see the airport and runway. Let there be low clouds, rain, snow or other visibility-reducing conditions and the ILS is essential.

The figure below includes the arrangement of the ground-based components of an ILS system. Briefly, what the ground-based system does is to broadcast very precise directional signals. These signals provide a lateral and vertical path to the runway. The lateral (centerline) and vertical (glide slope) signals are usable within 18 NM of the runway.

All ILS systems broadcast marker beacons. These are directed upward within a relatively narrow

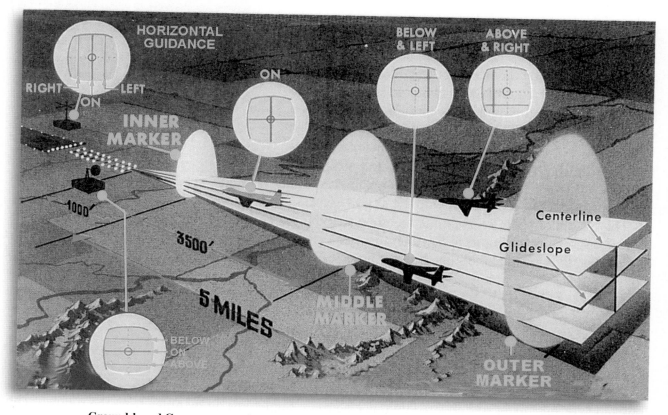

Ground-based Components and Instrument Indications of an Instrument Landing System (ILS).

space, and they serve as checkpoints to tell the pilot the airplane's position. Some ILS systems have three marker beacons: the outer, the middle and the inner. However, only two such beacons are found at most airports—the outer and the middle. Marker beacons generally tell the pilot that they are at an important place along the approach. For instance, a marker might indicate that the aircraft should have its gear down, or that it is time to decide if you can see the runway to land or need to go-around and try another approach.

Equipment in the airplane to use the ILS consists of a glide-slope receiver and a marker-beacon receiver. Glide-slope and azimuth information are displayed on a VOR course indicator. This course indicator (also called navigation indicator) has a localizer needle (vertical) and a glide-slope needle (horizontal). The localizer needle operates in the same manner as when its receiver is tuned to a VOR station. For the ILS, it shows the pilot whether the airplane is right or left of the centerline. The glide-slope needle shows whether the airplane is above or below the glide slope. By proper manipulation of the airplane's flight and power controls, the pilot can keep the craft on a perfect flight path to visual contact with the runway.

The marker-beacon receiver has a light display for showing passage over each marker beacon. Passage over the outer marker causes a blue light to flash; passage over the middle marker is indicated by the flash of an amber light; and, if an inner marker is present, a white light flashes upon overflight. As the airplane crosses each marker beacon, a tone is also heard over the radio speaker if this feature is selected on the intercom panel.

Use of the ILS requires that the pilot locate the system. The standard way this is done is through the combined efforts of the pilot and the FAA air traffic controller. The FAA controller directs the pilot toward an intercept of the intended ILS using his area radar. In the meantime,

Course Deviation and Glide Slope Indicator

the pilot has tuned one of the navigational receivers to the ILS frequency. Upon intercept of the ILS, communications are established with the airport control tower for landing.

There is much more to using the ILS than we have stated here, and it isn't as simple as it seems. If you can imagine trying to follow the directions shown by the ILS while doing the tasks required of precision flying and at the same time communicating with airport control tower personnel, you get more of an idea of its complexity.

Microwave Landing System (MLS). In Europe, the microwave landing system is replacing the instrument landing system discussed above. The advantages to all of aviation are many, but the primary advantage is that the MLS is more efficient than the ILS.

Where the ILS produces narrow beams for guidance to the runway, the MLS broadcasts much wider beams—both horizontally and vertically. In fact, the MLS can create an electronic funnel that spreads horizontally as much as 120 degrees and vertically as much as 20 degrees. You can imagine how much of the airspace is covered by this electronic funnel just a few miles from the runway. This wide-mouthed funnel is easy to enter because the intercept can be made from any angle and from any distance within range of the system.

The MLS also has a precision back-course guidance that can help pilots continue to navigate as they go-around from a poor approach. This guidance provides the pilot reassurance as he reenters the weather and can no longer see the airport.

Differential GPS Landing Systems. So, what could a very accurate GPS guidance system be used for by the pilot? How about highly accurate landings? Because GPS signals are not transmitted in any particular direction, precision approaches can include curved paths and tiered altitudes. In fact, a GPS approach can take virtually any shape, as it is computer generated.

Approaches have always been a point of discussion with the communities that surround airfields. Noise and other environmental concerns affect the people in the airport community. GPS approaches can be molded to the community's needs and still satisfy the aviator. That is the goal of any good navigation system.

A Safe Landing

Key Terms and Concepts

- Global Coordinate System
- grid system (graticule)
- great circles and small circles
- latitude and longitude
- prime meridian
- hemisphere
- mercator and conic projections
- sectionals
- relief and contour lines
- hydrographic and cultural features
- civil, military, and joint-use airports
- controlled airspace
- airways
- special-use airspace
- true course vs. magnetic course
- compass deviation
- true airspeed vs. ground speed

- wind and the wind triangle
- pilotage
- dead reckoning
- aircraft radio
- FAA
- VOR and TACAN Receiver (VORTAC)
- radial
- Automatic Direction Finder (ADF)
- Distance Measuring Equipment (DME)
- weather and ground radar
- Long-Range Navigation (LORAN)
- Global Positioning System (GPS)
- Inertial Navigation System (INS)
- Area Navigation System (RNAV)
- Instrument Landing System (ILS)
- Microwave Landing System (MLS)
- Differential GPS Landing System

? Test Your Knowledge ?

FILL IN THE BLANKS

1. *A grid may be made to provide a system of _____ on a map.*
2. *This is done by drawing _____ and _____ lines on the map and putting numbers and _____ on the lines.*
3. *By reading across and down the grid to the point of _____, any location can be found.*
4. *Relief is a term used to describe _____.*
5. *Relief on an aeronautical chart is depicted by _____, _____, and _____.*
6. *Water is a useful navigational aid because a pilot can identify a lake by comparing its actual shape, as seen from the _____, to the shape shown on the _____.*
7. *Very small towns are shown by a _____.*
8. *Mines are charted as _____ and _____.*

9. On a map, highways are printed as black or _____ lines.

10. Victor airways are based on the locations of _____ _____ stations called VORs.

11. The two types of airspace clearly marked on charts for pilots to avoid are called _____ and _____ airspace.

12. MOA means _____ _____ _____ and indicates airspace where _____ flight-training activities are conducted.

13. Low-level _____ _____ appearing on sectional aeronautical charts are called MTRs.

14. Some major factors that must be considered by all navigators are: determining the _____ line and the magnetic _____, allowing for compass _____, maintaining proper _____, determining true _____, and determining the wind _____ and _____ in order to correct for wind drift.

15. Pilotage means navigating by reference to _____.

16. Preparation for pilotage navigation could involve the following four steps: (a) drawing a _____ line, (b) marking the answer to a visible landmark in _____-mile segments, selecting land marks to be used as _____, and (d) using brackets to help maintain the proper _____ over the ground.

17. Navigation involving the systematic consideration of all factors which will and could affect a flight is called _____ _____.

18. The ADF only shows the direction of a _____ station; it makes no allowance for the effects of _____.

19. The DME shows the number of _____ _____ the airplane is from the radio station.

20. While weather radar does show areas of precipitation, its most important function is to show _____ ahead of the aircraft.

21. The nationwide VOR system consists of directional broadcasting _____ stations.

22. Each station broadcasts two signals; one is _____ while the other is _____.

MULTIPLE CHOICE

23. The prime meridian is the starting point for
    a. latitude.
    b. longitude.
    c. graticules.
    d. projection.

24. The equator divides the northern and southern
    a. meridians.
    b. longitudes.
    c. hemispheres.
    d. none of these.

25. By definition, hemisphere means
    a. half of a plane.
    b. half of a sphere.
    c. a whole sphere.
    d. all of these.
26. The basic grid system of latitude and longitude lines is called the
    a. graticule.
    b. conformal.
    c. coordinate.
    d. topographic.

TRUE OR FALSE

27. A great circle is any circle on the earth's surface that is made by a plane passing through its center.
28. Any circle other than a great circle is a small circle.
29. Coordinates are read first according to longitude and then according to latitude.
30. The broadest airport classifications are civil and military/joint-use.
31. In joint-use airports, facilities aren't necessarily shared by the military and civilians.
32. The FAA is the regulatory body for all of aviation.
33. Controlled airspace is serviced by air traffic controllers.
34. The largest area of controlled airspace is called the international control area.
35. High-altitude airways are clearly defined on sectional charts.
36. Low-altitude airways are also known as Victor airways.
37. The wind triangle is constructed to find the true heading that compensates for the effect of wind.
38. As a navigational aid, the aircraft radio is useful as a communications link with authorities who control aspects of navigational flight.
39. The VOR allows pilots to fly directly to or from VOR stations.
40. The VOR does not automatically compensate for the effects of wind.

SHORT ANSWER

41. Describe parallels and meridians in terms of longitude and latitude.
42. List a cause of magnetic variation.
43. State three factors affecting compass deviation.

44. The text listed 10 steps in planning navigation according to dead reckoning. Place the appropriate numeral (1-10) next to the correct step.

    ___ *Determine the compass heading.*
    ___ *Determine the time en route.*
    ___ *Determine magnetic variation and magnetic heading.*
    ___ *Determine fuel usage.*
    ___ *Determine the wind correction angle, true heading, and ground speed.*
    ___ *Select checkpoints.*
    ___ *Check the weather.*
    ___ *File a flight plan.*
    ___ *Estimate the true airspeed.*
    ___ *Draw the TC line.*

45. What are the two surface-based transmitters required in the LORAN system?
46. List the three basic components of the inertial navigation system. What does this system provide for the navigator?
47. What are the two types of GPS systems and who might use each?
48. Name three types of landing systems.

PART THREE

The Aerospace Community

The aerospace subject is very large and diverse. As seen in previous chapters, there are many subject areas. So far you have learned about history, weather, space and aerodynamics. Now you will learn more about specific functions of aircraft, organizations, training and careers. Together these all makeup the aerospace community. Only when all subject areas discussed in this book are working together do we see the whole picture. Each part may stand alone, but doesn't tell the whole story. Each plays a vital role in the aerospace community, but without them altogether, there would not be a synergistic effect. The loss or slowdown of progress in one area would have negative impacts across the entire community. A recent economic boom has invigorated the aerospace community. Commercial aviation is expanding at record paces. Technology has played a key role in this boom.

This boom has brought many challenges and benefits that will continue into the future. This will help to ensure the aerospace community will be more and more a part of everyone's life.

The All-new, World-class Denver International Airport

bjectives

Identify the different parts of a typical airport and describe their functions.
Describe how runways are numbered.
Know the difference between a controlled and uncontrolled airport.
Describe the different lights and their meanings on an airport.
Describe three concerns and challenges to a typical airport.

The Airport

Airports come in all sizes and shapes. Some airports are grass fields located on farms, while others are downtown in major cities encompassing tens of square miles. Airports can be civilian, military or a combination of both. They can be for public, private or military use. They can also be for large commercial air carrier operations or for the smaller general aviation aircraft. Regardless of size and function, they all exist for the basic purpose of launching and recovering aircraft. They are madeup of several parts, each providing an essential service to accomplish the basic functions of the airport.

Runway

The most important part of the airport is the runway. With the exception of helicopters, the runway is needed for all aircraft to takeoff and land. The runway can be made of grass, gravel, concrete, or asphalt. All runways are identified by a number. The number is the first 2 digits of a compass direction rounded to the nearest 10 degrees. For example, if a runway faces west or 265 to 274 degrees, it is numbered 27. When going the opposite direction on the runway, it changes its number to the reciprocal compass heading. In this example, it would be 09 because 180 degrees from 270 is 090 degrees. Some airports have several runways with the same direction. These runways are given a letter to tell them apart from the other ones, such as 23L for left, or 23R for right. Runways also have other markings on them. A dashed, white line down the center identifies the centerline and a solid white line on each side marks the edge. Special markings identify the runway for use in bad weather. These markings are usually large white blocks that start at the approach end and stop several thousand feet down the runway. All of these different markings tell the pilot something about the runway, just as markings on a road tell drivers about the road.

At night, runways have steady white lights on the edges and sometimes down the middle. At the end of the runway are red lights and at the beginning are green lights. Larger runways can also have approach lighting. These are lights before the actual runway. Usually they are on poles that slope downward towards the threshold or beginning of the runway. They are used by the pilot to line up the airplane with the runway and, in bad weather, help the pilot to find the runway. The approach lights usually flash in sequence so a pilot can more easily see which direction the runway is pointing. Some lighting is pilot-controlled and is available at some smaller airports. Pilots tune in a specific radio frequency and key their microphone. The number of times the microphone is keyed determines the intensity of the lighting. To conserve electricity, the lights shut off automatically after about 15 minutes.

Taxiways

Taxiways are the roads that aircraft use to get to the runway. Pilots taxi their aircraft from one spot on the airport to another by using these taxiways. Each airport has its own pattern of taxiways. The most common taxiway is called the parallel taxiway. It gets its name because it parallels the runway. Taxiways are usually narrower than runways and have different markings and names so pilots do not

Aerial View of an Airport Showing Runways, Taxiways and the Ramp Area

confuse them with runways. Letters instead of numbers name taxiways. An example of this would be taxiway "C." The centerline is a solid yellow line instead of a dashed white line and solid yellow lines sometimes mark the sides.

Ramp and Hangars

The ramp and hangars are the parking spots for aircraft. The ramp is a large paved area for parking airplanes. Most large aircraft are parked outside on the ramp because of the large open space and expense of a hangar. Most smaller aircraft are placed in hangars. A hangar is nothing more than a garage for airplanes. It provides a protected place for the aircraft from weather damage.

It also is handy for aircraft maintenance. Aircraft parked on the ramp are usually tied down. This is true only for light aircraft because strong winds can easily lift a small airplane and damage it. The ramp is where loading and unloading of airplanes takes place. There are many vehicles on the ramp to perform services for the aircraft. They can bring fuel, baggage, passengers and maintenance personnel to the aircraft. It is a very dangerous place to be. A person on the ramp must constantly watch for aircraft taxiing or starting their engines. Vehicles driving on the ramp also pose a threat to people working on the ramp.

Control Tower

The control tower is often the first thing noticed at an airport. It is usually the highest structure on the airfield. The height is necessary so the tower controllers can see all the movement on the airport. This helps them to reduce congestion between aircraft and vehicles moving about the airfield. The tower has many functions. Its primary function is to control the runway. It does this by giving permission to aircraft for takeoff or landing. Permission is also given to vehicles for maintenance on the runway. This could be to fix holes, remove snow or repair lights. The goal is to restrict all traffic on the runway to only those approved by the tower. The tower also controls the movement of aircraft on the ground. They watch all aircraft and give permission for them to move. They are like traffic police that direct the flow of aircraft to avoid collisions.

The tower is also the source of the Automated Terminal Information System (ATIS). ATIS is a voice recording of a tower controller. The recording tells pilots about the wind, clouds, visibility and any restrictions that the runways may have. It is updated at least every hour. During changing weather conditions, it is changed much more frequently. ATIS allows the tower controllers to direct their attention to controlling traffic rather than to discussing the weather and restrictions with aircraft. To perform all these functions, they use different radio frequencies. This ensures separation of the functions because different permission or information is given on different frequencies.

Control Tower

Some airports do not have control towers. There are many more airports without towers than with towers. These airports are called uncontrolled airports. At these airports, pilots must use common procedures to reduce the chances of collisions on the ground and in the air. Most of the uncontrolled airports are not very large and most small airplanes fly in and out of these airfields. Larger commercial airliners almost always land and takeoff at controlled airports. Some airports have towers, but may not operate 24 hours a day. During times when they are not operating, the airport changes from a controlled airport to an uncontrolled airport.

FBO is a term that many pilots and ground support use in daily conversations; however, few outside the aviation world know what it means. An FBO is a Fixed-base Operation. The FBO is basically a service station for airplanes. The FBO is where most of the activity occurs at smaller airports and it can be a small office or a large building complete with several hangars. The purpose of the FBO is to provide some essential services to pilots. They provide pilot training and instruction, fuel, maintenance, rental aircraft, aircraft sales and

charter flights. Not all FBOs offer all of these services, but most provide at least a few.

Passenger Terminal

The passenger terminal is found at larger airports. At smaller airports, passengers are usually found at the FBO. Terminals are designed to handle people, baggage and cargo. Most have large waiting rooms for passengers to relax while waiting to board their aircraft. They have places to eat, purchase tickets and rent cars. Some large passenger terminals have jetways. These are long, square tubes that reach out to the aircraft and allow passengers to walk to the aircraft and board without stepping outside. Underneath the terminal are places for transferring baggage and cargo from one aircraft to another or to the baggage claim area. Aircraft park on the ramp next to the terminal at places called gates. Gates are places where passengers wait to board their airplane. Large terminals have many gates to accommodate all arriving and departing aircraft.

Passenger Terminal

Other Facilities

There are numerous other facilities located at airports. One is the National Weather Service, which is found at medium and large airports. It provides weather information to Flight Service Stations (FSS). The FSS provides all types of weather information to pilots. It gives forecasts and current weather along the route of flight. The FSS also takes care of flight plans and can help pilots with special requests. Flight plans are a description of the planned route of flight an aircraft is going to take to get somewhere.

The fire station is an essential service at the airport in case of an accident. At larger airports, there are several stations located at different parts of the airport. Many large airports have what looks like a burned out aircraft surrounded by water. This is a fire training area. Firefighters occasionally set the aircraft on fire and practice putting the fire out to improve their skills.

There are also facilities for storing auxiliary equipment. This equipment is used to service aircraft before and after flights. It also requires a place for storage and maintenance.

One navigation aid that is very familiar at night is the rotating beacon. This beacon is used by pilots to help them locate the airport at night or in bad weather. At civilian airports, it consists of a green light and a white light. It is frequently located atop the tower or on top of another tall structure, such as a water tower. It rotates in a circle and can be seen for many miles. A military field also has a beacon, but has a device that splits the white light into two beams. When viewed, it looks like a green flash, then two quick white flashes. This difference helps pilots to distinguish between the two types of airports.

Airport Concerns and Challenges

One of the biggest concerns of airports is wildlife. Sometimes animals, especially birds, wander into the path of aircraft on the runway. Aircraft striking wildlife has caused many aircraft accidents. Birds are the biggest problem.

Larger game animals are another wildlife hazard. Airports sometimes use cattle grates and fences to keep animals away from the runway. Grates are placed across roads where the road passes through a fence. Sometimes these efforts fail and animals are tranquilized and moved, or simply killed.

The noise factor is another concern. Airplanes are not very quiet when operating near the ground. When encroachment becomes a problem, airports develop noise abatement procedures. These usually involve a very quick climb by the aircraft after takeoff. The aircraft also try not to fly over certain areas on the ground. Communities can help to minimize the encroachment problem by not allowing building near airports.

2/2/2000 08:28

Birdstrike Damage

A Look at the Future

An aircraft known as the *tiltrotor* may revolutionize both military and commerical aviation in the near future. Because of its vertical takeoff and landing capabilities, it has the potential to serve without an airport. Because of its high speed, once it reaches straight and level flight, it can travel between airports much faster than a helicopter. It has the potential to fly from the center of one city to the center of another population center almost as quickly as a turboprop aircraft. This aircraft may be the future of short-term air travel, and airports may be used only for very long-distance flight operations.

The Tiltrotor *(Bell Helicopter Textron)*

Key Terms and Concepts

- airports
- uncontrolled airports
- runways
- runway designations
- threshold
- taxiways
- ramps
- hangars

- control tower
- Automated Terminal Information System (ATIS)
- Fixed-Base Operation (FBO)
- passenger terminal
- Flight Service Station (FSS)
- encroachment
- noise abatement procedures

? Test Your Knowledge ?

MATCHING

1 Match the terms:

a. runway
b. control tower
c. taxiways
d. ramp
e. passenger terminal
f. FBO
g. hangar
h. Flight Service Station

(1) planes use these to get from one place to another on an airport
(2) parking area for aircraft
(3) place to protect smaller aircraft from the elements
(4) primary function is to control the runway
(5) similar to a service station for aircraft
(6) place to board aircraft and retrieve baggage
(7) provides weather forecasts to pilots, assists with flight plans
(8) surface aircraft use to takeoff and land

FILL IN THE BLANK

2. An airport with an operating control tower is a _____ field.
    An airport without a control tower is an _____ field.
3. A _____ field has a beacon with one green and two white rotating lights.
4. Taxiway lights are _____ colored.
5. The lights used by the pilots to line up with the runway are _____ lights.
6. Runway edge lighting is _____ colored.

TRUE OR FALSE

7. Some runways have lights that can be adjusted in intensity by the pilot tuning the designated frequency and then keying his microphone.
8. Taxiways are the same width as runways, but are identified by a letter rather than a number.
9. Aircraft starting engines, taxiing aircraft and numerous vehicles are several of the dangers posed to personnel working on the ramp of an airport.

SHORT ANSWER

10. Your airplane lines up on the runway and the compass heading reads 257 degrees. What is the runway number? After landing on another runway, your compass reads 033 degrees. What is that runway number? How are parallel runways delineated?
11. What does the acronym ATIS stand for? What is it? How does it help the congested environment near an airport?
12. List the three major challenges facing airports today.

11 AIR CARRIERS

Aviation is divided into separate categories with specific functions. This chapter will focus on air carriers, both large and small. Although quite different in size and function, they all have in common the movement of people and cargo from one place to another. This chapter will describe these categories and their functions in the aviation community.

bjectives

Define air carriers.

Describe why the Airline Deregulation Act had more serious effects on the older airlines than on the newer ones.

Define modern airliner, all-cargo carrier and regional/commuter carrier.

Major Air Carriers

In this chapter, we will categorize the air carriers as follows:

1. Modern Airliners: The largest carriers in terms of the number of passengers carried regardless of the length of the routes.
2. Cargo Carriers: These carriers carry mainly freight but now are also allowed to carry passengers.
3. Regional-commuter Aircraft: These are smaller airlines that carry passengers within a certain limited geographical region. They serve many of the smaller cities that the larger airlines have dropped.

The first category we will discuss is the major air carrier aircraft. In this case, the payload includes the passengers and their baggage, as well as airmail, air cargo and anything else that the airlines carry for the purpose of making money.

The air carriers include the companies generally referred to as commercial airlines. There are several other groups not normally considered airlines also included in the air carrier category. These include carriers that transport only cargo and the commuter air carriers. The thing that all of them have in common is that they all fly on regular schedules and they are all transporting people or cargo as a commercial business.

The air carriers are considered common carriers along with the railroads, bus lines and steamships. Common carriers are in business to serve the public, and thus, they are very closely regulated and controlled to ensure the safety of the public. The Federal Aviation Administration (FAA) is in charge of regulating the safety of the airlines and of controlling the flight of all air traffic while flying over the United States.

Prior to 1978, the Civil Aeronautics Board (CAB) very strictly regulated the fares and routes of the air carriers. Fares could not be changed without CAB approval, and every airline was restricted to flying only certain routes.

The Airline Deregulation Act of 1978 changed everything. This act allowed the airlines free entry into the air routes of the nation. This means that the airlines were allowed to start flying on new routes without approval of the CAB.

The idea behind this decision was that as more airlines began flying certain routes, competition would cause fares to be reduced. This happened on certain routes, but something else occurred. As the airlines began flying more profitable routes, they began to cut back their services on the less profitable routes. In some cases, they actually eliminated stops in certain smaller, unprofitable cities.

The result of this was twofold. First, many new airlines sprang up, both to provide service to the smaller cities and to compete with the larger airlines. Secondly many of the existing airlines merged to form larger airlines. In 1978, there were 36 scheduled airlines serving the United States. In 1988, this had grown to 76 even though there had been mergers and bankruptcies in the airline business.

Immediately after deregulation, many of the older airlines began to have serious financial problems.

A Large Airport Terminal with Many Commercial Departures

These problems were caused by a number of factors. The airlines were suddenly faced with competition on air routes, which they previously monopolized. Not only were new airlines beginning to fly on these air routes, but many of them charged lower fares. The older, established airlines had very high labor costs. The new, smaller airlines were nonunion; therefore, the employees were paid less. These savings were passed on to the passengers. Operating costs skyrocketed as fuel prices tripled because of the energy crisis, and interest rates soared because of the inflation of the late 1970s. Many of the older airlines had ordered new fuel-efficient aircraft to cut down on fuel costs. However, when these new, higher-priced aircraft were delivered, the airlines did not have the money to pay cash for them and they had to pay 15 to 20 percent interest on their loans to pay for the aircraft. The newer airlines were buying cheaper, used aircraft and did not have these large interest payments. To further compound the problem, the recession of the 1970s and early 1980s reduced the number of passengers, and the air traffic controllers' strike reduced the number of flights to and from many areas.

Modern Airliners

These carriers are the most common and most familiar to the general population. Their job is to haul passengers to all parts of the world in only hours. The aircraft in this category generally carry over 100 passengers, with some carrying over 500 passengers. Most major carriers only travel from large city to large city. This ensures most of the seats on the airplane are filled. Airlines are businesses and empty seats do not generate income. The major airlines fly all sizes of aircraft, depending on the size of the cities being served. In this section, we will emphasize the larger, long-range aircraft that the major carriers use to serve their larger markets.

Boeing 747

This is the largest commercial airliner ever built and it deserves the name jumbo jet. There have been about 700 of the giant Boeing 747s built in 15 models. The 747-100 and 747-200 have been produced in

The Boeing 747(*Boeing Photo*)

the greatest numbers. Both models are similar in that they can carry up to 500 passengers. Most often, however, they are configured to accommodate 48 first-class and 337 coach passengers. The passenger compartment is huge, measuring 187 feet long, 20 feet wide and 8 feet high. Its floor area measures 3,529 square feet (an average-size American home has about 1,700 square feet).

A fully loaded 747 can weigh as much as 870,000 pounds (435 tons). The 747-200 has a fuel capacity of 51,430 gallons of fuel. If you had an automobile that got 20 miles to the gallon and you drove it 17,000 miles per year, it would take you over 60 years to burn this much fuel.

Boeing also makes a 747-200F, an all-cargo version. We will discuss this aircraft in the section dealing with all-cargo carriers.

The latest model of the 747 is the Model 400. It has the same fuselage dimensions as the Model 500, but it has more range, better fuel economy and lower operating costs. It entered service with Northwest Airlines in the fall of 1988.

The Model 400 has a range of 8,200 miles which is 1,150 miles greater than the Model 300. On one of its early test flights (June 27, 1988), the first Boeing 747-400 took off at a gross weight of 892,450 pounds—the heaviest mass ever lifted by an aircraft.

McDonnell-Douglas DC-10/MD-11

The second jumbo jet to enter service was the McDonnell-Douglas DC-10. By the beginning of 1987, 357 DC-10s in 3 models were flying with the world's air carriers. The DC-10-10 is the standard version and the DC-10-30 and DC-10-40 are the extended-range intercontinental versions. There are also two convertible passenger/cargo models designated the DC-10-10CF and the DC-10-30CF.

The DC-10 is smaller than the 747. It is about 44 feet shorter (181 feet), has a 30-foot-shorter wingspan (165 feet) and weighs about 250,000 pounds less.

The DC-10 can carry between 255 and 380 passengers, depending on the design. The maximum operating range is from 3,600 miles in the Model 10 to 6,100 miles in the Models 30 and 40.

In November of 1982,

The MD-11

a new designation system for McDonnell Douglas commercial aircraft combined the "M" of McDonnell and the "D" of Douglas. First aircraft to use the designation was the DC-9 Super 80, which became the MD-80.

The MD-11, the world's only modern large, wide-cabin trijet, offers a highly sophisticated flight deck system controls that substantially reduces pilot workload. Advances in aerodynamics, propulsion, aircraft systems, cockpit avionics and interior design contribute to the performance and operating economy of all MD-11 models. The MD-11 is 18.6 feet longer than the DC-10 trijet and carries about 50 more passengers. It was first delivered in 1991.

Lockheed L-1011

Lockheed entered the commercial jet transport field with the introduction of the L-1011 jumbo jet in 1972. This was the first commercial airliner that Lockheed had produced since the Electra.

The L-1011 is very similar to the DC-10 both in external appearance and performance, and was produced in three models. Three British-built Rolls-Royce turbofan engines power all L-1011s. The 747s and DC-10s are powered by US-manufactured Pratt and Whitney and General Electric turbofans. Rolls-Royce engines are available on special order.

Both the DC-10 and the L-1011 were originally designed to be profitable on high-density short-to-medium-length routes. They were built to meet the airlines' needs to carry larger passenger loads than the current medium-range jets and still be able to operate from comparatively short runways. After they were introduced into service, the DC-10 and the L-1011 became so popular that the airlines wanted to use the same type of aircraft on longer routes. This led to building longer-range models. The outward appearance of the longer-range models is the same as the shorter-range ones. The long-range models have larger fuel tanks in the wings and, sometimes, higher thrust engines. The long-range version often has a shortened fuselage. This reduces the number of passengers the aircraft can carry. It also allows the weight of the fuel the aircraft carries to be increased by the amount the passenger weight is reduced. As an example of this, the original model of the L-1011 has a maximum range of 3,600 miles, while the long-range version has a maximum range of 6,100 miles. Production of the L-1011 stopped in 1984.

Airbus A-300B

The latest entry into the wide-body jumbo jet field was the A-300B Airbus. An international corporation (Airbus Industrie) made up of industries from England, France, Germany, the Netherlands and Spain builds this aircraft. The French are manufacturing the nose section, lower center fuselage and engine pylons. Germany is responsible for the forward fuselage, the upper center fuselage, the rear fuselage and the vertical tail. England is building the wings; the Netherlands builds the wing control surfaces; and Spain builds the horizontal tail surfaces, fuselage main doors and landing-gear doors.

The engines are American-made, but are assembled in France and Germany. All of the parts are shipped to France for final assembly.

The A-300B is smaller than the DC-10 or the L-1011. It is about 11 feet shorter, weighs about 100,000 pounds less, and carries between 220 and 320 passengers. Two General Electric turbofan engines mounted under the wings power the Airbus.

Airbus has two long-range aircraft—the A-330 and the A-340. The A-330 is a twin-engine, medium-range aircraft, and the A-340 is a four-engine (the first four-engine aircraft ever for Airbus), long-range aircraft. The A-340 is not as large as the Boeing 747, but it is much larger than current Airbuses.

Boeing 767

In 1982, the first of the new Boeing 767s went into service with the major carriers. United Airlines was the first to fly the 767 and Delta was second. This aircraft uses the latest technology in design, new engines and computerized flight controls. Not only does this provide better fuel efficiency, and thus better profits for the airlines, it also provides for the ultimate in comfort, convenience and safety for the passengers.

The Boeing 767-200

The 767 is a twin-engine, wide-body jetliner, but it is not as wide as the 747. The 767 fuselage is 15 feet wide compared with 20 feet for the 747. The tourist-class cabin features seven-abreast seating with two aisles. The 767 typically carries all passengers (18 first-class, 193 tourist) in mixed-class seating or 230 in all-tourist configuration. The size of the 767 can best be demonstrated by comparing it with the 747. The 767 is 70 feet shorter (159 feet vs. 231 feet) and has a wingspan that is 39 feet shorter (156 feet vs. 195 feet). Also, the 747 maximum takeoff weight is more than twice that of the 767 (710,000 pounds vs. 300,000 pounds).

The basic version of the 767 can serve such medium-length routes as San Francisco to Chicago, Los Angeles to Miami, or London to Cairo. The advanced transcontinental version (767-300) can operate nonstop between New York and Los Angeles.

Boeing 777

The 777 family is designed to fill the size gap between the 767 and 747. The market-driven 777-200 twinjet seats from 305 to 328 passengers in a typical three-class configuration. The initial 777-200, which was first delivered in May 1995, has a range of up to 5,925 miles.

The 777-200ER (extended range) was first delivered in February 1997. This model is capable of flying the same number of passengers up to 8,861 miles.

Boeing 777

The latest derivative is the 777-300, a stretched version that provides seating for 328 to 394 passengers in a typical three-class configuration. The first airplane was delivered in 1998.

Boeing is studying new versions of the 777-200 that could fly nearly 10,000 miles, as well as a longer-range version of the 777-300.

Boeing 727

This is the most successful airliner ever built in terms of numbers. A total of 1,831 of these aircraft were produced, and every air carrier in the free world is currently flying this aircraft. Of the 1,831 727s built, 1,500 are still flying today. The three engines mounted on the rear of the aircraft and the T-tail are the unique features of the 727. The first model (727-100) can carry up to 131 passengers and has a range of about 2,500 miles. The later "stretched" 727-200 can handle up to 189 passengers and has a range of up to 2,900 miles.

Boeing 737

Boeing 737

The 737 is a twin-engine, short-range jet transport which entered airline service in April 1967. Still in production, the 737 will eventually surpass the 727 in terms of the number built. Depending on the model, the 737 can carry from 110 to 190 passengers. The 737 is attractive to the airlines because its fuselage is the same diameter as the 727. This offers better passenger comfort. This feature is also attractive because many parts are interchangeable between the 727 and 737. The advanced 737s can also operate from runways as short as 4,000 feet, and some can even operate from unpaved runways. This provides many small communities with jet service where it was previously unavailable.

Boeing 757

Another new, advanced-technology jet for the 1990s is the short-to-medium-range Boeing 757. This aircraft is being manufactured as a replacement for the older 727s and DC-9s, which are aging.

The 757 is a twin-engine airliner with the same fuselage diameter as the 727. With six-abreast seating, the 757 can carry 178 passengers in mixed first-class/economy seating or up to 220 in all-tourist configuration.

The 757 has an overall length of 155 feet 3 inches. Its wing makes use of the same advanced technology used in the 767 and spans 124 feet 6 inches. The advanced flight deck employs the same technological concepts as the 767 Boeing jetliner.

As a replacement for the DC-9 and 727 aircraft, the 757 is attractive to the largest airline market in the world—the short-haul market. Currently, 70 percent of all jet passengers in the world fly on trips of less than 2 hours duration. On these short-duration flights, turnaround time becomes very important. The 757 is precisely suited for these routes. It offers the same number of seats as the larger trijets, with

65 percent more flights per day. Compared to current larger trijets, it will cut airplane-mile costs by 40 percent. This cost-cutting combination makes it the world's most economical short-to-medium range jet transports.

Because it consumes less fuel per seat, the 757 saves money and/or provides additional revenue on fixed fuel allocations. For example, 10 of the 757s replacing equal numbers of 727-100s can save about $15 million a year (based on fuel costs at 60 cents a gallon). If fuel costs are $1 per gallon, about $25 million can be saved. The 10-airplane 757 fleet can provide 70 percent more seat-miles or $60 million in additional revenue given an equal amount of fuel.

Savings with the 757 are not limited only to fuel. The 757 is certificated for a two-crew member operation, whereas the 727s they replace are all operated by three crewmembers. This factor can result in a $9 million per year savings for a 10-aircraft fleet. New, lower-maintenance systems can save the same 10-aircraft fleet an additional $2 million per year.

The Boeing 757

McDonnell-Douglas DC-9

This aircraft is the mainstay of the national carriers. Six models of the twin-engine DC-9 have been produced. About 900 are still in service today. The DC-9 can carry 90 to 172 passengers and has a range of from 1,000 miles to almost 1,500 miles. Their reliability and ease of maintenance make them a favorite with the smaller airlines.

The sixth and latest model of the DC-9 is the MD-80 series. This aircraft entered airline service in October 1980 as the first of the new, high technology jet airliners. The DC-9 Series 80 is 147 feet long, has a wingspan of 107 feet and can carry up to 172 passengers.

Air Cargo Carriers

It is important to understand that all of our major air carriers also fly a great deal of air freight in addition to their passengers, and they also have airplanes that are designed to carry only cargo. The important difference is that before the Airline Deregulation Act of 1978, the all-cargo carriers were prohibited from carrying passengers, and they still carry very few.

The all-cargo carriers fly a wide variety of cargoes— from livestock and machinery to fresh flowers and fruit. Their major market is a medium or long route where speed of delivery is of prime importance. They cannot compete with railroads or truck lines on short distances (under 500 miles) or for cargo where speed is not important. If time is not a factor, cargo will usually be shipped by rail or roadway.

The aircraft flown by all-cargo carriers have been modified to carry freight. They resemble jet airliners, but the seats have been removed and special cargo-handling equipment has been added. Although bulk cargo is carried, the carriers are increasingly, turning to containerized cargo. This means that loose cargo is packed into large containers, which are designed to fit the contours of the aircraft. These containers permit easier handling and reduce losses from theft. There are two basic all-freight aircraft operated by these carriers—the McDonnell-Douglas DC-10-30CF and the Boeing 747F. Some of the all-cargo carriers are flying the civilian version of the C-130 Hercules. They also are still flying some converted piston-engine aircraft such as DC-6s and even some DC-3s.

McDonnell-Douglas DC-10-30CF

This is a convertible passenger/freighter version of the DC-10 airliner. It can carry a payload of 155,000 pounds at 550 mph over a 4,000-mile range. The aircraft can be converted from full-cargo configuration to full-passenger configuration, or it can be part passenger and part cargo. There are about 35 of these DC-10s in service with the all-cargo carriers.

Boeing 747F

This is the giant of the air freight world. It is capable of carrying a payload of 200,000 pounds (100 tons) a distance of 3,500 miles at 575 mph. The nose section of the 747F is hinged so that it opens upward. This will allow straight-in loading of large cargo. The 747F has made possible the economic air transport of large pieces of cargo which previously had to go by rail. Bulldozers and other road-working equipment have been carried by air, and even small herds of livestock like sheep and cattle have been carried by air. When time is important, many companies now think nothing of shipping large cargo by air.

Boeing 747F

Regional/Commuter Carriers

The final group of air carriers we will discuss are the airlines that serve very small cities or cities with little air traffic. These commuter airlines came into existence in the 1960s. When the major carriers began buying larger jet-powered aircraft, they found they could not economically serve many of the small communities. In some cases, the airports in the small communities could not handle the heavier and faster jet aircraft. The Civil Aeronautics Board allowed the major carriers to leave these small cities to the commuter airlines. This ensures that the smaller communities will continue to have air service, but allows the larger carriers to get out of an unprofitable market.

The Airline Deregulation Act of 1978 was good for the regional-commuter carriers. As the larger airlines dropped their less profitable routes, the regionals moved in to provide service. Many of the commuter carriers that were in existence in 1978 have grown quite rapidly and many others have been formed. A recent occurrence is for the regionals to affiliate with one of the major carriers and serve smaller communities around one of the major carrier's large hubs. The commuter carrier is a regularly scheduled airline and must meet all FAA safety requirements.

The average trip length for commuter airlines is several hundred miles, and the average load is about 20 passengers. This means that the type of aircraft they use is different than other air carrier aircraft. In most cases, commuter aircraft are twin-engine (for safety reasons) aircraft. Many of the very small regional airplanes have reciprocating engines, rather than turboprop or jet engines, because jet fuel is not available at all of the airports they serve. Most of the large regionals fly turboprop aircraft.

As the regional airline market developed, the airlines found that they had to turn to foreign-built aircraft. The US aircraft manufacturers had spent all their time building larger aircraft. In 1986, Boeing Aircraft bought out DeHavilland of Canada and entered the turboprop manufacturing business.

Swearingen SA-266 Metro II

This aircraft was designed as a commuter airliner, and it offers the commuter passenger the same luxury as larger airliners. The Metro II can carry up to 20 passengers or 5,000 pounds of payload. It is pressurized and can cruise at 20,000 feet at 280 mph. The range of the Metro II is more than 500 miles, and it operates off runways as short as 3,000 feet.

Short-takeoff-and-landing (STOL) aircraft are also finding their way into the commuter fleet. Their advantage is that they can operate off very short (less than 2,000 feet) runways and even ones that are not paved.

Shorts SD-3-30 (England)

The Shorts SD-3-30 is a STOL aircraft and carries up to 30 passengers or 5,900 pounds of cargo. The twin-turboprop engines allow it to cruise at 185 mph over a 1,000-mile range. It can takeoff in as little as 1,800 feet.

Beechcraft 99

This is a twin-turboprop airliner, which can carry up to 15 passengers or 5,000 pounds of payload. It can operate off 2,000-foot runways. It cruises at about 250 mph and has a range of 400 to 500 miles. The B-99 is not pressurized so it cannot fly above 12,000 feet.

Dehavilland DHC-7 (Dash 7) (Canada)

One of the larger of the commuter aircraft, the Dash 7 is a four-engine turboprop aircraft that carries 50 passengers. The Dash 7 is a STOL aircraft, which can operate off very short runways. It has a range of up to 1,400 miles at 225 mph. Another attractive feature is the larger size of the passenger cabin. Whereas most commuter aircraft have two-abreast seating in a very small cabin, the Dash 7 has 6 feet 4 inches of stand-up headroom and a cabin width of 8 feet.

British Aerospace Company

British Aerospace of England manufactures three aircraft that are widely used by regional carriers. Two of them—BAE Jetstream 31 and the ATF—are twin-turboprop aircraft, and the third—the BAE 146 —is a four-engine, turbofan-powered aircraft. The Jetstream 31 is the smallest, carries 18 to 19 passengers, and has a range of 700 to 800 miles. The ATF carries 60 to 70 passengers and has a 1,000 mile range. The BAE 146 is manufactured in two series: the 100 carries 82 to 93 passengers and has a range of 1,000 to 2,000 miles, and the 200, which is larger, carries 109 passengers to about 1,500 miles.

Embraer (Brazil)

This South American Company builds two twin-engine turboprop aircraft used extensively by our regional carriers. The EMB 110 Bandeirante carries 21 passengers and has a 1,200-mile range. In 1985, Embraer brought out its larger EMB 120 Brasilia, which carries 30 passengers and has a range of 1,000 to 1,800 miles.

Fokker (Netherlands)

Historically, the Fokker Company is best known for World War I Axis fighter planes. Aviation historians have given the Fokker D-7 the honor of being the best aircraft to have been built in WWI. Manfried von Richthofen, the famous Red Baron, achieved much of his success in a Fokker Dr1 triplane.

In today's aviation world, the Fokker Company is dedicated to more peaceful pursuits. They are one of the premier builders of short-range commercial aircraft, most notably the F-27, the F-50 and their newer turbofan aircraft the F-28 and F-100.

The F-100 is the latest entry by Fokker and is a modern jet aircraft in every sense. It will carry 100 passengers and has a range of about 1,500 miles.

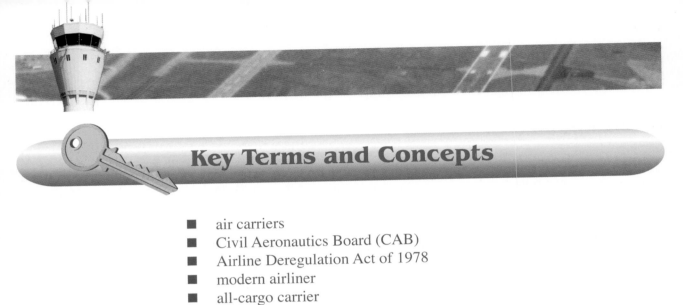

- air carriers
- Civil Aeronautics Board (CAB)
- Airline Deregulation Act of 1978
- modern airliner
- all-cargo carrier
- regional commuter carrier

? Test Your Knowledge ?

SELECT THE CORRECT ANSWER

1. The *(747/L-1011)* is the largest commercial airliner ever built.
2. The *(DC-10/A-300/727)* is also called the Airbus.
3. The *(DC-9/727/737)* was the most successful airliner ever built in terms of numbers.
4. **(Seventy/ninety)** percent of jet passengers fly on trips less than (2) hours in duration.

MATCHING

5. **Match the terms:**
   - a. *modern airliner*
   - b. *all-cargo carrier*
   - c. *regional-commuter carrier*

   (1) **smaller airlines that carry passengers in a limited geographical region**
   (2) **largest carriers in number of passengers carried**
   (3) **handle mainly freight, but now are allowed to carry passengers**

FILL IN THE BLANKS

6. All-cargo carriers are not competitive with railroads and truck lines for _____ _____ or where _____ is not important.

7. The big three U.S. manufacturers of passenger airliners are _____, _____ and _____.

8. Prior to 1978, the Civil Aeronautics Board (CAB) very strictly regulated _____ and _____ of the air carriers.

9. The average trip for _____ airlines is several hundred miles with an average load of _____ passengers.

TRUE OR FALSE

10. The Airline Deregulation Act of 1978 had more of an effect on air carriers since they were founded than any other piece of federal legislation.

11. Flying older aircraft and having non-union employees helped new airlines keep prices low to attract passengers away from the established airlines.

12. All major US aircraft manufacturers have multiple airplanes to serve the needs of regional airlines.

13. Since they are smaller, commuter carriers are not subject to the FAA safety requirements.

14. Most air cargo carriers fly freight versions of passenger airliners like the DC-10 or 747.

SHORT ANSWER

15. What do all air carriers have in common?

16. What was accomplished by the Airline Deregulation Act of 1978?

17. Why did the Airline Deregulation Act of 1978 affect the older airlines more significantly?

18. What is the name of the European aircraft consortium?

19. What are the advantages of containerized cargo for the all-cargo carriers?

GENERAL AVIATION

General aviation is defined as all civil aviation other than flying done by scheduled air carriers and government agencies. It is the largest segment of the aerospace industry. Very few people realize the size and importance of this branch of aerospace. There were over 190,000 civil aircraft in the United States in the late nineties. Of that number, nearly 10,000 civil aircraft were used as licensed air carriers.

There are over 633,000 certified pilots in the United States today. The aircraft they fly are categorized as: (1) instructional, (2) personal, (3) sport, (4) business and (5) commercial aviation.

bjectives

Define general aviation.
Name the five groups into which general aviation is separated.
Describe the typical instructional aircraft.
Discuss two basic trainer aircraft.
Describe the process of getting a private pilot certificate.
Describe the typical personal aircraft.
Define sport aviation.
List and describe the purposes of the seven divisions of sport aviation.

Instructional Aviation

The first category of general aviation, deals with aircraft used specifically to teach someone to fly. Whether a pilot is flying a Boeing 747, or just a small single-engine personal aircraft, entry-level flight training is a requirement.

A pilot usually learns to fly in general aviation or in the military. Instructional flying accounts for about 13 percent of all the hours flown in general aviation. In the late nineties, there were approximately 14,000 aircraft being used in flight training and a total of 4,500,000 hours were logged.

Ninety percent of all instructional aircraft are small single-engine airplanes. At most flight schools, you will currently find either Cessna 152s or 172s being used. Other company models, such as those built by Piper and Beechcraft, are used, but their current production is primarily focused on higher performance pleasure and business airplanes.

There are also opportunities for pilots who seek training in other aircraft types. These include multi engine reciprocating, turbopropeller-powered, turbojet-powered, helicopters, gliders, and hot air balloons.

Pilot Certification

An individual who wants to learn to fly will usually go to a certified flight instructor (CFI). The student's flight training includes both ground school (classroom work on various aspects of flying) and flight instruction (actually flying the aircraft). Prior to flying alone (solo), the student must acquire an FAA student pilot certificate by passing a standard FAA Class III Medical Examination, which is given by an FAA-designated medical doctor. This student certificate must be endorsed by the flight instructor prior to the first solo flight and again prior to the first solo cross-country flight. At some point in the training, the student must be certified by an instructor as being prepared to take the FAA written examination. This is the goal of ground school preparation. After passing the written examination and completing all flight requirements, the flight instructor recommends the student for a flight test, which is administered by a FAA-certified examiner. Successful completion of this flight test earns the coveted private pilot certificate. The pilot may then fly unsupervised and carry passengers—but not for hire.

A person interested in becoming a pilot has several options available. After completing the private pilot license, or certificate, there are several higher levels of training available. These include the commercial, the ATP (Air Transport Pilot), and flight instructor's certificate. Also, there are ratings that can be added to these certificates. For example, there is an instrument rating, a multi-engine rating, a rotorcraft rating, a glider rating, an airship rating, and a free balloon rating.

The majority of pilots have received their basic instruction in either Cessna or Piper aircraft. They are small, two-seat aircraft with small engines. They have a low cruising speed and are very easy to fly. These characteristics help develop confidence in the beginning student. The fact that they are also inexpensive to buy, operate, and maintain makes them attractive to flight schools.

One of the greatest training planes of all time, the Piper J-3 *(EAA)*

Cessna 152

This is the successful Cessna 152. Thousands of pilots have received their entry-level flight training in this aircraft.

This basic trainer went into production in 1978 to replace the well-established Cessna 150. It is 24 feet long, has a 33-foot wingspan and a maximum gross weight of 1,670 pounds. It is powered by a 110-horsepower Lycoming four-cylinder engine. At 8,000 feet and using 75 percent power, the Cessna 152 will cruise at 100 mph for about 650 miles. The fuel economy factor is 28 miles per gallon of fuel, which is excellent for an airplane.

Since World War II, a number of training aircraft have come and gone. Thousands of pilots received their licenses in airplanes like the Piper Cherokee 140, the Beechcraft Skipper, and Luscombe Silvaire. They were great little airplanes but for one reason or another, they were discontinued from the offerings of their companies.

During the 1970s and 1980s, threats of lawsuits plagued America's general aviation "entry level" flight training and many manufacturers considered two-place training airplanes to be too great a risk. However, the Cessna 150s, 152s, Piper Cherokee 140s, Piper Tomahawks, Beech Skippers and others are still being used by many flight schools despite their age. Can you imagine taking driver's education in a 1966 Chevy? In the world of general aviation flight training, however, that is exactly the case and these old airplanes just keep on flying and doing their job well!

If an individual wants to fly a multi-engine aircraft, he or she must get a multi-engine rating. This rating allows the pilot to fly only the type of multi-engine aircraft in which the instruction is received. To fly another type of multi-engine aircraft, the pilot must have that type aircraft added to his or her pilot certificate by taking additional instruction in that type aircraft.

Personal Aviation

Most people are surprised to learn that personal flying accounts for only 24 percent of all hours flown by general aviation aircraft. Generally, people think of all general aviation aircraft as small "puddle jumpers" being flown by an individual for fun or for personal transportation. The news media generally refers to private airplanes as all non-air carrier and non-military aircraft. This category of general aviation is the largest both in terms of the number of hours flown and the number of aircraft.

Personal aviation is the use of an aircraft for other than business or commercial use. It is often called private aviation, although this term is often misused by the news media. The private plane is used in the same way and for the same purposes as a private car. It may be used to carry the family on a vacation, to take friends to a football game, or just for the fun and relaxation of flying. The thing to remember is that you cannot tell a personal aircraft from any other type of general aviation aircraft just by looking at it. The only difference is in its use.

From the early 1920s until the beginning of the 1980s, names like Cessna, Beechcraft and Piper were synonymous with general aviation. The vast majority of all the general aviation aircraft flying anywhere in the world were manufactured in the United States. Most of them were built by Cessna, Piper and Beech Aircraft, and were built before 1980.

The Air Force Academy T-41

Beech Aircraft Company

Beech produced six aircraft models that fit into our definition of the typical personal aircraft. All of them are all-metal, low-wing monoplanes. As an example, let's take a look at the Bonanza F33. Of the six, only the Bonanza is still in production.

The Bonanza F33 is a descendant of one of the most recognizable of all aircraft, the V-tail Bonanza. The Bonanza F33 has a 285-horsepower Continental engine and a constant-speed propeller. The tricycle gear is retractable. It has a large 1,300-pound payload and is fast (150 to 200 mph). It also has a long range (800 to 1,000-miles). The Bonanza is a very reliable airplane and can be equipped with many options including an autopilot. Many consider it the finest single-engine, fixed-wing aircraft built today.

Beechcraft are prestigious aircraft and, like prestigious automobiles, have a great deal of standard equipment.

The Beechcraft Bonanza *(EAA)*

Cessna Aircraft Company

The Cessna Aircraft Company produced eight different models of the four-place personal aircraft. All of them are high-wing monoplanes and are among the most successful airplanes in the aviation industry.

They are the only all-metal, high-wing aircraft manufactured in the United States. Their "home base" is Wichita, Kansas, which is sometimes referred to as the "Air Capital of the World."

Cessna has been building aircraft since 1927 and is the world's largest manufacturer of general aviation airplanes. It has produced a total of 179,000 aircraft. However, production of all entry-level aircraft ceased in 1986. In the 90's, Cessna once again started manufacturing the 172 Skyhawk and 182 Skylane aircraft.

The Cessna 172 Skyhawk has a 160-horsepower Lycoming engine and a fixed-pitch propeller. It also has fixed (non-retractable) landing gear. The Skyhawk has a payload of

Cessna 172 Skyhawk

950 pounds, a cruising speed of 116 to 135 mph and a maximum cruising range of 695 miles. This was the best selling of all Cessna aircraft and the one most often purchased as a "first" aircraft.

The Cutlass RG was the least expensive retractable-landing-gear aircraft offered by Cessna. The retractable landing gear reduces drag, thus increasing performance. The Cutlass has a 1,120-pound payload and the 180-horsepower Lycoming engine provides a cruising speed of 139 to 161 mph. The maximum cruising range is 967 miles.

The Cessna 185 Skywagon is a "tail dragger." You will notice in the figure that the Skywagon has

Cessna's venerable Skywagon

its main landing gear set more forward than the other aircraft. Also, in place of the nosewheel the Skywagon has a tailwheel. This arrangement causes the Skywagon to sit on the runway with its nose high, whereas tricycle-gear aircraft sit level. This nose-high attitude makes it more difficult to see straight ahead while taxiing the aircraft; however, taildraggers have other advantages. The Skywagon has a 300-horsepower Continental

engine which gives it a cruising speed of 130 to 170 mph and a maximum range of 750 miles.

The 210 Centurion was a "top of the line" in Cessna personal aircraft. The Centurion is powered by a 300-horsepower Continental engine, which drives a three-bladed, constant-speed propeller. It has a 1,650-pound payload and a maximum range of 1,250 miles. The Centurion cruises at 175 to 193 mph. For those who can afford it, the Centurion is probably the roomiest and most comfortable four-place aircraft built in the United States.

Mooney Aircraft Company

The Mooney 201 is an all-metal, low-wing aircraft with a retractable tricycle landing gear. It has a payload of about 1,000 pounds and a 1,100-mile range. The Mooney 201 is powered by a 200-horsepower Avco Lycoming engine, which gives it a cruising speed of 160 to 190 mph. There's an interesting bit of trivia about Mooney. At one point in their manufacturing history, they produced an airplane that had a Porsche engine in it!

The Mooney 201

Piper Aircraft Company

Piper Aircraft Company has been building airplanes since 1929; although prior to 1937, it was known as the Taylor (Brothers) Aircraft Company. Throughout the years, Piper has had a reputation for reliability and simplicity. Piper is one of the "big three" of general aviation. At one time, Piper manufactured nine models of personal aircraft. They were all-metal, low-wing monoplanes. Today, it produces six piston-engine aircraft under the name of the New Piper Airplane Company.

One of Piper's most popular aircraft is the Arrow. It has a 200-horsepower Lycoming engine and a cruising speed of 142 to 165 mph. The payload for the Arrow IV is 1,125 pounds and the maximum range is 850 miles.

The exotic Piper Malibu is a six-place aircraft that was introduced in 1983. The Malibu holds several single-engine speed records including Oakland, California, to Honolulu, Hawaii, with an average speed of 200.2 mph. The Malibu is powered by a 310-horsepower Continental turbocharged engine and is pressurized to fly at altitudes up to 25,000 feet. Its cruising speed at optimum altitude is 250 mph, and has a range of up to 1,700 miles.

Piper PA-18 Super Cub was first offered in 1949. This makes it a record holder for the longest continuously produced airplane in American aviation history. There have been over 40,000 Super

Cubs produced since it was introduced, and Piper still builds the Super Cub, but only on special order. The Super Cub is the only high-wing aircraft manufactured by Piper and is also the only fabric covered one. The latest Super Cubs are equipped with 150-horsepower Lycoming engines. The first model was powered by a 90-horsepower Continental. It is a small, two-place airplane that cruises at 105 to 115 mph and has a 460-mile range.

The New Piper Archer III

Sport Aviation

Sport aviation is often called "flying for fun." It is basically flying for some purpose other than transportation or business. Some people do it as a hobby, some for relaxation, some for competition (racing) and some for the thrill of it (aerobatics). Whatever their motive, sport aviators comprise a small but enthusiastic segment of aviation.

Sport aviation is generally broken down into the following divisions: (1) homebuilts, (2) ballooning, (3) soaring and gliding, (4) antique aviation, (5) racing, (6) aerobatics (stunt flying) and (7) ultralights. With the exception of ultralights, all other forms of sport aviation require the pilot to have at least a private pilot certificate.

Homebuilts

This phase of sport aviation combines the love of flying with the hands-on hobbies of woodworking, fabrics, welding, metal working and composite construction. In this endeavor, the pilot actually builds the airplane either from a kit or from a set of plans. For many, the incentive is that they can become an airplane owner by building their own aircraft much more cheaply than by buying one. They can also build an airplane that is sportier looking than a factory-built airplane, or they can even build a replica of a famous "warbird." The prices vary from only a few hundred dollars for the plans to complete kits costing well over $100,000. A variety of engines are available from two-stroke to modified automotive 4s, V-6s, V-8s and custom built V-12s.

The FFP Classic

This homebuilt airplane was constructed by a group of advanced aeronautics students at Littleton High School, Littleton, Colorado.

A homebuilt aircraft must pass FAA inspections, and it is certificated in a special category as an experimental aircraft. In order to qualify for the special certificate, 51 percent or more of the fabrication must be done by the homebuilder. One major consideration of homebuilding is the commitment of time. It is not uncommon for an airplane to take 5 years to complete. Too often, many projects are abandoned because of the time involved.

Ballooning

In the past few years, many sport aviators have turned to hot-air ballooning for recreation. These aircraft include the large envelope (gasbag), which is usually made of polyester and a basket suspended under the envelope. The basket carries the passengers, flight instruments, propane gas and the burners that keep the envelope inflated.

The envelope is inflated first by using a large fan to blow air into the round opening at the bottom of the envelope. After the envelope has air in it, the burner is lighted and the hot propane flame heats the air inside. To make the balloon rise, the air is heated more. To make the balloon descend, the burner is shut off allowing the air inside to cool down. For more rapid descents, there is a vent shaped like a parachute, in the top of the envelope. This allows a large volume of hot air to escape.

The balloons are equipped with an altimeter, rate-of-climb indicator, envelope temperature gauge and compass. They also have a two-way radio for communications with the ground.

Balloon enthusiasts believe this is the ultimate in aviation sport. Balloons are carried along by the wind, and the pilot controls the direction by finding winds blowing in different directions at various altitudes.

Soaring and Gliding

There is a group of aviators who fly unpowered sailplanes. Their sport is often called soaring or gliding, but there is a big difference between the two. Gliding is the controlled descent of an unpowered aircraft while soaring is flying without engine power and without loss of altitude. If a sailplane is towed up to altitude and after release it descends to a landing, that is gliding. Similarly, if a person with a hang glider jumps from a high place and descends to a landing, that is gliding. Soaring, on the other hand, involves finding and riding air currents so that the aircraft remains aloft or even gains altitude.

A hot air balloon takes off from the Montgolfier Balloon Port near Denver, Colorado.

Soaring is a well-organized and competitive sport. There are soaring meets with prizes given for highest altitude, longest-duration and longest-distance flights. This aspect of sport aviation is much more popular and much larger in number of pilots soaring in Europe than in the United States.

Sailplanes are necessarily very lightweight. They must produce a great deal of lift at relatively low speeds in order to remain airborne. For lightness, most competitive sailplanes are constructed of aluminum tubing or wood, covered with fabric or fiberglass over a foam-sandwich material.

The TG-4A sailplane was used to train Air Force Academy cadets.

For many years, the best competitive sailplanes came from Europe, but now the United States is manufacturing a few which match the best of the Europeans. Schweizer Aircraft Corporation is the leading US manufacturer. They build training sailplanes, family sailplanes, and medium- to high-performance competitive sailplanes. Two examples are the SGS 2-33A and the SGS 1-35. The SGS 2-33A is a two-place training and family sailplane. This 600-pound aircraft is only 26 feet long and has a 51-foot wingspan. Its fuselage is fabric with a fiberglass nose, and it has an all-aluminum wing.

There are about five other sailplane manufacturers in the United States. They produce quality sailplanes both in kit form and as factory-produced aircraft.

Antique Aviation

This segment of sport aviation involves either finding and restoring a vintage aircraft or building replicas of old airplanes from original plans. This phase of sport aviation attracts the same type of people who collect antique automobiles, furniture and other items. They want to preserve these pieces of the past because they are irreplaceable.

In order to qualify as an antique, an aircraft must be at least 20 years old. This area of sport aviation is very expensive and generally attracts people from the higher-income levels. When restoring an old aircraft, it is often impossible to obtain the parts you need, so they have to be handmade. For example,

Antique Airplane *(EAA)*

One of the great warbird trainers,
the Consoldated Vultee BT-13 *(EAA)*

to restore a Piper J-3 Cub may cost $20,000 in addition to the $3,000 to $5,000 purchase price. Some of the very rare aircraft can easily cost over $100,000.

The warbirds aviation buffs collect, restore, and fly aircraft that served during times of conflict. These include World War I, World War II, Korea, Vietnam and Desert Storm.

Some of the most popular are the P-40, P-51 Mustang, P-47 Thunderbolt, AT-6 Texan, Supermarine Spitfire, Hawker Hurricane, Messerschmitt Bf l09 and Mitsubishi A6M Zero. This phase of antique aviation is fast becoming the most expensive of all. In 1961, a person could buy a P-51 for about $1,500. Today, the cost can easily exceed one million dollars. They are becoming scarce, their parts are hard to find and labor costs to work on them are skyrocketing.

Racing

Each year the National Championship Air Races are held in Reno, Nevada. This is a pylon race where the airplanes race around markers (pylons), with the racers flying about 50 to 200 feet above the ground. The low altitude and high speeds put a great strain on the aircraft and the pilots.

The racing aircraft are classified according to size and power. The unlimited class is made up of World War II fighter aircraft, and they will race at speeds in excess of 400 mph. The other categories include the AT-C (which is limited to AT-6 aircraft only) and the Formula One category. The Formula One racers are small single-place (20-foot wingspan, weighing about 850 pounds) aircraft, powered by small 100-horsepower engines. They reach speeds of over 200 mph when racing.

Aerobatics

The most familiar aspect of sport aviation is the air show with all its special flying events. The main event in these air shows is aerobatics, which used to be called stunt flying. This activity is too precise to be called stunting now, especially when a team performs the aerobatic maneuvers. More truthfully, it should be called precision flying.

Aerobatic flying requires aircraft that can withstand tremendous forces and that can fly upside down, right side up, and everything in between. It also requires a particularly skillful pilot. The pilot must have very good vision and distance judgment, and must be able to think and react calmly while under a great deal of pressure. Many of the best aerobatic pilots in the world are women.

Aerobatic Biplane

Some of the maneuvers seen during a typical aerobatic performance are loops, the hammerhead stall, rolls, Cuban 8s, the Immelmann, spins and the splits.

Some of the aerobatic aircraft used by pilots in the United States are the Bellanca Citabria and the Cessna 150 Aerobat, both production-models. Also, many US pilots use several smaller biplanes, like the Pitts Special.

Ultralights

These small, lightweight aircraft began as powered hang gliders. Ultralight pilots feel that this is the only area of powered flight with the freedom to fly whenever and wherever one desires. Ultralight aircraft do not require FAA certification and pilots do not need a license or medical examination.

In the 1970s, ultralights were all "foot-launched." This meant that the aircraft was picked up and launched by running along the runway with it until flying speed was attained. These early ultralights had no landing gear, but today many have wheels.

Power plants for ultralights must be small and lightweight because of the weight restrictions involved. Ultralights are relatively inexpensive ($5,000 to $20,000) and are available either assembled or in kit form.

In this chapter, we have discussed three areas of general aviation—instructional, personal and sport. These three areas involve learning to fly and the fun activities in aviation. In the next chapter, we will talk about general aviation, which is directly or indirectly related to business.

Ultralight Aircraft

Fisher Flying Product FP202 Ultralight

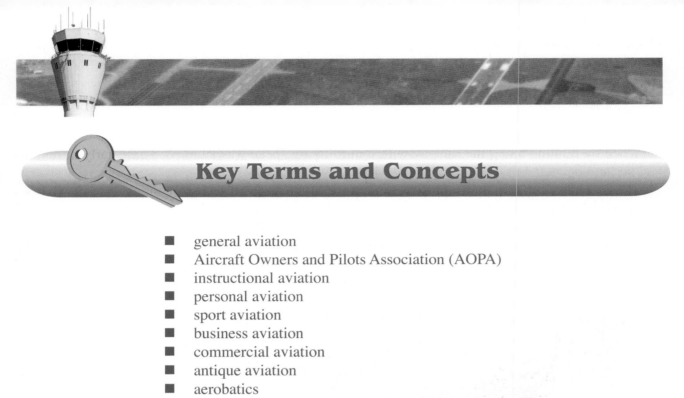

- general aviation
- Aircraft Owners and Pilots Association (AOPA)
- instructional aviation
- personal aviation
- sport aviation
- business aviation
- commercial aviation
- antique aviation
- aerobatics
- ultralights

? Test Your Knowledge ?

SELECT THE CORRECT ANSWER

1. **(Ultralights/Antique aircraft)** *are relatively inexpensive, ranging from $5,000 to $20,000.*
2. **(Beech/ Cessna/ Piper)** *is the largest manufacturer of general aviation aircraft in the world.*
3. *Homebuilt aircraft must pass* **(FAA inspections/AOPA inspections)** *and then it is certified as a/an* **(homebuilt aircraft/experimental aircraft)**.

FILL IN THE BLANKS

4. _____ *is defined as all civil aviation other than flying done by the scheduled air carriers and government agencies.*
5. *Just over 20 percent of general aviation is* _____ *while almost 80 percent is either directly or indirectly* _____ .
6. *Ninety percent of the instructional aircraft are* _____ .
7. *The two companies with the most name recognition in personal and trainer aircraft are* _____ *and* _____ .

8. Fill in the blanks with the names of the divisions of sport aviation:

_____Use small, light weight aircraft requiring no license

_____Involves finding and riding air currents to remain aloft

_____Aircraft includes the gasbag, basket, instrument, burner, propane

_____Contest where planes fly around pylons

_____Involves the controlled descent of unpowered aircraft

_____Should really be called precision demonstration flying

_____The pilot actually constructs their own aircraft

_____Involves restoring vintage airplanes or building replicas of them

TRUE OR FALSE

9. Flight training is a highly competitive business and manufacturers provide considerable assistance.

10. One of the incentives of homebuilts is that you can become an aircraft owner for substantially less money.

11. Racing aircraft are classified according to size and power.

12. Soaring is more popular in the US than in Europe.

13. The lift for balloons is provided by heating helium.

SHORT ANSWER

14. List the five groups of general aviation

15. Describe the typical instructional aircraft.

16. Describe the typical personal aircraft.

17. What are some of the reasons given to enjoy sport aviation?

BUSINESS AND COMMERCIAL AVIATION

This category of general aviation is one of the largest in terms of hours flown. Business aviation is the use of a private- or company-owned general aviation aircraft for business purposes. Business aviation is usually divided into two groups according to who is flying the aircraft. If an individual personally pilots an aircraft used by a business in which he or she is engaged, it is classified as a business aircraft. If, on the other hand, a professional pilot flies a company or corporate aircraft to transport employees and/or property, the airplane is classed as an executive aircraft.

The executive aircraft is usually larger and more luxurious than the business aircraft. The majority are multi-engine and one-third are jet powered. In general, they are used to carry very important people over medium-length distances in comfort and at relatively high speeds. To these people, time means money and getting them to their destination in the minimum amount of time is very important.

There are over 55,000 aircraft in the business aviation category. The vast majorities of the business aircraft are single-engine piston aircraft. About 33 percent of the executive aircraft are either turboprop or turbojet powered. In the business aircraft category, only about one percent are turbine powered.

Looking at these figures, there are some generalizations that can be made. A typical executive transport is a twin-engine aircraft and is almost as likely to be turbine powered as piston powered. These types of aircraft are in areas where the pilot must have special training, a multi-engine rating and at least a commercial license. If the aircraft is turbine powered, another rating is required.

These executive aircraft are also very expensive, as we shall see later. On the other hand, the typical business aircraft is almost certain to be piston powered and is three times as likely to have a single engine as twin engines.

The typical business aircraft is similar to the typical personal aircraft in that it is a single-engine, four-place airplane. However, the business aircraft is probably better equipped. Because it is important in some businesses to be able to fly even in bad weather, the typical business airplane is well-equipped with instruments. Almost all business aircraft pilots are instrument rated.

There are three areas of concern in aviation today, and they play an important part in the decision of which aircraft to buy for use in a business. These three areas are (1) fuel efficiency, (2) noise and (3) cost effectiveness.

Raytheon Premier I and Hawker Horizon *(Courtesy of Raytheon)*

bjectives

Define business aviation.

Describe the two categories of business aviation.

Describe a typical business aircraft and a typical executive aircraft.

State the importance of fuel efficiency, noise and cost effectiveness as they apply to business aviation.

Identify at least two business aircraft.

Identify at least two executive aircraft that are piston powered, two that are turboprop powered and two that are turbojet powered.

Define commercial aviation.

Describe the two subdivisions of commercial aviation.

Differentiate between air taxis and rental aircraft.

Discuss six different non-transportation areas of commercial aviation.

Fuel Efficiency

The cost of aviation fuel has increased by 700 percent since 1973. It is possible that it will become necessary to cut petroleum use to avoid a major shortage in future years. The increase in fuel costs and possible fuel shortages have forced businesses to buy the most fuel-efficient aircraft available. These restrictions have also forced the aircraft industry to build more economical engines and more efficient wings and airframes to get more mileage out of each drop of fuel. Beech Aircraft Company has also looked at alternative fuels for general aviation aircraft. In 1982, they converted a Sundowner to burn liquefied natural gas as a fuel.

In determining fuel efficiency, it is necessary to look at airplanes a little differently than automobiles. With the family car, the only figure we are concerned with is miles per gallon. The Federal Government is forcing the automobile manufacturers to increase the miles per gallon their automobiles achieve.

Of course, many small cars, both foreign and domestic, get much better mileage. Many small cars claim more than 40 miles per gallon. This is possible because the cars weigh less and have smaller engines. Weight and size (horsepower) affect mileage. We also know that speed affects mileage in automobiles. The faster we drive, the more fuel we burn.

All of these things, weight, engine size and speed, also affect the fuel efficiency of the airplane. The main reason for using an airplane for business is to save time. If a business airplane can get executives to a business meeting faster than the commercial airlines, the money saved in terms of salaries justifies the travel.

In figuring the fuel efficiency of an airplane, the distance, number of passengers and amount of fuel used are all considered. For example, if an airplane carrying four people (pilot plus three passengers) flew 250 miles and burned 30 gallons of fuel, the mileage would be 33.3 passenger miles per gallon (250 x 4/30 = 33.3).

Noise

The Federal Government placed limitations on the amount of engine noise an aircraft can produce. Many communities close their airports to jets at night. These restrictions are for environmental reasons and are getting more severe. The aircraft manufacturers are building quieter jets, and many businesses are turning to these quiet aircraft.

Cost Effectiveness

In the past, many businesses bought aircraft based on speed plus the length of the longest trip their employees traveled. This led to aircraft that were underutilized. For example, if a company makes only one 2,000-mile trip a year and all the rest are only 300 miles, that company really doesn't need an airplane with a 2,000-mile range. It would be better to buy an airplane with a 500-mile range (which would be cheaper) and use the airlines for the 2,000-mile trip. For instance, a twin-engine turboprop aircraft can make a 500-mile flight in 2 hours 15 minutes, while a turbojet can make the same flight in 1 hour 50 minutes. The turbojet saves 25 minutes on the flight. However, it costs a great deal more to buy and it burns 600 gallons more fuel on the trip. Is the saving of 25 minutes worth the additional cost? Many businesses are starting to look more closely at these things.

Let's compare some of the aircraft used in business aviation. For our discussion, we will look at executive aircraft and business aircraft separately.

Executive Aircraft

The executive aircraft market is a very competitive business. Many manufacturers, both US and foreign, are building high-quality aircraft to meet the needs of today's corporations. To get some idea of the importance of airplanes in business today, let's look at some figures compiled by the National Business Aircraft Association (NBAA) in 1996.

Of the Fortune 500 companies in the United States, 335 had at least one aircraft. That's twice as many as those without aircraft. Sales of all Fortune 500 aircraft operators were $4.1 trillion, while sales of non-operators totaled $900 billion. Operators collectively had over $8.4 trillion in assets, non-operators' assets only totaled $3.2 trillion. The net income of all operators was $261 billion, non-operators' total income was $40 billion.

The results of this survey were obvious. The largest and most successful of the US corporations own and operate a sizable fleet of very expensive aircraft. Since these companies are very cost conscious, they must have determined that business aviation helps them make money.

Earlier, we said that the typical executive aircraft is a twin-engine aircraft and nearly as many are turbine powered as are piston powered. In our discussion here, we will cover the larger, multi-engine piston aircraft. We will discuss the twins that are turbocharged and pressurized, as well as the turboprop aircraft and turbojet executive aircraft. The single-engine aircraft and smaller twins will be covered under the business aircraft section.

Multi-engine Piston Aircraft. The two largest aircraft in this category are the Beechcraft Duke B-60 and the Cessna 421C Golden Eagle III. Both of these aircraft are out of production, but several thousand were built. Both carry six passengers in addition to the pilot. The performance of the two aircraft is very similar. Two 380-horsepower engines power the Duke, while the Golden Eagle III's

Cessna 421 Golden Eagle

Cessna 340

engines are rated at 375 horsepower each. The Golden Eagle III will takeoff a little quicker than the Duke and has about a 100-mile-longer range.

To fly a 500-mile flight under identical conditions, both of these aircraft would burn about 75 gallons of fuel each. With a pilot and five passengers on board, this figures out to be 40 passenger miles per gallon. Some of the other pressurized, turbocharged twins are the Beech Baron 58, the Aerostar 602P, and the Cessna 414, 340A and T337G Skymaster.

All of these aircraft carry a pilot and five passengers except the Skymaster, which carries one less passenger. Each aircraft differs slightly from the others, and each will suit the needs of certain customers.

There are many fine turbocharged-, twin-, and piston-engine aircraft that are not pressurized. The only disadvantages to these unpressurized aircraft are in passenger comfort and speed. The unpressurized aircraft cannot fly as high as pressurized ones and this means a bumpier ride. Also, the unpressurized aircraft causes more ear discomfort when climbing and descending

Cessna produced three aircraft (303T, 402C and 404) in this class, Piper built six (Turbo Seminole, Seneca III Aerostar 600S, Navajo C/R, Chieftain), and Beech had one (Baron 58TC).

Within this class of twins, the Piper Commuter is the largest, carrying a pilot and 10 passengers. The Cessna Titan and Piper Chieftain both carry nine passengers in addition to the pilot, and the Navajo C/R and 402C both carry a pilot and seven passengers. The remainders, except for the Turbo Seminole, are designed to carry a pilot and five passengers.

The Turbo Seminole carries four passengers including the pilot. We should mention that these are maximum passenger

Beech Baron 58

loads and if this many passengers are carried, the baggage and fuel loads are limited. Care must be taken with all these twins not to overload them because they will not carry a full load of passengers, plus baggage and/or fuel. Of course, the manufacturer will customize the interior of the aircraft to meet the customers' needs. Many only have two seats and a couch for seating, but may also have a galley and a lavatory.

Turboprops. The next step above the largest piston twin is the turboprop twin. The big difference between them is in the power plants. The largest piston twins have engines of about 375 to 400 horsepower. The turboprops have engines rated as high as 850 horsepower. This increase in horsepower offers two advantages, the aircraft can be larger and fly faster. This is the major selling point for the turboprop executive aircraft.

It isn't until you get beyond the range of the piston-engine twins that the turboprops begin cutting time off trips. It will actually take a turboprop a little longer to make a 500-mile trip than a piston-engine twin. This is because it takes longer to climb to the higher cruising altitude of the turboprop. However, on a trip of 1,000 miles, the turboprop will save a lot of time because the piston-engine twin will have to stop for refueling.

On the other hand, the price of a turboprop is much higher; in most cases, nearly three times as much as the most expensive pressurized twin. They will have to decide if there are enough long trips with several passengers to justify the additional expense of a turboprop.

Some of the twin-engine turboprop aircraft are large enough that they are widely used by the commuter airlines. We have already discussed them in the chapter dealing with air carriers. Here, we will be dealing only with those twin turboprop aircraft that carry 15 or fewer passengers. The following chart shows a comparison of several turboprop executive aircraft as to size, engines and range.

The Swearingen Merlin IVA is the largest of the turboprop executive aircraft, closely followed by the Beech Kingair BE300. Both of these are available with either commuter-type seating or in executive versions with plush interiors. The Piper Cheyenne also fits into this class and claims to be quieter and smoother than other turboprops.

Some of the less expensive turboprops, such as the Piper Cheyenne II or the Beech Kingair C90A, are not as plush inside. They are almost as fast and cost hundreds of thousands dollars less.

The newest and the most radical of the turboprop executive aircraft is the Beechcraft Starship 1. It is built entirely of composite materials using a design by Mr. Burt Rutan (builder of the Voyager aircraft). Its twin, turboprop pusher engines are mounted at the rear of the wings, and the aircraft is equipped with a canard on the nose. The Starship will carry 8 to 11 passengers, fly at more than 300 mph and has a range of about 1,500 miles. In addition to being constructed of composites, the Starship will use the latest technology in its avionics, including digital instrumentation and CRT displays.

Turbojets. These aircraft are often called bizjets, or corporate jets, and are the top-of-the-line for executive aircraft. The chart in the figure on turboprops above shows the performance and the price of the bizjets both are high. A corporate jet is expensive to buy

TURBOPROP, TWIN ENGINE			
NAME OF AIRCRAFT	SEATS	CRUISING SPEED (MPH)	MAX RANGE (MILES)
Beechcraft Kingair C90A	6-10	250	1,500
Beechcraft Kingair B200	8-15	300	2,700
Beechcraft Kingair BE300	8-15	275	2,000
Piper Cheyenne III	9-11	315	2,330
Sweringen Merlin IVC	13-16	305	2,500
BAe Jetstream 31	9-18	260	1,600
Beechcraft Starship 1	8-11	330	1,500

TURBOJET, TWIN ENGINE EXCEPT (3)			
NAME OF AIRCRAFT	SEATS	CRUISING SPEED (MPH)	MAX RANGE (MILES)
Canadair Challenger	11-28	485	4,400
Cessna Citation III	8-10	460	3,000
Dassault Falcon 200	10-12	470	3,000
Dassault Falcon 50 (3)	12-14	480	4,800
Gates Learjet 35A	10-12	480	3,000
Gates Learjet 55A	12	480	3,500
Gulfstream IV	22	500	5,000
BAe 800	8-14	490	3,200
Israel Westwind 1	7-10	460	3,000
Beechcraft BE-400	10	435	2,300

Kingair C90A *(Beechcraft photo)*

and to operate. Even the smallest bizjet will burn over 100 gallons of fuel per hour and larger ones can burn almost 300 gallons per hour. However, remember during that hour you may be carrying 10 people over 400 miles. In order to justify owning a corporate jet, it is usually agreed that a company would have to fly more than 135,000 miles per year. This amounts to about 300 hours of flying per year, or 25 hours per month.

Beechcraft Starship 1

In the turbojet area, Gates Learjet leads all other manufacturers in numbers of aircraft. Their production at the end of 1987 totaled nearly 1,600 aircraft. In 1981, Gates Learjet introduced a new series called the Learjet 55. The 55B can be recognized by the vertical winglets at the tips of the wings. These winglets reduce drag and enhance thrust, thereby improving the aircraft's performance. The 55 series has been certificated to operate at 51,000 feet, the highest altitude of any business or executive jet. Grumman has also incorporated the winglets into their Gulfstream III and IV, as has Israel Aircraft in its Westwind 2.

There is quite a bit of difference in the amount of room inside the cabin of the various business/ executive jets. In most of them, the dimensions are about 5 feet wide by a little over 4 feet high. You can see that it would be very difficult to get up and walk around in a cabin this size. There are some that are considerably more roomy, and the trend seems to be toward larger cabins. The Gulfstream has a cabin that is over 7 feet wide and over 6 feet high. The Israel Westwind series

Gates Learjet

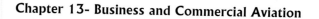

is also over 6 feet high and 6 feet wide, as is the Learjet Longhorn series. Of course, to be larger on the inside, the aircraft has to be larger on the outside, as well as heavier. This leads to larger engines and more fuel consumption. The result is that you have two classes of business/executive jets small (Learjet, Citation, etc.) and large (Gulfstream, Jetstar, etc.). The cost of the aircraft also goes up as the size increases.

Beechjet

Cessna Citation

With today's emphasis on ecology and pollution, another important feature in turbojet aircraft is noise. The FAA has established maximum noise levels, which all jet aircraft had to comply with by 1990.

Another consideration when buying a business/executive jet is the length of available runways. The shorter the takeoff and landing distance, the more airports available to you. Here again, the Cessna Citation leads the field. It is able to take off and land in less distance than others in its class.

Canadair is no more although it lives on as an initial in Bombardier's CRJ regional jets.

The Canadair Challenger began as a project for an advanced-technology bizjet by William Lear, developer of the Learjet. It was then called the Lear Star 600. Canadair Limited purchased the production rights from Lear, renamed the aircraft the Challenger and began production of the prototype in 1976.

The Challenger was the first production aircraft to use supercritical wings. The latest high-bypass turbofan engines power it. The engines (Avco Lycoming ALF 502) produce 7,500 pounds of thrust, giving the 40,000-pound aircraft the highest thrust for its weight of any bizjet.

These innovations allow this aircraft to takeoff quicker, climb faster, fly farther and have better fuel efficiency than any aircraft in its class. The Cessna Citation III is the latest model of the popular Citation jets. It is considerably larger than earlier Citations, being more than 8 feet longer and weighing 7,000 pounds more than the Citation II. The Citation III has supercritical wings and a 3,650-pound-thrust turbofan engine. It is similar in size and performance to the Learjet 55, but it has more range, burns less fuel at normal cruise speed and costs more than $1 million less than the 55.

Beech Aircraft bought the Mitsubishi Diamond Jet Corporation. They sold the Diamond Jet aircraft under the name of Beechjet BE-400. The Beechjet 400, after Raytheon bought the line and mixed it in with the Hawker line, is now called the Hawker 400.

Business Aircraft

As we mentioned earlier, 78 percent of all business aircraft are single- and piston-engine aircraft and another 21 percent are twin- and piston-engine aircraft. We mentioned many of the single-engine aircraft in the section which dealt with personal aviation and will not repeat them here. Any of the single-engine aircraft manufactured by Beech, Cessna, Piper, Mooney, Rockwell, Grumman, Bellanca, etc., can be and are used as business aircraft. In this section, we will deal with only one single-engine aircraft, the Piper Malibu. We mention it because it is a single-engine aircraft built in the United States, which is pressurized. The remainder of our discussion will deal with twin- and piston-engine aircraft and will be limited to the smaller, unpressurized and non-turbocharged twins.

The Piper Malibu is powered by a turbocharged, 310-horsepower piston engine. It can cruise at 248 mph at an altitude of 20,000 feet using 75 percent power. This altitude places the pressurized Malibu above most weather.

Business Twins. The light twin aircraft offers two advantages to the business person. First is the peace of

The New Piper Malibu Mirage

mind the second engine adds to the reliability of the aircraft. However, the pilot must be aware of the single-engine capability of the aircraft and not overload the aircraft. Second, the light twin will carry more payload at only a slightly higher cost than the heavy single-engine aircraft. The fuel efficiency of the twin will be almost the same as a single when all seats are full.

Remember, in most business aircraft, the business person is also the pilot. So, if the aircraft is listed as a six-place aircraft, this includes the pilot. Many times, a business person may not want to carry this many passengers. He or she may want to carry cargo instead. In this case, he or she can remove the seats and carry as much as 1,000 pounds of payload, or in some cases more.

Helicopters. Although there are several different types in service, most are Bell 206 Jet Rangers and McDonnell-Douglas 500Ds. Business and executive helicopters have the same advantages as helicopters in general. They can takeoff and land from a small area rather than from a large airport. This is attractive to some companies, particularly if they have several plants within a few hundred miles of each other. The range and speed of a helicopter are very limited when compared to other executive aircraft, and if the helicopter has to land at a regular airport, it loses its advantage over conventional aircraft. However, if a helicopter pad is available at both the origin and the destination, a helicopter will save time over any conventional aircraft built on flights up to 250 miles.

Commercial Aviation

This is another term that causes a lot of confusion. Many people immediately think of the air carriers (airlines) when they hear the term commercial aviation. This is because the air carriers have been called commercial airlines for years. Remember, air carriers (commercial airlines) carry passengers or cargo for hire on a scheduled basis. Commercial aviation is a segment of general aviation, which deals with using general aviation aircraft for hire as a commercial (money making) business. The secret words here are "for hire."

Commercial aviation is subdivided into two groups. Aircraft that produce income by transporting people or cargo on demand (air taxi/charter) and those that generate income with no transportation function involved.

Transportation

Air taxis and charter services provide transportation on a nonscheduled or demand basis. People needing to travel to a city not served by an air carrier and needing to get there in a hurry can go to the local airport and hire an aircraft and a pilot to fly them there. Most of the air taxi customers are business people who cannot afford to own their own aircraft, but need to get somewhere in a hurry. There is also some emergency transportation.

A company may need to get a part to one of its plants in a hurry or a medical patient may need to get to a hospital, so time is an important factor. These would be considered air taxi or charter operations. There are special FAA regulations which govern these operations. The pilot must have at least a

commercial pilot certificate and an instrument rating. The aircraft must have special instrumentation to allow it to fly in bad weather. The aircraft must also comply with special safety regulations.

Depending on the distance to be flown, the size of the load, the time factor and weather conditions, an air taxi may be as small and as simple as a Piper Cherokee or as large and as complex as a Gates Learjet. Helicopters are also used as air taxis. Many of these helicopters are used to transfer people and supplies to and from the offshore oil-drilling platforms. Before helicopters were available, this transportation was done by boat and many hours were required for each trip. Now it only takes a few minutes. This becomes very important during hurricane season when it is necessary to evacuate the platforms quickly.

Rental aircraft are sometimes included in the commercial aviation category and, at other times, they are included with the instructional aircraft. In this case, an individual hires an aircraft, but he or she also serves as the pilot rather than to hire one. Rental aircraft are also required to meet very strict safety and maintenance requirements.

A rental aircraft can be as plain or as fancy as the renter wants or can afford. Depending on the aircraft, a rental may cost from $50 per hour to over $2,000 per hour.

Nontransportation

In the nontransportation area of commercial aviation, we find agricultural application, aerial advertising, aerial photography, construction, fire fighting, pipeline/power line surveillance, fish and wildlife conservation, and logging.

In many of these areas, the use of aircraft is the only way to accomplish the task economically. This is particularly true in the use of helicopters. The helicopter is expensive to buy and very expensive to operate, but it is so versatile that it is often the least expensive way to accomplish the task.

Agricultural Application. Agricultural aircraft include both fixed-wing and rotary-wing aircraft. They seed, fertilize and apply pesticides to almost 200 million acres of farmland annually. Ninety percent of the US rice crop is seeded by air. One airplane can seed more acreage in an hour than a tractor can in a whole day. It also will use only one-ninth the amount of fuel that the tractor uses.

Agricultural aircraft face some very special requirements and they have developed into a special type of aircraft. Let's look at a couple of the most common agricultural aircraft.

The Cessna Ag Husky and the Schweizer Super Ag-Cat are manufactured specifically for agricultural applications. They all carry heavy payloads (1,900 to 5,000 pounds), have powerful (300- to 600-horsepower) engines and have high-

Cessna Ag Husky and Ag Truck

lift wings. The Ag-Cat is a biwing aircraft, while the Ag Husky is a monoplane. Both are very maneuverable and are noted for their ruggedness and reliability. They fly long hours under rough conditions. They are very expensive.

Helicopters are being used more and more in agricultural applications. They can get into smaller fields and can cover the ends and corners of fields with obstructions better than fixed-wing aircraft. Also, the downwash of the rotor blade causes the spray to be distributed more evenly and on the undersides of the leaves. Helicopters are more expensive to buy and to operate than fixed-wing aircraft, and they do not carry as large a payload. They do have one advantage in that they can be loaded with spray right in the field without being flown back to a landing strip like the fixed-wing airplane.

Two spray helicopters often seen are the Bell Model 47G and the Bell Model 206B Jet Ranger. Another, which is seen occasionally, is the Branbly-Hynes B-2. The 47G and the B-2 are both piston-engine helicopters, while the 206B is turbine-powered. The 206B has the largest payload, about 1,500 pounds. The 206B is also the fastest. But helicopters seldom spray at a speed of over 60 to 75 mph, so speed is not an important factor.

Helicopters, like this Hughes 500 C, play a vital role in both civilian and military aviation. *(EAA)*

Aerial Advertising. The public seldom sees most other uses of aircraft in the nontransportation commercial field. An exception is aerial advertising, which is specifically designed to be seen. Most of you have seen an aircraft towing a banner over a sports stadium or at a county fair. Another example of this use, which most of you have seen, is a Goodyear blimp. There are three of these large dirigibles in service across the United States; the *America,* the *Columbia* and the *Enterprise.* They are often leased by one of the television networks to give an aerial view of a major sporting event. Two of the blimps are equipped with a large, lighted display area on the side of the gasbag. This display area is used for advertising at large sporting events. Another method of aerial advertising, which is seen less often, is the skywriter. An acrobatic aircraft is equipped to inject oil into

The Budweiser Blimp, A-60 Plus Lightship, is 132 feet long, 44 feet high and cruises at 32 mph. It contains 70,000 cu. ft. of helium and features special internal illumination that makes it glow at night. *(EAA)*

the engine. This oil burns causing dense smoke. The specially trained pilot then uses his aircraft to write a message with this smoke hundreds of feet high in the sky.

Aerial Photography. This use of aviation has developed from taking simple pictures from the air to highly specialized photography using special films. The big advantage of aerial photography is that a single picture can cover a large area (often hundreds of square miles). Using infrared film and special filters, aerial photography can be used to spot and map crop damages due to disease or insects. Healthy plants appear red in these pictures and the diseased ones are dark. These types of pictures are valuable to foresters and farmers in stopping the spread of disease. This technique has been extended to space where satellites are taking these same types of pictures.

Firefighting. Many of you have seen television news broadcasts showing airplanes being used to help battle forest fires. These aircraft are used to deliver people and equipment into remote areas and to drop fire-retardant chemicals on the blaze. Many ex-World War II aircraft, such as the TBM torpedo bomber, the B-17 and the PBY Catalina are used for these missions. All of them are very stable, can fly very slowly and carry large payloads.

Fish and Wildlife. For many years, fish and wildlife people have been using aircraft to assist them. Airplanes stock many remote, high mountain lakes. The small fish are placed in water-filled plastic bags. As the airplane flies over the lake, at quite a low altitude, the bags are dropped. The plastic bags burst upon striking the surface of the lake, but most of the fish are uninjured.

In the mountainous areas of the Pacific Northwest, aircraft are used to manage wildlife such as deer and elk. Not only do the rangers take a census of the animals from aircraft but they also herd them from one area to another to prevent overgrazing of the range. Occasionally, during a severe winter, aircraft are used to drop feed to the herds.

Patrol Aircraft. Many utility companies hire pilots to fly along their pipelines or power lines to inspect them. These pilots fly at low altitudes looking for broken insulators, faulty transformers or downed power lines. Using aircraft, a pilot can patrol more distance in a day than can be patrolled in a week by a land vehicle. Often the areas are so remote that the only other way the patrol can be made on land is either on foot or horseback.

Industrial Uses. Another area, which has grown in the past few years, is the use of helicopters in many types of construction and in logging. It is in these jobs that the versatility of the helicopter is really shown.

In construction of power lines, helicopters often are used to carry preassembled towers to the location where they are to be erected. The helicopter can hold the tower in place, while a ground crew fastens it to the foundation. Helicopters have been used to place air conditioners on the roofs of high buildings and to place the antenna at the top of television towers, which are several thousand feet high.

Helicopters are also being regularly used around oil fields. They carry and place large loads, transport people and cargo. This is particularly true for offshore oil rigs.

The logging operations in Washington and Oregon provide one of the most fascinating uses of helicopters. Converted Sikorsky S64 Skycranes and Vertol CH-47 Chinooks are used to transport huge loads of logs. Many of these areas were so inaccessible that trucks could not be brought in to carry out the logs. Now, they are being harvested, and the logs are carried out by helicopter. The S64 is the largest helicopter in the United States and can carry payloads as heavy as 20 tons. The CH-47 can lift about 11,000 pounds, but can be operated much cheaper than the S64. In the past, these helicopters have been available only as military surplus. Now, however, the market has grown significantly and Boeing Vertol has built a commercial version of the Chinook.

Key Terms and Concepts

- commercial aviation
- air taxis
- rental aircraft
- STOL
- VTOL
- UAV
- business aviation
- business aircraft
- executive aircraft
- corporate jet
- charter services
- agricultural applications
- aerial advertising
- aerial photography

? Test Your Knowledge ?

FILL IN THE BLANKS

1. _____ involve hiring a _____ and an _____ to fly you to your destination while _____ allow you to be the pilot if you are qualified.
2. The light, twin aircraft offers the advantages of _____ _____ _____ and _____ to the business person.
3. The _____ is the only single-engine aircraft built in the US that is pressurized.
4. Commercial aviation is divided into two categories—_____/_____ that produce income by transporting people or cargo on demand, and those that generate income with no _____ _____ involved.

5. Fill in the blanks with nontransportation areas of commercial aviation:

_____ Fixed- and rotary-wing aircraft seed, fertilize and apply pesticides
_____ Towing a banner or using the blimp to circle a stadium or county fair
_____ Conducting simple picture taking or highly specialized photography
_____ Deliver people and equipment to remote areas or dropping chemicals
_____ Stock high mountain lakes, herd animals or drop feed in the winter
_____ Inspect power- or pipe-lines for damage
_____ Hauling pre-assembled units out to be bolted in by ground crews
_____ Transporting huge loads from areas too remote to access by truck

TRUE OR FALSE

6. Nearly two thirds of the Fortune 500 companies own aircraft for business purposes.
7. It will actually take a turboprop longer to fly a 500-mile trip than it would a piston engine aircraft due to climbing to a higher cruising altitude.
8. The Beech Starship I is built of composite materials using a design by the builder of Voyager, Mr. Burt Rutan.
9. Helicopters can easily be used to haul power line towers out to the installation location.
10. In the past, many business aircraft were over-utilized because they let the longest trip made during the year be the guidance as to which aircraft they purchased.

SHORT ANSWER

11. What is the definition of business aviation?
12. What distinguishes between business aircraft and executive aircraft?
13. Describe a typical business aircraft.
14. Describe a typical executive aircraft.
15. Name the three factors important in selection of aircraft for business aviation and the reasons for them.
16. What does commercial aviation refer to?

It was during World War II that aircraft became an important part of military strategy. The airplane dominated all aspects of warfare, from bombardment to invasion and even naval battles. Since World War II, this has become even more evident. The Korean War, the Vietnam conflict and Desert Storm have proven that control of the air is a prerequisite to winning on the ground.

The US military aircraft in this chapter were developed to deter a major nuclear war and to win a conventional war, if necessary. We will divide these aircraft into combat (bombers and fighters) and noncombat (reconnaissance and observation aircraft, transports, tankers and trainers). Combat aircraft are specifically designed for a combat role. Noncombat aircraft are designed for support roles. However, many noncombat aircraft become involved in combat action while performing their support roles.

Objectives

Describe the functions of the major categories of military aviation.
Identify at least two aircraft in each of the major categories of military aviation.
State what the letter designation of specific military aircraft means.

Combat Aircraft

The cost of modern-day combat aircraft has become so high that the trend is toward building a single aircraft that can perform several roles. For example, the F-14 was originally designed as a fighter, but has been modified as an attack and reconnaissance aircraft.

Many military people feel that if you try to design an aircraft to perform several different missions, it will not be able to do any of them well. They feel a fighter should be designed to function only as a fighter and an attack aircraft only for that role. On the other side are the people who have to get the most airplane they can for the money spent. They would like to have one aircraft that could perform every type of combat mission. The result is that a new combat aircraft is designed to perform one mission well and then changed to perform other tasks.

Bombers

Bombers are large, long-range aircraft with a mission to reach into the enemy's homeland and destroy the ability to wage war. The targets are the factories where the enemy's weapons are produced, military bases and population centers. They can also attack troops along a battlefront. A bomber usually is able to carry either nuclear or conventional bombs. The United States has three bombers in

its inventory— the Boeing B-52, the B-1 and the B-2.

B-52. The B-52 bomber was designed by the Boeing Company in the late 1940s, and the prototype first flew in April 1952. It has gone through eight model changes, and the B-52H is currently in the inventory. A total of 744 B-52s were built with the newest being completed in October 1962. Currently, only the B-52H remains operational.

The B-52H is powered by eight turbofan engines that provide a speed of about 660 mph and a range of up to 10,000 miles. With aerial refueling, the B-52H can extend its range as much as necessary. The crew consists of a pilot, copilot, navigator, radar navigator and electronic countermeasure operator. It can carry nuclear or conventional bombs, and/or short-range attack missiles (SRAM) and air-launched cruise missiles (ALCM).

Boeing B-52 *(EAA)*

B-1. In June 1977, President Jimmy Carter stopped production of the Rockwell B-1A supersonic bomber. In his decision, he called for a continuation of the B-1 research and development program. The Air Force wanted 244 of the B-1As as replacements for the B-52s. Their argument was that the B-52s were old and that the B-1 aircraft could penetrate enemy defenses better than the B-52. Opponents said the B-1s were too expensive (about $250 million each) and they were not needed because missiles could do the job better.

The B-1B, approved by President Ronald Reagan in October 1981, is about the size of a Boeing 707 airliner, weighs about 477,000 pounds and carries a crew of four. As originally designed, the B-1A was to have a maximum speed of Mach 2.1 (1,400 mph) at 50,000 feet and a range of 6,100 miles without refueling.

There is very little external difference between the original B-1A and the new B-1B. The major changes

Rockwell International B-1B

are internal and include strengthening the structure to increase the gross (total) takeoff weight from 395,000 to 477,000 pounds. The B-1B can carry a variety of conventional weapons.

The B-1B is flown as a subsonic bomber at low altitudes, but can travel supersonically at high altitudes. It has a low-altitude penetration capability using terrain-following radar and is equipped with the latest in electronic countermeasure equipment. New technology has also been used to reduce the ability of enemy radars to track the B-1B or for enemy missiles to shoot it down. The first B-1B was delivered in December 1984, and final delivery of the 100 production models was made in early 1988.

B-2. The United States developed a new Advanced Technology Bomber (ATB), which is designated the B-2 and often called the "stealth" bomber. This aircraft has very high priority by the Department of Defense and has been kept very secret. Northrop Aircraft, with Boeing, builds the B-2. The B-2 is using the latest technology to make it invisible to enemy radar and infrared detectors, hence the name "stealth." It was developed to eventually replace the aging B-52 and compliment the B-1. It can carry a variety of conventional and nuclear weapons. The aircraft has a crew of two pilots. They share the workload with one pilot responsible for flying, while the other is bombing. An extremely capable and advanced aircraft, it is equipped with the latest in electronics technology. It was developed in almost complete secrecy and many of its advanced capabilities remain classified.

Northrop B-2 *(Boeing Photo)*

Fighters

Fighter aircraft have much in common regardless of which country builds them. Their basic mission is to destroy other aircraft and this dictates their design. They must be fast and maneuverable. They also carry various types of weapons. Most modern fighters are equipped with air-to-air missiles for use in long-range combat; bombs, machine guns and cannons for close-range combat.

As the speed of fighters increased after World War II, it became impossible for the pilot to fly the aircraft, aim the guns and navigate without assistance. This led to more electronic aids to accomplish these tasks. Today's fighters are equipped with so much electronic equipment that a second crew member sometimes is required to operate it.

Adding all of these systems and the additional crewmember adds weight to the aircraft. In the United States, we also add weight in the form of armor to protect the crew and the vital parts of the

aircraft. Weight is important because it affects speed, range and maneuverability. Lighter aircraft are faster and more maneuverable than heavy ones.

US fighters have traditionally been heavier than the enemy's aircraft. They have also been safer and more rugged. To make up for the disadvantage of weight, US pilots have better training and technology. This training and technology paid off. In the Korean War, US pilots shot down 14 enemy aircraft for every one we lost. Israeli pilots flying US aircraft in the Yom Kippur War of 1973 shot down 55 Arab aircraft for every aircraft they lost.

Technology and training played a big role in keeping American aircraft superior to those of the enemy. However, as technology changes, the aircraft must change to make use of it. This led to the so-called "arms race" and explains why aircraft that are suitable today may not be suitable in the future.

A-l0 Thunderbolt II. Although not a true fighter in the classic sense, the A-10 is a twin-engine, single seat, close-support aircraft. The A-10 carries up to 16,000 pounds of external armament and a 30-mm multibarrel cannon internally. The engines are mounted high up in the fuselage to protect them from hostile fire. The A-10 is heavily armored to help it survive, and its large fuel load allows it to remain in the battle area for a long time (up to 2 hours).

The United States has over 275 A-10 aircraft in its inventory. It carries a large variety of weapons. It is used primarily in support of ground forces and can defend itself with air-to-air missiles. Although slow, it is highly maneuverable and able to operate at extremely low altitudes.

F-15 Eagle. The F-15 Eagle is an all-weather, extremely maneuverable, tactical fighter designed to gain and maintain air superiority in aerial combat. The Eagle's air superiority is achieved through a mixture of unprecedented maneuverability, acceleration, range, weapons and avionics. It can penetrate enemy defenses and outperform and outfight any current or projected enemy aircraft. The F-15 has electronic systems and weaponry to detect, acquire, track and attack enemy aircraft while operating in friendly or enemy-controlled airspace. Its weapons and flight control systems are designed so one person can safely and effectively perform air-to-air combat.

The F-15's superior maneuverability and acceleration are achieved through high engine thrust-to-weight ratio and low-wing loading. Low-wing loading (the ratio of aircraft weight to its wing area) is a vital factor in maneuverability and, combined with the high thrust-to-weight ratio, enables the aircraft to turn tightly without losing airspeed.

The F-15 Eagle employs an advanced-technology engine (improved turbofan). It has a speed of more than Mach

F-15E *(Boeing Photo)*

2 and a range of more than 2,000 miles. Its twin turbofan engines develop 50,000 pounds of thrust and the combat-loaded Eagle weighs about 40,000 pounds.

The F-15 was designed specifically as an all-weather, air-superiority fighter, but it also has the ability to attack ground targets. It is armed with one 20-mm multi-barrel gun and with advanced air-to-air missiles. The ground attack version also carries a wide variety of precision and nonprecision weapons.

This single-seat aircraft first flew in July 1972. Its electronic equipment includes a lightweight radar system for long-range detection and tracking of small high-speed objects, such as enemy missiles. This system also ensures effective delivery of the F-15's weapon payload. The McDonnell-Douglas Company builds it. The F-15D is a two-seat trainer version of the F-15C. The F-15E is a two-seat, ground-attack version.

F-16 Fighting Falcon. The F-16 is a US Air Force lightweight fighter which entered service in 1978. The US Air Force purchased a total of 2,699 F-16s. More than 1,100 have been purchased by 16 foreign countries.

The F-16 is a reversal of the US Air Force trend to produce large, heavy fighters. It weighs only 15,000 pounds empty compared to the F-15's empty weight of about 30,000 pounds. The F-16 is a Mach 2 aircraft with a range of 2,200 miles. In an air combat role, the F-16's maneuverability and combat radius (distance it can fly to enter air combat, stay, fight and return) exceed that of all potential threat fighter aircraft. It locates targets in all weather conditions and detects low-flying aircraft in radar ground clutter. In an air-to-surface role, the F-16 can fly more than 500 miles, deliver its weapons with superior accuracy, defend itself against enemy aircraft and return to its starting point. An all-weather capability allows it to accurately deliver ordnance during non-visual bombing conditions.

The F-16 is being built under an unusual agreement creating a consortium between the United States and four

F-16 Fighting Falcon *(EAA Photo)*

NATO countries: Belgium, Denmark, the Netherlands and Norway. These countries jointly produced with the United States an initial 348 F-16s for their air forces. Final airframe assembly lines were located in Belgium and the Netherlands. The consortium's F-16s are assembled from components manufactured in all five countries. Belgium also provides final assembly of the F100 engine used in the European F-16s. The long-term benefits of this program will be technology transfer among the nations producing the F-16 and a common-use aircraft for NATO nations. This program increases the supply and availability of repair parts in Europe and improves the F-16's combat readiness.

F-117. The F-117A Nighthawk is the world's first operational aircraft designed to exploit low-observable stealth technology. The unique design of the single-seat F-117A provides exceptional combat capabilities. About the size of an F-15 Eagle, the twin-engine aircraft is powered by two General Electric

F404 turbofan engines and has sophisticated fly-by-wire flight controls.

The F-117A employs a variety of weapons and is equipped with navigation and attack systems integrated into a state-of-the-art digital avionics suite that increases mission effectiveness and reduces pilot workload. Detailed planning for missions into highly defended target areas is accomplished by an automated mission planning system developed, specifically, to take advantage of the unique capabilities of the F-117A.

The first F-117A was delivered in 1982, and the last delivery was in the summer of 1990. The F-117A production decision was made in 1978 with a contract awarded to Lockheed Advanced Development Projects, the Skunk Works, in Burbank, California.

F-14. The F-14 Tomcat is a supersonic, twin-engine, variable sweep wing, two-place fighter designed to attack and destroy enemy aircraft at night and in all weather conditions. Based on an aircraft carrier during normal patrols, it provides long-range air

F-117 Nighthawk *(EAA)*

defense for the carrier battle group. The F-14 tracks up to 24 targets simultaneously with its advanced weapons control system and attacks six with Phoenix AIM-54A missiles while continuing to scan the airspace. Armament also includes a mix of other air-to-air missiles, rockets and bombs. The F-14 is able to achieve Mach 2 and climb to an altitude of over 50,000 feet.

F/A-18. The F/A-18 is an all-weather fighter and attack aircraft. The single-seat F/A-18 Hornet is the nation's first strike-fighter. It was designed for traditional strike applications such as interdiction and close air support without compromising its fighter capabilities. With its excellent fighter and self-defense capabilities, the F/A-18 at the same time increases strike mission survivability and supplements the F-14 in fleet air defense.

F/A-18 Hornets are currently operating in 37 tactical squadrons from air stations worldwide, and from 10 aircraft carriers. In its

F-14 Tomcat *(EAA)*

F/A-18 Hornet *(Boeing Photo)*

fighter mode, the F/A-18 is used primarily as a fighter escort and for fleet air defense; in its attack mode, it is used for force projection, interdiction, and close and deep air support.

The F/A-18 Hornet was developed jointly by McDonnell-Douglas and Northrop Aviation. It is a lightweight carrier-based fighter with flight characteristics similar to the F-16 and capable of speeds of Mach 1.7. It entered service in 1982. Canada also flies the Hornet, which they designate the CF-18A.

F-22 Raptor. Lockheed developed a new air-superiority fighter to replace the F-15. It is called the F-22, the Advanced Tactical Fighter. The F-22 incorporates the latest in technology. It borrows from the research done in stealth, avionics and engines. The F-22 is unique in that it is the only aircraft in the world able to travel greater than Mach 1 without the use of afterburners. This flight regime has been named supercruise. The F-22 was incorporated into USAF inventory in December 2005.

YF-22A Raptor

Noncombatant Aircraft

The term noncombat is used to describe aircraft that were not designed specifically to participate in combat as were the bombers and fighters. Many of these noncombat aircraft, however, are fired upon while performing their support missions. The aircraft we will discuss in this section are grouped as reconnaissance and observation aircraft, transports and tankers, trainers and utility aircraft.

Reconnaissance and Observation Aircraft

These aircraft are used by the military to watch an enemy or potential enemy in order to keep track of what they are doing. These aircraft are called observation, patrol or reconnaissance aircraft depending on what they are watching.

We will discuss five of the US Air Force aircraft, which are classified as reconnaissance aircraft. These are the TR-1/U-2, SR-71, E-3A, E-4B and E-8.

TR-1/U-2 Dragon Lady. This high-flying aircraft was built in the 1950s as a top-secret spy plane. It is essentially a powered glider and can fly at extremely high altitudes (90,000 feet). At this altitude, it is out of range of enemy interceptors and antiaircraft. In 1960, a U-2 piloted by Francis Gary Powers was shot down over Russia causing an embarrassing international incident. The U-2 cruises at about 500 mph and has a range of about 4,000 miles. The newest tactical reconnaissance version of the U-2 is the TR-1.

SR-71 Blackbird. This is the world's highest flying and fastest aircraft. It is powered by two jet engines and operates at altitudes of 80,000 to 100,000 feet at a speed in excess of Mach 3 (2,000 mph). In 1974, an SR-71 flew from New York to London in 1 hour 55 minutes 32 seconds. This was nearly 3 hours faster than the previous record. Highly sophisticated cameras are used to take photographs from high altitudes. The Blackbird can photograph 60,000 square miles in 1 hour with three cameras. It is now retired from Air Force service, but continues to fly for NASA as a research aircraft.

E-3A Sentry. The E-3A AWACS (Airborne Warning and Control System) is based on the Boeing 707. It has a 30-foot radar dome on top of the fuselage and is loaded with electronic equipment. AWACS serves as an airborne command and control center. Its radar allows it to see what's flying in the battle area. It coordinates and controls the total air effort over this airspace. This includes fighter cover, attack aircraft, airlift and transport into and out of the battle zone, and reconnaissance.

SR-71 Blackbird

E-3A AWACS
(Boeing Photo)

E-4B. This is a version of the Boeing 747 jumbo jet. The E-4B serves as the National Airborne Operations Center for the National Command Authorities. In case of a national emergency, the aircraft provides a modern, highly survivable, command, control and communications center to direct US forces.

E-8. The Joint Surveillance Target Attack Radar System (J-STARS) is an airborne platform equipped with a long-range, air-ground surveillance system designed to locate, classify and track ground targets in all weather conditions. Its capabilities make J-STARS effective for dealing with any contingency, whether actual or impending military aggression, international treaty verification or border violation. The US Navy classifies its aircraft according to their specific jobs, such as antisubmarine patrol and surveillance.

Noncombatant Navy Aircraft

For antisubmarine patrol, the US Navy uses the P-3C Orion and the S-3A Viking. The Orion is a land-based aircraft and is used to search for submarines up to about 500 miles from shore. Beyond this range, the jet-powered Viking takes over. The Viking is a carrier-based antisubmarine aircraft. Both aircraft carry electronic equipment to detect the submarines and the weapons to destroy them.

Surveillance aircraft are carrier-based airplanes that fly ahead or around a task force keeping an electronic lookout for enemy ships or aircraft. The E-2C Hawkeye carries a large radar, which not only spots enemy aircraft, but directs fighters to as many as 70 at a time. The Hawkeye carries a crew of five and its twin turboprop engines propel it at nearly 400 mph.

Noncombatant Army Aircraft

Observation is the locating of enemy troops and the calling for air or artillery strikes on their positions. Some observation aircraft are armed so they can provide support until attack aircraft arrive. We will discuss OV-10A used by the US Air Force, Navy and Marines.

OV-10A Bronco. This aircraft was specially designed as a forward-air-control and quick-response aircraft. It is heavily armed with four machine guns and up to 3,600 pounds of bombs. The Bronco provides a strong ground support until the attack aircraft arrives. If the enemy troop concentration is small, the OV-10A may neutralize it without calling in an air strike.

Transports and Tankers

The combat aircraft (fighters, attack aircraft and bombers) may be the glamour planes, but they could not operate without the support of transports and tankers. The mission of the transport aircraft is to airlift personnel and materiel to wherever they are needed. They also evacuate the wounded from the battle area. Airlift is generally broken down into either strategic or tactical airlift. Strategic airlift is transportation of personnel or cargo between theaters of operation. Tactical airlift is transportation within a theater of operation. Using the war in Southwest Asia as an example, strategic airlift was between the United States and the Persian Gulf, and tactical airlift was within Saudia Arabia, Kuwait, Oman or Bahrain.

Transport planes are not generally considered combat planes because they are usually unarmed. Tactical airlift often involves delivering cargo directly into a battle zone. They often land to deliver their cargo and/or to pick up wounded while under hostile fire.

C-5 Galaxy. The US Air Forces' largest aircraft, the C-5 was built primarily to provide massive strategic (intercontinental) airlift for combat supplies. It can haul 265,000 pounds of cargo and virtually any piece of army equipment, including tanks and helicopters. The capabilities of this aircraft became obvious to the world during its service in Southeast Asia and especially during the Yom Kippur War

The C-5B is officially known as the Galaxy, but pilots call it *"Fred."*

in the Middle East in 1973. Using the C-5, the United States was able to resupply Israeli forces very quickly after their initial losses of aircraft, tanks and other equipment, thereby enabling the Israelis to launch successful counterattacks.

The C-5 is massive; nearly 248 feet long with a wingspan of more than 222 feet. When empty, it weighs more than 520,000 pounds and when fully loaded, it weighs 764,500 pounds. Powered by four huge turbofan engines, each developing 41,000 pounds of thrust, the C-5 can carry 49,000 gallons of usable fuel. When fully loaded, it can travel 5,500 miles at speeds up to 471 mph.

The C-5, built by Lockheed, won a series of design competitions with the Boeing and Douglas aircraft companies. The C-5 first flew in 1968, and the first operational deliveries to the US Air Force took place in 1969.

In 1982, the US Congress authorized production of 50 C-5Bs, an advanced version of the Galaxy. The first delivery was made in 1986, and the final aircraft was delivered in early 1989.

The C-5 has a basic crew of five and is capable of in-flight refueling. Although it can carry troops, it is primarily a cargo hauler. The C-5's big-load delivery role is shared by the C-141 Starlifter.

C-141B Starlifter. The Starlifter has been the backbone of our strategic airlift. Although the Starlifter is smaller than the Galaxy, it is by no means a small aircraft. It can carry 45 tons of cargo and has a range of up to 6,000 miles. Beginning in 1976, Lockheed began modifying all of the C-141As to C-141Bs. The project was completed in 1982. This modification consisted of stretching the fuselage by 23 feet and adding an in-flight refueling capability. It was retired in 2006.

C-130 Hercules. Like the C-5 and the C-141, the Hercules is built by the Lockheed-Georgia Company. The Hercules is much smaller than the C-5 or the C-141 and is turboprop-powered rather than turbojet-powered. However, the C-130 has to be considered one of the most successful aircraft of all times. The C-130 is also one of the most highly modified of all airplanes. Over thirty models have been produced and are used by 52 foreign countries and by the US Air Force, Navy, Marine Corps and Coast Guard. It is used as a transport, a tanker, a gunship and a reconnaissance aircraft. It is also used for search and rescue, communications, weather observation and to launch drones (unmanned aircraft). The C-130 has a cruising speed of about 350 mph and can carry up to 92 troops or 45,000 pounds of cargo.

Lockheed C-130 Hercules

VC-25A, the President's airplane is also known as Air Force One.

MILITARY AIRCRAFT LETTER AND NUMBER DESIGNATIONS

The letters and numbers that designate military aircraft, such as B-52H, are easy to read once you know the system. The prefix letter or letters indicate the mission or type of aircraft. The numerals indicate the specific make and model. The suffix letter indicates major design changes in series. Thus, B-52H means bomber, model 52, seventh major design change (after A). In this case, the H model differs from the G model in that it has turbofan engines rather than turbojet engines - a change considered important enough to rate a new suffix letter.

Sometimes, there are two or even three prefix letters to be read in combination. These are arranged in a certain order (explained below along with examples). First, let us list prefix letters. The following list is not complete, but covers the military aircraft mentioned in this chapter. The same system is used for aircraft of all US military services.

A   Attack (for use against enemy ground targets only)
B   Bomber
C   Cargo or passenger
E   Electronic (special surveillance equipment such as early-warning radar)
F   Fighter (air-to-air capability).
H   Helicopter (single or final prefix only); search and rescue or other air rescue service mission (first prefix only)
K   Tanker
O   Observation
P   Patrol; applied to shore-based US Navy reconnaissance and antisubmarine warfare aircraft
R   Reconnaissance (photographic or electronic)
S   Search; applied to carrier-based reconnaissance and antisubmarine warfare aircraft
S   Strategic (unique case of SR-71)
T   Trainer
U   Utility (usually a small aircraft; miscellaneous uses)
V   Staff (aircraft with interior furnished for staff or key-personnel transportation–first prefix letter only)
V   Nonrotary VTOL or STOL aircraft (final prefix letter only)
W   Weather (aircraft with meteorological equipment permanently installed)
X   Experimental
Y   Prototype (aircraft procured in limited quantities to develop the potentialities of the design)

COMBINATION PREFIXES

The prefixes listed below are the three types: (1) current status (examples are X and Y), (2) modified mission - meaning purpose for which the aircraft is now used if converted from some other use, or (3) basic type, original mission (or intended mission if preceded by X or Y). When combination prefixes occur, they are arranged in the above order. Even three-letter prefixes are sometimes used. An example is YAT which means a prototype of an attack aircraft converted from a trainer. The following examples should help clarify the prefixes:

EC-121 Electronic (early-warning) aircraft modified from C-121 cargo aircraft
HC-130 Search and rescue aircraft modified from C-130 cargo aircraft
WC-130 Weather airplane, also modified from C-130
HH-3   Search and rescue helicopter
OV-10   Observation airplane with STOL capability
VC-137 Staff aircraft modified from cargo or passenger aircraft (NOTE: the combination CV would mean something different–a cargo plane with STOL or nonrotary capability, the designation CV-2 was formerly used for what is now the C-7 Caribou)
YF-12A Prototype of a fighter
F-12   Same as YF-12A (short informal designations like this are often used instead of full designation)
XB-70   Experimental intended as bomber
X-19   Experimental (no specific intended mission)

KC-135 Stratotanker. The military version of the Boeing 707 is the C-135. The C-135 has been produced in several models. The KC-135 tanker and the WC-135 weather aircraft are the best known. They are used for aerial refueling of bombers, fighters and attack aircraft. The KC-135 can carry about 120,000 pounds of transfer fuel. The crew consists of two pilots, one navigator and a boom operator, who is enlisted and actually refuels the aircraft. The KC-135 also carries a wide variety of cargo. They transport passengers, cargo and still refuel aircraft on a single mission. Most KC-135s have been reengined with new, high-bypass turbofan engines. They are designated KC-135R. This significantly increased their efficiency and range. As the C-141 has been slowly phased out, the KC-135 has been filling in the gap for cargo transport.

KC-10 Extender

KC-10A Extender. This advanced tanker/cargo aircraft was selected as an eventual replacement for some of the older KC-135 tankers. It is a modified McDonnell-Douglas DC-10 series 30CF. Bladder fuel cells were added in the lower cargo compartments, which can hold 193,000 pounds of fuel. The aircraft can also be used as a cargo aircraft with a maximum cargo payload of 169,000 pounds. The combined tanker/cargo capability has been used in deployment of fighter squadrons overseas. The Extender is able to refuel the fighters while en route and also carry the support equipment and personnel. The first KC-10A was delivered to the US Air Force in March 1980.

C-9 Nightingale. The McDonnell-Douglas DC-9 commercial jetliner has been modified into two models for the military, the Air Force C-9A Nightingale and the Navy C-9B Skytrain. The Nightingale is a medical airlift transport, which can carry 30 to 40 litter patients or more than 40 walking patients. The crew consists of the flight crew plus two nurses and three aeromedical technicians.

The C-9B Skytrain is used as a personnel transport. It is outfitted like the DC-9 airliner and has the same flight characteristics.

C-17 Globemaster III. The C-17 Globemaster III is the newest, most flexible cargo aircraft to enter the

C-17 Globemaster III *(Boeing Photo)*

airlift force. The C-17 is capable of rapid delivery of troops and all types of cargo. It can deliver the cargo directly to forward bases on unimproved fields. The C-17 has a crew of three and entered Air Force service in 1993. It replaces the C-141B.

Trainers

All pilots, regardless of the type of aircraft they fly, must first go through flight training. After pilots learn to fly, they must continue their training. Every time pilots change from one type of aircraft to another, there is training involved. In this section, we will deal only with the trainers used in learning to fly.

Some Air Force pilots receive their initial flight training in the Cessna T-3 Firefly. Graduating from the T-3, the student will move to the Cessna T-37B. The T-37 is a subsonic jet that seats a student and an instructor side by side. Following instruction in the T-37, the student goes into advanced training in the supersonic T-38 Talon or the T-1 Jayhawk. The Talon can fly at Mach 1.2 and carries the student and instructor seated in tandem (one behind the other). It is used for fighter pilot specific training. The T-1 is used for pilots who will be flying bomber or transport aircraft.

T-34 Mentor

T-37 "Tweet" *(EAA)*

Navy pilots receive their basic training in the T-34C Turbo Mentor. This high-performance trainer is built by Beech Aircraft and carries an instructor and student in tandem. It is powered by a 550 horsepower turboprop engine and can fly over 300 mph. After basic training, the Navy pilot moves up to the jet-powered T-45 Goshawk. This primary jet training aircraft can fly at about 650 mph and is used to teach gunnery, bombing and how to operate from an aircraft carrier.

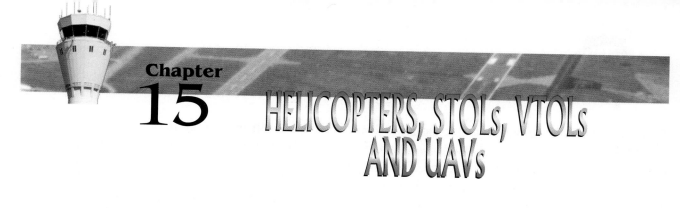

Chapter
15
HELICOPTERS, STOLs, VTOLs AND UAVs

Objectives

Identify at least two heavy lift helicopters.
Identify at least two light lift helicopters.
Define STOL and VSTOL.
Define UAV.

Vertical and short takeoff aircraft are known as V/STOL. The most common type of VSTOL aircraft is the helicopter. Since a helicopter can takeoff and land vertically it is also known as a VTOL aircraft.

Helicopters are used in civilian and military for transportation. In the military, they are also used for attack missions. Some drawbacks to helicopters over fixed wing aircraft are maintenance, vibration, and speed. Even, Igor Sikorsky admitted that. Advances in technology have reduced vibration.

The main historical advance that made helicopters more useful was the gas turbine engine. This enabled greater lifting loads and speed.

Most modern helicopters make extensive use of composites such has fiberglass and carbon epoxy. Helicopters for the US Army are usually named after Native American Tribes. The US Army is the lead service for helicopter research and development.

Helicopters

Military

While many designs have military uses, attack helicopters are almost entirely in the military domain, although there are some Cobras in private ownership. The main U.S. attack helicopters are the AH-1 *Cobra* and AH-64 *Apache*.

Attack

AH-1 Cobra. The *Cobra* was a development of the UH-1 *Iroquois* soley for the attack mission. Although the US Army retains some Cobras, they are being retired. Several other countries still operate them. The newest Cobra in the US inventory is the AH-1Z *Super Cobra*. It is a development of the earlier AH-1W. The AH-1Z has a four-bladed rotor and a new cockpit. It is powered by two General

Electric (GE) T-700 engines each producing 1500 SHP. It is built by Bell Helicopter Textron, Inc.

AH-64 *Apache.* The AH-64 *Apache* was developed by Hughes Helicopters. The company was originally founded by Howard Hughes. The company was subsequently bought by McDonnell Douglas then Boeing. A version of the same engines that power the Super Cobra is used in the AH-64 *Apache*. The latest variant of the *Apache* is the AH-64D. The AH-64D has a millimeter wave radar that enhances its attack capabilities.

Both aircraft can carry an assortment of weapons ranging from the Hellfire missiles to 2.75 in rockets. The AH-64 has a 30mm gun; the *Cobra* has a three-barreled 20mm cannon.

AH-64A Apache *(Boeing Photo)*

Transport

Transport helicopters by their nature can be military or civilian. There are three categories of transport or cargo helicopters. They are heavy lift, medium lift and light lift or utility. An example of heavy lift is the CH-53. An example of medium lift is the H-46 *Sea Knight,* and an example of utility is the UH-1 *Iroquois*.

Heavy Lift

Sikorsky H-53. The US helicopter with the heaviest lift capability is the CH-53E *Super Stallion*. It is built by Sikorsky Aircraft. It can vertically lift up to 32,000 lbs. It is powered by three 4380 SHP GE T-64 engines. Its seven-bladed main rotor has a diameter of 79 feet and its overall length is 99 feet.

Boeing CH-47 Chinook *(EAA)*

It is an outgrowth of the earlier CH-53D *Sea Stallion* which is still operated by the US Marines. The CH-53D has two engines each with 3200 SHP. The CH-53D has a six-bladed main rotor with a diameter of 72 feet. The range of the CH-53E can be extended using aerial refueling. A replacement for CH-53E is currently under development, it is the CH-53K.

Boeing H-47. The heavy lift machine for the Army is the CH-47 *Chinook*. It is built by Boeing Helicopters. It comes in several variants. The CH-47D is the most common. These are being replaced by, and upgraded to, CH-47Fs. Special Operations uses both the MH-47E and MH-47G. They are powered by two Lycoming T-55s, which put out over 4800SHP each.

Medium-lift

Boeing H-46. Medium lift is defined by the H-46 *Sea Knight*. The H-46 was built by Vertol, which later became Boeing Helicopters. It is a development of the earlier tandems designed by Frank Piasecki. It is powered by two GE T-58 engines of 1600 SHP each. It is 84 feet long. The H-46 served with both the US Navy and the US Marine Corps. It has been replaced in the Navy by the MH-60S *Knighthawk* and is being replaced in the Marine Corps by the V-22 *Osprey*. Some H-46s may remain in service until 2020.

Sikorsky H-3 Sea King. The Sikorsky H-3 has served in many roles for many services: antisubmarine warfare, search and rescue, and transport. The H-3 has largely been replaced by the H-60. In the Air Force the HH-3E was replaced by the MH-60. The HH-3E had been known as the "Jolly Green Giant" during the Vietnam War. In the Coast Guard, the HH-3F *Pelican* was replaced by the MH-60J. The Navy used the SH-3 as search and rescue and transport aircraft, they have been replaced by the SH-60F, HH-60H and MH-60S. The VH-3D is one of the select few to fly the President and other dignitaries. When the President is aboard they are known as "Marine One" The VH-3 was scheduled to be replaced by the VH-71 *Kestrel* also known as the US 101. This is the US version of the European Helicopter Industries EH101 built by Great Britain (Westland) and Italy (Agusta). However, this was cancelled. The VH-3 is now scheduled to be replaced by the VXX.

Utility

Bell H-1. The most famous of all utility helicopters is the Bell UH-1 *Iroqouis*. It is nicknamed the *Huey*. It is the most built U.S. helicopter of all time with production topping 16,000 machines.

It was originally designated the Bell XH-40. Then later, the HU-1; the name *Huey* comes from the HU-1 designation. The designation was later changed again to UH-1, however the nickanme stuck. It was Larry Bell's most successful design. However, he died the same day the XH-40 first flew. The latest variant of the *Huey* is the UH-1Y which has the same rotor system, engines, and transmission as the AH-1Z.

Bell Jet Ranger. Another light utility helicopter is the Bell *Jet Ranger.* Although used in the civilian market, many variants are used by the military. They include the OH-58 *Kiowa* and TH-67 *Creek* for the Army and TH-57 *Sea Ranger* for the Navy. Both the TH-57 and TH-67 are used for training. The OH-58D is a scout, observation and light attack helicopter. They are all powered by various versions of the Allison/Rolls Royce C250 engine. The ARH-70, *Arapaho* was a new scout helicopter based on the Bell 407, similar to Bell *Jet Ranger* and designed to replace the cancelled RAH-66 *Commanche*. It was cancelled in 2008.

Another light helicopter is the H-6 *Cayuse*. The H-6 was originally built by the Hughes Helicopter Company. As stated above, the helicopter company was acquired first by McDonnell Douglas then Boeing. It is used in several variants. The US Navy had the TH-6, which has now been retired, the Army had the OH-6 and Special Operations has the AH-6 and MH-6. They

UH-60A *Black Hawk*

are powered by a version of the same engine that powers the *Jet Ranger.*

UH-60. Although developed as a replacement for the UH-1. The *Blackhawk* spans the space between utility and medium lift. First developed by Sikorsky as the UH-60 *Blackhawk,* versions are now in use by all services and many foreign countries. The US Army operates the UH-60 *Blackhawk;* the US Navy operates the SH-60B, SH-60F, MH-60R, HH-60H, MH-60S; the US Coast

Coast Guard HH-60J *Jayhawk*

Guard operates the MH-60J, the US Marine Corps operates the VH-60N to transport the President and the US Air Force operates the MH-60G. All H-60 production variants use versions of the GE T-700 engine used in the *Apache, Super Cobra* and UH-1Y *Huey.*

UH-72. Many other new developments are underway. The UH-72A *Lakota* is a United States Army light utility helicopter that entered service in 2006, built by the American Eurocopter division of EADS North America. It is a military version of the Eurocopter EC 145 modified to the Light Utility Helicopter (LUH) requirements for the US Military. The UH-72 is being bought for the Army Guard to replace the UH-60. It is also in use by the U.S. Navy Test Pilot School. In June 2006, the US Army had selected it as the winner of its LUH program with 300 aircraft planned. The fielding of the LUH was part of an Army effort to transform its aviation capability through the deliberate reinvestment of funds from the canceled RAH-66 *Comanche* program. The Army National Guard will receive the majority of the 322 new aircraft. Initial aircraft will be used for medical evacuation missions.

Civil

The civil market operates many similar machines to the transport helicopters operated by the military. In the heavy lift role, they operate the *Chinook* as the Boeing 234 and the Sikorsky S-64 *Skycrane*. The military S-64 was also known as the CH-54. It is no longer in use by the US military. In the light lift role they operate the Bell 206, 406, 427. The civil variant of the H-60 is the Sikorsky S-70 a lighter machine known as the S-76 is also operated. Many older military machines are still operated such as the Bell 47 *Ranger* made famous in Korea by MASH units.

Bell 222. This aircraft utilizes the latest technology to produce a fast, quiet, long-range helicopter. The 222 is aimed at the executive aircraft market, as well as other commercial uses. It carries up to 10

passengers or 2,700 pounds of useful load. Its hoist is rated at 4,000 pounds. The twin 600-horsepower turbine engines give the 222 a top speed of 180 mph and a range of about 400 miles.

McDonnell-Douglas 500D. The MD Heliocopters MD 500 series is an American family of light utility civilian and military heliocopters. The MD 500 originated as the Hughes 500, a civilian version of the US Army's OH-6A *Cayuse/Loach*. The series currently includes the MD 500E, MD 520N, and MD 530F. The 500E replaced the 500D in 1982. The 500E had a pointed nose and greater head and leg room. The 530F was a more powerful version of the 500E. The MD 520N introduced a revolutionary advance in heliocopter design as it dispensed with a conventional tail rotor in favor of the no tail rotor (NOTAR) system. The NOTAR is popular with law enforcement because of its very low noise levels.

Sikorsky S-76. Another helicopter, which was developed specifically for the civilian market, is the Sikorsky S-76. Much of the new technology developed for the UH-60A is used in the S-76. It is aimed at the executive aircraft market and is available in several plush interiors. The S-76 is powered by two 700-horse-power turbines that give it a maximum cruising speed of 160 to 170 mph and a range of up to 450 miles.

Sikorsky S-76

	S-70B	*S-76*
Crew	pilot, copilot + 12	pilot, copilot + 12
External lift	12,000 lbs	13,500 lbs
Max speed	193 mph	193 mph
Range	460 miles	460miles

Sikorsky has used the latest in soundproofing and antinoise, antivibration technology to make the S-76 one of the smoothest and quietest helicopters ever built. The S-76 is also designed as an instrument flight rules (IFR) helicopter, which allows it to fly in all but the worst types of weather. More than 800 have been ordered and 650 have been delivered to customers in 23 countries.

Other Light Helicopters. There are three other US light helicopters, which we will discuss before looking at some foreign-made aircraft. The closest thing to helicopters for personal use are the small aircraft manufactured by Brantly-Hynes, Enstrom and Schweizer (now part of Sikorsky). All three of these aircraft utilize reciprocating engines rather than turbines. These are just about the only helicopters still being manufactured with piston engines.

The Brantly-Hynes H-2 is a two-place helicopter powered by a 180-horsepower reciprocating engine. The H-2 has a useful load of 670 pounds, cruises at about 100 mph and has a maximum range of 250 miles.

Enstrom Helicopter Corporation makes four models of small helicopters, all of which are three-place aircraft. They are all powered by 205-horsepower reciprocating engines and, in two of the models, the engines are turbocharged. The Enstrom 280C has a useful load of 850 pounds and cruises at about 100 mph. The range with maximum fuel is about 250 miles. Enstrom uses fiberglass and aluminum exclusively in its construction.

Schweizer Helicopter builds a civilian version of the small, reciprocating-engine helicopter that was developed by Hughes Aircraft for pilot training by the Army. This aircraft, designated the 300C, is a three-place aircraft that cruises at about 90 mph and can carry a useful load of 1,000 pounds for 200 miles.

Foreign-built Helicopters

Three foreign manufacturers are dominant in the manufacture of helicopters. They are Aerospatiale of France, Messerschmitt-Bolkow-Blohm (MBB) of Germany, and Agusta of Italy. Aerospatiale is far larger than the other two and sells many times the aircraft as MBB and Agusta combined.

Aerospatiale. This is the national aerospace industry of France, and it is currently producing 10 different models of helicopters. They range in size from the five-place *Gazelle* to the 22-place *Puma*.

The most popular Aerospatiale helicopters in the United States are the seven-place *Alouette III* and the *Puma*. A new helicopter, the SA 365N *Dauphin 2,* is also becoming popular, particularly with the off shore oil platform users. The *Dauphin 2* is competitive with the Bell 222.

Agusta. This Italian company markets one helicopter, the 109A Mk II, which is imported into the United States by the Atlantic Aviation Corporation. The 109A Mk II is a light-haul, twin-turbine helicopter, which is being advertised as a high-technology competitor of the Bell 222 and the Sikorsky S-76. The 109A can carry up to eight people or 2,400 pounds of useful load. It cruises at about 175 mph and has a range of about 350 miles. There are about 30 of these helicopters imported into the United States each year. The A139 is now uses by police forces.

MBB. Marketed by MBB Helicopter, Inc., the MBB BO 105 CBS light helicopter is imported from Germany. The BO 105 is a twin turbine-powered aircraft with a useful load of 2,300 pounds. It can lift 2,000 pounds with its external hoist. The range (300 miles) and speed (150 mph) are about the same as other light twin, turbine-powered helicopters. In addition to being used as an executive aircraft, the BO 105 is popular for use in supply of offshore oilrigs.

V/STOL Aircraft

V/STOL in all its forms encompasses many types of lifting and many operational techniques. Broadly they can be categorized as VTOL – vertical take off and landing, STOL short takeoff and landing; with the components: VTO - vertical takeoff, STO - short takeoff, VL - vertical landing, SL - short landing. These can be combined to give you: STOVL - short takeoff vertical landing, VTOSL vertical takeoff short landing; practicality limits most aircraft to STOVL .

There are differences of opinion as to whether STOL is worthwhile when the full Vertical Takeoff and Landing (VTOL) capability is another goal being pursued. Most agree, however, that the pursuit

of STOL is a worthwhile effort and will not be made obsolete by VTOL progress for many years to come. As things look now, STOL can be more easily combined with better all-around aircraft economy and performance. Full VTOL capability demands more engine weight, more fuel consumption, and less payload.

In war, there will always be situations in which STOL is not good enough and only VTOL airplanes or helicopters can be used. An example is rescuing a downed flyer from a jungle or supplying troops in battle. In other military situations, however, advanced STOL

The Ryan X-13 was an early experiment in VTOL technology.
(San Diego Aerospace Museum)

capability would be highly useful. Higher-performance STOL airplanes could use short, unprepared landing strips, and could transport personnel and supplies over long distances faster than present-day helicopters. STOL attack or fighter planes could be dispersed over many small military bases rather than a few large ones.

Vertical/Short takeoff aircraft have been around for many years. Unfortunately not many military VSTOL aircraft have reached production. The exceptions are the AV-8 *Harrier* and V-22 *Osprey*. The third member of this family is the V/STOL variant of the F-35 formerly known as the Joint Strike Fighter. The F-35 *Lightning II* will replace the F-16, F-18C, A-10, AV-8B, as well as the *Harrier* in other countries.

V-22 Osprey. The V-22 *Osprey* is an outgrowth of tiltrotor technology developed by Bell Helicopter in the XV-15 during the 1970s and XV-3 during 1950s. It is a multimission V/STOL aircraft. The V-22 is produced as a joint venture between Bell and Boeing Helicopters with sub assemblies built in 48 states. As stated above, it is replacing the H-46. It has two 38-foot proprotors, meaning they can be used as helicopter rotors in hover or tilted forward and used as propellers. The V-22 has two Rolls Royce T-406 engines of 6000 SHP each. These engines and their associated transmissions are cross-shafted to each other meaning one engine can drive both rotors. The span across the two side by side prop rotors is 85 feet. The V-22 is 58 feet long. To date, over 100 have been built and delivered to the U.S. Air Force (CV-22) and Marine Corps (MV-22).

AV-8 Harrier. The AV-8 *Harrier* was developed from the XV-6A *Kestrel*. Many versions are in

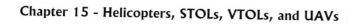

CV-22 Osprey

AV-8 Harrier *(Boeing Photo)*

service world wide. It came to attention when the British used it in the Falklands War in 1982. Although some were lost to ground fire not a single one was lost in air-to-air combat. The US Marine Corps initially ordered the AV-8A *Harrier* then the AV-8B *Harrier II.* The AV-8B makes larger use of composites and has a larger wing. The British developed the GR9 which has now been discontinued.

XV-6A

Compound Helicopters

These machines use lift compounding and or thrust compounding to achieve better performance than standard helicopters. The most recent compounds are the Sikorsky X-2 the Eorocopter X-3 and the X-49A *Speedhawk* modified by Piasecki Aircraft. The X-49A first flew in June 2007.

Possibly the most famous compound was the AH-56 *Cheyenne*. It had both a tail rotor and pusher propeller. It was cancelled due to cost. The AH-56 was built by Lockheed aircraft and was an outgrowth of their earlier XH-51. Both aircraft had very stiff or rigid rotors. The AH-56 was powered by the General Electric T-64 engine

X-49A

346

similar to what was used in the H-53.

Compound helicopters can be heavy lift machines as well. The Soviets had the biggest one, the Mi-12, also known as the V-12, or *Homer* to NATO. The Mi-12 lifts 55,000 pounds of payload vertically, or 66,000 pounds with a short takeoff run, to a service ceiling of 11,500 feet.

AH-56

The Mi-12 is a four-engine, two-rotor aircraft with the counter-rotating rotors mounted on the ends of wings on each side rather than fore-and-aft like most helicopters. The high wings are braced with struts and the span over the rotors is 219 feet 10 inches.

Soviet Mi-12

Uninhabited Air Vehicles (UAVs)

Unmanned or uninhabited aerial vehicles have been around since WWI. They can range in size from the size of an insect to the largest of aircraft. Among the first was the Kettering "Doodle Bug". Unmanned or remotely piloted vehicles continued on in to WWII. During Korea and Vietnam they were again used. Some examples were remotely piloted versions of manned vehicles. Some were dedicated designs developed specifically for unmanned use.

During the 80's UAVs began to emerge in earnest. Today they have grown in size to perform virtually any mission a manned platform can perform. They come in all classes; rotary and fixed wing.

Large

Helios. The largest UAV yet flown was the Helios operated by NASA. It had a 247 foot wing span. (that is larger than a C-5 or a B-36). It was lost in 2003. It set an altitude record of 96,863 feet.

RQ-4. The Northrop Grumman RQ-4 *Global Hawk* is powered by a Rolls-Royce/Allison F-137 turbofan. The

The Helios Prootype flying wing is shown over the Pacific Ocean during its first test fight on solar power rom the U./S. Navy's Pacific Missile Range Facility in Hawaii *(Boeing Photo)*

airframe has prominent nose bulge houses a wideband SATCOM antenna. . The vehicle can reach an altitude of 65000 feet and has an endurance of 40 hours. It is about the size of a U-2.

MQ-9 Reaper *(Boeing Photo)*

Medium

In the medium size class is the General Atomics RQ-1 *Predator*. An armed variant, the MQ-9 *Reaper* is also in use. In the rotary wing world, the RQ-8A and RQ-8B *Firescout* operated by Army and Navy are in use. They are based on the Hughes 269 manned helicopter. The *Eagle Eye* is a Tilt Rotor UAV that was explored by the Coast Guard. The Northrop Grumman RQ-5 *Hunter* is a pusher-puller propeller-driven UAV similar in configuration to the Cessna 337 *Skymaster* but much smaller.

Small

Small UAVs are some times known as Tactical UAVs.

One of the first to appear was the RQ-2 *Pioneer*. Developed by IAI in Israel; then further developed in the US. It has operated from land bases as well as ships. On ships it operated from the battleships and later from Navy LPD-type ships. LPDs are landing ships for personnel and include a well deck to operate landing craft or hovercraft. The *Pioneer* is no longer operated by the US Marine Corps.

CL 327 *(Boeing Photo)*

The Canadair company fielded the CL 227, 327, and 427. These UAVs used a Williams gas turbine engine similar to the engine used in cruise missiles. It had two contrarotating rotors similar to a coaxial helicopter.

Another small UAV is the *ScanEagle* built by the Insitu company and marketed by the Boeing Company. It weighs 44 lb and is powered by a modified 3W 28i engine. Versions of this engine are in use by the radio controlled airplane hobby industry. From the beginning a major hurtle for small UAVs has been their fuel. If used on a ship heavy fuels such as jet fuel (JP5 or 8) or diesel are much preferred to gasoline. Boeing/Insitu appears to have solved this problem. They are presently testing a heavy fuel engine. The *ScanEagle* is used by the USAF, Marines, and Navy as well as several foreign countries.

Other small UAVs are the *Manta* and RQ-7B *Shadow*. The *Shadow* is operated by the US Army. Yet even smaller UAVs are being fielded. They are known as micro UAVs. One of these is the Honeywell MAV.

A major challenge in the small UAV world is how the small vehicles react to air as a fluid. This science involves the use a term known as Reynolds number. UAVs contain every bit of technology that their larger manned cousins carry. UAVs are also used to research flight conditions which have not yet been attained by manned aircraft. Some examples are the X-36 and X-51.

Boeing X-36 Unmanned Tailless Agility Research Aircraft *(Boeing Photo)*

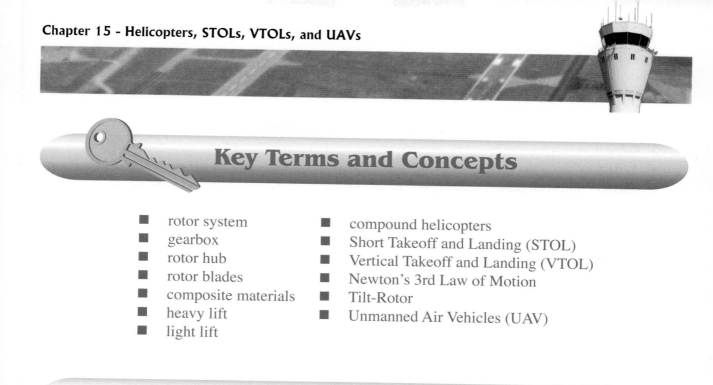

Key Terms and Concepts

- rotor system
- gearbox
- rotor hub
- rotor blades
- composite materials
- heavy lift
- light lift

- compound helicopters
- Short Takeoff and Landing (STOL)
- Vertical Takeoff and Landing (VTOL)
- Newton's 3rd Law of Motion
- Tilt-Rotor
- Unmanned Air Vehicles (UAV)

? Test Your Knowledge ?

SELECT THE CORRECT ANSWER

1. The dividing line in the text for deciding whether a helicopter is heavy-lift or light-lift is a useful load of (**4,000** / **5,000** / **6,000**) pounds.

2. Generally speaking, (**compound** / **hybrid**) helicopters go further than (**compound/hybrid**) helicopters in combining the airplane and helicopter.

3. There is debate within the aerospace community whether (**VTOL/STOL**) will have much value after (**VTOL** / **STOL**) is fully developed.

4. UAVs have been in wide usage since the (**Vietnam** / **Korean** / **Gulf**) War.

5. The USAF standardized definition of STOL is an aircraft with the ability to clear a (**50** / **100** / **200**) foot obstacle within (**1,000** / **1,500** / **2,000**) feet of commencing takeoff role and to stop within (**500** / **1000** / **1500**) feet after passing over a (**50/100/200**) foot obstacle when landing.

MULTIPLE CHOICE

6. Which of the following was not a drawback to helicopters that has been improved or eliminated due to advancements in technology?
   a. High maintenance
   b High noise levels
   c. Controlability problems
   d. Slow cruise speeds
   e. Vibration

7. Which of the following is not a dominant foreign manufacturer of helicopters?
   a. Schweizer
   b. Aerospatiale
   c. Messerschmitt-Bolkow-Blohm (MBB)
   d. Agusta
8. Which of the following is not a major US manufacturer of helicopters?
   a. Lockheed Martin
   b. Boeing
   c. Bell
   d. Sikorsky

FILL IN THE BLANKS

9. The _____ is a _____ using a tilt-rotor designed developed for _____ US military.
10. By applying _____ (for every action there is an equal and opposite reaction), VTOL capability is achieved.
11. UAV missions are classified as either _____ or _____, depending on whether or not the UAV is used to destroy a target.

TRUE OR FALSE

12. Although initially designed for military use, heavy lift helicopters are being used more frequently in the civilian market.
13. The helicopter was first put into use after World War I.
14. Many helicopters are produced in both civilian and military versions.
15. A drawback to helicopters is their inability to accomplish a transoceanic flight.
16. In-flight aerial refueling has yet to be adapted for helicopters.

There are many aerospace organizations that promote aerospace functions. Most of the ones discussed in this chapter are very well known. Several are important governmental aerospace organizations, but each has its own area of responsibilities. There are far too many non-governmental organizations that center on aerospace vehicles to mention in this book. Two of the largest and well-known organizations discussed are AOPA (Aircraft Owners and Pilots Association) and EAA (Experimental Aircraft Association). They both are very large organizations that promote the aerospace environment and are concerned with a wide variety of aerospace topics. There are also many industry related aerospace organizations. This chapter will cover several aerospace organizations. All of these organizations do their jobs very differently from each other, but all provide an immense service to the population.

bjectives

Outline the history of the Federal Aviation Administration (FAA).
Describe the FAA air traffic control system.
Describe the FAA system of flight standards.
Discuss the FAA National Aviation Facilities Experiment Center and the FAA Aeronautical Center.
Explain the responsibilities of the National Transportation Safety Board.
Describe the function of NASA.
Describe the function of the ICAO.
Discuss the makeup and the role of the Civil Reserve Air Fleet.
Describe the three missions of Civil Air Patrol.
Describe the functions of AOPA, EAA.

Governmental Organizations

Federal Aviation Administration

The Federal Aviation Administration (FAA) is the United States Government agency that is responsible for regulating air commerce. It helps by improving aviation safety, promoting civil aviation, a national system of airports, and developing and operating a common system of air traffic control for all aircraft.

History

The regulation of air traffic by the United States Government began with the passage of the Air Commerce Act of 1926. This law gave the Federal Government the responsibility for the operation and

maintenance of the airway system over the United States, including all aids to air navigation. It also authorized the Department of Commerce to develop a system of regulations, which would provide safety in air commerce. The Bureau of Air Commerce was established within the Department of Commerce to carry out these programs.

The first safety regulations developed were the requirements for registration and licensing of aircraft, and the certification and medical examination of all pilots. The Bureau of Air Commerce did much to improve aviation radio and other navigational aids. It also promoted airport construction throughout the country, but it did not provide financial assistance for building airports.

Civil Aeronautics Act - 1938. By 1938, the carrying of airmail and passengers had increased significantly, making new legislation necessary. The new law governing civil aviation was called the Civil Aeronautics Act of 1938. This act placed all air transportation regulations, both economic and safety, under three separate agencies. The first was the Civil Aeronautics Authority, which established policies governing the safety and economics of air transportation. The second was the Office of the Administrator of Aviation, which was formed to carry out the safety policies of the Civil Aeronautics Authority. The third was the Air Safety Board, which was formed to investigate aircraft accidents.

In 1940, the Civil Aeronautics Act was amended, and the three agencies were reduced to two. The Civil Aeronautics Board (CAB) took over the policy-making responsibility in both safety and economic matters. It also assumed the accident investigation duties of the Air Safety Board. The second agency was the Civil Aeronautics Administration (CAA). It was charged with executing the safety regulations developed by the CAB and with operation of the airway system. The CAA was placed under the Department of Commerce.

Federal Airport Act - 1946. The Federal Airport Act of 1946 provided for the CAA to design a system of airports throughout the United States using federal funds for their development. This legislation was needed because of the tremendous increase in aviation activity after World War II. The Federal Airport Act of 1946 was amended several times, but it remained in effect until the Airport and Airway Development Act of 1970 was passed in June 1970.

Federal Aviation Act - 1958. The Civil Aeronautics Act remained in effect for 20 years (1938 - 1958) before the regulation of civil aviation was again changed by the Federal Aviation Act of 1958. The biggest change provided by this act was that the CAA, which was part of the Department of Commerce, became an independent agency—the Federal Aviation Agency (FAA). The Federal Aviation Act of 1958 removed the responsibility for developing safety regulations from the CAB and gave this responsibility to the newly formed FAA. In effect, this gave the FAA the responsibility for both developing safety regulations and enforcing them. The CAB retained its responsibility for economic regulation of air commerce and the investigation of aircraft accidents.

Department of Transportation Act - 1966. The final change in the status of the FAA came with the Department of Transportation Act, passed in 1966. This act placed all public transportation under a single manager, the Department of Transportation. The duties and responsibilities of the FAA remained unchanged, but the name was changed to the Federal Aviation Administration. During its history, the

present-day FAA has been called the Bureau of Air Commerce, the Administration of Aviation, the Civil Aviation Administration and the Federal Aviation Agency.

Duties and Responsibilities

Air Traffic Control. One of the FAA's biggest tasks in the area of aviation safety is the control of air traffic. Air traffic control is concerned with keeping aircraft safely separated to prevent accidents. This is necessary while aircraft are taxiing, taking off, climbing, en route, and approaching and landing. The FAA also provides preflight and in-flight services to all pilots for air traffic control and safety purposes.

Air traffic control is accomplished by establishing certain parts of the airspace as controlled airspace and by requiring that all aircraft flying within this controlled airspace follow certain rules and regulations.

There are two types of facilities that control the Instrument Flight Rules (IFR) traffic flying within the controlled airspace. The first type is the Airport Traffic Control Tower, which controls traffic departing or arriving at certain airports. The control tower is equipped with complex electronic equipment and is operated by highly skilled FAA air traffic controllers. The tower also controls aircraft taxiing on the ground. As would be expected, the busier the airport and the more types of aircraft it handles, the more restrictive are the rules and regulations. Certain large metropolitan airports require all aircraft using the facility to be equipped with various types of traffic control equipment. Some of this equipment is

Based on the volume of aircraft traffic handled, the Flight Service Station provides by far the most service, including in-flight information and assistance in the event a pilot becomes lost or is having trouble. Pictured here is the FAA Flight Service Station in Denver, Colorado.

355

very expensive, and many general aviation pilots cannot afford it. They are restricted from using these large airports.

After the IFR aircraft leaves the immediate area of the airport, the controller in the tower will "hand it off" (transfer it) to another air traffic controller in the second type of facility known as the Air Route Traffic Control Center (ARTCC). The ARTCC assigns the aircraft a certain altitude and a specific route to follow to its destination. The pilot must not change the route or the altitude without permission. As the flight continues, the aircraft is transferred from one ARTCC to another. The flight is under positive control at all times, and no other aircraft is allowed to enter that aircraft's "piece of airspace." The ARTCCs follow the flight on radars and are in voice communications at all times. Commercial airliners, general aviation, and military aircraft all use the same traffic control system when flying within the controlled airspace using IFR.

The FAA also provides assistance to pilots who do not fly within the controlled airspace. These are mostly general aviation pilots since most airline and military aircraft are required to fly IFR at all times. This assistance is provided by the Flight Service Station (FSS). The FAA personnel who work in the FSSs provide preflight information such as weather information, suggested routes, altitudes, etc., to pilots. In addition, the FSS provides in-flight information, via radio, and assistance in the event a pilot becomes lost or is having trouble. Based on the volume of aircraft traffic handled, the FSS provides by far the most service. This is not surprising since they handle mostly general aviation traffic, which includes over 90 percent of all pilots and aircraft.

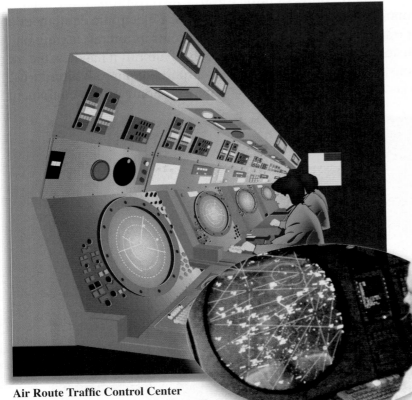

Air Route Traffic Control Center Showing Radar Console with Controller

The control towers, centers, and flight service stations are all connected and work closely together to keep a safe and orderly flow of traffic. The system is currently very heavily loaded. The FAA is modernizing and updating all of its equipment to handle the increase in traffic.

Airway Facilities. The nation's airways are a 250,000-mile system of highways in the sky which pilots follow from takeoff to landing. Currently, the heart of the system is the Very High Frequency Omni-Directional Range (VOR) system, which covers the United States. These VORs are used for navigation along the airways. The FAA is responsible for operation and maintenance of these facilities. They also own and maintain other radars, instrument landing systems and communications at the various airports. These facilities are checked regularly by specially instrumented FAA aircraft.

Flight Standards. The FAA is responsible for ensuring that all pilots and aircraft are safe through enforcement of a system of flight standards. These standards ensure that all aircraft are airworthy, all airmen (pilots, navigators, air traffic controllers, engineers, mechanics, etc.) are competent and all regulations and procedures are followed.

All new models of aircraft, engines, instruments or other components must meet very rigid safety standards before the FAA certifies them. When a manufacturer brings out a new aircraft, the FAA works with the engineers and designers during construction of the prototype. It is then thoroughly ground-tested and flight-tested before being given a type certificate. This certificate confirms that this type of aircraft has met FAA standards of construction and performance. A production certificate is later provided, which shows that the manufacturer can duplicate the aircraft that was type certificated. The production certificate allows the manufacturer to continue to produce that type of aircraft. As each production aircraft is built, it must be issued an airworthiness certificate, which ensures that it has been tested and is safe for use.

Even after an aircraft starts flying, the FAA continues to check its safety. They control aircraft maintenance programs by setting times for inspection and overhaul. The FAA also certifies the repair and overhaul facilities to ensure that the aircraft receives proper maintenance and repair.

Before flying an aircraft, a pilot must have a FAA-issued pilot certificate. There are many types of certificates, but in all cases, they certify that the holder has passed medical examinations. The FAA also requires that a physical examination and a flight-check ride with a flight instructor be completed every 2 years.

Research and Development. The National Aviation Facilities Experiment Center (NAFEC) is the FAA's research and development center. This center, located in Atlantic City, New Jersey, is involved in research to upgrade our airway systems, to improve aircraft instruments and systems, and to reduce the workload on the pilot in the aircraft and the controller on the ground. All of these efforts are expended to make flying easier and safer.

The NAFEC is currently working on new types of airway navigational systems, which will reduce the congestion of our airways in the future. Another area, which they are working on, is new instrument landing systems which would allow aircraft to land safely in any type of weather regardless of visibility.

They are also involved in research on collision avoidance systems for use in aircraft. This would provide a warning to both pilots any time two aircraft were on a course that would lead to a collision. The system would also tell the pilots the type of evasive action to take to avoid a collision.

Aeronautical Center. Another facility operated by FAA is the Aeronautical Center in Oklahoma City, Oklahoma. This multi-million dollar facility is the home of the FAA Academy, which is the training center for FAA operational personnel. They train the personnel who operate the ARTCCs, FSSs and airport control towers. In addition to training FAA control tower operators, they also train controllers for the military and for many foreign countries. The academy is also the training ground for the engineers and technicians who install and maintain the electronic equipment used for navigation, communications and air traffic control. Finally, the academy also provides initial and refresher training for their maintenance inspectors. The Civil Aeromedical Institute (CAI) is also located at the Aeronautical Center. The CAI operates the program for medical certification of all airmen. It is also involved in research to identify human factors that cause aircraft accidents and how to make accidents more survivable. The Aeronautical Center is also the home of the people who write the airmen examinations, develop the airworthiness standards for all civil aircraft, and keep all the records of airmen and aircraft. The pilots and aircraft that fly the inspections of the airways and airport control and communications equipment are also based at the Aeronautical Center.

National Transportation Safety Board

The National Transportation Safety Board (NTSB) is a five-member board appointed by the President, with the advice and consent of the Senate. The members of the NTSB are appointed for a term of 5 years and, like the CAB, there can be no more than three members from any one political party.

The NTSB is responsible for determining the cause, or probable cause, of any transportation accident. Under the chairman of the NTSB, the Bureau of Aviation Safety carries out these duties in the area of aviation. The Bureau of Aviation Safety makes rules governing accident reporting. They also investigate all aircraft accidents (they have delegated this duty to the FAA in the case of general

Experts will be assisting in determining the cause of this crash.

aviation accidents), report the facts relating to each accident and the probable cause, and make recommendations to FAA as to how to prevent similar accidents. The NTSB maintains its own technological division, which provides engineering and technical assistance in areas of aerodynamics, structures, propellers, power plants, instruments, electronic aids to navigation, human factors, etc. These experts are available to assist in determining the causes of various accidents. They also assist the manufacturers in making their aircraft safer.

The result of these agencies working together to promote aviation safety is an air transportation system that is safer than any other form of public transportation.

National Aeronautics and Space Administration

The National Aeronautics and Space Administration (NASA) is a government organization that is very well known throughout the world. Most everyone thinks space exploration when they think NASA. It is much more than just space. You will be learning a great deal about NASA in the following chapters about space; mostly about the spacecraft and not the organization itself.

NASA's budget is under one percent of the federal budget, or over $13 billion, and is divided into four strategic enterprises. They are Science, Aeronautics, Space Operations, and Human Exploration and Development of Space. To support these strategic enterprises, NASA employs 18,500 civil servants and is divided into nine field centers, the contractor-operated Jet Propulsion Laboratory and the Wallops Flight Facility. Each of these facilities directly supports one or more of the strategic enterprises.

NASA's mission statement is threefold and is directly supported by the strategic enterprises. The first part is to explore, use and enable the development of space for human enterprise. The second part is to advance scientific knowledge and understanding of the earth, the solar system and the universe and use the environment of space for research. The third part is to research, develop, verify and transfer advanced aeronautics, space and related technologies. NASA contributes a great deal to the goals of the United States and the world. It promotes economic growth and security to America by conducting aeronautics, and space research and development in partnership with industry, academia and other federal agencies to keep America capable and competitive. It helps to preserve the environment through studies of earth as a planet and a system, enabling the world to address environmental issues. It engages the educational world by directly supporting and encouraging

America leads the world in aerospace technology. *(EAA)*

learning through its many educational endeavors. It also promotes world peace through the exploration and discovery of the universe for all mankind.

NASA research has many great spin-offs of technology to our society. Our space program did not directly develop such things as solid-state televisions, pocket calculators or microwave ovens, but these items and thousands more are spin-offs of aerospace technology. Other things we can list are glasses that darken as the light becomes brighter, digital watches and tiny nickel cadmium (NiCad) batteries. Small hearing aids in the bow of your glasses and artificial pacemakers for heart patients are also spin-offs of aerospace technology.

In the area of materials, we have new temperature-resistant metals, extra strong plastics, bonded lubricants, super insulators and composite materials, which were developed for our space effort. These are now being used in aircraft, automobiles, sporting goods, houses, etc. How do you judge the value of these spin-off products? The answer will vary for each individual. If you are one of the more than 2,000,000 people being kept alive by an artificial heart pacemaker, your answer will probably be that it is very valuable.

International Civil Aviation Organization (ICAO)

The ICAO is an international organization dedicated to standardizing aviation functions. Originally started on December 7, 1944, it was completely ratified by the member countries on April 4, 1947. Later that year, it became a special agency of the United Nations linked to the Economic and Social Council. Today, almost all nations of the world follow the ICAO rules.

The primary ICAO activity is standardization. It provides a means and forum for countries to standardize the many activities associated with aviation. Some of the subject areas standardized are rules of the air, aeronautical meteorology, aeronautical charts and symbols, air traffic services, search and rescue, aeronautical information services, airspace designations, airports and even language. The universal aviation language is English. All pilots and controllers in foreign countries must be able to speak and understand English to use the ICAO system. These standards are constantly reviewed for changes as technology changes aviation. The overall goal of the ICAO is to make the skies safer and more prosperous for all aircraft. Without these standards in place, international air travel would be very close to impossible. The ICAO has made air travel a much safer and easier place in which to operate.

Civil Reserve Air Fleet

The Civil Reserve Air Fleet (CRAF) is composed of commercial airliners, which have been designated by the Department of Defense for use in time of national emergency. These aircraft are long-range jet transports, which have been specially equipped so they can be quickly converted for military use. The CRAF is subject to call on a 24-hour notice. However, the CRAF is more than just aircraft, it also includes aircrews and maintenance crews supplied by the airlines.

When activated, the CRAF would provide the armed forces with modern, fast aircraft capable of airlifting troops and supplies to any point on the earth's surface. The capability of the CRAF continues to expand as more of the newer and larger jumbo jets are added to airline service.

The CRAF was established to assist the military in case of a national emergency, but it is also available for use in case of a natural disaster. In this case, only a small portion of the CRAF would be activated to provide airlift assistance to earthquake, flood or drought victims.

Civil Air Patrol

National Headquarters Civil Air Patrol, Maxwell Air Force Base, Alabama

The Civil Air Patrol (CAP) is a federally chartered, private, nonprofit corporation and is also the official civilian auxiliary of the United States Air Force. The over 60,000 volunteer members are aerospace-minded citizens dedicated to service for their fellow Americans. CAP has three basic missions—emergency services, aerospace education, and cadet programs.

Emergency Services. CAP uses more than 580 corporate-owned and 4,400 member-furnished aircraft to fly various emergency missions. These include search and rescue (SAR) missions for downed aircraft, lost hunters, fishermen, children, etc.; disaster relief missions for natural disaster; and, emergency airlift missions of sick or injured persons, as well as transporting blood and body organs.

Aerospace Education. CAP conducts an aerospace education program for its membership and for the general public. This program develops an awareness and appreciation of the aerospace world

in which we live. CAP's involvement in aerospace education includes sponsorship of workshops for teachers, and development of curriculum and other materials to help teach aerospace education to all grade levels.

CAP Emergency Services

Aerospace Education in All Grades

Cadet Programs. CAP cadets are young men and women, ages 12 to 21, who are interested in aerospace and in community service. The cadet program is structured to use aerospace as a vehicle to help teach leadership and management skills, moral leadership and physical fitness. The program emphasizes activities and involvement of the cadets.

CAP was founded in 1941, and for 60 years, the CAP members have been involved in service to their communities and their nation.

CAP Cadets experience flight.

Nongovernmental Organizations

Aircraft Owners and Pilots Association (AOPA)

AOPA was founded in 1939 to support the views and rights of aircraft owners and pilots. It has continuously built on this premise. Today, it is the leading voice among aircraft owners and pilots to Congress and the FAA. It continuously monitors the government very carefully and, in partnership with the government, strives to make the skies safer for all who use it. One of the most renowned suborganizations within AOPA is the Air Safety Foundation.

Founded in 1950, the Air Safety Foundation is the nation's largest organization dedicated to providing aviation education and safety programs for general aviation. It accomplishes this through researching accidents, distributing safety related materials to pilots, conducting training and providing free public-service aviation safety seminars.

Experimental Aircraft Association (EAA)

One of the fastest growing areas of aviation is the homebuilt market. The EAA was formed to help builders to safely construct and fly their aircraft. It is one of the largest general aviation organizations, along with AOPA. Its local chapters provide builder training and education. EAA supports all sport aviation including antique aircraft, warbirds and ultralights. It also works with the government to ensure the voice of general aviation is heard and understood. Each year, it

EAA Headquarters, Oshkosh, Wisconsin *(EAA)*

holds one of the largest airshows in the world at Oshkosh, Wisconsin. During the weeklong airshow, it becomes the busiest airport in the world, logging more takeoffs and landings than the busiest commercial airports in the world. At the airshow, there are many events that teach and inform builders and pilots on new rules and laws, building techniques and new aircraft. It also sponsors workshops and provides hands-on training in aircraft construction and maintenance.

The EAA Annual Fly-in in Oshkosh is the world's largest airshow. *(EAA)*

Industry Organizations

The aerospace industry is composed of hundreds of companies, large and small, that are involved in some form of manufacturing related to aircraft, missiles, spacecraft and their parts and accessories. Fifty-two of these industries belong to a professional organization—the Aerospace Industries Association (AIA). Some of the industries that belong to AIA are the Boeing Company, Northrup-Grumman Corporation, Bell Helicopter, Textron, Lockheed-Martin Corporation, Honeywell Incorporated, General Dynamics, Raytheon Corporation, General Electric Company and McDonnell-Douglas Corporation. Many of the manufacturers of general aviation aircraft like Cessna, Piper, Beech, etc., are not members of AIA, but they have their own professional organization—General Aviation Manufacturers Association (GAMA). There are about 54 manufacturers that belong to GAMA including many that build engines (Lycoming), instruments (NARCO), radios (King) and other equipment for general aviation aircraft.

The industries, which are involved in aerospace manufacturing, are considered high-technology industries. This means that the areas they work in are involved in the most modern, up-to-date areas of applied research. Because of the highly technical nature of the work in the aerospace industries, the personnel tend to be very skilled and more highly trained than in the average manufacturing industry. This is true for production workers, managers, scientists and engineers. As a result, salaries generally average higher in the aerospace industries.

Key Terms and Concepts

- Federal Aviation Administration (FAA)
- Air Commerce Act of 1926
- Civil Aeronautics Act (1938)
- Civil Aeronautics Board (CAB)
- Civil Aeronautics Administration (CAA)
- Federal Airport Act of 1946
- Federal Aviation Act of 1958
- Air Traffic Control
- Instrument Flight Rules (IFR)
- Air Route Traffic Control Center (ARTCC)
- Flight Service Station (FSS)
- National Aviation Facilities Experiment Center (NAFEC)
- Civil Aeromedical Institute (CAI)
- National Traffic Safety Board (NTSB)
- Bureau of Aviation Safety
- National Aeronautics and Space Administration (NASA)
- International Civil Aviation Organization (ICAO)
- Civil Reserve Air Fleet (CRAF)
- Civil Air Patrol (CAP)
- Aircraft Owners and Pilots Association (AOPA)
- Experimental Aircraft Association (EAA)
- Aerospace Industries Association (AIA)
- General Aviation Manufacturers Association (GAMA)

? Test Your Knowledge ?

SELECT THE CORRECT ANSWER

1. The (**FAA / CAB**) *has responsibility for economic regulation of air commerce and the investigation of aircraft accidents.*
2. The (**FSS / IFR**) *provide preflight information such as weather, suggested routes, and altitudes to pilots.*
3. The (**NAFEC / Bureau of Aviation Safety**) *conducts research to upgrade the airway system, improve aircraft instrumentation, and reduce the workload on pilots and controllers.*
4. The (**NTSB / FAA Aeronautical Center**) *investigates all transportation accidents.*
5. (**NASA / NAFEC**) *controls the contractor operated Jet Propulsion Laboratory and the Wallops Flight Facility.*
6. (**IFR / ICAO**) *is a special agency of the UN linked to the Economic and Social Council.*

FILL IN THE BLANKS

7. *The _____ (FAA) was created as an _____ _____ by the the Federal Aviation Act in 1958. It replaced the _____ _____ _____ (CAA), which had been under the Department of _____. As such, the FAA was now tasked with both developing _____ _____ and _____ them. In 1966, the name was changed to _____ _____ _____ (still abbreviated FAA) and they were placed under the Department of _____, with all other public transportation.*
8. *_____ _____ _____ _____ controls the aircraft while on the ground and during takeoffs and landings. After takeoff, they are handed off to _____ _____ _____ _____ _____, who assigns a specific route and altitude to fly. The flight is under _____ _____ at all times, as the aircraft is passed from one sector to another. As the aircraft approaches its destination, it is again handed off to the _____ _____ for its arrival instructions.*
9. *FAA flight standards ensure that all _____ are airworthy by being type certified, and that all _____ meet competency requirements through checkrides and evaluations.*
10. *_____ is the universal language of aviation.*
11. *The _____ _____ _____ _____ is the international organization dedicated to standardizing aviation functions.*
12. *_____ was founded in 1939 to support the views and rights of its members, and as their voice to Congress and the FAA.*
13. *The _____ _____ _____, one of the largest general aviation organizations, was formed to help builders safely construct and fly their aircraft.*

TRUE OR FALSE

14. The FAA currently falls under the Department of the Interior.
15. NASA research has provided many great spin-off technologies to our society.
16. The heart of the airways system in the United States is the Very High Frequency Omni-Directional Range system, which covers the country.
17. CRAF only applies to aircraft, not crews or maintenance personnel.
18. The Civil Air Patrol is federally funded, public and unofficial auxiliary to the USAF.
19. The Air Safety Foundation is a small organization providing aviation education and safety programs for commercial aviation under the auspices of the FAA.

SHORT ANSWER

20. What does the acronym NAFEC mean? What is it? Name three areas where they are currently working on improvements mentioned in the text.
21. What is done at the FAA Aeronautical Center?
22. What does the acronym NTSB mean? What is their primary responsibility?
23. What are the three main tenets of the NASA mission statement?
24. What does the acronym CRAF mean? What will it do for the Department of Defense?
25. Briefly describe the three missions of the Civil Air Patrol.

Our present day aerospace society is complex and dynamic. It will become more complex as technology advances and the population increases. Aerospace brought about change. The advent of space exploration in 1957, coupled with the beginning of commercial jet aviation in 1958, created an environment where the quest for knowledge became one of our nation's greatest industries. Suddenly, it was not only acceptable, but actually popular to do research.

This brought about what many have called the "knowledge revolution." The computer was developed and refined, enabling people to store and analyze the tremendous amount of data created by aerospace-related industries. During the first decade of the space exploration program, more new knowledge was created than in the entire past history of mankind.

This quest for knowledge placed a great demand on our educational community. We needed, and still need, well-trained people to work in our aerospace community. The highly technical nature of aerospace itself demands training beyond the high school level. The special aptitudes and skills students possess and the courses they take in high school, technical schools and college are important considerations in preparing themselves for an aerospace career.

The term aerospace *is often misunderstood. Some think it is an area where spacecraft orbit. Aerospace is actually a compression of aeronautics (the science of flight within Earth's atmosphere) and space flight (the movement of a vehicle beyond the atmosphere). Aerospace embraces the full spectrum of flight, and the aerospace industry that manufactures the components and equipment for things that fly.*

Aerospace *comprises the atmosphere of Earth and surrounding space. Typically the term is used to refer to the* ***Aerospace industry****, which researches, designs, manufactures, operates, and maintains vehicles moving through air and space. The aerospace field is diverse, with a multitude of commercial, industrial, and military applications.*

Objectives

OBJECTIVES:

Explain how the aerospace age has affected education and training.

Describe the relationship between aptitudes and careers.

List several reasons why junior colleges are popular and serve the educational needs of many people.

Describe the type of training available at technical/vocational schools.

Describe how institutes differ from junior colleges and technical/vocational schools.

Describe the types of aerospace courses taught in 4-year colleges and universities.

Compare the type of education received in a 4-year college with that received in a junior college, a vocational/technical school or an institute.

List four ways that the Air Force helps to train and educate their personnel.

Describe the AFROTC program.

Discuss the Air Force Academy's role in preparing officers for the US Air Force.

State what service the Community College of the Air Force provides to Air Force personnel.

Aptitudes and Aerospace Careers

The special talents and natural abilities that a person possesses are called aptitudes. The figure on page 364 shows some of these aptitudes, i.e., mechanical, verbal, numerical, social and artistic. People with a good mechanical aptitude find it easy to repair, adjust or assemble machinery. Verbal aptitude is important in jobs related to any form of communication, such as reading, writing and speaking.

Numerical aptitude makes mathematics very easy and is important to people seeking employment using calculators or computers.

Air Force Pilots

There is a definite relationship between aptitudes and a person's success in certain occupations.

People working in professions related to their aptitudes are usually happier in their careers. The figure on the next page shows the relationship between various aptitudes and those aerospace occupations in which they are important.

The aerospace industries and government agencies employ aerospace personnel in many thousands of different job categories.

Aptitudes in the areas listed in the chart may lead to satisfaction and success in hundreds of additional aerospace jobs requiring similar abilities. Frequently, there are relationships between aptitudes and the school subjects you may like or dislike, those that are difficult, and those in which you may excel. The chart on the next page shows the association of selected school subjects with representative aerospace occupations in which they have primary importance.

An occupation should provide much more than a means of making a living. It should be interesting, pleasant and provide satisfaction and self-respect in addition to financial rewards. The choice of a particular occupation requires complex decisions involving such factors as general ability, special aptitudes, health, learned skills and family status, as well as the opportunities for necessary education and employment.

You may wonder how your aptitudes compare with those necessary in particular aerospace jobs. You are probably interested in discovering how your personal traits can be used to the best advantage. Questions may also arise concerning the educational requirements for different vocations. Answers to these and many other questions about selecting the best vocation may be obtained in part from persons in your community. With the aid of standard inventory blanks, aptitude scales, interest surveys, and other materials for the measurement of personal traits, your teacher, principal or school counselor may give you objective information about your interests, personal aptitudes and general ability.

Vocational guidance services listed in your telephone directory and operated in your community as nonprofit organizations provide excellent assistance of this type. Local offices of your state employment commission offer vocational counseling services in addition to current occupational information.

APTITUDES AND AEROSPACE CAREERS

Aptitudes	Related Vocational Activities	Selected Aerospace Age Careers
Mechanical	Equipment Development Aircraft Maintenance Machinery Repair	Aeromechanical Engineer Astronautical Engineer Production Technician Power Plant Mechanic Instrument Repairman
Verbal	Speaking and Writing Giving Instructions Persuasive Activities	Flight Instructor Public Relations Director Air Traffic Controller Military Information Specialist Airline Sales Representative
Scientific	Research and Invention Experimentation Scientific Investigation	Aeronautical Engineer Physical Chemist Research Metallurgist Astrophysicist Aeromedical Lab Technician
Manipulative	Equipment Operation Machinery Control Instrument Supervision	Aircraft Pilot Flight Engineer Radar Specialist Machine Tool Operator Production Expediter
Numerical	Mathematical Calculations Arithmetic Reasoning Computational Activities	Data Processing Engineer Aircraft Navigator Research Mathematician Industrial Accountant Airline Statistician
Administrative	Managerial Activities Supervisory Responsibility Secretarial Duties	Research Project Director Management Engineer Airport Operator Military Administrative Officer Stenographer
Social	Service, Advice and Assistance to Individuals and Groups	Aviation Psychologist Personnel Manager Flight Nurse Training Director
Artistic	Self-expression Through Design Drawing and Other Creative Skills	Design Engineer Airline Architect Photographic Technician Technical Illustrator Scale Model Builder

Aerospace Careers and Training

Professional, vocational, educational counselors and private employment agencies operated in your community as business enterprises provide similar assistance. Persons entering the military receive extensive counseling and guidance to help with their proper assignments. Regardless of the choice you make as to the career you want to enter, you will need to receive additional education and training.

Let's look at some of the advanced training available for persons interested in aerospace. In order to keep the U.S. as the world leader in aerospace technology development and manufacturing, we need the best engineers, scientists and technicians possible. If you're interested in mathematics, flight, engineering, science, physics or electronics, you might just be a perfect candidate for a high-flying career in aerospace.

This could be your "office" in your future! Boeing 777 cockpit (*Boeing photo*)

The first step toward exploring the cutting-edge aerospace industry is simple, and the best starting point or source for universities and colleges with aerospace programs, Technical schools, military service, scholarships, internships, and job opportunities is right here. A degree is not as important as the needed training, on the job training, or hands on experience. All of these go together to equip you with what is needed to get the job you want in the aerospace career fields.

You need to know what you are interested in, hence the "know thyself" rule. What do you have an aptitude for and what do you personally have an interest in? The table above should help you in answering this question. You can get to your goal via a degree, or technical training and several years of experience. Both approaches will get you the job you seek in the future. If you cannot afford college enlist in the military and let them train you at any number of really good service technical schools. This is the equivalent of community college training for free. You will graduate from a service technical training school and spend two to four years mastering your skills through on-the-job-training and eventually training others yourself. When you exit the service or are discharged you will have your Associate of Arts degree finished (or nearly completed), certificates of training in a technical field as well as several years experience. All of this plus the military security clearance you will have been granted while serving in the military make you very competitive in the aerospace job market.

You are reading this because you have an interest in aerospace and have many questions you would

like answered such as:

What sort of skills do you need for a job in the aerospace industry? The skills vary according to the position you are seeking, but generally a vocational degree or higher are required. Being comfortable with computer technology is a must.

Do aerospace jobs pay well? Yes they do. Because of the high technology nature of the industry, aerospace jobs pay 50 percent greater than other manufacturing sectors.

What courses should I take in high school to prepare for a career in aerospace? A well-rounded education is desirable with an emphasis on math, science and computer technology. Heading for vocational school or off to college will determine what courses you should take. Check with your guidance counselor.

How important is education to getting a job in a good engineering firm? Education is very important, particularly in the aerospace industry where peoples' lives depend on the products you develop. An aerospace engineering degree can equip you for many different positions in design, testing, verification, project management or even sales. Complex products require knowledgeable people in many different roles.

Let us survey some aerospace jobs and see what they are, or do. It starts with school and some basic learning like you are doing right now. One needs to enjoy aviation, space related activities, or geography. One needs to be "curious" and enjoy solving problems. To work in an aerospace career field, one does not need an aerospace college degree, but it helps open doors. A person needs a certain level of math and science understanding to work in space related operations. A college degree is the normal entry requirement, as well as a very clean police record for the required higher security clearances.

If you are working with satellites or the information they are handling (imagery, communications, etc.) you must have a security clearance. A record of drug usage, drinking, financial problems, and excessive speeding tickets will end your career even before you begin it.

Community Colleges

The community colleges, or junior colleges as they are also called, have become very popular in recent years and more are being built every year. Why the popularity? The community colleges are dispersed within the various states to make them more accessible to prospective students; students that can live at home and commute to school. Therefore, they are less costly. Also, the community college attendee is more likely to find a job to pay for, or help pay for, education at this level. This happens because they earn an Associate of Arts Degree (AA). An Associate of Arts Degree is a college degree awarded after the completion of about 20 classes. It either prepares students for a career following graduation or allows them to transfer into a Bachelor's Degree program.

Community colleges offer the same courses that students take during the first 2 years at a 4-year college and, at most of them, students can specialize. For example, many provide a 2-year education that is especially tailored to the future engineer (aeronautical or otherwise) or to the future physician. Credits earned in this manner are transferred to a 4-year college or university, and the student proceeds to earn his or her Bachelor's Degree.

In addition to the basic preparatory courses of study, which are common to further study in engineering, medicine, business, etc., the community colleges offer special terminal courses. These terminal courses will vary from college to college because they are usually established to fulfill the needs of prospective employers (industries) found within a local, state or regional area. As a result of the growth of new technologies created by aerospace developments, more and more community colleges offer courses that prepare students for vocations in the aerospace industry (air transport and aerospace manufacturing) and related fields (government and military).

Common to most of the community colleges will be a continuation of studies in language, mathematics, history and certain other subjects that were begun in secondary school. In any event, the amount of exposure to these basic subjects will depend on which of the curricula a student chooses.

Compared with workers whose highest level of educational attainment was a high school diploma, workers with an Associate Degree averaged an extra $128 a week in 2001, according to the Bureau of Labor Statistics (BLS). People with Associate Degrees also are more likely to find jobs: the unemployment rate in 2001 was more than 30 percent lower for Associate Degree holders compared with high school graduates. And, according to several academic studies, advantages in the job market might be even greater for those just starting their careers and for those who work in a career related to their degree.

Technical & Vocational Schools

Curricula designed to prepare students for studies beyond community college level place more emphasis on basic subjects. On the other hand, curricula that are highly specialized and terminal (non-degree) place more emphasis on the subjects students will study. These schools prepare you to take an examination to obtain a required certificate for employment.

Technical/vocational schools provide the majority of the formal technical educational courses. In this type of school, many people learn the special trades and skills that are applicable to the aerospace industry. A person planning to become an aircraft welder, an electronics technician or an aircraft power plant mechanic should seek the nearest technical/vocational school and obtain details on what the school has to offer. Let's take a quick look at what you would study if you were to decide to specialize as an aircraft airframe and power plant mechanic:

Aircraft basic science
Covering and finishing
Aircraft sheet metal
Assembly and rigging
Aircraft wood work
Auxiliary systems
Aircraft welding
Radio, electricity and instruments
Aircraft electricity

Rocket engines
Aircraft power plants (introduction)
Power-plant installation and test
Induction, fuel and oil systems
Repair stations (organization, management and operation)
Aircraft propellers
Aircraft hydraulics and pneumatics
Turbine engines (operation, maintenance overhaul)

How long does it take to complete one of the courses of study described above? Like Community Colleges, it takes about 2 years. This time can be shortened to perhaps 15 calendar months if the student

continues studies without a vacation break. Examples of aviation maintenance programs or Courses:

Associate of Occupational Science in Aviation Maintenance Technology is designed to not only provide you with the proper knowledge and skill levels to excel in aircraft maintenance but you will earn a AA degree. That degree may lead to job advancement in the future. This training provides you with the proper knowledge and skill levels required to pass the A&P license tests administered by the Federal Aviation Administration (FAA).

Aviation Maintenance Technician (AMT) Programs are designed to provide students with the proper knowledge and skill levels to excel in their

Welding is utilized in many construction and manufacturing businesses.

chosen career field as an AMT or as a aircraft service technician. This training prepares students with the knowledge and skill required to pass the A&P exam administered by the FAA to gain entry level employment in aviation and other maintenance fields as inspectors, installers, parts managers, and equipment or service technicians.

Aviation Maintenance Technical Engineer (AMTE) Programs prepare students for the airframe and powerplant FAA license exams and additionally the avionics program for the FCC licensing exam.

Airframe Maintenance Technician Programs are designed for a person who desires to work with airframes and other similar structures. Tasks may include performing assembly, repair, rigging and inspections on a variety of control systems. This training can prepare a person for entry level employment in aviation maintenance, or in service technician positions throughout the world.

People who graduate from this type of school go directly into the work force of private industry or government. Usually there is a short period of further training sponsored by the employer. This is necessary because no two companies use the exact same manufacturing or work procedures and the new employee's skills must be adjusted to the employer's methods of doing things.

Institutes

Institutes like the technical/vocational schools and community colleges (terminal courses), place more emphasis on subjects that are essential to doing the job for which the student is preparing. However, there will be several courses in the humanities (rather than subjects in science) that will help give the student a well-rounded education. Also, unlike community colleges and technical schools, students enrolled in institutes will earn a Bachelor of Science (BS) degree.

Students attending an institute may concentrate in aerospace engineering, electronic engineering, mechanical engineering, aeronautical engineering, and aircraft maintenance engineering technology, aviation management and mathematics. Aerospace engineering is a curriculum that has evolved because of space developments. This type of engineering education prepares a person to work on either aircraft or spacecraft design and production programs—hence the title "aerospace." Listed on the below are the subjects to be mastered over a 4-year period by the aspiring aerospace engineer.

Engineering education
prepares a person to work
in many areas of the
aerospace field.

Freshman and Sophomore Years:

- English composition and literature
- Economics
- US History
- Oral communication
- Political science
- Technical report writing
- Chemistry
- Electronic engineering—introduction
- Engineering: orientation, drafting
- Engineering mechanics: dynamics, statics
- Mathematics: calculus, analytic geometry, computer programming, advanced engineering mathematics
- Mechanical engineering: engineering materials and design
- Physics: mechanics, thermodynamics and electrostatics, atomic physics and quantum mechanics

Junior and Senior Years:

- Aerospace engineering: guidance and control systems
- Electronic engineering: electrical network analysis, electronic circuits, linear systems analysis
- Engineering: engineering design, engineering economy, systems engineering
- Engineering mechanics: strength of materials, fluid mechanics, aircraft structures
- Mathematics: complex variables, probability and statistics
- Mechanical engineering: thermodynamics, engineering metallurgy, heat transfer

The curriculum shown above is an example taken from one institute. A comparable curriculum for the aerospace engineering degree may be slightly different at other institutes. Language studies in composition, technical report writing and oral communication prepare the aerospace engineer to communicate with fellow engineers and the public. Of course, the several courses in mathematics are essential to physics and engineering studies.

Aerospace Schools and Flight Training

The aviation industry is a multifaceted, dynamic career field that involves the interaction with, management of, and operation of aircraft. With the extensive career opportunities that exist within the aviation industry, there are many undergraduate programs for students to choose from. Regardless of whether a student majors in commercial aviation, aviation management or air traffic control their degree program will include studies that involve aviation safety, aviation law, and business management as well as aircraft operations. In addition to seeking a job position flying for an airline or corporate flight department, you can obtain employment in areas such as managing an airport, air traffic control, working in aviation for many government agencies or operating aviation related businesses.

What Kinds of Students Major in Aviation / Flight Training? Many Aviation careers require at least a bachelor degree in aviation science, civil aviation or a related field, with courses in aerodynamics, aircraft systems, navigation, human factors, aviation management, aviation law, air transportation and aviation safety.

Is Aviation / Flight Training the right major for you? Take the MyMajors Quiz and find out if it is one of your top recommended majors: http://www.mymajors.com/college-major-quiz.cfml

What Courses Do Aviation / Flight Training Majors Take? The required and elective courses you would take for Aviation/Flight Training majors vary considerably among institutions. Courses are listed here that are illustrative of the breadth of topics you are likely to experience were you to major in this field:

- Advanced Aircraft Systems
- Air Traffic Control
- Airport Operations
- Aviation Safety
- Flight Physiology

- Aeronautics
- Air Transportation
- Aviation Law
- Business Management

Four-year Colleges/Universities

Entry into a college or university is recommended for those who intend to earn a degree, and either do or do not know how they will use their education. The college or university offers a much broader education to its students than they can get in a junior college, a vocational/technical school or an institute because they can choose from more electives in both humanities and science areas. The person who wants to specialize immediately upon beginning the freshman year can do so in somewhat the same manner as in the institute, but they will have to take more courses in humanities. Aspiring engineers, for example, begin introductory engineering courses as freshmen. For the person who hasn't decided on a specialized

course of study when entering a college or university, the final decision on the area of major study can be postponed until the beginning of the sophomore or junior year. There is only one drawback to this approach for those who decide on an engineering major. It will take additional study to complete the engineering requirements if the prerequisite subjects were not taken during the first 1 or 2 years. This means that if one doesn't plan ahead, the total time involved for the basic engineering degree could be as long as 6 years.

Curricula vary in colleges and universities. This is particularly true with the elective courses. Today's forward-looking educators have taken steps to help students understand the aerospace world and the changes brought about by aerospace developments. Many colleges and universities now offer courses especially tailored for this purpose. Some colleges provide flight training as an elective for the entire student body and as a required course for certain major fields of study.

Several universities developed curricula which are especially designed for aerospace careers. These particular institutions now afford an aerospace minor for students who are majoring in some other subject. They also provide a special 2-year program for students who want to become professional pilots, but also want to expand their education beyond what is needed to master the art of powered flight. The institution also gives credit for pilot certificates earned. In addition to these special courses, a person can receive a bachelor of science degree in either aerospace administration or aerospace technology, and a master of education degree in aerospace education.

The curriculum for aerospace technology was designed for students who intend to become professional pilots or who want to work within the various technical fields found in the aerospace industry. It contains a mixture of courses from engineering and other curricula.

Of particular interest is the curriculum for the degree in aerospace administration because it is relatively new and was designed to prepare a person for an administrative or managerial position in the aerospace field. Let's see what kinds of courses are given in this curriculum:

Freshman Year:

Theory of flight	Plane trigonometry
FAA regulations	Science
English composition	Technical drawing
College algebra	General metals

Sophomore Year:

Meteorology
Science
Navigation
American people

Flight instruction
History
Prose fiction
General psychology

Junior Year:

Propulsion fundamentals
Aircraft operation & performance
Principles of economics
Statistical methods
Basic electrical fundamentals (plus electives)

Alternating current theory
Principles of accounting
Principles of management
Data processing

Senior Year:

Aerospace vehicle systems
Aerospace internship
Management
(plus a certain number of electives and the courses needed to complete the requirement for a minor.)

Note that this curriculum gives the student a very broad but in-depth sampling of courses that pertain to specialized areas in the aerospace field. At the same time, it provides a good background in those subjects that a person needs to know to become an administrator or manager.

Military Technical Training Schools

The serious, determined student will find it possible to get the education wanted and needed from civilian schools. If funds are low or nonexistent, the student can work while going to school, borrow the needed funds (to be repaid after graduation), win scholarships, obtain federal assistance or enter a co-op plan with an industry (student alternates full-time work periods with full-time school periods).

Training plays a key role in all of America's Military branches. Whether you're joining right out of high school or after earning a college degree, you'll have the opportunity to advance yourself at all stages of your career. The Air Force alone conducts nearly 4,000 technical training courses. Through any of a variety of training centers and training programs, depending on your position in the military, your training will be hands-on. Your trainers: the most knowledgeable around, with real-world experience. Your equipment: beyond cutting edge.

No matter what you do or where you go, you'll get the best training around. Each branch of service uses the best schools to train its personnel. If you choose the Marines or Air Force, do not be surprised if you go to a technical training school that is run by the Navy, and vice versa. In fact, the Navy has been recognized as one of the world's top training organizations by Training magazine. The magazine's list evaluated demonstrable results, innovation, success factors, training strategic goals and objectives.

Training Centers that Reflect the Mission

If you enlist, your first training will take place at a basic training facility, unique to your branch of the service. While it's called boot camp, it's really a huge campus that includes both classroom and lots of hands-on training, and learning to become a member of your branch of the service. When you graduate from "boot camp" or "basic training" you will move on to your specialty, MOS, or AFSC training. This training is from a few weeks to over a year in length depending on the "job" you have signed up for. No matter what the training, when you finish it, you will be at an apprentice or journeyman level, have one or more certificates and be ready for more on-the-job training and gaining experience in your trade or specialty.

Advanced and Specialized Training

Through extensive classes and on-the-job training, you will have learned the fundamentals of your chosen technical field. There are numerous opportunities to take on advanced training courses, and they are recommended once you have the basic fundamentals of your job mastered, and have satisfied a minimum time-in-the job requirement. You could even earn an Associate's or Bachelor's degree. For a list of all training available, you can consult the Catalog of Navy Training Courses (CANTRAC), of if you are in the Air Force, the Base Education Center will assist you via the Community College of the Air Force.

Community College of the Air Force

When you join the United States Air Force, you're automatically enrolled in the Community College of the Air Force. It's not only America's largest community college, but it's also the only degree-granting institution in the world dedicated entirely to Air Force personnel. The Community College of the Air Force is also a unique combination of on-duty and voluntary off-duty courses with classes and times that are flexible to meet your needs.

Since 1972, enlisted men and women in the Air Force have had their own community college. The Community College of the Air Force helps airmen and noncommissioned officers by translating what they have learned in Air Force technical training and on-the job training into college-level semester hours. Air Force enlisted members can then credit those hours toward an Associate of Arts Degree related to their Air Force job.

The Community College of the Air Force is a worldwide multi-campus college. The seven major technical schools, the professional military education system and the field training detachments are affiliated with the Community College of the Air Force. Enrollment in the college is voluntary, but many enlisted people enroll because they know that planning for the future includes the need to document the technical education they receive in the Air Force. You'll work toward your Associate of Arts Degree in applied science in one of five career areas — aircraft and missile maintenance, electronics and telecommunications, allied health, logistics and resources or public and support services. You'll be earning college credit just for doing your job while gaining invaluable experience to help your career take off.

When an enlisted person enrolls in the Community College of the Air Force, he or she receives a transcript with the credits granted for Air Force courses completed. For example, by completing Basic Military Training (BMT) airmen earn 4 semester hours of Physical Education. The Community College of the Air Force maintains a computerized record of each student's educational progress. This record will automatically pick up all applicable Air Force courses and translate them into semester hours and into civilian educational terminology. Students are able to add civilian courses, which may then be applied toward an Associate of Arts Degree.

Degree programs include a minimum of 64 semester hours of Air Force and civilian instruction including:

- 24 semester hours in technical education directly related to the student's Air Force career area.
- 21 semester hours in the area of general education (courses include humanities, math, natural sciences, physical education and communication skills) and 6 semester hours in management education.

Pararescue Trainees

The remaining hours are technical or general education hours and are usually elective options. The Community College of the Air Force offers Associate of Arts Degrees in more than 70 programs. Some are in career areas such as aircraft and missile maintenance, electronic and telecommunications, health care sciences, management and logistics and public and support services.

When a Community College of the Air Force student leaves the Air Force, he or she can take the transcript or can write for one later. It's a document easily understood by potential employers, trade unions and college officials. The transcript is valuable whether or not the individual completes an Associate of Arts Degree.

Air Force Reserve Officer Training Corps

The Air Force Reserve Officer Training Corps (AFROTC) is the primary source of commissioned officers for the Air Force. The program is offered on the campuses of most colleges and universities.

Two commissioning programs are available through AFROTC for college students. Freshmen may enroll in the 4-year program, and students with at least 2 years of undergraduate or graduate work remaining may apply for the 2-year program. The two programs are open to both men and women.

ROTC Cadets

Both 4-year and -year cadets attend e Professional Of- cer Course (the st 2 years of the FROTC program). he 4-year cadets so take the Gener- Military Course he first 2 years), hich consists of 1 ur each week in the classroom and 1 hour of leadership laboratory (military training and leadership). Class- room instruction time for the Professional Officer Course is 3 hours weekly, plus 1 hour of leadership laboratory. Four-year cadets must complete a 4-week field training course during the summer between their sophomore and junior years. Two-year cadets complete a 6-week field training course (which makes up for the General Military Course) before entering the program. Scholarships are available to qualified cadets in both the 4- and the 2-year AFROTC programs.

Each scholarship provides full tuition, laboratory expenses, incidental fees and a reimbursement for textbooks. While all cadets receive a monthly, nontaxable subsistence allowance of $100 in their junior and senior years, scholarship cadets receive this allowance for the duration of the scholarship.

In either program, there are certain commissioning requirements. The cadet must successfully complete the Professional Officer Course and field training, must earn at least a Baccalaureate Degree, must agree to accept a commission in the United States Air Force if it is offered and must agree to serve for a period of not less than 4 years on active duty after being commissioned.

Pilot candidates must serve several more additional years after completion of pilot training than do non-flying officers. Navigator candidates must also serve several more years after completion of navigator training than non-flying officers.

AFROTC cadets who volunteer and are qualified for Air Force pilot training take their first step toward winning their wings through the Flight Instruction Program (FIP), which is provided at no cost to the cadets. The program is conducted during the 24 months prior to the commissioning. It serves as a test of the cadets' aptitude and interest in flying before attending undergraduate pilot training as an officer. High school students who have successfully completed at least 2 years of the Air Force Junior ROTC program (AFJROTC) may receive credit for a portion of the General Military Course, if they elect to enroll in the 4-year college ROTC program.

The US Air Force Academy

On an 18,800-acre site located near Colorado Springs, Colorado, the Air Force Academy ranks among the nation's finest colleges and universities. Appointees to the Academy receive a 4-year college education in addition to military and physical training. The academic curriculum consists of studies in both the humanities and the sciences. Successful completion of the prescribed courses leads to a Bachelor of Science degree and a commission as a second lieutenant in the Air Force or one of the other armed services.

By authorization of Congress, the Air Force Academy maintains a strength of 4,500 cadets. This equalizes the student strength of the Air Force, Army and Navy academies. US senators and Representatives make most of the yearly appointments to the Air Force Academy. The nominees are selected by members of Congress from eligible young people in their states or districts who have applied for an appointment.

Application for appointment to the academy must normally be made during the year before the applicant wants the appointment—in other words, during their junior year in high school. Of special interest to AFJROTC students is the fact that five students from each high school may be nominated to compete for authorized vacancies in the academy. To be eligible, the student must have successfully completed the AFJROTC program at his or her school and be awarded a Certificate of Completion and a high school diploma. The aerospace education instructor recommends the best-qualified applicants to the high school principal, who in turn, submits the nomination to the academy.

A prospective appointee, male or female, to the Air Force Academy must meet the following requirements:

- Be at least 17-years-old and not have passed his or her 22nd birthday on July 1 of the year of admission.
- Be a citizen of the United States. (This does not apply to allied students).
- Be of good moral character.
- Be unmarried and have no dependent children. Any cadet who marries while at the Academy will be discharged.
- Be in good physical condition.
- Have a good scholastic record.
- Have demonstrated a potential for leadership in extracurricular activities.
- Have a strong desire to become a cadet and have an interest in serving as an Air Force officer.

A successful candidate for admission must assume certain obligations and sign an agreement to that effect. The candidate must agree to complete the course of instruction unless disenrolled by competent authority. The candidate must accept an appointment as a commissioned officer upon graduation, and serve in one of the armed services for at least 6 years. If authorized to resign before the sixth anniversary of his or her graduation, the candidate must serve as a commissioned officer in the Reserve component of the service until such sixth anniversary is reached. If disenrolled from the Academy, the candidate will be subject to the separation policies employed by all service academies.

The Air Force offers a comprehensive range of academic courses, in addition to leadership and military training, physical education and athletics. Cadets may select their major from numerous courses offered within the fields of science and engineering, or social studies and humanities. The academic program of the Academy includes graduate-level courses, which may be applied toward a Master's Degree under a cooperative arrangement between the academy and various civilian universities in less than 1 year after graduation. Graduate programs include both science and engineering fields, and social sciences and humanities.

In conjunction with the Academy, the Air Force conducts the Air Force Academy Preparatory School. It is for selected members of the regular and reserve components of the Air Force and for unsuccessful candidates for the academy whose records indicate that they could improve their chances of receiving an appointment by additional academic preparation. The preparatory school provides an 11-month course of intensive instruction in English and mathematics to assist students in preparing for the entrance examinations. It also prepares the students for the academic, military and physical training programs of the academy.

You finish Your Education, and Ask, "Is There Life after School?"

After all the work and completing your aerospace education, how do you find the right job for your future? Below is a series of steps that have been proven to work. There is no quick answer or timetable unless your father owns a factory and names you the vice-president. The steps to a career begin while you are in college or in a training school as an intern. Remember that word "intern" is the key. The steps listed below build upon one another and should result in a career you enjoy, in a location you choose and at a salary you are comfortable with. This last sentence is what you are now striving for

In a country with 7 - 8% unemployment statistics, you will have to do something to sharpen your competitive edge to get hired. In the following modules you will be introduced to several successful ways to put the edge in your favor, from writing a cover letter and Resume they will read, out-foxing the computer that "mines" key words out of your Resume, to how to dress and follow up on an interview.

The steps are:
- Internships
- Filling out the application correctly
- Cover letters to the hiring official
- A short and concise Resume
- Knowing where the work is located
- Knowing what the pay is in different locations across the country
- A successful interview

Aerospace Summer Internships

Summer internship jobs exist in most large aerospace corporations, across the country. Job assignments are primarily for college students at the sophomore level and above and are designed to give students the opportunity to work in scientific, technical, or administrative areas of the company. The difficulty and level of responsibility of each job depends on the needs of the project and the career interests and level of experience of the student.

These companies seek students majoring in science and engineering, computer science, mechanical engineering, aerospace engineering, information systems, and mathematics. All majors will be considered. Most companies offer competitive compensation, attractive working conditions and a professional environment. This an incredible way to get yourself in the door and to be considered for employment once you have your degree in hand a few years down the road.

Applications

Every company has a process they follow to hire new employees. Human Resources or HR as they are known has HR representatives go to the same schools to learn their job. You will have to play according to their rules, or read "What Color Is Your Parachute" and work it a little bit differently to get a job in spite of HR. Here is the accepted process at a glance. Generally this process begins with your application. In today's world applications tend to be on line.

Online Applications

Almost all applicants wanting to be considered for employment must complete an online application. The online application can be accessed through a company's "Search Jobs button" on the employment careers or opportunities web page. For most companies, in order to apply to a specific job or submit an online resume, applicants must register by creating a user name and password and entering a valid e-mail address.

Once your application and resume are submitted you can expect an online application to remain in a company's database for 12 months from the date of last activity, which includes updating the Resume and/or applying for a specific job opening.

Once you submit the application the company computer will match words in the company job description against your paperwork. As a rule anything less than a 75% match does not even go to an HR person to look at. Your application was dead on arrival. The secret here is to have done your research first, and worded your application against the job description you are applying for. For this reason alone you must make your Resume and cover letter mirror the job you are looking at.

A Short Concise Resume

A Resume is in simplest terms, a document that presents your abilities and work experience, if you have any, in a systematic way which gives the recruiter or an employer a general detailed overview of you as a prospective employee.

Writing a really great Resume is far from following specific rules and advice you hear from others. Some common notions like the Resume should just be a page long, etc. is very misleading. Every Resume is one-of-a-kind "marketing communication." It should be appropriate to the post applied for. It is about you, not fluff and pretty words and formats. Writing a Resume is something that follows a set pattern. It is a simple presentation of your achievements or strong points in your career, be it educational or professional. The format in which you are supposed to present the information is quite simple and devoid of any decoration.

Resume Importance

The importance lies in making the crucial first impression. If your Resume is well laid out, systematic, precise and to the point you are seen as sorted and organized. It is important because the Resume is what the employer or the recruiter sees, way before any interaction with you in person or on the telephone. Human Resources (HR) has to swim across the sheaf of papers and a pile of Resumes, and an impressive and well formatted resume with relevant highlighted points really stands out.

Resume Purpose and Focus

Your Resume is a tool for winning an opportunity for an interview. It wouldn't be wrong to say that it is also an advertisement of yourself in the job market. Keeping yourself in the employer's shoes is the key point here while answering the question as to what should be the focal point of a Resume. Ask yourself what makes you a perfect candidate for the said job. What does the employer really need and is looking for?

Resume Content

In short, the Resume content has to be convincing to the reader about how good, useful and profitable an employee you can be to them. So the content should invariably revolve around what you you done in the field or industry until now, what were your responsibilities, what were your targets, what was the work profile or nature of job, etc. Be sure to use words like: achieved, delivered, exceeded ex-

pectations, beat goals, acquired, etc. Companies want to see an inventory of achievement and success, not a history of menial tasks. If you are having trouble coming up with solid statements of achievement and results from your previous jobs, that's a problem.

Parts of Resume

Resumes are made up of two generic sections, namely, the first where you mention your qualifications or things that you have achieved so far, and the second the details of all the information you gave and proof for the claims you made for being hired.

Cover Letters

A Resume cover sheet or cover letter is a letter that goes with your Resume to the employer giving details on why you are applying. You need to send a cover sheet with all Resumes, always. Your Resume cover sheet has to be very specific to the company in which you are applying for employment.

Your resume cover page is one of the most critical pieces of your Resume marketing kit. Unfortunately, it is all too often completely overlooked by job seekers.

In the cover sheet, you can specify why you are sending the Resume and what exactly you have which will be useful for the company if it hires you. The cover page provides you with a number of advantages that you cannot hope to achieve with a stand-alone Resume. For example: the standard Resume is limited to one or two pages at a maximum. If your Resume is longer than this, you have already lost the ball game. With such a short amount of space, it can be difficult to broadcast the message that you are the ideal candidate. The cover page, however, allows you the opportunity to go into greater detail about your specific qualifications, skills and experience. It gives you a chance to truly shine. Cover letters are meant to introduce yourself briefly to your potential employer, creating in them a desire to know more about you and to want to meet you in person to discuss job opportunities.

Where the Jobs Are

Jobs in aerospace companies are located virtually everywhere, or in many different locations. Using a good search engine is the quickest way to look over a large area for jobs. The search engine web sites listed below will allow you to search jobs requiring a security clearance to jobs requiring none. The jobs go from entry level positions to masters of their trades. You are only limited by your imagination and time constraints to research the web and find the job you are seeking.

Printed or downloaded lists change daily. For that reason there are none here. Begin with the Job Search wizard sites below, and start your own search:

- www.avjobs.com/salaries-wages-pay/index.asp - updated daily (Job Title, Location, and Salary):
- http://www.salary.com/careers/layouthtmls/crel_narrowbrief_RD01.html

What do different Aerospace Career Fields Pay?

Wages vary from company to company, region to region and even state to state. Wages can even be different within the same company based on location or even seniority (length of employment/union rules). Alternatively, the amount earned after five (5) years or more is often much different than what you earn in the first year. Use these pages to discover the reality of "First Year Earnings" in the aviation industry.

The aviation industry offers career opportunities to suit many interests and backgrounds. As aviation remains an integral part of our society, there is still a growing need for qualified personnel. The Avjobs website above menu areas of Aviation Career Salary, Wages and Pay provides this look at salaries, wages and pay in the aviation industry for you as you plan for your future. The following web site is ideal for finding answers to your pay questions:

• http://www.avjobs.com/salaries-wages-pay/index.asp - (This web site is updated daily!)

Interviews

Your cover page memo and Resume addressed to the hiring person (not HR), opened the door for the interview. You told them you knew what they are looking for, and you are the right person for that job. It sounds simple, but the interview is the moment you confirm yourself as that person. There are several do's and don'ts that you need to remember and several additional things that separate the professional (you) from the also-ran's.

When asked to describe themselves, far too many job applicants start into a rant that covers their entire life history. What the employer is looking for with this type of question is your experience as related to the available position. They don't care about your childhood or how many kids you may have. They want to know what skills you have that qualify you to work with them and other aspects of your previous experience. Keep the personal details out.

Don't blow off the questions about your weaknesses and strengths. They are bound to come up in almost every interview you go to, so start preparing for them right now! This is a big question where many people destroy their chances of being hired, so it's important to spend some time learning the correct way to answer. Take a sheet of paper and draw a line down the center. Label one column "strengths" and the other "weakness." Take a few minutes to randomly list all of the appropriate characteristics for yourself in each column. Next, go through and cross out anything that is unrelated to employment and the specific position you are applying for. Finally, come up with one word for any words that are extremely similar, narrowing down each list as much as possible.

Even before you land a job interview, you should be learning about the most commonly asked questions and practicing your answers in the mirror at home. This will prepare you to give natural sounding answers in a very calm, natural tone in the interview. View the following web link to a job interview video and good luck: http://video.about.com/jobsearch/Preparing-for-a-Job-Interview.htm

Key Terms and Concepts

- aptitude
- curricula
- community colleges
- technical/vocational schools
- institutes
- four-year colleges & universities
- Air Force Reserve Officer Training Corps (AFROTC)
- Flight Instruction Program (FIP)
- Air Force Junior Reserve Officer Training Corps (AFJROTC)
- Air University Professional Military Education Courses
- Air Force Academy
- Air Force Academy Preparatory School
- Community College of the Air Force

? Test Your Knowledge ?

SELECT THE CORRECT ANSWER

1. There **(is / is not)** a correlation between your aptitudes and school subjects you like or dislike, and those that are easy or difficult.
2. **(Universities / Institutes)** offer only those courses and degrees designed for a specific career field.
3. Community colleges and vocational schools both take about **(2 / 4)** years to complete.
4. Technical/vocational schools provide the majority of **(formal technical education courses / associate degrees)**.
5. Enrollment in the Community College of the Air Force is **(voluntary / automatic)**.
6. After attending a technical school, there is usually a short period of **(adjustment to the working world / further training sponsored by the employer)**.

MULTIPLE CHOICE

7. Which is not true of the impact aerospace has had on education and training?
   a. It actually made it popular to do research.
   b. Its highly technical nature demands training beyond high school.
   c. It caused change leading to the so-called knowledge revolution.
   d. It caused only a temporary need for better-trained people.

8. Which is not a reason for the surge in junior or community college enrollment?
   a. Limited locations make them less accessible.
   b. Students can live at home and commute to school.
   c. They are generally less costly.
   d. Students can find employment to help pay tuition.

9. Which is not a course likely to be found at a technical/vocational school?
   a. Aircraft basic science
   b. Rocket engines
   c. Science
   d. Auxiliary systems

10. Which is not true of the Air Force Academy?
    a. It provides a four-year college education.
    b. You are commissioned as 2nd Lieutenant upon graduation.
    c. You must be between 17 and 22 to be admitted.
    d. The Fighting Falcons always beat Army and Navy teams.
    e. You must be unmarried and have no dependent children

11. Which of the following is not true of the AFROTC program?
    a. It has two and four year programs.
    b. The monthly stipend is only available to the four-year cadets.
    c. It incurs a four-year commitment to serve on active duty upon completion.
    d. Both programs require a field-training course.

FILL IN THE BLANKS

12. The special talents and natural abilities that a person possesses are called _____ .

13. Selecting an _____ based on your _____ may help you to _____ in it.

14. Aircraft welding is probably a course at a _____ _____ .

15. _____ _____ are those designed to fill the needs of local employers and are part of a non-degree program offered at community colleges.

16. _____ _____ _____ _____ _____ _____ is the primary source of commissioned officers.

17. In AFROTC, both 2- and 4-year cadets attend the _____ while the 4-year cadets also attend the _____ .

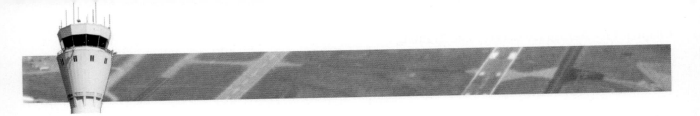

18. The _____ _____ _____ serves as a test of the cadet's aptitude and interest in flying before they attend Specialized Undergraduate Flying Training as an officer.

TRUE OR FALSE

19. During the first decade of the space exploration program, more knowledge was created than in the entire past history of the world.
20. Standard inventory blanks, aptitude scales, interest surveys and other materials can be used to determine your interests, special talents and general ability.
21. Junior colleges are declining in popularity because they no longer fill a need in the education of their students.
22. Credits earned at a community college are not transferable to 4-year schools.
23. The Air Force Academy Preparatory School is a mandatory, 11-week course for all in-bound freshmen.

SHORT ANSWER

24. What is the relationship between aptitudes and success in certain occupations?
25. Discuss what expectations you should have about an occupation.

PART FOUR

Air
Environment

The atmosphere is sometimes called "an ocean of air surrounding the earth." You might also find it referred to as an "envelope of air," or as a "gaseous covering." Both are acceptable, but in this chapter the atmosphere will not be given a descriptive name. Instead, it will be examined for what it is: gaseous fluid that reacts to any force.

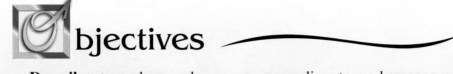

Objectives

Describe atmosphere and space as one medium termed aerospace.
Identify the atmospheric elements.
Recall the four ways of describing atmospheric regions.
Define the various atmospheric regions.
State the general characteristics of atmospheric pressure.
Define the atmospheric regions.
Describe the evaporation cycle.
State the difference between condensation and precipitation.
Identify the role of particulate matter in the water cycle.
Define water vapor, dew point temperature, solar radiation, sublimation, humidity, relative humidity and condensation nuclei.
Classify the four principal ways in which heat is transferred.
Define insolation.
Describe the importance of heat balance.
Explain the Coriolis effect.
Identify the types of pressure patterns used to depict pressure gradients on weather maps.
Describe the effect of gravity, friction and centrifugal effect (force) on the wind.
Explain the land and sea breeze phenomenon.
Describe how turbulence can form around mountains.
Describe the general characteristics of the jet stream.

What is the Atmosphere?

Before discussing the atmosphere, the two concepts "atmosphere" and "space" need to be clarified. Many people still believe the atmosphere and space are two separate regions. This is understandable knowing that an unprotected human being can live in the atmosphere, but not in space. We also know that the airplane can fly within the atmosphere, but cannot fly in space. For these reasons, it is natural for people to assume that space must be separate and different from the atmosphere.

The problem is in searching for the dividing line between space and the atmosphere. Even scientists disagree as to where the atmosphere ends and space begins. There are some people on earth who live, work and play high in the mountains where most of us would have difficulty breathing. These people, over generations, have adapted to living in the very thin atmosphere. Who is to say that people could not adapt to living at even higher altitudes if given enough time to do so? Airplanes can now fly much higher and in much thinner atmosphere than they once could. Thus, the dividing line between the atmosphere and space has, as far as people's activities are concerned, been moved higher and higher over a period of time.

No boundary line between atmosphere and space is found by looking at the composition of the atmosphere either. The only change is a gradual increase in the distance between the molecules and atoms that makeup the atmosphere. Considering these factors there is only one conclusion possible. The atmosphere and space are really

The Earth's Atmosphere

one medium which is best described by the compound term aerospace (aero means atmosphere, plus the word space).

For the purpose of this text, the word atmosphere will be used to describe the aerospace portion where humans do not require special life support systems and space will be used to define the area above the atmosphere where special equipment is needed.

Later, chapters will show in more detail how the earth's atmosphere is divided and named. Once beyond this measurable atmosphere, it is generally accepted that all else is space, and space extends in all directions for an infinite distance. The realm of "true" space has also been given names; these names—whether they pertain to the atmosphere, to space or to aerospace—are necessary as points of reference for the communication of thoughts and facts.

Describing the Atmosphere

The atmosphere is a complex mixture of molecules and atoms. It is not easily or quickly described, but there are three major ways to study the makeup of the atmosphere: its *elements*, its *regions*, and its *pressure*.

Atmospheric Elements

The atmosphere is composed of 78 percent nitrogen and 21 percent oxygen. This leaves only one percent to be made up by other permanent and variable gases. The other permanent gases are argon, neon, helium, methane, hydrogen and xenon. The variable gases are water vapor, carbon dioxide, ozone, carbon monoxide, sulfur dioxide and nitrogen dioxide. Added to this pure mixture there are also dust particles, hydrocarbons and other matter given off by vehicles and industries, the pollens of plants, and so forth.

Atmospheric Regions

Certain levels of the atmosphere can be identified according to general characteristics, or atmospheric regions. The four usual ways of describing these regions (also called atmospheric shells or layers) are by temperature distribution, physicochemical (physical and chemical properties) processes distribution, molecular composition and dynamic-kinetic (force-motion) processes.

Temperature Distribution. One of the most common and easiest ways to understand and describe the atmosphere is by temperature. There are four distinct regions of the atmosphere where the temperature distribution is different enough to warrant a different name.

The Troposphere and Tropopause. The troposphere is that region in which most people live, work, play and fly. It extends from the earth's surface to about 10 miles above the earth at the equator (55,000 feet). In the polar regions, the troposphere is only slightly more than 5 miles in height (28,000 feet). The reason for this is the change in the air temperature between the poles and the Equator. The prefix "tropo" means to turn or change (sphere = layer), and this is just what the troposphere does. The atmosphere within this region is constantly turning and changing as it produces what is known as weather.

In general, temperatures within the troposphere go down with increase in altitude at a fairly constant rate. There are many factors that affect this rate, but it is generally accepted to be a 2° Celsius (C) or 3.5° Fahrenheit (F) decrease with each 1,000 feet gained in altitude. This is known as the standard lapse rate (temperature).

The tropopause is at the top of the troposphere (where the atmosphere becomes stable). The tropopause is the dividing line between the troposphere and the next higher layer (the stratosphere). The tropopause is not a distinct dividing line. It undulates like the gentle swells of a calm sea as large areas of the atmosphere in the troposphere rise when heated and descend when cooled.

Also, there are "steps" within the tropopause. These steps are found where the jet streams occur. Jet streams are "tubes" of very high-speed air that encircle the Northern and Southern Hemispheres. These jet streams are the upper-level dividing lines between the polar troposphere and the equatorial (or tropical) troposphere.

The Stratosphere and Stratopause. The next region of the atmosphere is called the stratosphere. In this region, temperature goes up with increase in altitude. The stratosphere begins at 10 or so miles above the earth and extends upward to about 30 miles. From the base to the top of the stratosphere, the temperature goes up from about -60° C (-76° F) to about -40° C (-40° F). At 30 miles up, the warming trend stops and there is another dividing line called the stratopause.

The Mesosphere and Mesopause. The next region is the mesosphere. From the stabilized -40° C stratopause, the mesosphere first shows a marked increase in temperature to 10° C (50° F), then a decrease until at about 50 miles altitude where the temperature has dropped to as low as -90° C (-130°F). This point is called the mesopause.

Thermosphere. From 50 miles outward to about 300 miles, there is the region called the thermosphere. Here, the temperature increases again. How much it goes up depends on solar activity, but

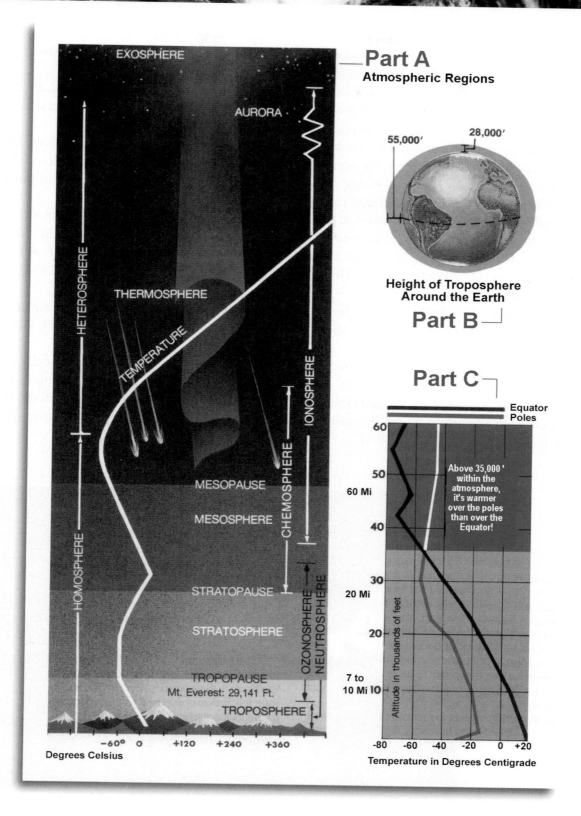

Part A
Atmospheric Regions

EXOSPHERE

AURORA

HETEROSPHERE

THERMOSPHERE

TEMPERATURE

IONOSPHERE

MESOPAUSE

MESOSPHERE

CHEMOSPHERE

HOMOSPHERE

STRATOPAUSE

STRATOSPHERE

OZONOSPHERE

NEUTROSPHERE

TROPOPAUSE
Mt. Everest: 29,141 Ft.

TROPOSPHERE

−60° 0 +120 +240 +360
Degrees Celsius

55,000'   28,000'

Height of Troposphere
Around the Earth
Part B

Part C

Equator
Poles

60

50

60 Mi

40

Above 35,000'
within the
atmosphere,
it's warmer
over the poles
than over the
Equator!

30

20 Mi

20

Altitude in thousands of feet

7 to
10 Mi 10

−80 −60 −40 −20 0 +20
Temperature in Degrees Centigrade

395

it is usually between 750° C (1,380° F) to 1,250° C (2,280° F). At this point, we are in space and temperature is a relative sort of thing. It depends on one's closeness to the sun and whether or not the thermometer is in direct sunlight or is shaded from the sun.

Physicochemical Processes Distribution. Atmospheric regions can also be described by the distribution of various physicochemical processes that happen in them. Included in this atmospheric classification are the ozonosphere, ionosphere, neutrosphere and chemosphere.

Ozonosphere. The ozonosphere is a special region, or global shell, that extends from about 10 to 30 miles altitude. In this region, the sun's radiation reacts with the oxygen molecules and causes them to pickup a third atom creating ozone. The ozonosphere performs the very important function of shielding us from ultraviolet and infrared radiation that could be fatal.

Ionosphere. The ionosphere begins at an altitude of about 25 miles and extends outward to about 250 miles. Because of interactions between atmospheric particles and the sun's radiation, there is a loss or gain in the electrons of the atoms and molecules, and thus the word "ion." The floor of the ionosphere reflects certain radio waves. This allows them to be received at stations far away from the broadcasting station.

Neutrosphere. The shell, or region, below the ionosphere that extends down to the surface of the earth is the neutrosphere. In this region, there is little ionization compared to that which takes place in the ionosphere.

Chemosphere. The neutrosphere, ozonosphere and ionosphere extend upwards (vertically) without overlapping. The chemosphere is vaguely defined. It overlaps the ozonosphere and ionosphere and begins at about the stratopause, includes the mesosphere, and sometimes the lower part of the thermosphere. This is an important region because of a number of important photochemical (radiant energy and chemical) reactions occur within it.

This is the ER-2 airborne science aircraft. It is used to study earth resources, celestial observations, atmospheric chemistry and dynamics, global warming and ozone depletion.

The DC-8 airborne laboratory conducts scientific studies in atmospheric chemistry, meteorology, oceanography and soil science.

Molecular Composition. Describing the atmosphere by its molecular makeup results in two main regions: the homosphere and heterosphere.

Homosphere. The homosphere extends from the earth's surface up to an altitude of about 60 miles. The prefix "homo" means same; thus, the homosphere is that region in which the gaseous composition and mixing are relatively constant, i.e., 78 percent nitrogen and 21 percent oxygen.

Heterosphere. The heterosphere (hetero is a prefix meaning different) begins around the 55- to 60-mile altitude. In the heterosphere the molecules and atoms of the gases are spaced much farther apart. At this altitude, gravity influences them according to mass and they take on a vertical arrangement. The heaviest molecular nitrogen and oxygen are found in the lower part of the heterosphere. The lighter atomic oxygen, helium and hydrogen are in the upper part.

Dynamic and Kinetic Processes. The exosphere is the top of the atmosphere above the heterosphere. The dynamic and kinetic processes that occur within the region determine the exosphere. In this region, the particles of the atmosphere move in free orbits subject only to earth's gravity. The bottom of the exosphere is estimated between 310 to 621 miles above the earth's surface. The upper boundary of the exosphere extends into space without end.

The exosphere begins in that region where the atmosphere's molecules and atoms are so far apart they would have to travel as far as 100 miles before running into another molecule or atom. Within this region an atmospheric particle with enough velocity can escape from earth's gravitational influence. This is why the lower part of the exosphere is also known as the "region of escape."

There are several other regional classifications of the atmosphere that describe a particular condition or process that occurs. The thermal structure or temperature distribution is the most important. Within this structure, the troposphere will receive the most emphasis as it is where most of us spend our lives and it is where "weather" takes place. For a summary of the different classifications of the atmosphere, refer again to the chart on page 383.

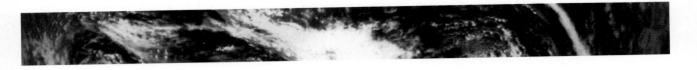

Atmospheric Pressure

Earth's gravitational force is what keeps atmospheric molecules from sailing off into space. This force becomes stronger the closer something is to the center of gravity. Earth's center of gravity is considered to be near its core; therefore, gravitational influence is greatest at or below sea level on earth.

Density indicates how tightly the particles of matter are packed together. This is also known as mass per unit volume. The density of air molecules decreases with increases in altitude. This happens for several reasons. Some molecules possess less mass than others. In addition, the molecules closer to the earth are under more gravitational influence than molecules higher up. The most significant fact is the weights of all air molecules press down upon all the other molecules below them. This is called pressure.

Pressure is exerted in all directions within a given volume of air. At sea level, the pressure aver-

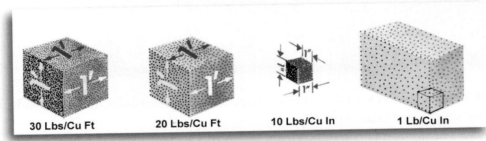

| 30 Lbs/Cu Ft | 20 Lbs/Cu Ft | 10 Lbs/Cu In | 1 Lb/Cu In |

Density: Mass Per Unit Volume

ages about 14.7 pounds per square inch. The reason 14.7 pounds is an average is that the pressure at any one point fluctuates as cells of higher or lower pressure are formed and move across earth's surface (this aspect of the atmosphere appears in a later section).

Air pressure decreases with gains in altitude because of the lessening effect of gravity and the greater distance between the numbers of molecules present. For example, the pressure at 18,000 feet (3.4 miles) is about one-half that at sea level. Going higher, to 35,000 feet (6.6 miles), we find the pressure less than one-fourth that of pressure at sea level. This rapid pressure decline continues the farther outward from earth's surface we travel, until there is no measurable pressure. This is why pilots of very high-flying aircraft and astronauts must wear pressure suits. If they did not wear these suits, the

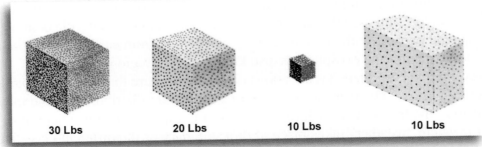

| 30 Lbs | 20 Lbs | 10 Lbs | 10 Lbs |

Mass: Amount of Material

"normal" pressure within their bodies would cause cells to rupture much like the way a balloon does when it rises into the upper atmosphere.

Roles of Water and Particulate Matter

Water in the Atmosphere. The water content of the atmosphere is almost restricted to the troposphere. There are occasions when a particularly heavy thunderstorm will produce enough energy to thrust part of its top into the stratosphere. Water may also be injected into the stratosphere by the engines of high-flying aircraft. Still, water is usually only found in the troposphere.

In the troposphere, however, water goes through a complete process cycle. From vapor, water goes to condensation then to precipitation.

As it goes through this cycle, it takes on several forms. Water is seen in liquid forms as lakes, rain, dew and even as perspiration on our bodies. It can be in solid form as ice, hail or snow. It also appears as fog and clouds—the condensation stage of its cycle.

Under normal conditions, water is not seen when it is part of the atmosphere—when it is a water vapor. If there is a relatively large amount of water vapor in the air, we say that it is humid, and when there is little water vapor, we say that the air is dry. However, no matter how dry the air may seem, there is always some water vapor present.

The air is said to be "saturated" when it cannot hold any more water vapor. The amount of water vapor that can exist in the air increases with rising temperatures. The higher the temperature of the air, the more water vapor the air per unit volume can hold before saturation is reached. The lower the air temperature, the less water vapor a given volume of air can hold before it becomes saturated. The term "dew point" is best defined as the air temperature at which saturation occurs. Thus, the amount of water vapor that can actually be in the air will depend on the temperature at any given time.

In addition to temperature, pressure also affects how much water vapor a per unit volume of air can hold. Air is a gas and gases expand when the pressure on them decreases. As we gain altitude, pressure decreases and the air expands. This leaves more room for additional water vapor to enter a given volume of air and increases its saturation point.

Thus, the water in the atmosphere that falls to earth, as well as the amount, will relate directly to the current temperature and pressure of the air. This concept is important in understanding the concept of relative humidity. The question at this point is how does water get into the air?

Evaporation. We know that temperature and pressure are the primary causes of water vapor in the air. What caused the vapor in the first place? The air is constantly gaining and losing water, and the water vapor gets into the air by a process called evaporation. Evaporation is the process by which liquid water molecules change to a gas or vapor state and enter the earth's atmosphere. The main factor in evaporation is temperature.

A simple example of evaporation due to temperature is seen with boiling water. The high temperature causes the water molecules to escape from the liquid surface and rise into the air. The molecules immediately condense as steam because they saturate the air into which they are escaping. Soon, the steam disappears as it evaporates into the surrounding air, because its dew point temperature has been raised by the warm water vapor. If this vapor-laden air comes in contact with a surface cooler than

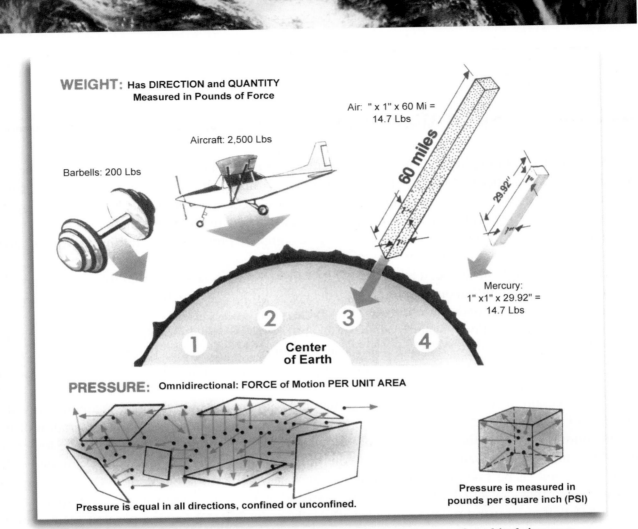

WEIGHT: Has DIRECTION and QUANTITY
Measured in Pounds of Force

Barbells: 200 Lbs

Aircraft: 2,500 Lbs

Air: " x 1" x 60 Mi =
14.7 Lbs

60 miles

29.92"

Mercury:
1" x1" x 29.92" =
14.7 Lbs

1   2   3   4
Center
of Earth

PRESSURE: Omnidirectional: FORCE of Motion PER UNIT AREA

Pressure is equal in all directions, confined or unconfined.

Pressure is measured in
pounds per square inch (PSI)

Weight is in one direction, while pressure is in *all* directions—both decrease when altitude increases.

it, the air temperature drops below its dew point and the vapor condenses into a liquid and the wall or ceiling becomes wet.

Evaporation of water on a global scale takes place in a manner similar to the example above, but it is much more subtle. Most of the water vapor in the atmosphere comes from the oceans and other large bodies of water. A process called solar radiation heats the water causing the evaporation. The warm moist air moves over cooler land and cools below its dew point causing the excess water vapor to fall back to the ground in some form of precipitation.

Another method of putting water vapor into the atmosphere is called sublimation. This happens when water molecules leave the frozen (solid) state and directly enter the atmosphere without first changing into a liquid. This process requires more heat energy than the evaporation process. You may have witnessed the sublimation process during the wintertime when snow on the ground disappears without having melted. Sublimation also describes the formation of frost. That is, water vapor doesn't condense first to a liquid before becoming frost; it goes directly from the vapor state to the frozen state.

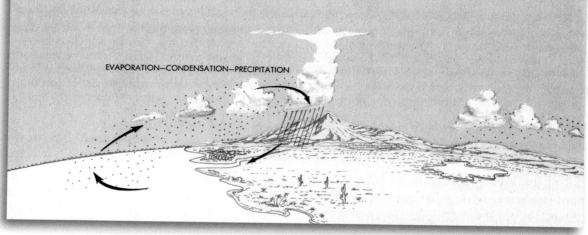

Evaporation Cycle

Humidity and Relative Humidity. Invisible vapor is the water form usually associated with humidity. While there are many ways of explaining humidity, the simplest approach begins by emphasizing that

1. temperature is the main cause of humidity and precipitation,
2. before precipitation can occur, there must be enough water vapor present,
3. the amount of water vapor the air is able to hold depends on the temperature of the air,
4. warm air can hold more water vapor than cold air and
5. as air cools, its ability to hold water vapor decreases.

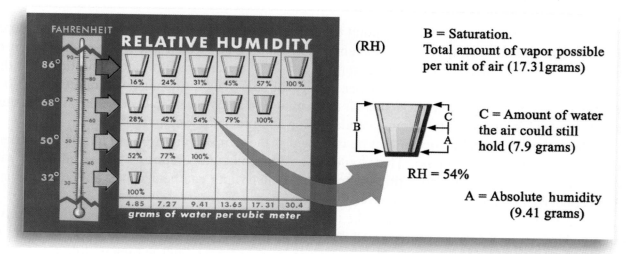

This chart shows relative humidity and temperature. When RH is 100% at a given temperature, the dew point is reached. It also shows that the ratio of A to B equals relative himidity and indicates how far away from saturation is the unit of air (C).

Humidity is the term that indicates the amount of water vapor in the air. Absolute humidity tells you the actual percentage of water vapor in the air at a given time. Relative humidity is the method used to tell you the amount of water vapor that can still enter an air mass before it becomes saturated. It is expressed as a percentage, which is the ratio of the amount of water vapor in the air to the maximum amount that the same volume of air could contain at a given temperature and pressure.

When the air is holding the maximum amount of water vapor for the existing temperature (i.e., 68° F) and pressure, the air is saturated (i.e., 17.31 grams) and the relative humidity is 100 percent. However, if the same unit of air were only holding a little more than half of the amount of water vapor it is capable of at that temperature, the relative humidity would be 54 percent (junction of 68° F and 9.41 grams). This would leave 46 percent more water vapor that the given air mass could hold at 68° F.

Looking at the figure on page 401 may make this relationship clearer. The ratio of A to B equals the relative humidity—a percentage indicator of how much more water (C) that the unit of air at 68° F could hold before reaching the saturation point (B), or 17.31 grams of water vapor. In this case, the unit of air could accept up to 7.9 grams more of vapor before it would be saturated. The relative humidity number is indicating how much more vapor the air is capable of holding at the time of measurement. This, in turn, gives a fair idea of when condensation and/or precipitation might occur—particularly important factors for pilots.

Condensation and Precipitation. Periodically, part of the water vapor in the air returns to a liquid or solid form and is seen as condensation or precipitation. Clouds, fog, dew and frost are forms of condensation. Rain, sleet, snow and hail are forms of precipitation. If visible water falls, it is precipitation; if it does not, it is condensation.

Condensation and precipitation occur due to lowered temperatures. Since cold air holds less moisture than warm air, simply lowering the temperature can increase the relative humidity. In doing so, the air holds less vapor and, if it is already saturated, the excess vapor condenses or turns into precipitation. If the temperature gets lower, and there is particulate matter in the air, the vapor can quickly change to a liquid state — a potential hazard to a pilot. If the air is cold enough, it can freeze and cause freezing rain — an even worse hazard for a pilot.

Dew Point Temperature. The dew point temperature is the key factor in condensation and precipitation. The dew point temperature is the temperature at or below which water vapor will condense. This does not say that there will be clouds, rain, snow, fog, etc., as a result of condensation. On the contrary, it indicates that some type of condensation will take place if the air temperature drops to a certain level. When compared to the actual air temperature, it also reveals how close the air is to saturation and how close the air is to forming condensation and precipitation.

Condensation and precipitation might be expected if the temperature dropped to 50° F (with no further vapor added to the air mass). This would be the dew point temperature. Relative humidity will have increased to 100 percent indicating that no more water vapor can be accepted into the air mass without condensation and precipitation probably occurring.

The difference between the actual and the dew point temperature is called the "spread." Relative humidity increases as the temperature spread decreases and is 100 percent when the spread is zero. At the dew point temperature, moisture in the air will condense to form clouds at higher altitudes and fog on the ground. Under the right conditions, precipitation could also occur. When the spread is within

4 degrees and the difference is getting smaller, fog should be expected.

Nothing about earth's atmosphere and its weather is simple, because of the almost constant changes experienced at any single location. For example, a parcel of air could have its water vapor content changed quickly if another parcel of air came along and the two merged their individual characteristics. That is, a warm and moist parcel that could mix with a cold and dry parcel.

If the mix were sudden, there would be some condensation because the temperature of the warm, moist air parcel would be lowered. At the same time, the cold, dry air parcel would be warmed. The net result would be a new parcel of air with a capacity for holding an amount of water vapor that would be somewhere between that of the warm air and the cold air before the mixing took place. In everyday weather, this sort of thing takes place all the time.

Particulate Matter

Dust and other very small particles called particulate matter play an important role in weather. If they were not present in the atmosphere, there would not be certain forms of condensation and precipitation.

These particles serve as a surface for condensation of water vapor and are called condensation nuclei. The molecules of water attach themselves to these nuclei if the temperature is right. Water molecules continue to accumulate until they can be seen in their familiar liquid or solid forms. For an idea of just how small the condensation nuclei might be, the diameter of a single condensation nucleus could be as small as 0.000000004 inch (four billionths of an inch).

═══ Atmosphere in Motion ═══

The atmosphere is in constant motion in all directions: up, down and sideways. This is why the weather is constantly changing. If a unit of air is thought of as being the center of a sphere, its movement can be in any of the directions possible from the center of the sphere outward. This unit of air can be very small or it can involve hundreds of cubic feet.

There are two primary causes of atmospheric motion: heat and the motion of earth. Heat comes from the sun, and is critical in keeping the planet inhabitable. Thus, it is essential to examine how this thermonuclear heating system works.

Heat and Temperature

The heat energy contained within the atmosphere is responsible for all the earth's weather processes. In review, remember the atmosphere is composed of molecules that are in constant motion. Because of this motion, the molecules possess energy. Heat is the sum total energy of all moving molecules within a substance. If something has a great deal of heat, the total energy of motion of all the molecules in the substance is high. Temperature, on the other hand, is a measure that expresses an average of the energy of molecular motion. Heat is a form of energy, and energy can be transformed and transferred.

Methods of Heat Transfer

There are four principal ways in which heat is transferred from one place to another. These are called conduction, convection, advection and radiation.

Conduction. When one molecule (energized to a higher level of molecular motion through the heating process), contacts another molecule, the second molecule absorbs some of this heat. This is why the air above a layer of hot concrete, for example, becomes warmer than other surrounding air. Heating by direct contact is called conduction.

Convection. Any heat transfer by vertical motion is called convection. An example is the rippling effect of air above a hot runway or highway in the summer. The air over these hot surfaces rises much more quickly than the air over surrounding surfaces. Thus, vertical currents are established in the atmosphere; some parcels of air are heated and rise, and other parcels of air are cooled and descend.

Advection. When the wind blows, it is simply movement by or within the local air mass. Since that air mass has a certain temperature, that temperature will be transferred horizontally over the surface of the earth by blowing winds or moving air masses. This process of lateral heat transfer is called advection. Advection is an important factor in the global circulation of air.

Radiation. The heat energy of the sun reaches earth as radiation. This method transfers heat energy without changing the temperature of anything between the source of energy and the object heated. Heat energy escapes a generating source in the form of waves. These radiant waves (or rays) are themselves a form of energy and are part of the electromagnetic spectrum, which includes visible light. When radiant energy from one object reaches another object and is absorbed, the radiant energy is changed into some other form of energy, often heat.

You can experience the effect of radiation, and its consequent heating effect, with an ordinary electric light bulb. Place your hand within one foot or so of a lighted bulb and hold it there for at least 30 seconds. The radiant energy from the light bulb will warm your hand considerably. The same effect can be felt with a flashlight, but your hand will have to be much closer to the flashlight because it generates much less radiant energy than the light bulb. The radiant energy that comes from the light bulb or the flashlight and warms your hand is the same principle as sunlight warming the earth.

Although radiant energy is never destroyed, it may be changed in many ways. Radiant waves may be absorbed or reflected by the clouds, scattered or reflected by dust in the air, or absorbed by the earth and converted into heat energy.

As stated before, the evaporation process requires a lot of heat (radiant energy). Although the radiant energy is absorbed by the water, there is no increase in the temperature of the water vapor that results; no heat is lost.

When the water vapor later condenses, heat is released and does affect the temperature of the surrounding air. This heat is known as the latent heat of condensation. This is a point to be remembered, since the heat released in this manner is a prime source of atmospheric energy. It is this latent heat energy that fuels such violent atmospheric disturbances as thunderstorms, tornadoes and hurricanes.

Insolation

The rate at which the earth's surface is heated by solar radiation is called insolation. The amount of insolation received at any point on the earth's surface depends on several factors: the angle the sun's rays make with the horizon (called the angle of incidence), the distance of the earth from the sun and the amount of radiation absorbed by the atmosphere. On clear days more radiation reaches the earth's surface than on cloudy days. Very dense cloud formations may reflect as much as three-fourths of the radiant energy from the sun.

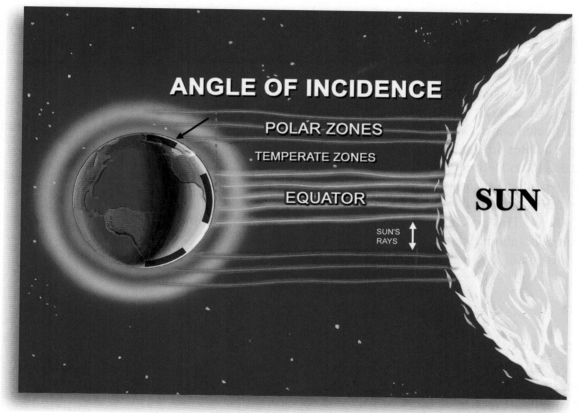

ANGLE OF INCIDENCE

POLAR ZONES

TEMPERATE ZONES

EQUATOR

SUN

SUN'S RAYS

Insolation varies with latitude.

Insolation is greatest in the equatorial zone. The sun's rays are nearly perpendicular to the earth's surface. Therefore, more radiant waves per equal area (hence, more heat) reach the equatorial zone than reach the temperate zones, and more reach the temperate zones than reach the polar zones.

The Heat Balance

If there were no balance of heat between the earth, its atmosphere and space, the earth would become increasingly warmer. This does not happen because the insolation is in turn radiated back from the earth into space or the atmosphere.

It is estimated that of all the solar radiation arriving at the top of the atmosphere, 25 percent is reflected into space by clouds and atmospheric dust, 15 percent is absorbed directly into the atmosphere, and 50 percent reaches the earth. Of the 20 percent absorbed directly into the atmosphere, 4 percent eventually reaches the earth as diffused sky radiation. Thus, about 55 percent of all the incident solar radiation reaches the earth and heats it.

The heated earth's surface, in turn, radiates infrared rays upward. Part of these rays (about 39 percent) are absorbed by the atmosphere are convert-

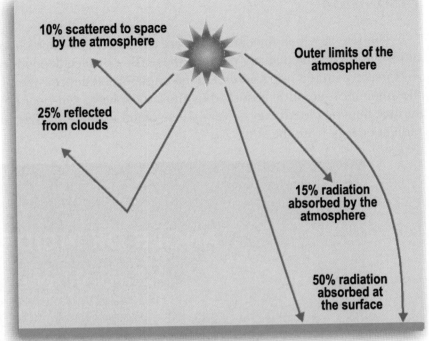

Solar Radiation

ed into heat. This process provides the principal source of heat for the troposphere. The rest of the infrared rays (about 8 percent) escape into space with no heating effect. The radiative processes that tend to maintain the earth's heat balance are also chiefly responsible for worldwide weather.

Wind

Heated air rises. It rises because the heat applied to it has decreased its density to the point where it is lighter in weight than the surrounding air, and the surrounding, cooler air pushes the parcel of lighter air upward. This same effect can be seen in the flight of a hot-air balloon.

When this heated air rises, cooler, higher-pressure air flows sideways to fill the lower-pressure area created. This lateral movement is referred to as wind. Basically, the same type of exchange takes place on a global level, but in much larger proportions. All along the equatorial zone the air is heated more than at any other area. In the polar regions, where the angle of incidence is least, the least amount of heating takes place. The general trend is, therefore, for the cold air from the polar region to flow toward the equatorial zone. This occurs while the heated air of the equatorial zone is rising and drifting toward the poles.

The rotation of the earth complicates this simple concept of wind. The rotation causes the alternating heating and cooling of the equatorial and other regions during day and night. Perhaps the most significant influence on the creation and flow of wind is the spinning planet and the resulting Coriolis Effect.

Global Winds

Coriolis Effect

The atmosphere is a part of the earth held by the earth's gravity. However, the atmosphere is not rigidly attached to the earth. The atmosphere may move with relationship to the earth, and the earth may move with relationship to the atmosphere.

The earth rotates on its axis in such a way that an observer in space over the North Pole would see the earth turning in a counterclockwise direction. The rotation of the earth influences any object moving over its surface. This influence is called the Coriolis Effect after the French physicist who first explained it in 1835.

The Coriolis Effect can be illustrated by imagining the earth as the turntable on a record player with the center of the turntable representing the North Pole and the rim being the Equator.

1. Place paper on top of the turntable and cut it to the same circular dimension.
2. Start the turntable rotating in a counterclockwise direction.
3. Using a ruler and pencil, quickly draw a straight line from the center (North Pole) to the rim (Equator) of the rotating turntable.

To the person drawing the line, the pencil line traveled in a straight line. When the turntable is stopped, it can be seen. The line is not straight but is curved to the right or west. Similarly, a line drawn from the rim (Equator) to the center (North Pole) of the turntable, the line would curve to the left or east.

Anytime the atmosphere is in motion, the Coriolis Effect caused by the rotation of the earth influences it. The heated air rises over the Equator and begins to travel toward the poles. However, the Coriolis effect acting on this mass of moving air will deflect it to the east in the Northern Hemisphere. By the

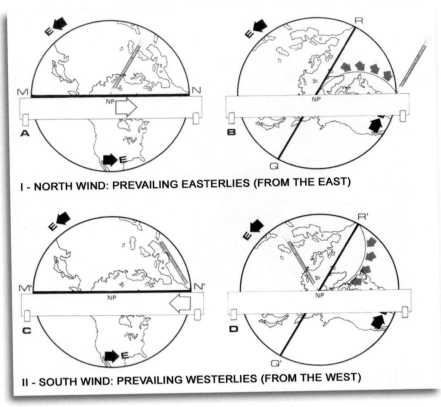

I - NORTH WIND: PREVAILING EASTERLIES (FROM THE EAST)

II - SOUTH WIND: PREVAILING WESTERLIES (FROM THE WEST)

Example of the Coriolis Effect

time this air mass reaches 30° N latitude, it is no longer traveling north. It has been deflected and is moving straight east. As the mass of air cools, it becomes denser and sinks toward the earth, creating a high-pressure belt at this latitude.

As the air pressure builds up within this belt, some of it is forced downward toward earth's surface. A portion flows toward the Equator along the surface; another portion flows toward the pole along the surface. As these surface winds move toward the poles and the Equator, the Coriolis Effect again comes into play, deflecting the moving air masses.

The air flowing from 30° N latitude toward the Equator is deflected toward the west. This creates the trade winds that blow toward the southwest in the Northern Hemisphere. The air flowing from 30° latitude toward the North Pole is deflected toward the east. This creates the prevailing westerlies that blow toward the northeast between 30° N latitude and 60° N latitude. The same conditions occur in the Southern Hemisphere, but the directions of flow are reversed because the direction of rotation in the Southern Hemisphere is clockwise.

At the same time, some of the air aloft continues to flow toward the poles, cools, settles to the surface, and begins a return trip toward the Equator. The warmer surface air moving up from latitude 30° overruns this colder air and produces a high-pressure condition in the polar zones. When the polar high pressure becomes sufficient, massive cold-air surges break out of the polar zones. These surges of air move toward the Equator and cause the changing weather conditions of the middle latitudes.

The Pressure Gradient

Several factors cause the atmosphere to be a constantly changing landscape of invisible mountains and valleys. The major influences are the uneven distribution of oceans and continents, the seasonal temperature changes, the heat transferring qualities of different earth surfaces and daily temperature changes. The high-pressure areas of the atmosphere are the mountains and the low-pressure areas are the valleys. The wind flows from these high-pressure mountains into the low-pressure valleys.

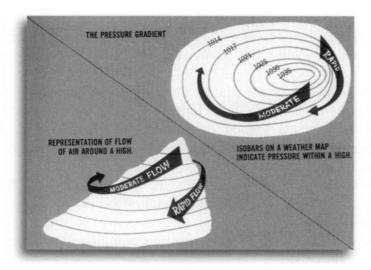

The Pressure Gradient

The slope of the high-pressure mountain is called the pressure gradient. On weather maps, its degree of steepness is shown by lines called isobars. Isobars are drawn through points of equal sea-level atmospheric (barometric) pressure. They identify five different types of pressure patterns—highs, lows, cols, troughs, and ridges. A high is a center of high pressure surrounded by lower pressure, and a low is a center of low pressure surrounded by higher pressure. A col is a "saddle-back" area between two highs and two lows. An elongated area of low pressure is called a trough. An elongated area of high pressure is called a ridge.

Other Factors Affecting the Wind

Other factors that affect the circulation of the air (wind) are gravity, friction and centrifugal effect (also known as centrifugal force). Gravity tends to pull the air downward and produce a graduated air-density distribution, with the greatest air density near the earth's surface. Friction tends to slow air movement from the earth's surface up to 6,000 feet or more.

Centrifugal force acts on air moving in a curved path, and decreases its speed within a low-pressure area and increases it within a high-pressure area. In the Northern Hemisphere, the air flows clockwise around the high-pressure area (an anticyclone) and counterclockwise around a low-pressure area (a cyclone). In the Southern Hemisphere the directions are reversed.

It should be noted that at an altitude where surface friction ceases to affect wind movement, the wind always blows parallel to the isobars. At this level (called the wind level), pressure gradient, centrifugal effect, and the Coriolis Effect are in balance. The wind at this level is called the gradient wind. Its speed is always inversely proportional to the distance between the isobars. This means that when the isobars on a weather map are far apart, the wind is weak; when they are close together, the wind is strong. Aviators always try to take advantage of favorable winds, and plan and navigate their flights accordingly.

Local and Surface Air Movements

The general circulation of the air is complicated by the irregular distribution of land and water areas. Different types of surfaces vary in the rate at which they absorb heat from the sun and transfer heat to the atmosphere. Seasonal changes and daily variations in temperature also affect this rate of transfer.

In some regions, local low-pressure areas form over hot land surfaces in summer, and over the warmer water surfaces in winter. Convection currents are formed along shorelines. These currents are

heated air rising upward, which cause advection currents (wind) to flow from the water over the warmer land during the day. During the night, convection currents develop over the warmer-than-land water and cause the wind to blow from the land toward the water. This phenomenon is known as the land and sea breeze.

Local air circulation of limited scope is caused by variations in the earth's surface. Some surfaces— such as sand, rocks, plowed areas and barren land—give off or reflect a great amount of heat. Other surfaces—such as meadows, planted fields and water—tend to retain heat. Rising air currents are encountered by aircraft flying over surfaces that give off considerable heat, while descending air currents are encountered over surfaces that tend to retain heat.

Moving air flowing around obstructions tends to break into eddies. On the leeward (opposite of the windward) side of mountains, there are descending air currents. Such conditions cause turbulent air. The stronger the wind, the greater the descending air currents and turbulence. Aviators flying into the wind toward mountainous terrain should place enough distance between their aircraft and the mountaintops to avoid dangerous descending air currents.

Land and Sea Breeze Phenomenon

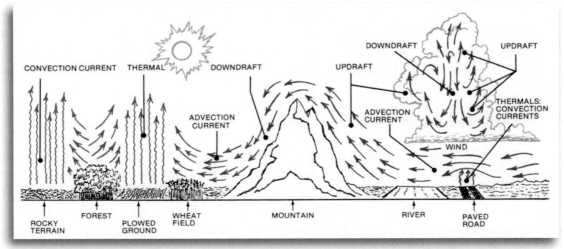

Thermals, advection currents, convection currents, wind, updrafts and downdrafts affect air movement.

410

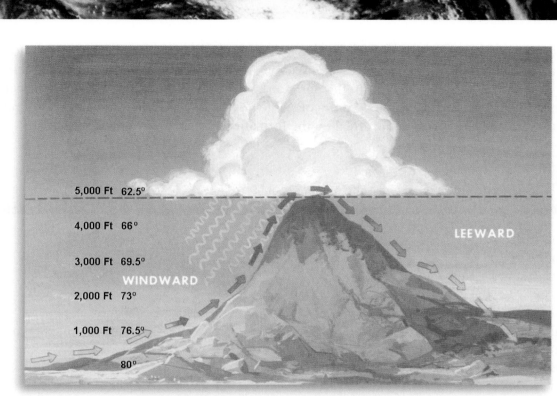

5,000 Ft	62.5°
4,000 Ft	66°
3,000 Ft	69.5°
2,000 Ft	73°
1,000 Ft	76.5°
	80°

WINDWARD

LEEWARD

Descending Air Currents on Leeward Side of a Mountain

The Jet Stream

The jet stream, as mentioned earlier, is a comparatively narrow current of air that moves around the Northern (and Southern) Hemispheres of the earth in wavelike patterns. It might be compared to a "river" of wind moving at high speed. The jet stream varies from about 100 to 400 miles wide and 1 to 3 miles thick. Its strongest winds are generally encountered above 30,000 feet. Jet-stream winds usually have a speed of 150 to 300 mph, but speeds up to 450 mph have been recorded. Its general motion is from west to east.

The jet stream shifts position frequently and actually migrates with the seasons. Sometimes two streams flow across the United States, one along the northern border and the other well toward the south. The cruising range of aircraft flying downwind within a jet stream is greatly increased. Pilots anticipating high-altitude or long-range flights attempt to discover the location of the jet stream and use it to their advantage.

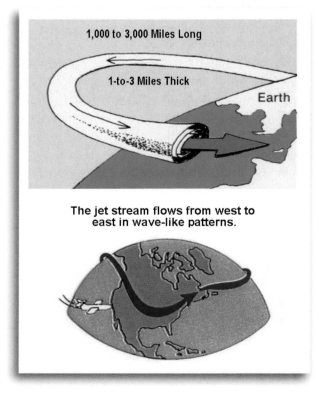

1,000 to 3,000 Miles Long

1-to-3 Miles Thick

Earth

The jet stream flows from west to east in wave-like patterns.

411

For several decades now, meteorologists have studied jet streams and how they affect the movements of air masses. While the relationship is still unknown, there is a common agreement that jet streams may act as a barrier between cold air in the north and warm air in the south. During their snakelike meandering, the streams appear to allow some cold air to flow southward and warm air to flow northward. These flows undoubtedly have some affect on the formation of cold and warm air masses.

Key Terms and Concepts

- atmosphere
- aerospace
- atmospheric elements
- four ways to classify atmospheric regions
- temperature distribution: troposphere, stratosphere, mesosphere, thermosphere
- physicochemical process distribution: ozonosphere, ionosphere, neutrosphere, chemosphere
- molecular composition: heterosphere and homosphere
- dynamic and kinetic processes: exosphere
- density, pressure and mass
- condensation
- humidity and relative humidity
- saturation
- dew point
- evaporation
- solar radiation
- sublimation
- condensation and precipitation
- fog
- particulate matter
- condensation nuclei
- heat and temperature
- conduction
- convection
- advection
- radiation
- insolation
- Coriolis Effect
- pressure gradient
- isobars
- centrifugal force
- land-sea breeze phenomena
- jet stream

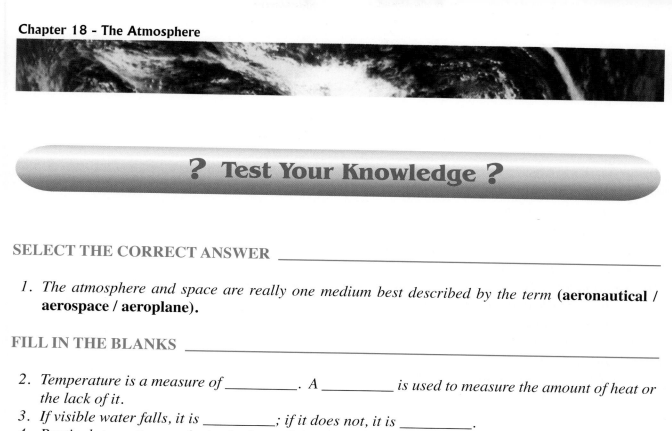

? Test Your Knowledge ?

SELECT THE CORRECT ANSWER

1. The atmosphere and space are really one medium best described by the term (**aeronautical / aerospace / aeroplane**).

FILL IN THE BLANKS

2. Temperature is a measure of _____. A _____ is used to measure the amount of heat or the lack of it.
3. If visible water falls, it is _____; if it does not, it is _____.
4. Particulate matter can be in the form of dust, dirt, smoke, exhaust fumes or even salt particles. If the temperature is right, these particles can serve as _____ for _____.
5. The following terms are part of the _____ cycle:
    dew point temperature
    solar radiation
    sublimation
    saturate
6. The difference between the actual and the dew point temperature is called the _____.
7. The rate at which the _____ surface is heated by _____ radiation is called insulation.
8. The radiation processes that tend to maintain the earth's _____ _____ are also chiefly responsible for worldwide weather.
9. Wind is generally referred to as a _____ movement of air.
10. The rotation of the earth affecting anything moving over its surface is one way of defining the _____.

MATCHING

11. Heating by direct contact
12. Process of lateral heat transfer
13. Heat transfers by vertical motion
14. Heat energy of the sun-reaching earth

a. Radiation
b. Advection
c. Convection
d. Conduction

MULTIPLE CHOICE

15. *Centrifugal effect acts on air moving in a curved path and decreases its speed within a low-pressure area and*
    a. *decreases it within a high-pressure area.*
    b. *increases it within a high-pressure area.*
    c. *stops it within a high-pressure area.*
    d. *none of the above.*
16. *Friction tends to*
    a. *have no affect on air movement.*
    b. *increase air movement.*
    c. *slow air movement.*
    d. *all of the above.*
17. *Gravity tends to pull air downward with the greatest air density*
    a. *near the earth's surface.*
    b. *next to the jet stream.*
    c. *at the tropopause.*
    d. *near the sun.*
18. *Unequal heating by the sun's rays of land and water areas causes*
    a. *the land and sea-breeze phenomena.*
    b. *the thermal downdraft.*
    c. *winds to stay aloft.*
    d. *none of the above.*
19. *Different types of earth's surfaces vary in the rate at which they*
    a. *reflect the sun's heat and transfer the sun's heat to the atmosphere.*
    b. *absorb the sun's heat and transfer the sun's heat to the atmosphere.*
    c. *absorb the sun's heat and transform heat to the atmosphere.*
    d. *avoid the sun's heat and reflect heat to the atmosphere.*
20. *Jet streams shift positions frequently and*
    a. *have some effect on the formation of cold and warm air masses.*
    b. *can be compared to a river of air.*
    c. *actually migrate with the seasons.*
    d. *all of the above.*

TRUE OR FALSE

21. *Density is the comparison of how heavy something is to the space it fills.*
22. *Liquid water will evaporate only if there is space in the air for the water vapor molecules to occupy.*
23. *A high is a center of high pressure surrounded by higher pressure.*
24. *An elongated area of high pressure is called a ridge.*

25. *A low is a center of low pressure surrounded by even lower pressure.*
26. *An elongated area of low pressure is called a trough.*
27. *A col is a "saddleback" area between a high and a low.*

SHORT ANSWER

28. *Explain the difference between humidity and relative humidity.*
29. *Cite examples of how heat energy can be transformed and transferred.*
30. *Review the term standard lapse rate and solve the following problem: You are at the ocean beach on a hot summer day and the thermometer registers 92° F. What would be the temperature reading for the pilot directly above you flying at 8,000 feet?*
31. *The following examples involve atmospheric pressure. Give a brief explanation of each.*
    a. *The doors on a new car will not close unless a window is partially open.*
    b. *Your ears "pop" if you go up or down a mountain.*
    c. *You usually make two holes in the top of a metal can in order to remove the liquid.*

Chapter 19 WEATHER ELEMENTS

Meteorologists, who are also called weather forecasters, define weather as "the condition of the atmosphere at any particular time and place." In simpler terms, the weather is the day-to-day changes in atmospheric conditions.

The weather is usually described by its elements. These include temperature, air pressure, humidity, clouds, precipitation, visibility and wind.

Everything the atmosphere does, plus the activity of the sun, affects the weather and can be considered weather elements. Thus, this chapter will first examine various weather elements within the larger categories of air masses and fronts, clouds and terrain factors. Then we will analyze wind shears and clear-air turbulence. Some of the unique weather patterns affecting the United States will end this chapter.

You are encouraged to develop a mental picture of the weather parts and to have a general understanding of how all the parts interact to cause weather—both good and bad.

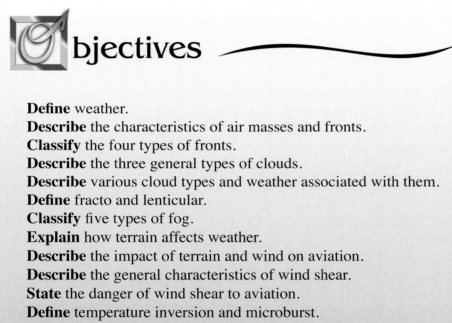

Objectives

Define weather.
Describe the characteristics of air masses and fronts.
Classify the four types of fronts.
Describe the three general types of clouds.
Describe various cloud types and weather associated with them.
Define fracto and lenticular.
Classify five types of fog.
Explain how terrain affects weather.
Describe the impact of terrain and wind on aviation.
Describe the general characteristics of wind shear.
State the danger of wind shear to aviation.
Define temperature inversion and microburst.
Identify causes of clear-air turbulence.
Classify types of clear-air turbulence.
Define wake turbulence.

Air Masses and Fronts

An air mass is a large body of air. It usually covers an area 1,000 or more miles across. It generally has the same temperature and moisture content within the entire mass. The temperature and moisture characteristics of the air mass are similar to those of the area in which the air mass originates.

Air Mass Type and Origination

A polar air mass (P) is cold and a tropical air mass (T) is hot. A maritime air mass (m) is humid and a continental air mass (c) is dry. Maritime air masses are formed over water and continental air masses are formed over land. Aviators and meteorologists in the United States are mainly concerned with two air masses — those that move southward from polar regions and those that move northward from tropical regions.

Here are the air mass classifications:

cA = **continental arctic**
cP = **continental polar**
cT = **continental tropical**
mT = **maritime tropical**
mP = **maritime polar**
mE = **maritime equatorial**

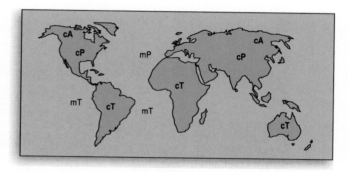

Characteristics of Air Masses

The characteristics of an air mass depend on four things: the surface over which it forms, the season, the surface over which it travels and the length of time it has been away from its source. The general movement of the atmosphere across the United States is toward the east. Air masses originating in the tropical and equatorial areas move toward the northeast. Those originating in the arctic and polar areas move toward the southeast. Cold air masses move more rapidly than warm air masses. The weather generally depends on the nature or origin of an air mass or the interaction of two or more air masses.

As an air mass moves away from its source, its original characteristics are changed by the earth's surface over which it passes. It may become warmer or colder, absorb or lose moisture, rise over mountains or settle into valleys. However, an air mass is not likely to lose all of its original characteristics.

Fronts

The boundaries between air masses of different characteristics are called frontal zones or fronts. A front moves along the earth's surface as one air mass displaces another. If a cold air mass replaces a warmer air mass, the boundary is called a cold front. If a warm air mass replaces a cold air mass, the boundary is called a warm front. When there is a big temperature and humidity difference between the two air masses, weather changes along the front will be severe.

Cold Front. The cold front's general direction of travel across the United States is from the northwest to southeast. Cold fronts travel very far south, even in the summertime. The energy of a cold front depends on the amount of cold air that comprises the high-pressure cell behind it.

An Approaching Front *(NOAA Photo Library)*

The front is the leading edge of the air mass and is formed at the junction of this high-pressure cold air with lower-pressure warm air. Since the cold air is denser, it pushes under the warm air forcing it upward. How much weather is associated with a cold front's movement depends on the condition of the warm air with which it is colliding. In the western states, the warm air is often dry. As a front moves through, the only noticeable change is a shift of wind, cooler temperature and possibly blowing dust.

As the "typical" cold front approaches the southern and eastern states, it encounters warmer vapor-laden air and problems for aviators begin. As the warm, humid air is forced upward, it cools and water vapor condenses into clouds creating thunderstorms. If the movement of the cold air mass is rapid, and if there is abundant water vapor ahead of it, very violent weather can occur. Lines of thunderstorms (squall lines) develop well ahead of the front—from 50 to 150 miles. These squall lines are in addition to the thunderstorms immediately ahead of the front.

Somewhere along the cold front there will be a low-pressure cell. In the area around this cell, the weather will be at its worst. Almost any type of cloud can be found here because this is where the amount of water vapor is high and the temperature and dew point temperature are very close. Therefore, as the air is lifted, only a slight drop in temperature causes condensation. If the season is summer, aviators can expect very poor visibility, exceptionally low clouds and a lot of rain. Winter makes the low-pressure area even more miserable for aviation because of freezing rain and snow.

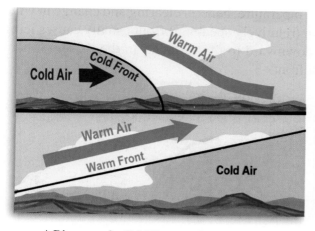

A Diagram of a Cold Front and a Warm Front

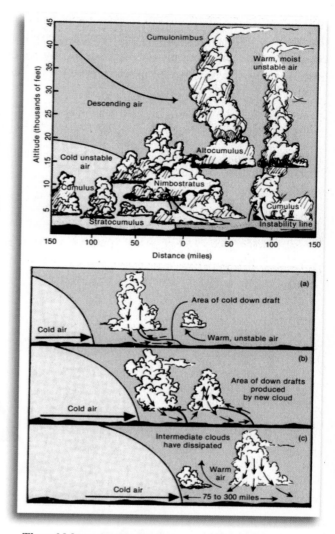

The cold front (top) produces a squall line (bottom) resulting in very violent weather.

Warm Front. Although both cold fronts and warm fronts can exist without the associated low-pressure cell, the condition is not common. Therefore, the usual warm front is connected to a low-pressure cell, extends eastward from it and travels northeastward. Now, if the low-pressure cell did not move, the warm front would travel counterclockwise around the cell until it dissipated. However, the normal cold-front, low-pressure cell, warm-front complex involves movement of all three components; thus, the low-pressure cell tends to travel eastward/northeastward across the United States, taking the warm front with it.

Since warm air is less dense than cool or cold air, the leading edge of a warm front slips upward and over the cooler air forming a wedge shape. The warm air rises slowly and its rate of cooling is slow, which results in delayed condensation of the water vapor. The approaching warm front is announced by the appearance of cirrus (high, thin, wispy clouds). The cirrus may be as much as 1,000 miles in advance of the front. As the front approaches, other types of clouds are present and the sky gets darker and darker. Eventually, rain begins to fall.

The above description of an approaching warm front is typical. However, fronts do not always act in this typical manner. For instance, a warm front may also cause violent thunderstorms, if the air in front of it is highly unstable. The atmospheric conditions ahead of and behind fronts are key in determining what kind of weather will occur.

Near the frontal boundary, clouds usually are low, there is gentle rain and visibility is poor. Often, the falling of warm rain into the cooler air near the surface causes fog. Fog is the archenemy of avia-

419

tion activities. After the front passes, there is a rise in temperature, general clearing and change in wind direction. In the winter months, the passage of a warm (relatively speaking) front usually causes icing conditions at very low altitudes, which may extend downward to the surface. In the more northern latitudes, snow may also be associated with the warm front.

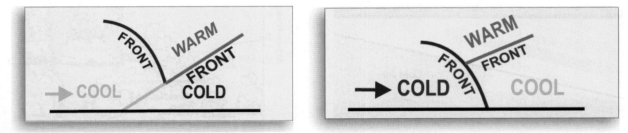

Diagrams of Warm and Cold Occluded Fronts

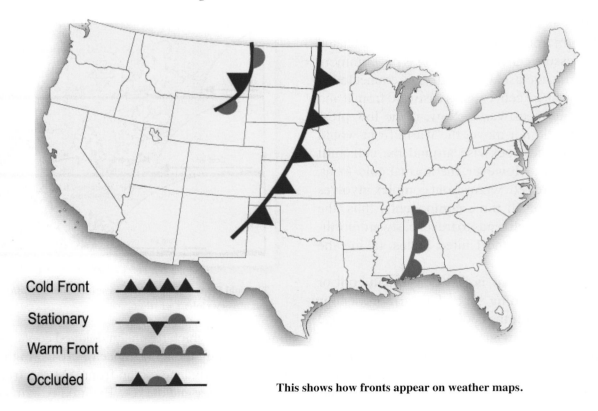

This shows how fronts appear on weather maps.

Stationary Front. When air masses lose their "punch" and are not replacing one another, a stationary front develops. The weather along a stationary front can be very bad for aviation. In parts of the country where there is a large amount of moisture, just about every form of weather can be found along the stationary front. There may be very slow-moving thunderstorms at some locations. At other locations, there may be large areas of drizzle and fog.

Near the trailing edge of any front, there will be a stationary-front condition because a frontal zone cannot go on forever. Such "trailing-edge" stationary fronts are caused by the great distance between the pressure cell and the end of the front attached to it. When the distance becomes great enough, the identity between cold and warm air is lost. The front in that area no longer exists.

Occluded Front. Another type of frontal development is called an occlusion or occluded front. It is formed when a warm air mass, lying between two cold air masses, is lifted up by the cold air mass behind it. The rapidly lifted warm air cools and creates a low sometimes causing severe precipitation to occur. Such a front will also cause the usual cold-front and warm-front weather. As the occluded front passes, there is little change in the temperature of the ground air, because at that level, there is only a change of cold air masses.

Clouds

The previous chapter explained how condensation takes place. Condensation is also how clouds form. Clouds will form wherever the dew point temperature and water vapor happen to be collocated within the atmosphere.

Clouds form at different altitudes above the surface, varying from hundreds to thousands of feet. They take on characteristic shapes according to altitudes, temperatures and the movement of the atmosphere at their levels.

Cloud Types

The three general types of clouds are cumulus (piled up), stratus (layered), and cirrus (high, thin appearance). All other types come from these three, and we usually talk about them as low, middle and high clouds.

Low. Beginning at the lower altitudes, between 300 and 6,500 feet, the stratus, cumulus, stratocumulus, cumulonimbus and nimbostratus types of clouds are found. Stratus means to stretch out and/or cover as a layer. Cumulus means a piling up of

Cumulus

Stratus (Note Tower Fading in Cloud)

Cirrus

rounded masses; thus, the cumulus cloud looks bumpy. Nimbo is the combining term to indicate that a cloud is at the moment producing precipitation or is capable of producing precipitation. This precipitation is more closely associated with rain, but it also includes snow and sleet.

Middle. The middle clouds are first identified by the prefix "alto" (high, but not highest). At middle altitude, which is between 6,500 feet and 20,000 feet, the stratus and cumulus shapes are found, but are known as altostratus and altocumulus. Nimbostratus can be classified here too.

High. At 20,000 feet and up, cirrus types appear. Cirrus means wispy or fleecy. There are cirrus, cirrostratus and cirrocumulus. Cirrus are thin and lacy. Cirrostratus are slightly thicker and look more like a layer. Cirrocumulus are similar to cirrostratus, but have a slightly bumpy appearance.

Fracto and Lenticular. Another combining term associated with the various cloud types is "fracto," which means broken and/or ragged. Thus, we can combine fracto with stratus to describe a broken stratus layer—fractostratus.

There is a special type of cloud that frequently forms as strong winds sweep up and over the tops of high mountains. It is called a lenticular formation and its name is the result of its lens-like shape (double convex). A lenticular can, and does, form over other than mountainous areas, but the classic lenticulars are more frequent in the mountains.

What do these cloud types mean? Stated simply, they tell what can be expected with regard to turbulence, visibility and precipitation. Following will be a study of the cloud types and their general characteristics in more detail. First, however, the reader must understand that these characteristics are probabilities and averages. No one can point to a particular type of cloud and guarantee the exact conditions that will be found near it.

Stratus and Altostratus

Stratus has a smooth appearance. It indicates to pilots that no turbulence (bumpiness) is associated with the cloud. However, the stratus may be nothing more than fog that has developed at the surface and risen a hundred or so feet above the surface. The stratus may or may not produce some type of

Altostratus

precipitation. If precipitation does occur, it will be light drizzle in the summer or light snow in the winter. The reason why simple stratus produces so little precipitation is that it is relatively thin. For a cloud to produce significant precipitation, a thickness of 4,000 feet or more is the norm.

To aviation, stratus can cause problems. Low stratus can create visibility problems for pilots. It can hide the fact that they are flying into or toward very unfavorable or dangerous weather. Thus, stratus can be a hazard to aviation because of reduced or obscured visibility.

The simple altostratus usually is relatively thin, perhaps more so than the lower-level stratus. It produces a gray or bluish veil through which the sun may be dimly seen. Due to its altitude—particularly in the winter months—it may contain ice crystals and supercooled water droplets. If the altostratus does produce precipitation, it will be very light.

The cirrostratus appears at high altitudes and is very, very thin. It is composed entirely of ice crystals. The light of the sun or moon refracted by these crystals can sometimes cause a halo effect around the sun or moon.

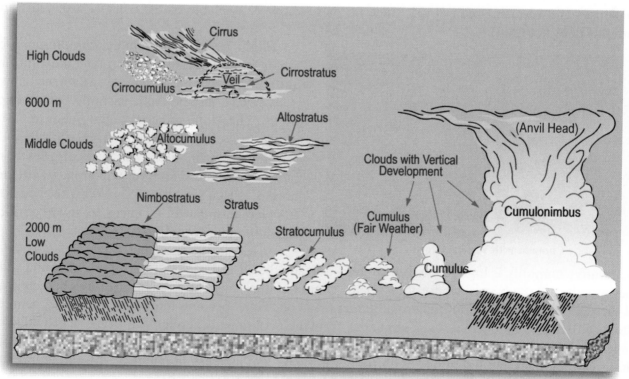

The 10 Basic Cloud Types

Stratocumulus

The similarity of stratocumulus to stratus lies in the layering characteristic only. This cloud has numerous bumps on the topside and usually is rather thick. Heavier rains and snow can be expected from this type of cloud. Turbulence of varying intensity can also be expected nearer the bottom of the layer.

To pilots, the appearance of stratocumulus is a warning that flying under these clouds most likely will bring low visibility and probably strong turbulence. Flying over these clouds is not wise either. The stratocumulus can mask higher and more severe cloud buildups.

Stratocumulus

Cumulus with Vertical Growth

Cumulus alone has a harmless, puffy, cotton-ball appearance with a horizontal dark base. It is known as fair-weather cumulus. It develops from thermals or updrafts of heated air containing a relatively small amount of water vapor. Upon reaching the dew point temperature at altitude, the vapor condenses and forms a small cloud; since no more vapor is available or the thermal dissipates, the cumulus does not grow.

Cumulus with Vertical Growth

Flight below fair-weather cumulus can be rather bumpy because the airplane flies into the updrafts beneath the clouds. However, no danger is involved—just the slight discomfort of a choppy flight. Therefore, aviators find it better to climb above such clouds and enjoy a smooth ride.

However, cumulus with vertical growth, or building cumulus, deserves attention. It will produce at least a strong rain shower with moderate to severe turbulence. Chances are it will develop into a thunderstorm.

Vertical-growth cumulus can be expected if the relative humidity is high, the temperature is hot, and the air is unstable. Thus, the spring and summer months are the best times for this type of cloud buildup. Very strong updrafts are characteristic of these clouds as they build higher and larger. As conditions become more favorable, two or more clouds will merge and form an even larger cell from their combined energies. This type of growth continues until the cloud becomes a cumulonimbus. As a cumulonimbus, it has developed precipitation along with thunder and lightning. With further building and increase in intensity, the cumulonimbus is called a thunderstorm.

Type	CLOUDS Approximate height of bases (feet)	Description	ASSOCIATED WEATHER Precipitation types	General
Cumulus	1,500 10,000	Brilliant white in sun, dark blue or gray in shadows detached domes or towers, flat bases	If building rain or snow showers	Good surface visibility and fair weather, if not building. If building, high winds, turbulence
Altocumulus	6,500-16,500	White or gray layers. rolls or patches of wavy, solid clouds	Intermittent rain or snow, usually light	Turbulence likely: generally good surface visibility
Stratocumulus	A few feet above surface to 6,000	Gray or blue; individual rolls or globular masses	Light rain or snow showers	Strong gusty surface winds, particularly if ahead of a cold front turbulence
Cumulonimbus	1,500-10,000	Large, heavy, towering clouds; black bases; cauliflower-like or anvil-shaped tops	Heavy showers: possibility of hail	Associated with severe weather, turbulence, high surface winds; surface visibility usually fair to good outside of precipitation
Stratus	A few feet above surface to 3,000	Low, gray, uniform, sheet-like cloud	Light drizzle, light snow	Poor surface visibility, air smooth
Altostratus	6,500-16,500	Gray or blue veil or layer of clouds; appears fibrous; Sun may show as through frosted glass	Light continuous precipitation	Usually poor surface visibility; air smooth moderate surface winds
Nimbostratus	1,500-10,000	Dark gray, thick, shapeless cloud layer (really a low altostratus with precipitation)	Continuous precipitation	Visibility restricted by precipitation; air smooth; calm to light surface winds
Cirrus	16,500-45,000	White, thin, feathery clouds in patches or bands	None	If arranged in bands or associated with other clouds, usually a sign of approaching bad weather
Cirrostratus	16,500-45,000	White, thin cloud layers; looks like sheet or veil; halo around moon or sun	None	Often a sign of approaching bad weather; surface winds bring overcast skies
Cirrocumulus	16,500-45,000	Thin clouds in sheets; individual elements look like tufts of cotton	None	Indicate high-level instability

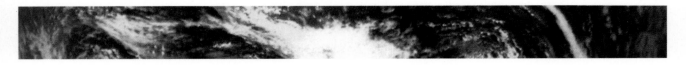

The chief danger with vertical growth or building cumulus clouds is extreme turbulence inside the cloud. Some pilots try to fly through the gaps or holes between developed thundershowers or thunderstorms. Unfortunately, cell merger can close the gaps faster than some planes can make it through. Then clouds, turbulence and rain suddenly surround the pilot.

The degree of turbulence in a building cumulus can be seen if you will take the time to watch one. The top continues to gain altitude and round protrusions build quickly, swirling upward, outward and downward from the rising column. Although the buildup looks graceful and appears to be at slow-motion speed, this is not the case. It is an illusion brought on by the distance between you and the cloud. Perhaps a better illustration of the latter point would be a modern, jet transport aircraft and its contrail, which seem to be creeping across the sky, while the actual speed involved may be 600 mph. The various cloud types, and the weather associated with them, are summarized in the table on page 425.

Altocumulus

Cirrus and Cirrostratus Clouds

Fog Types

Fog is a surface-based cloud because it develops within the atmosphere. It is considered separate of clouds because of how it is formed. It is a cloud in contact with the ground. There are five types of fog: radiation, high-inversion, advection, evaporation and upslope.

Radiation fog is so named because it forms at night when land surfaces radiate much of the heat absorbed from the sun back into space. The cool land surface in turn cools the air near it (by conduction) to below the dew point and fog is formed. High-inversion fog is actually a low cloud; it is formed by condensation of water vapor at or near the top of cool air that is covered by a warmer air layer. Advection fog is formed when wind blows moist air over a cold surface and the surface cools the air to its dew point temperature. Evaporation or steam may occur when cold air moves over warm water; the

water's normal evaporation process saturates the cooler air with water vapor, and the dew point is reached. Upslope fog results when wind carries moist air up a mountain slope or sloping land until the air is cooled.

Terrain Factors

You learned earlier that terrain has a very significant influence on how much solar radiation is absorbed or reflected by the earth's surface. The

Fog Rolling In Under the Golden Gate Bridge

presence of mountain ranges in the path of a weather front can change the characteristics of the front greatly. Gentle, rolling hills also contribute to the manufacture of weather.

An excellent example of mountains as weather makers is the High Sierra in California. Maritime tropical air masses coming into Southern California are filled with moisture and heat. Directly in the usual path of these air masses is a popular ski area and just a few miles past it is one of the driest spots in the world-Death Valley. What happens to the moisture in an air mass from the time it leaves the Pacific Ocean until it passes over Death Valley?

As the air mass enters the United States, the mountains cause it to rise. As it rises, it cools and loses practically 100 percent of its moisture on the western slopes of the mountains in the form of snow. This accounts for the excellent ski conditions. As it descends the eastern slopes, this dry air is heated and absorbs the small amount of moisture in the vicinity of Death Valley. This process is repeated again and again all over the world in the Himalayas, the Alps, the Caucasus and other mountain ranges where windward (facing the wind) slopes are moistened with rain and snow, and where leeward slopes are dry.

Along many seacoasts, there is a breeze from the sea by day. This moist, relatively cool air rises and heats as it passes across land. Clouds form a short distance inland and may bring showers by afternoon. At night, the land cools more rapidly than the sea, the current is reversed and the breeze blows from land to sea.

Wind blowing toward, or with, land formations that slope gently upward carries moisture-laden air to the altitude where its dew point temperature is located and condensation can occur. The reverse can happen if the wind forces clouds, which have already formed, downward into warmer air. The clouds will again become water vapor.

At any time the flow of wind is interrupted, turbulence develops. The severity of the turbulence depends on wind speed and the complexity and height of the obstruction to the wind. Gentle rolling

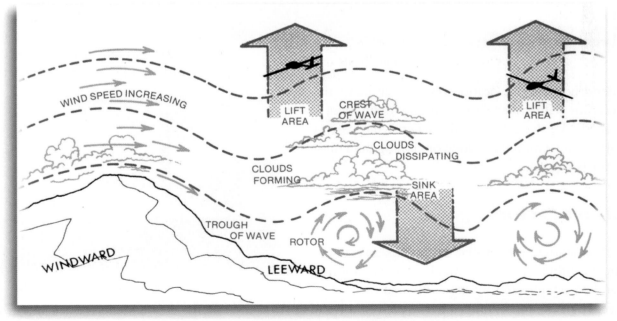

The Results of Strong Winds Crossing a Mountain Range.

hills, for example, will produce a mild turbulence for hundreds of feet above them. In the areas of the country where there are mountains, turbulence can be severe.

Even if the atmosphere is stable, a strong wind striking a mountain or range of mountains may produce little turbulence on the windward side. However, the leeward side will be very dangerous to flying. Turbulent downdrafts will be created and they can force an airplane into the side of the mountain with little or no warning.

When the wind strikes mountains at 50 mph or more, the result is extreme turbulence. The effect of this turbulence can be seen by the types of clouds formed—if sufficient water vapor is present. At or slightly below the elevation of the mountain crest, there may be what is known as rotor clouds. These clouds show by their shape and motion that the air coming over the mountain is spinning on an axis that parallels the mountain's linear shape. Higher up, there probably will be the lenticular-type clouds that we mentioned earlier. These lenticulars form at the crests of atmospheric waves, which develop as the force generated by the wind striking the mountain is transmitted upward.

For aircraft, flight into the area where rotor clouds are located must be avoided because of the danger of structural damage. Flight at higher altitudes, where the wave formations are located, produces inaccurate readings on the aircraft altitude indicator. Readings may be off as much as 1,000 feet. This is caused by the differences of atmospheric pressure within the wave formations. However, mountain waves are good news to at least one segment of aviation. Sailplane enthusiasts find the mountain wave to be the ideal weather condition for sustained and very high flight. By flying the crests of such waves, the sailplane pilot can gain and maintain altitudes that would not otherwise be possible.

Wind Shear

Wind shear is an atmospheric condition in which changes in speed and direction of the wind occur. At one level, the wind is traveling in one direction, while at an adjacent level either the wind is traveling in a different direction or the air at that level is calm. Turbulence is located at the junction of the two atmospheric layers involved in the wind shear phenomenon.

Aviators may experience horizontal wind shear when there is a temperature inversion. That is, nighttime radiation cooling may produce a layer of cool, calm air at the surface extending to a hundred or so feet above the surface while air above this layer is warm and moving. This kind of atmospheric condition is dangerous to aircraft during takeoff and landing because of the possibility of very abrupt changes in airspeed. The amount of danger depends on how fast the warm upper layer of air is moving and the direction of the aircraft's flight.

Vertical currents of air (updrafts or downdrafts) are forms of wind shear too. The strong vertical current near the approach or departure end of a runway can change the airspeed and flight path of an airplane greatly. This sort of air current is often experienced in a mild form during the summertime. The small airplane can be bounced up and down as the pilot tries to maintain a smooth and correct descent toward the runway. No matter how much the pilot tries to manipulate the controls, these summertime vertical air currents can make the descent seem very erratic.

The downdraft shear, or microburst, associated with large thunderstorms, can be particularly dangerous. The force of such downdrafts has caused even large airliners to strike the ground before reaching the runway. Microbursts, perhaps more than any other type of wind shear, have been the cause of aviation tragedies across the world.

A microburst is caused when a column of air is quickly cooled (usually by rain) and rapidly falls towards the earth. The air speed in a microburst often exceeds hurricane force and the resulting damage closely resembles that of a tornado. Recently, commercial aircraft and airports have been equipped with special doppler and infrared radar that can detect microbursts and give pilots enough warning to avoid them.

Diagram of a Microburst or Downdraft Shear.

Clear Air Turbulence

Turbulent air can be signaled by the presence of certain cloud types. However, clear air turbulence (CAT) may exist at different places and altitudes, but be completely invisible. The causes of such turbulent air may be one or a combination of the conditions discussed earlier: vertical growth if currents, wind shear and obstructions (such as mountains) to wind flow.

Since CAT cannot be seen, the first actual knowledge of the existence of a CAT area comes to the meteorologist, or weather service specialist, from pilots who fly into it. Pilots radio their location and the severity of the turbulence encountered to the weather service. This information is then made known to other pilots so those who will fly through the same area can be prepared.

The probability of CAT can be expected, even if it cannot be seen. Light CAT usually is found in hilly and mountainous areas even when winds are gentle. Light turbulence also occurs below 5,000 feet when the air is colder than the earth's surface (soon after the passage of a cold front), and at anytime the wind is blowing about 20 mph.

Turbulence can be further classified as light, moderate, severe and extreme. There are no ironclad criteria for designating these levels of turbulence, because how much turbulence exists depends on the person reporting it and the type of aircraft flying through it. It is generally agreed that the following sensations and reactions describe the various levels of turbulence: light—occupants of aircraft may be required to use seat belts, but objects in aircraft remain at rest; moderate—aircraft occupants must wear seat belts and unsecured objects move about; severe—aircraft may at times be out of control, occupants are thrown against seat belts and unsecured objects are tossed about; extreme—entire aircraft may be tossed about and is practically impossible to control. Structural damage to aircraft may result.

In addition to nature's CAT, there is one man-made type of CAT. This is called wake turbulence

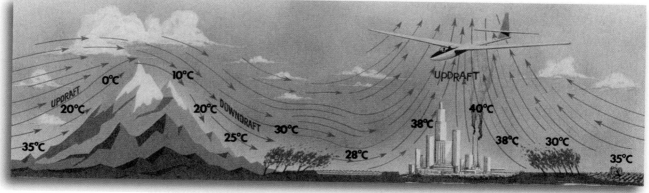

Some Causes of Clear Air Turbulence

and is caused by large aircraft in flight. As the wings of these large aircraft slice through the atmosphere, air spilling over and around their wingtips forms a vortex—a twisting, horizontal column of air that possesses a tremendous amount of energy. These vortices can have the same effect on small aircraft as severe CAT.

Under landing and takeoff conditions, the small airplane that flies into a vortex may strike the

ground before its pilot can re-gain control. Aviators, there-fore, must be wary of natural and man-made atmospheric turbulence.

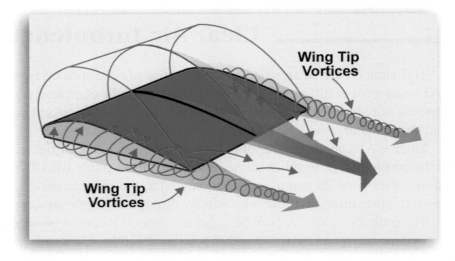

Formation of Wake Turbulence

Unique Weather Patterns

El Niño and La Niña. The cyclical warming of the east Pacific Ocean sea water temperatures off the western coast of South America directly influences the weather patterns all over the world. When the normal pattern is disturbed, there are significant changes in weather patterns in the United States and across the world. The El Nino occurs when warm waters move in and displace the colder waters for a longer than normal period of time. A La Nina is the opposite, i.e., ocean temperature off the coast of South America is colder than normal for a longer than normal period. This also impacts weather patterns across the world.

Key Terms and Concepts

- weather
- air masses: polar, tropical, maritime, continental
- fronts: cold, warm, stationary, occluded
- cloud types: cumulus, stratus, cirrus
- nimbo and alto
- fracto and lenticular
- five types of fog: radiation, high-inversion, advection, evaporation, upslope
- windward, leeward and rotor clouds

- wind shear
- microburst
- levels of turbulence: light, moderate, severe, extreme
- clear air turbulence (CAT)
- wake turbulence

? Test Your Knowledge ?

MATCHING

1. Moist and warm air mass formed over subtropical waters.
2. Body of air with generally the same temperature and moisture content.
3. Boundary between two air masses.
4. Cold and dry air mass.
5. Moist air is blown over a cold surface.
6. Moist air is carried by wind up a mountain until the air is cooled.
7. Actually a cloud.
8. Forms at night when the land surface cools the air above it to below the dew point.

a. **Air mass**
b. **Front**
c. **Maritime tropical**
d. **Continental polar**
e. **Upslope fog**
f. **Advection fog**
g. **Radiation fog**
h. **High-inversion fog**

FILL IN THE BLANKS

9. Whatever the atmosphere is doing at any time is one way of defining _____.
10. _____, _____ and_____ are the general types of clouds.
11. All other types of clouds come from the above three and are classified according to _____.
12. Stratocumulus is likely to produce precipitation in the form of _____ or _____.
13. Altostratus produces moderate surface _____.
14. The _____ cloud is most often associated with violent weather.
15. _____, _____ and _____ have no types of precipitation associated with them.
16. _____ and _____ are closest to the surface of the earth.

MULTIPLE CHOICE

17. Wind shear involves changes in speed and direction of the wind
    a. horizontally.
    b. downwardly.
    c. upwardly.
    d. all of the above.
18. A microburst is a threat to aviation and is associated with
    a. temperature inversion.
    b. horizontal movement.
    c. thunderstorms.
    d. updrafts.

19. Which of the following means a piling up of rounded masses?
    a. cumulus.
    b. stratus.
    c. cirrus.
    d. nimbostratus.

TRUE OR FALSE

20. An occluded front occurs when a warm air mass is "sandwiched" between two cold air masses.
21. A stationary front has a lot of movement along its edge.
22 A cold front's general direction is from southeast to northwest.
23. Warm fronts are usually associated with low-pressure cells.
24. The term lenticular results from the concave-shaped cloud that forms over mountains.
25. Fracto is a term only associated with rain clouds.
26. Terrain factors may be one of the factors causing clear air turbulence (CAT).
27. The turbulence classifications of light, moderate, severe are the same for all pilots.
28. Wake turbulence is produced by large aircraft only on landing.

SHORT ANSWER

29. Is it generally safer for the pilot of a small aircraft to fly on the leeward side or the windward side of a mountain range? Give reasons for your answer.
30. If you are flying at 7,000 feet on the windward side of a 15,000-foot mountain range, what affect will its rotor clouds have on your flight?

Chapter
20   AVIATION WEATHER

Previous weather chapters indicated the importance of weather conditions to aviation activities. This chapter will take a closer look at what weather can do with aviation. While factors such as turbulence and thunderstorms will again be studied, this time they will be investigated more thoroughly.

bjectives

Describe weather conditions that reduce visibility for aircraft.
Identify the forms of turbulence hazardous to aircraft.
Classify the types of icing hazardous to aircraft.
Define CAVU, hydroplane, VFR, IFR, and AGL.
Explain the three stages in the development of a thunderstorm.
Describe the general characteristics of a tornado.
Explain the Fujita-Pearson Scale.
State the general characteristics of a hurricane.
Explain the Saffir-Simpson Scale.
Explain the developmental stages of hail.
Describe the hazards of severe weather to aviation.
Identify the beneficial effects of severe weather.
Define thunder, lightning, tropical depression, tropical storm, cyclone, and good and bad weather.
Describe the characteristics of Arctic weather.
State the classifications of tropic weather.
Identify the hazards of Arctic and tropic weather to aviation.
Define equatorial trough.

Weather Hazards

If the sky is clear of clouds, if the winds are calm, if the air is cool and if there is no haze, the weather is Ceiling and Visibility Unlimited (CAVU). It is time to fly! This is a rare condition of the atmosphere even in a local area. Much of the time when aviators fly, they encounter some type of weather condition that could be hazardous to their flight, especially if they fly long distances.

What are these weather hazards to aviation? Basically, they include any weather condition that produces an in-flight reduction of visibility, turbulence for the aircraft in flight, icing on the aircraft itself or within its power plant while in flight.

An airplane moving on the ground can also experience weather problems. Wet runways can cause an airplane's tires to hydroplane (slide on a film of water), making braking ineffective and causing skidding. Wet runways can affect both takeoffs and landings. Similar incidents or accidents have occurred when a runway was glazed with ice or covered in snow too deep for the aircraft's landing gear to work properly.

T38 -As in the Clouds

F-16 Landing on a Rain-slick Runway

Reduced Visibility

Visual Flight Rules (VFR). These are the general weather conditions the FAA considers a pilot can expect at the surface. VFR criteria mean a cloud ceiling greater than 3,000 feet and greater than 5 miles visibility. If any clouds are around, the noninstrument pilot must stay clear of them.

Instrument Flight Rules (IFR). Weather conditions at an airport during which a pilot must use instruments to assist takeoff and landing. IFR conditions mean the minimum cloud ceiling is greater than 500 feet and less than 1,000 feet, and visibility is greater than 1 mile and less than 3 miles.

Clouds, Rain, Snow, Fog and Obstructions. Visibility is reduced to zero if an airplane is flying within a cloud. Different types of fog pose a hazard to all aviation activities, and this includes up-to-date military and civilian aircraft—if you can't see the landing area or runway, it isn't safe to land. Rain, especially intense rain, can reduce visibility to the hazard level and snow greatly reduces visibility.

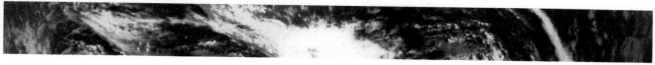

A B-1B taking off in foggy conditions.

The possibilities for landing accidents are increased when visibility is reduced. This same danger is also present in flight and is greatest for those pilots who are not trained to fly according to IFR and/or are not flying aircraft equipped for IFR flight.

For example: (1) pilots of different aircraft may not see each other until a midair crash is inevitable, (2) an improperly set altimeter could cause a plane to fly into a mountain because it is hidden by clouds, fog, rain, etc., and (3) across the land, there are very tall towers (up to 2,000 feet above ground level), which pose a hazard to flight. These towers are clearly marked on aeronautical charts; however, mix the presence of such a tower with greatly reduced visibility and the possibility of collision with the tower is increased.

In addition to clouds, rain, snow and fog, what else can cause reduced visibility? Haze and smoke, blowing dust, blowing sand, blowing snow and a condition that may occur where there is snowfall called "whiteout" can reduce visibility.

Haze and Smoke. Earlier study defined a temperature inversion as the condition where cooler air is overlain by warmer air. This condition can result from several causes, but the net result is a stable atmosphere. That is, the air doesn't mix through convection to disperse the particulates of dust, pollen, smoke and so forth. The wind is calm so the haze and smoke cannot move laterally out of the area. If this condition persists for several days, the visibility will become progressively poorer.

This atmospheric condition is especially common in the heavily populated and heavily industrialized areas of the country. It is noticeable in the early morning because radiation cooling the earth's surface during the nighttime has, in turn, cooled the air near the ground level and lowered the ceiling of the haze layer.

As is often the case, the sun will warm the cool, hazy air and cause it to expand upward. Visibility at surface level becomes better and is quite acceptable to the surface traveler but not to the aviator.

What seems to be ample visibility upon takeoff suddenly becomes what appears to be a complete obstruction to visibility at 1,000 feet

Industrial areas may produce haze and smoke.

above the surface. Visibility is satisfactory up and down, but the pilot may feel very apprehensive about what could come out of the murk ahead. The actual visual range at this altitude may very well be more than the FAA's acceptable 3 miles. Yet, visual perception while traveling well over 100 mph may interpret this much visual range as a wall just beyond the airplane's nose.

Particularly in the summertime, haze and smoke within a stable high-pressure cell may extend upward more than 10,000 feet during the heat of the day. Most small aircraft fly lower than this altitude. To them, the greatest surprise is the thundershower or thunderstorm that lies hidden within the area of haze and smoke. However, the weather service and FAA flight service personnel can warn of this type weather, if the aviator asks for such information by radio. When haze and smoke are present, the best preventive measure a pilot can take is to get a thorough weather briefing before flying.

Blowing Dust, Blowing Sand and Blowing Snow. Blowing dust of significant proportions is found in the relatively dry areas of the country. This condition develops when the air is unstable and there are strong winds. The horizontal wind picks up dust or soil particles while strong convective currents (vertical winds) carry it upward into the atmosphere. Working in combination, these winds can spread dust over hundreds of miles and upward to 15,000 feet. Visibility in these dust storms is reduced in all directions. The operation of an aircraft within a blowing-dust area is unthinkable. When in flight and approaching blowing dust, pilots have only one choice—to turn toward an airport that is clear and land.

Blowing sand is much more localized than dust. It occurs only in desert regions and only when the wind is strong enough to lift loose sand. Being much heavier than dust, the blowing sand is seldom lifted more than 50 feet above the surface. Still, this condition would prohibit an aircraft from taking off or landing.

Strong winds also are the cause of blowing snow. For this condition to exist, the snow must be lifted to a height of at least 6 feet. The frequency of blowing snow is much greater in the areas of the country where dry, or powdery, snow is more likely to fall. To the aviator, this blowing snow causes the same problems as fog, and it can reach 1,000 feet above the surface.

Aircraft taking off in snowy conditions.

Whiteout. This condition is more frequent in the arctic areas, but it can occur anywhere there is snow-covered ground. It is not a physical obstruction to visibility; it is an optical phenomenon. Whiteout requires a snow-covered surface plus a low-level cloud deck of uniform thickness. With the sun at an angle of about 20 degrees above the horizon, its light rays are diffused as they penetrate the cloud layer. This causes them to strike the snow-covered surface from many angles; thus, shadows are not produced. These diffused light rays are reflected back and forth between the surface and the base of the cloud layer. The net effect is the loss of any reference to the horizon and of other references needed for depth perception. People, buildings, trees, and all other dark objects cast no shadows during a whiteout, so they all seem to float in space—not very conducive to the landing of an airplane.

Turbulence

Recall the atmospheric conditions that bring about turbulence, including the high-altitude types of clear air turbulence (CAT) which commercial jetliners sometimes encounter. The most important thing to remember about normal atmospheric turbulence is that you know it exists with cumulus, rotor and lenticular clouds, but CAT is where you find it (fly into it, in other words). The turbulence, or wake turbulence, created by aircraft is a form of CAT, but all aviators know that it exists if they see the airplane that creates it.

Wake turbulence has become more and more of a concern to light-aircraft pilots because it grows more severe as larger aircraft are built and flown. It results when air spills over and around the airframe and wingtips of an airplane.

There is some wake turbulence associated with all aircraft—even the lightest ones. It is not dangerous until the aircraft creating it are large enough and heavy enough to produce sizable and strong swirling air currents called wingtip vortices.

The vortices (from each wingtip) might be described as horizontal tornadoes. Their strength is greatest immediately behind the aircraft and varies with the size, speed and flight attitude of the aircraft. The vortices tend to settle between 500 to 800 feet below the parent aircraft's flight level and tend to remain there, spinning and waiting for an unsuspecting lighter-weight aircraft to come along.

The vortices will remain active well after the aircraft that spawned them has passed. How long they remain active depends on how stable the atmosphere is at their level.

Knowing that dangerous vortices are present behind the larger aircraft, the light-aircraft pilot best avoids them by staying clear of

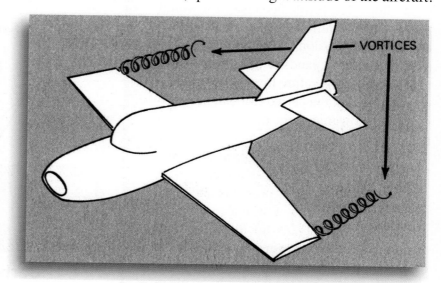

Small airplanes produce wingtip vortices.

them. If at the same altitude, the pilot of the small aircraft should climb well above the other aircraft's flight path. If the small aircraft is 1,000 feet below the flight path of the larger plane, there should be no problem; yet, it wouldn't be a bad idea to descend still more just in case the difference in altitude has been misjudged. Now, if it isn't advisable to climb or descend, what should the light-aircraft pilot do? The answer is to turn in the opposite direction and fly parallel to the other aircraft's flight path until a separation of 15 to 20 miles is obtained.

The greatest danger of wake turbulence is found at and near airports, and the first reason is obvious —this is where airplanes are concentrated. The second reason is that the large jets create the most severe wingtip vortices when they are taking off or landing. Their wings are at a greater angle of attack, which generates larger vortices that possess greater energy than vortices generated when in cruising flight.

Icing

Icing is a definite weather hazard to aircraft. Already mentioned was the fact that a runway covered with even a thin film of ice can cause loss of directional and braking control. In takeoff and in flight, the threat of ice hazard is increased.

Winter brings on icing conditions; however, ice is present, or potentially present, somewhere in the atmosphere at all times no matter what the season. What is critical is the altitude of the freezing level, which may be around 15,000 feet during summer and perhaps as low as 1,000 feet above ground level (AGL) on warm winter days.

Carburetor Ice. When the temperature and dew point are close, it is certain that water vapor is condensing within the carburetor of an aircraft reciprocating engine; and, if the engine is run at low speed, the condensation is turning into ice. This is why some engine manufacturers recommend that carburetor heat be applied when the throttle is retarded for prolonged descent and prior to landing. Ice forms because of lowered temperature within the carburetor as a result of fuel/air expansion within the carburetor system (as gas expands or as its pressure is reduced, its temperature lowers). The coldest point within the carburetor can be 40° F or more below that of the air through which the airplane is flying.

Glaze and Rime Ice. Glaze and rime are names given to the ice that forms on an airplane's windshield, its propeller and other aerodynamic surfaces. Glaze ice is formed and builds quickly as an airplane flies through supercooled rain droplets. These droplets instantaneously turn to ice as they strike the airplane. This is what happens in a surface-level ice storm when power lines

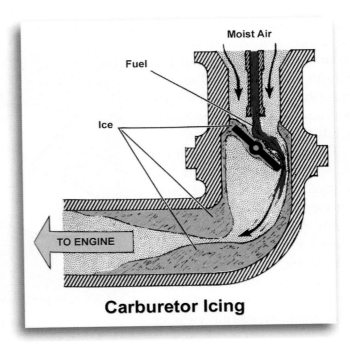

Carburetor Icing

440

and trees are broken from the weight of the ice that continues to accumulate.

This rapid increase of weight on an airplane in flight is a dangerous factor, but the greatest problem is the changing of the shape of the airfoil. The shapes of the wings and tail surfaces (airfoils) contribute to lift and the propeller's airfoil provides thrust. If ice distorts these shapes, lift and thrust will be adversely affected.

Rime ice has that frosty appearance seen on the walls of frozen-food lockers. It forms when the airplane is flying through supercooled clouds. It normally is no problem, but if it is allowed to accumulate, it will reduce lift and become a danger to flight.

Frost. Frost is another ice factor deserving mention. Frost would appear to be an inconsequential thing that develops on cold fall or spring mornings, and soon melts after the sun rises. However, frost disturbs the airflow enough to reduce the lift efficiency of aerodynamic surfaces.

This isn't to say that an airplane will not fly when there is frost on its wings, because it will. However, the danger becomes apparent at takeoff. The partial loss of lift caused by frost makes a much longer takeoff run necessary and reduces the rate of climb. On a relatively short runway, the result can be—and has been—a flight that ends just beyond the runway.

The larger, more complex aircraft are equipped to break or melt ice as it is formed—even on pro-

Frost on a Parked Airplane

pellers. On the other hand, the great majority of aircraft flying today are not equipped to combat icing conditions, and aviators who fly them must be prepared to recognize atmospheric conditions that can cause icing. With the assistance of weather and flight service specialists during the flight-planning stage, all pilots should be able to avoid flight through areas where icing is likely.

Severe Weather

The National Weather Service's severe weather classifications are based upon destructive effects with regard to man-made features. For example, a 40-knot (46-mph) wind has enough force to harm lightweight structures. Hail of 1/4-inch diameter can shred certain crops. Thus, the same weather is certainly a threat to aircraft. The violent "big three"—thunderstorms, tornadoes and hurricanes—pose the greatest in-flight hazards.

Thunderstorms

A thunderstorm may be defined as any storm accompanied by thunder and lightning. Lightning is the flash of light produced by electrical discharges in a thunderstorm area. Thunder is the sound sent out by rapidly expanding gases along the lightning's trail. It is attended by some form of precipitation and can cause trouble for aircraft in the form of turbulence, icing and poor visibility. The more severe thunderstorms produce hail and, in some cases, tornadoes. The thunderstorm is local in nature and is always produced by the growth of a cumulus cloud into a cumulonimbus cloud.

The severe elements of the thunderstorm are the result of the convection currents (vertical air movements) within the cloud. Individual thunderstorms are rarely larger than 10 miles in diameter, and they usually last no more than 1 1/2 hours.

Dangerous Lightning

Thunderstorms often form along weather fronts and appear to march across the land in lines of storms. This is the case when the local weather forecaster announces that a line of thundershowers is approaching and that thunderstorm warnings are in effect for the next few hours.

Thunderstorms are best studied by dividing them into three separate stages. They are cumulus (or building) stage, the mature stage and the dissipating stage.

The Cumulus Stage. Most cumulus clouds do not become thunderstorms, but all thunderstorms are born in cumulus clouds. The main feature of this first stage of the thunderstorm is the updraft: a large air current flowing upward from the ground through the chimney-like cloud. The updraft may reach speeds of over 3,000 feet per minute and altitudes of 40,000 feet or more. During this stage, water droplets grow to raindrop size as the cloud builds upward into a cumulonimbus cloud.

Thunderstorm Stages

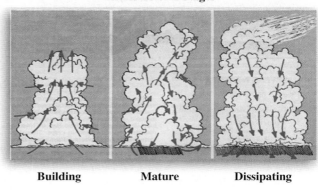

Building   Mature   Dissipating

The Mature Stage. The mature stage of a thunderstorm is marked by the beginning of rain at the earth's surface. The raindrops (or ice particles) have become so large that the cloud's updraft can no longer support them, and they begin to fall. As they fall, the raindrops drag air behind them causing the characteristically strong downdrafts of mature thunderstorms. These down drafts spread

Lightning Cloud

out horizontally when they reach the surface, producing strong, gusty winds, sharp drops in temperature (because the air was chilled at high altitudes) and a sharp rise in pressure. As the downdrafts continue to build and spread, the updrafts weaken and the entire thunderstorm eventually becomes an area of downdrafts.

The Dissipating Stage. The downdrafts produce heating and drying causing the rainfall gradually to cease and the thunderstorm to dissipate or weaken. During this stage, the cloud develops the characteristic anvil shape at the top and may take on a stratiform (layered) appearance at the bottom. This stage is usually the longest of the three stages of a thunderstorm's life. Sometimes, the same conditions that cause thunderstorms can also bring on a much more destructive type of storm, the tornado.

Tornadoes

A tornado is a local storm that focuses nature's most destructive force on a small area. It consists of violently swirling winds with rapidly rising air at its center. The tornado is small and usually short of life, but because of its violence, it is probably the most feared storm of all.

Tornadoes occur with severe thunderstorms. Their circular whirlpools of air take the shape of a funnel or tube hanging from a cumulonimbus cloud. The rotating column of air in a tornado may range in diameter from 100 feet to half a mile.

If a tornado touches the ground, its path may be very erratic. (Technically, if the funnel does not reach the ground, the storm is not a tornado, but a funnel cloud.) It may touch the ground at some points along its path and completely miss other points. Its boundaries of complete destruction may be fairly well-defined. It may destroy houses on one side of the street and leave those on the other side untouched.

The very low pressure of tornadoes gives them great suction. They can lift objects as heavy as automobiles and rooftops of houses and carry them for considerable distances. They have been known to suck water from creeks and ponds.

Tornadoes occur most often in North America and in Australia. They have been observed in every state in the continuous United States, but most frequently in the central part of the nation. They occur most often in the spring and in the afternoon hours, approaching with a very loud roar like a railroad train or a flight of airplanes. Tornadoes are more numerous in the spring (March, April and May) and in the late fall (September through December).

It is very difficult to forecast tornadoes. The storm usually lasts only a short time and is primarily a local condition. The conditions identified as favorable to tornado production include an active cold front separating maritime tropical air from polar air.

In the same area, there is a strong high altitude jet of cold air from the west crossing a tongue of moist air from the Atlantic or the Gulf of Mexico. Doppler radar gives the ability to "see" inside storms and identify rotating air masses. This has greatly increased the warning time given for people to take shelter.

Dr. Fujita and Allen Pearson of the Severe Weather Forecast Center in Kansas City developed a tornado classification system. It has quickly become the standard method to describe tornadoes around the world.

Tornadoes

Fujita – Pearson Tornado Intensity Scale

Type	Wind Speed	Possible Damage
F0 (Light)	40-72 mph	Minor roof, tree and sign damage
F1 (Moderate)	72-112 mph	Roofs damaged, weak trailers flipped and torn apart, cars thrown from roads
F2 (Considerable)	113-157 mph	Strong buildings unroofed, weaker buildings destroyed, trailers disintegrated
F3 (Severe)	158-206 mph	Outside walls of strong buildings blown away, weaker buildings completely swept away
F4 (Devastating)	207-260 mph	All interior and exterior walls of strong buildings blown away, cars thrown 300 yards or more in the air
F5 (Unbelievable)	261-318 mph	All types of buildings completely blown away

Hurricanes

Second only to tornadoes in damaging effects, and even more dangerous to people and property, is the hurricane. This storm is a strong tropical cyclone with winds that often surpass 100 mph and have been clocked at more than 200 mph. Tropical cyclones occur around the world. They are known as "typhoons" in the western Pacific, "baguios" in the South China Sea, and "cyclones" in the Indian Ocean.

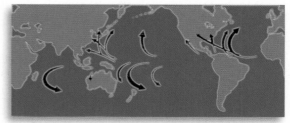

A hurricane is a large, revolving storm with a calm center—called the eye—resulting from the speed of the whirling winds around the low-pressure core. It is an area of convective action, with the air moving upward in spirals around the eye. The calm center (eye) averages around 15 to 20 miles in diameter. The hurricane itself is usually several hundred miles across.

Origins and Paths Typical of Tropical Cyclones

Hurricanes that affect the United States originate over the warm tropical waters of the Atlantic and Pacific Oceans, the Gulf of Mexico and the Caribbean Sea. August, September and October are the peak months of the hurricane season.

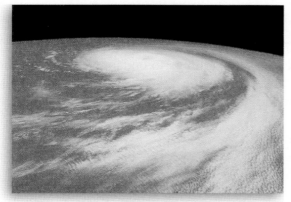

Hurricane

Hurricanes receive their energy from the heat given off by the condensation of moisture in the warm air. Heat lowers the atmospheric pressure and wind begins to flow into the heated (low-pressure) area. The Coriolis Force deflects that wind, setting up the typical cyclonic movement of winds at less than 39 mph. At this point, the storm is called a tropical depression and many such storms never grow beyond that level.

The next step is the level of tropical storm. In this stage, winds range between 40 and 74 mph. When wind speeds reach or exceed 75 mph, the tropical cyclone is called a hurricane. In the early 1970s, Herbert Saffir and Dr. Robert Simpson (then director of the National Hurricane Center) developed a scale to express hurricane intensity. It is known as the Saffir-Simpson Scale. It rates potential damage that can be done by a hurricane based on barometric pressure, wind speeds and storm surge. The easiest correlation is by wind speed as shown in the table on page 446.

Heavy rainfall accompanies the hurricane with individual convective showers and thunderstorms lining up in a circular pattern around the eye of the hurricane. Heavy rainfall often continues after the hurricane moves inland, even after the wind circulation decreases. Flood damage is often a major problem associated with hurricanes. Cooler surface temperatures over the land or over nontropical seas help to bring on the weakening of the hurricane. Other factors are the loss of moisture, the inflow of air from the land and the increase in surface friction over the land.

The National Weather Service (NWS) keeps a constant watch for hurricane development, especially during the hurricane season. Using weather aircraft and satellites, the NWS can track the movement

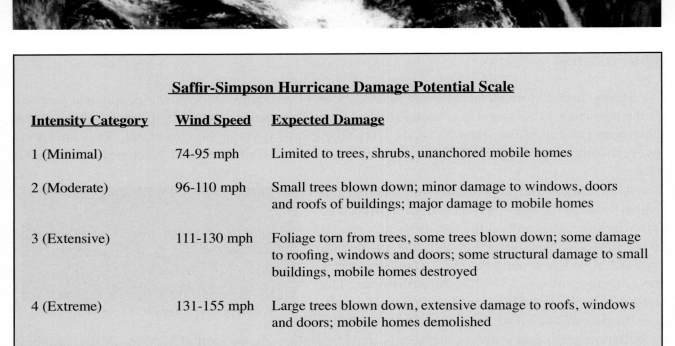

Saffir-Simpson Hurricane Damage Potential Scale

Intensity Category	Wind Speed	Expected Damage
1 (Minimal)	74-95 mph	Limited to trees, shrubs, unanchored mobile homes
2 (Moderate)	96-110 mph	Small trees blown down; minor damage to windows, doors and roofs of buildings; major damage to mobile homes
3 (Extensive)	111-130 mph	Foliage torn from trees, some trees blown down; some damage to roofing, windows and doors; some structural damage to small buildings, mobile homes destroyed
4 (Extreme)	131-155 mph	Large trees blown down, extensive damage to roofs, windows and doors; mobile homes demolished
5 (Catastrophic)	156+ mph	Considerable damage to roofs, extensive shattering of windows, widespread structural damage to all kinds of buildings

and development of cyclonic areas in the tropics, and can issue warnings to endangered areas. The conditions that cause hurricanes last longer than those causing tornadoes; therefore, hurricane development is easier to predict. Although satellites have made the prediction of hurricane paths much

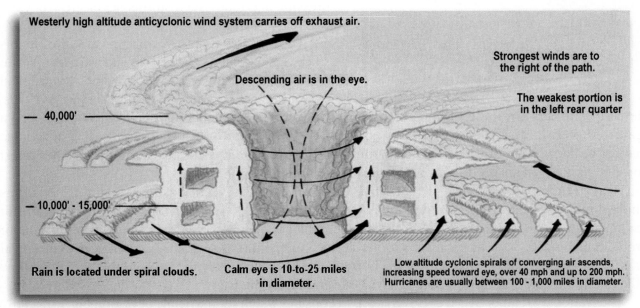

Cross-sectional Drawing of a Hurricane

more accurate, they still behave in unexpected ways and specific warnings cannot be 100 percent correct.

What do hurricanes mean to aviation, since only specially equipped meteorological research aircraft fly into them? They mean stay well clear, and this means hundreds of miles. It is not unusual for the cyclonic wind flow of the larger hurricanes to have a diameter of 500 miles, and they have been known to be much larger. A variety of weather will be associated with the system—everything except blizzards and dust storms. Hurricanes breed thunderstorms and, in many cases, tornadoes within the areas they affect. Knowing the perils of turbulence, thunderstorms and tornadoes to aviation, it is obvious why the hurricane is to be avoided.

Hail

Previous study related how hail is formed within the thunderstorm prior to falling to the ground. However, its importance as a hazard to aviation deserves special emphasis.

In the first place, hail may very well be within a building cumulus cloud before any type of precipitation falls to the surface. At this developing stage, the hail pellets may not be very large because strong air currents still are able to carry them about within the clouds. Even so, the combined velocity of

Hail this size can do quite a bit of damage.

an aircraft and hail give these small pellets a tremendous amount of energy.

Under these conditions, and especially if the pellets are hard because of exceptionally cold temperature at their level, the aircraft will experience some damage. The damage may be no more than many small dents in the aircraft's outer cover, but this is a very costly experience for the aircraft owner. Fender and body work on an airplane costs several times that of an automobile.

Hail Damage to an Aircraft Wing

Encounters with larger hail are even more damaging. Hail of the sizes, weights and velocities produced by thunderstorms in the western and mountainous areas could literally rip a small airplane apart if it were to fly into such an area. This reference is to hailstones approaching the diameter of a baseball, which, it is estimated, occurs in one out of about 5,000 thunderstorms. On the other hand, which of the 5,000 storms will contain hail of this size can't be predicted.

An example of what hail and intense rain can do to a jetliner occurred in 1977. In this instance, the storm area was producing thunderstorms with tops reaching 40,000 feet—a good indicator of high intensity. Radar showed heavy precipitation with indications of hail. The crew of a DC-9 elected to penetrate the storm area rather than avoid it and ran into one of the storm cells somewhere between 14,000 and 17,000 feet. Hail and rain pulled into the aircraft's engines caused the engines to stall and flame out. This also caused internal damage to the engines. The net result was the DC-9 making a crash landing and 63 of the 85 persons on board being killed.

Hail, therefore, is a definite hazard to flight, no matter how large the airplane. The only way to avoid it in flight is to stay well clear of the thunderstorms that produce hail.

Beneficial Effects

These severe or extreme forms of weather usually are referred to as bad weather because they may bring harmful effects to people and property. Of course, weather in itself is neither good nor bad. Any kind of weather may be considered good or bad depending on what is needed. Warm, sunshiny periods may be thought of as good weather, but can become bad if they last too long and cause shortages of moisture or even drought.

When the needed rain comes, suddenly the wet weather is good. However, if the rainy period lasts too long, it becomes bad weather again since floods may occur. What is needed is a balance of different types of weather.

In the same way, these forms of severe weather are neither good nor bad. Their effects on people and property are often devastating, but they are beneficial in the natural scheme of the earth's weather. They act to balance different forces at work in the atmosphere. They dissipate (break up) concentrations of energy in the forms of heat and atmospheric pressure that could, indeed, make the earth uninhabitable. It is true that these types of weather are often violent and, because of this, they are justly feared.

Arctic and Tropic Weather

People living in the temperate zones of the world are likely to consider arctic and tropical weather patterns as extreme. Natives of those regions, though, think of their weather as normal. Arctic weather and tropical weather are interesting to study and are important to weather in middle or temperate latitudes.

Aircraft in Arctic Weather

Arctic Weather

The Arctic is of passing interest to the student of weather, mostly because it causes the coldest air masses. While these air masses affect weather at lower latitudes, weather in the Arctic, unpleasant as it may seem, is not a major factor in most of our lives. It is included here because it may be a point of curiosity and because aviators fly there.

Mountains around the arctic Circle hold arctic air masses in the area. The Arctic Circle is a circle of latitude that marks off the earth's northern frigid zone. It is parallel to the equator and lies at approximately 66° north latitude. Because temperatures are so cold, the air has little moisture and little evaporation takes place. Precipitation (usually snow) in the Arctic is light, ranging from 3 to 7 inches per year in the coastal areas to 5 to 15 inches in the interior. This compares with some of the desert areas of the United States.

Cloudiness is at a minimum during the winter and at a maximum during the summer and fall. Strong winds occur frequently during the fall and winter. Winds stronger than 100 mph are not uncommon along the Greenland Coast during the winter.

Arctic winters are characterized by frequent windstorms and well-defined frontal passages. Visibility is a major problem at low levels in the Arctic due to fog haze, blowing and drifting snow, and peculiar light conditions including the dreaded whiteout.

Tropic Weather

The tropics feature weather quite differently from the Arctic, and not just in temperature. Fronts are rare in this area and there is much moisture in the air, especially in the oceanic and coastal regions. Continental tropical weather, however, can be quite different from oceanic and coastal tropical weather.

Oceanic Weather. Clouds cover about half the sky over the tropical oceans outside the equatorial trough. The equatorial trough is an area of low pressure and light winds near the Equator, varying from north to south of that line with the changing seasons. It is also the area in which the northeast and southeast trade winds converge (come together), and it is sometimes referred to as the intertropical convergence zone. Some amount of unsettled convective weather is found in this area at all times. When the wind convergence gets strong, thunderstorms develop that may produce wind gusts of up to 70 mph. Normal cloudiness includes a line of cumulonimbus clouds with sheets of cirrus clouds spread north and south of them.

In the oceanic zones outside the equatorial trough, the cumulus clouds yield showers in local areas, but outside the showers, visibility is good. Temperatures rarely vary from day to day or month to month, and humidity remains almost constant.

Continental Weather. Continental tropical weather and climate are quite different from oceanic tropical weather. It is subject to extreme variation because of the different features of the land: coastal mountain ranges, altitudes, wind flow patterns and rate of evaporation from surrounding ocean surfaces.

In Africa, various combinations of these factors produce tropical weather ranging from the hot, humid climate of the lower Congo River, to the arid Libyan Desert, to the snowcapped mountains of Kenya. Snow can also be found on the higher mountain peaks in the Hawaiian Islands.

In the arid areas behind coastal mountains, daytime temperatures may exceed 100° F, but nighttime temperatures in the desert regions may go below freezing. "Dry" thunderstorms produce sudden, violent squall winds and may cause severe dust storms or sandstorms, and precipitation often evaporates before it reaches the ground.

Where no mountains or high terrain are present to obstruct the flow of maritime air onshore, the warm, moist air influences wide continental areas in the tropics. Cloudiness and precipitation are at a maximum over these jungle regions and tropical rain forests. Thick, early morning steam fog often forms in the jungles. There is also a good bit of cloudiness over these areas. Occasional heavy rains, with descending cold air currents, can drive nighttime temperatures down to about 60° F, some 30 degrees below normal daytime ranges.

Island and Coastal Weather. Weather conditions are similar along coastal areas and over the various mountainous islands of the tropics. During the day, as warm, moist air moves inland and is lifted over the terrain, large cumuliform clouds develop. While these clouds are common in coastal areas, the lifting of moist air on the windward side of mountainous islands also produces towering cumulus clouds. These clouds frequently may be seen from long distances, indicating the presence of islands.

These islands, especially when mountainous, also have an interesting effect on rainfall. The almost-constant trade winds result in a predominantly onshore wind on one side of an island, while the opposite side has an offshore wind most of the time. These two sides of an island are referred to as the windward and leeward sides, respectively.

Precipitation and cloudiness are considerably heavier on the windward side than on the leeward. An example is the island of Kauai, Hawaii, where Mount Waialeale receives the highest average annual rainfall of all rain measured in the world, 460 inches. Only 10 miles away, on the leeward side of Kauai, sugarcane plantations must be irrigated.

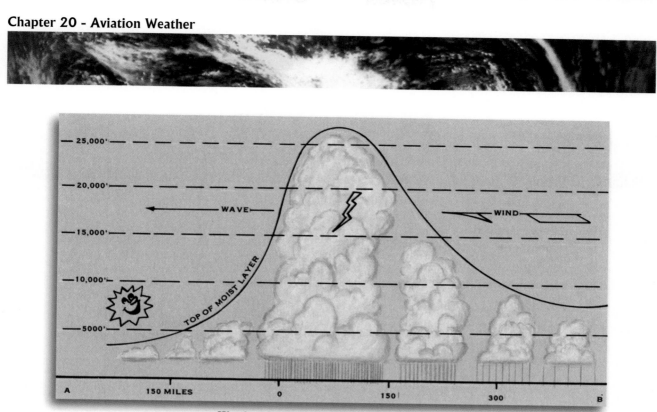

Weather Occurring with an Easterly Wave

One of the major factors influencing tropical weather is the easterly wave. This is a common tropical weather disturbance that normally occurs in the trade-wind belt. Easterly waves of the Northern Hemisphere have advance winds blowing somewhat more northerly than the usual trade-wind direction. As the wave line approaches, the atmospheric pressure falls.

The wind shifts to the east as the line passes. The typical wave is preceded by fair weather, but followed by much cloudiness, low cloud ceilings, rain, and, usually, thunderstorms.

Easterly waves are more numerous and stronger during summer and early fall. Their effects occasionally reach as far north as the Gulf Coast area of the United States. They frequently affect Hawaii and are commonly observed in the West Indies. A wave that is hardly noticeable on the weather chart may one day deepen rapidly and, by the next day, become the spawning ground of a tropical cyclone (hurricane).

Key Terms and Concepts

- Visual Flight Rules (VFR)
- Instrument Flight Rules (IFR)
- haze and smoke
- blowing sand, dust, and snow
- whiteout
- vortices
- icing
- freezing level

- glaze and rime ice
- frost
- thunderstorm
- tornado
- hurricane (typhoon and cyclone)
- hail
- arctic and tropical weather

? Test Your Knowledge ?

MATCHING

1. *Perfect flying conditions*
2. *Flying strictly by eyesight*
3. *Sliding on a film of water*
4. *Usually associated with low ceiling and visibility*
5. *Any level above the ground*

a. **IFR**
b. **Hydroplane**
c. **CAVU**
d. **VFR**
e. **AGL**

MATCHING

6. *Another name for a hurricane*
7. *First stage of a hurricane*
8. *Produced by electrical discharge*
9. *Pre-hurricane winds of 40-74 mph*
10. *Depends on what is needed*
11. *Produced by violent expansion of the air*

a. **Tropical depression**
b. **Lightning**
c. **Good and bad weather**
d. **Tropical storm**
e. **Cyclone**
f. **Thunder**

FILL IN THE BLANKS

12. _____ is a condition that results in an optical phenomenon.
13. Visibility equals zero if you fly in a _____.
14. _____ _____ occurs most often in dry areas.
15. Intense rain and snow can reduce visibility to the _____ level.
16. _____ _____ is seldom lifted more than 50 feet above the surface, but is still threatening when taking off or landing.
17. A temperature inversion is most often the culprit for the hazards of _____ and _____.
18. To the pilot, _____ _____ causes the same problem as fog.
19. _____ are clearly marked on charts and have proper lighting, yet can pose a hazard.
20. Wake turbulence presents a hazard to light aircraft because the _____ of larger aircraft remain indefinitely and are invisible.
21. CAT is hazardous because pilots cannot _____ it.
22. Hail may form whenever a _____ is present and may be within a building _____ cloud before any precipitation falls to the ground.
23. Hail can damage aircraft as well as crops. An in-flight aircraft can receive damage to its _____ and _____.
24. Severe weather is beneficial in that it acts as a balance _____ breaking up _____ that could make the earth _____.

MULTIPLE CHOICE

25. The icing that forms when an aircraft is flying through supercooled clouds is called
    a. carburetor.
    b. glaze.
    c. frost.
    d. rime.
26. Icing which seems insignificant, but can affect takeoffs, is called
    a. carburetor.
    b. glaze.
    c. frost.
    d. rime.
27. Icing which results from supercooled rain droplets that turn to ice as they hit the aircraft is
    a. carburetor.
    b. glaze.
    c. frost.
    d. rime.

28. *The aircraft engine could stop running in flight if water vapor condenses and turns into ice within the*
   a. *carburetor.*
   b. *glaze.*
   c. *frost.*
   d. *rime.*

TRUE OR FALSE

29. *There are three stages in hurricane development.*
30. *Hurricanes receive their energy from heat given off by the condensation of moisture in the warm air.*
31. *Typical hurricane movement is to the west or northwest.*
32. *The forward speed of a hurricane matches its wind speed.*

PART FIVE

Rockets

ROCKET FUNDAMENTALS

There is an explanation for everything that a rocket does. The explanation is most always based on the laws of physics and the nature of rocket propellants. Experimentation is required to find out whether a new rocket will or will not work. Even today, with all the knowledge and expertise that exists in the field of rocketry, experimentation occasionally shows that certain ideas are not practical.

In this chapter, we will look back in time to the early developers and users of rocketry. We will review some of the physical laws that apply to rocketry, discuss selected chemicals and their combinations, and identify the rocket systems and their components. We also will look at the basics of rocket propellant efficiency.

bjectives

Explain why a rocket engine is called a reaction engine.

Identify the country that first used the rocket as a weapon.

Compare the rocketry advancements made by Eichstadt, Congreve and Hale.

Name the scientist who solved theoretically the means by which a rocket could escape the Earth's gravitational field.

Describe the primary innovation in rocketry developed by Dr. Goddard and Dr. Oberth.

Explain the difference between gravitation and gravity.

Describe the contributions of Galileo and Newton.

Explain Newton's law of universal gravitation.

State Newton's three laws of motion.

Define force, velocity, acceleration and momentum.

Apply Newton's three laws of motion to rocketry.

Identify two ways to increase the thrust of a rocket.

State the function of the combustion chamber, the throat, and nozzle in a rocket engine.

Explain which of Newton's laws of motion is most applicable to rocketry.

Name the four major systems of a rocket.

Define rocket payload.

Describe the four major systems of a rocket.

List the components of a rocket propulsion system.

Identify the three types of rocket propulsion systems.

Name the parts of a rocket guidance system.

Name four types of rocket guidance systems.

Define specific impulse.

Define density impulse.

History of Rocketry

Rocketry is based on the propelling of a vehicle by a reactive force. The action of the rocket's exhaust gases produces a reaction, forcing the rocket in the opposite direction; therefore, a rocket engine, or motor, is a reaction engine. Jet engines, which power most airliners, are also reaction engines. However, there is a distinct difference between the two types of engines. A jet engine generates its reactive force by burning a mixture of air with a fuel; the rocket engine does not use air. The rocket carries everything it needs to generate a reactive force; this allows the rocket to operate in the atmosphere and in space.

Rocketry is not a new concept and was not born out of our efforts to explore space. As early as 1220, and perhaps even earlier, rockets were used by the Chinese, who were also the first to use the rocket as a weapon of war. In 1232, the Chinese used rocket "fire arrows" at the battle of Kai-feng Fu.

Much later, in 1405, a German engineer by the name of Konrad Kyeser von Eichstadt devised a rocket that was propelled by gunpowder. The French used rockets to defend Orleans against the British in 1429 and again at the siege of Pont-Andemer in 1449.

During the Thirty Year War (1618-1648), rockets weighing as much as 100 pounds were fired. These rockets exploded and sent small pieces of metal in all directions. In 1668, a German field artillery colonel, Christopher Friedrich von Geissler, experimented with rockets weighing over 100 pounds. By 1730, a series of successful flights had been made. Rockets saw extensive use in India when they were fired at the British in the battles of Seringapatam (1792 and 1799).

The news of India's success with rockets caused Colonel William Congreve, a British artillery expert, to experiment with rockets. He standardized the composition of gunpowder explosives, added flight-stabilizing guide sticks and built the first viable launching pad. He was able to increase the rocket range from approximately 300 yards to several thousand yards. Approximately 25,000 Congreve rockets were used in 1807 at the battle of Copenhagen.

In the War of 1812 between Britain and the United States, the British formed a rocket brigade. This brigade saw action in the Napoleonic Wars at Leipzig in 1813 and at Waterloo in 1815.

William Hale, an English engineer, solved the problem of stabilizing rockets in flight without a guiding stick. He used spin stabilization for his rockets, which were fitted with angled exhaust tubes that spun the projectile during flight.

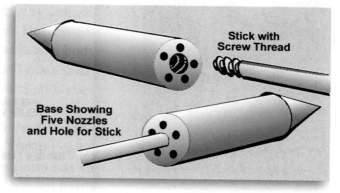

Congreve's Rocket with Stabilizing Stick

Hale's Rocket

457

module payload. Of course, the ultimate payload was the astronauts, materials and the data returned from the Moon.

Today, the payloads of large US rockets consist primarily of Earth satellites and deep space vehicles. Most military rockets have payloads of explosives, which are called missiles. These explosives can include nuclear and thermonuclear "bombs." Of course, the payloads of the smallest military rockets are conventional-type explosives especially designed to destroy specific types of targets such as airplanes, tanks and hardened command posts. To clarify, a "rocket" is any device that uses rocket propulsion (which would include retro-rockets and breaking rockets). A missile does not have to be rocket propelled, but usually is, and is typically thought of as a weapon which is directed at an enemy target. A launch vehicle is a rocket that takes a payload to high altitudes or outer space. Many early launch vehicles were converted military missiles, the Redstone, Atlas, and Titan are a few examples.

The Airframe System

The airframe system of a rocket, like that of an aircraft, serves to contain the other systems and to provide the streamlined shape. The airframe must be structurally strong and capable of withstanding heat, stress and a great deal of vibration. At the same time, it must be as lightweight as possible. Every pound of weight saved in the airframe allows an additional pound of weight to be added to the payload.

The Atlas missile was a prime example of how engineers design an airframe that was both strong and lightweight. The skin of this missile also served as the wall of the propellant tanks. This eliminated the need for separate internal tanks and provided great savings in weight. The skin of the Atlas was thinner than a dime and when it had no propellany aboard, it had to be pressurized to keep it from collapsing.

Precision is the watchword in making a rocket airframe. Techniques used to manufacture rocket airframe parts include machining, forging casting, spinning and extruding. To attain the required precision essential in building a rocket, the knowledge of the scientist and the skill of the technician are required to ensure the accuracy of each manufacturing technique—from the blueprint to the launch pad.

One of the most spectacular airframes ever constructed for a US rocket was that of the massive Saturn V launch vehicle. In its Apollo lunar (Moon)

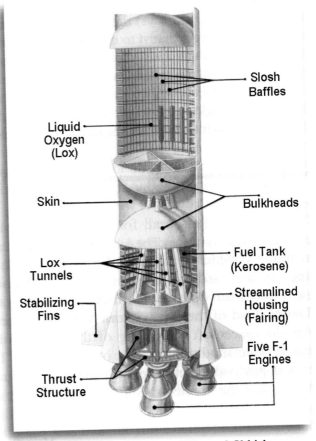

First Stage of the Saturn V Launch Vehicle

flight configuration, the Saturn stood 363 feet tall. Of course, this included the payload of astronauts and the subvehicles that were delivered to the vicinity and surface of the Moon.

Saturn's first-stage airframe had a diameter of 33 feet and its length was 138 feet. This diagram shows the major components of the first stage's airframe. Beginning at the bottom was the thrust structure that contained the vehicle's five F-1 engines.

The thrust structure was a complex group of beams and braces made mainly of aluminum alloy plus some steel. Surrounding the thrust structure was a skin assembly that provided additional strength and better aerodynamics, lessening the effect of drag caused by the rocket pushing its way through the air.

Other aerodynamic features attached to the thrust structure included fairings and fins, as seen in the illustration. The fairings were drag reducers. The fins helped stabilize the rocket's flight while it was climbing rapidly through the atmosphere.

Fuel and oxidizer tanks made up the greater portion of the Saturn's first-stage airframe (this is true with all liquid-propellant rockets). The walls of these tanks formed a large part of the rocket's exterior surface or skin. Within each of the tanks were slosh baffles that added strength to the airframe, while serving another purpose. The other purpose was to stabilize the propellant's motion as the rocket vibrated and tilted in flight. Without such baffles, the liquid oxygen (oxidizer) and kerosene (fuel) would setup sloshing and swirling motions that would make the rocket uncontrollable.

What is labeled skin in the figure is also known as the intertank structure. The interstage structure was similar and included that skin portion used to join the three rocket stages. While the propellant tank walls exposed to the airstream were smooth, the metal "skirts" forming the intertank and interstage structures were corrugated. This corrugation was necessary to give greater strength to a relatively thin part of the structure.

Although the airframes of all liquid-propellant rockets possess certain characteristics of the Saturn V's structure, there are differences. These differences depend on the size and purpose of the rocket. Again, in the design and construction of airframes for rockets, the primary objective is to build a structure that will withstand all anticipated stresses while using the least possible weight.

Propulsion System

The rocket propulsion system includes the propellant used, the containers for the propellant, all plumbing that may be required to get the propellant from the containers to the engine, and the rocket engine itself. In other words, everything directly associated with propelling the rocket is part of the propulsion system.

From our previous discussion of the Saturn V's airframe, you can see that areas of the airframe may also serve as part of the propulsion system. Propellants are classified as liquid or as solid. Liquid propellants are carried in compartments separate from the combustion chamber. Solid propellants are carried in the

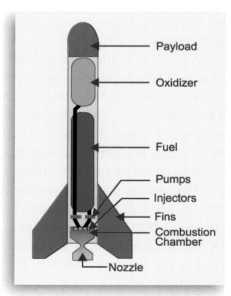

Liquid Propulsion System Components

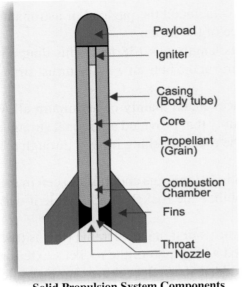

Solid Propulsion System Components

Labels: Payload, Igniter, Casing (Body tube), Core, Propellant (Grain), Combustion Chamber, Fins, Throat, Nozzle

combustion chamber. The two types of propellants lead to significant differences in engine structure and thrust control.

Propulsion systems used in rocketry may be generally classified as chemical, gas-heating and electric systems. Those considered chemical systems usually involve the mixing and burning of a chemical fuel and a chemical oxidizer to produce the hot, expanding gases needed to provide thrust. The gas-heating system design would use an external heat source to heat and cause the propellant to build the pressure necessary to provide thrust by exiting the exhaust nozzle at high velocity. Electric systems use magnetic fields and currents to propel matter in small amounts.

Guidance System

The "brain" of a large, sophisticated rocket is its guidance system. The guidance system is a self-contained electronic unit that employs a computer and an inertial platform and may also have a star-tracking unit for space navigation. The computer is programmed for the desired flight trajectory before launch. Of course, there is also a radio link between the rocket's mission controllers and its guidance system. This link allows changes to be made in instructions to the rocket's guidance system, and it also functions, more or less, as a direct control in the event the on-board guidance system experiences a partial malfunction.

In comparison to the rest of the rocket, the guidance system is exceptionally small. The miniaturization of electronics is the explanation for its small size. The electrical power needed flows through miniaturized circuits, and the wire connecting the various components is correspondingly lightweight.

Again, the Saturn V as an example, gives an idea of how relatively small a guidance system is in comparison to the rest of the rocket. This photograph shows the entire instrument unit being fitted atop the 22-foot-diameter third stage. The actual inertial guidance system was only a part of the total instrument unit.

The guidance system senses the rocket's motion and this data is fed into the system's computer. If the rocket is not flying according to the planned trajectory, impulses for correcting the trajectory are sent to the control system.

Coupled with an inertial guidance system may be an automatic celestial navigation unit,

The Saturn V's Instrument Unit

466

or "star tracker." However, a star tracker is justified only for spaceflight where it is exceptionally important to keep a spacecraft on the correct flight path.

Although rocketry is involved in making course corrections for the flight of spacecraft, we are hesitant to associate the star-tracker unit with the guidance system for rockets. The spacecraft itself is really the payload of a rocket launch vehicle whose guidance system initially placed the spacecraft on the correct flight path. Even so, a star-tracker unit can be linked to the primary guidance system of any rocket vehicle.

When we leave the larger, more sophisticated rockets and look at the smaller ones, we find there are several other types of guidance systems. These smaller rockets are within the area of military use; they are missiles. Of course, the largest of these missiles use the inertial guidance system too. These large missiles are capable of doing more than delivering a destructive device over intercontinental distances; they could be used (as some models have) as launch vehicles for spacecraft.

The smaller rocket missiles that have a guidance system usually are known as short-range missiles. Such missiles may be guided to their targets by the command of a human director. Other missiles' guidance systems may require that they "home in" on the target that is radiating heat or light. Still other missiles are built to fly along a beam that is aimed at and kept on the target. These guidance systems, which are in addition to the inertial system, are the command system, the homing system and the beam-rider system.

Control System

Again, we must think of the guidance system of a rocket as being its "brain." It doesn't matter if this "brain" is within the rocket as a self-contained unit (such as the inertial system) or mainly outside the rocket (such as a command system). Whatever the rocket's guidance system dictates should be done to keep on the correct flight path must be carried out by another system—the control system.

While in the atmosphere, control systems for rockets can work much like those of an airplane. Once the rocket climbs to where the air is very thin, other methods need to be considered. One way to change the rocket's flight path is to change the direction of the exhaust stream. Another way is to use small rockets along the side of the rocket near the nose and tail of the airframe to redirect the rocket. Variations or combinations of the systems control large and small rockets. (These same systems can also be used in the atmosphere.)

Specific Impulse and Density Impulse

The effectiveness of either type of propellant is stated in terms of specific impulse or density impulse. The word impulse means thrust and is the measure of how much thrust will be obtained from a propellant.

Specific impulse (I_{sp}) is the number of pounds of thrust delivered by consuming one pound of propellant (oxidizer/fuel mixture) in one second. If, for example, a pound of common black powder burns up in one second and produces 100 pounds of thrust, the specific impulse of this batch of powder is 100 seconds. Packing one pound of this powder into a rocket motor and igniting it would give our rocket a 100-pound kick that would last for one second. Now, how high or far our rocket travels depends on several factors; such as the total weight of the rocket and the design of the rocket motor.

Let's suppose we do not want to burn all this powder at one time. We do not need 100 pounds of thrust to lift our rocket because the entire rocket weighs only 2 pounds, including the black-powder propellant. What we want to do is spread the total thrust available over a longer period of time.

For instance, we would use a long-tube design for the motor. This would allow only a small portion of the powder's total surface to be exposed to the burning process. Let's say that this arrangement of the propellant extends the burning time to 10 seconds. In effect, we have divided our 100 pounds of thrust by 10, which gives us 10 pounds of thrust per second until the propellant is burned up.

Taking this example to the extreme, if we could cause the same powder (propellant) to burn for 100 seconds, then we would have one pound of thrust per second. (However, our two-pound-weight would not move in the vertical direction.)

When you see the symbol I_{sp} and a number following it, you should remember that the number represents the seconds during which 1 pound of thrust could be provided by burning 1 pound of propellant. For example, if a propellant has an I_{sp} of 500, it means that burning 1 pound of this propellant will produce 1 pound of thrust for 500 seconds or 500 pounds of thrust for 1 second (or any of an infinite of variations, such as 1,000 pounds of thrust for 1/2 second, 2,000 pounds for ¼ second, or 4,000 pounds for 1/8 second).

Specific impulse is not the only measure that is considered when choosing a propellant for a rocket. Density impulse is another measure of a propellant's thrust according to the volume involved. The propellants for the Saturn V's second stage are a good example. They were oxygen and hydrogen. This combination gives a specific impulse of 364 seconds. Yet, a pound of these propellants takes up a lot of space (volume) because of the relatively light density of hydrogen, even in liquid form.

The weight of the structure, or airframe, needed to contain this volume somewhat offsets the advantage of a high I_{sp}. The density impulse for oxygen/hydrogen is 90.

Another propellant composed of red fuming nitric acid (RFNA) as the oxidizer and aniline as the fuel has a specific impulse of 200 and a density impulse of 310. So why wasn't the RFNA/aniline propellant used for the Saturn V second stage? Very simply, the people managing the program had to consider many factors other than specific and density impulses. These factors included cost, ease and safety of handling the propellant, and stability of the propellant. The decision reached, therefore, was a compromise after considering all factors and all possible combinations of oxidizers and fuels.

Key Terms and Concepts

- reaction engine
- Earth's gravitational field
- spin stabilization
- gravitation
- gravity
- Newton's law of universal gravitation
- Newton's three laws of motion
- force
- velocity
- acceleration
- momentum
- combustion chamber
- throat (of a rocket engine)
- nozzle (of a rocket engine)
- payload
- four major rocket systems—airframe, propulsion, guidance and control
- propulsion systems—chemical, gas-heating, electric
- guidance—inertial, command, homing, beam-rider
- specific impulse
- density impulse

? Test Your Knowledge ?

SELECT THE CORRECT ANSWER

1. (**Galileo / Newton**) *conducted experiments from the Leaning Tower of Pisa.*
2. (**Galileo / Newton**) *proved that objects of varying weights strike the ground at the same time, if released at the same time.*
3. *The* (**Germans / Chinese**) *were the first to use a rocket at a weapon of war.*
4. *Dr.* (**Oberth / Goddard**) *is recognized as the "Father of Modern Rocketry."*
5. *Rockets were first attached to aircraft in* (**World War I / World War II**).

MATCHING

6. **Match the scientist with his contribution:**

   a. *Konrad Kyeser von Eichstadt* (1) Used spin stabilization for his rockets
   b. *Colonel William Congreve* (2) Made first computations for rocket flight into space
   c. *William Hale* (3) Built the first viable launching pad
   d. *Konstantin Tsiolkovsky* (4) Devised first rocket propelled by gunpowder
   e. *Dr. Robert Goddard* (5) Used more powerful liquid propellants
   f. *Dr. Hermann Oberth* (6) Developed method to correct deviations from flight path

7. **Match the terms with their correct definitions**

   a. *force* (1) The product of mass and velocity
   b. *acceleration* (2) The cause of motion
   c. *velocity* (3) Application of force over time
   d. *momentum* (4) Rate a body moves when force is applied

MULTIPLE CHOICE

8. *Which is not a major system of modern rockets?*
   a. *The airframe*
   b. *The payload*
   c. *The propulsion*
   d. *The guidance*
   e. *The control*

9. *Which of the following doesn't apply to the airframe system?*
   a. *It provides a streamlined shape.*
   b. *It contains the other systems.*
   c. *It must be strong and heavyweight.*
   d. *It must withstand heat, stress, and vibration.*

10. *Which is not a propulsion system used in rockets?*
    a. *Chemical*
    b. *Gas heating*
    c. *Nuclear*
    d. *Electric*

11. *Which is not a part of the guidance system?*
    a. *A computer*
    b. *An inertial platform*
    c. *A star-tracking unit*
    d. *Controls for the engine*

FILL IN THE BLANKS

13. Newton identified _____ _____ , which is the tendency of a rotating body to move away from its center of rotation.
14. Newton's _____ law of motion states a body at _____ and a body in _____ tend to remain in their respective states unless _____.
15. Newton's _____ law of motion states that for every action, there is a_____ .
16. Rockets were replaced as a significant military weapon when artillery developed _____.
17. Whatever the rocket is carrying is defined as the _____.
18. Propellants are classified as either _____ or _____.

TRUE OR FALSE

19. Mutual gravitation exists between all bodies, regardless of size.
20. After World War II, both the Soviets and Americans acquired German rocket experts.
21. The skin of the Atlas rocket was so thin that, if not fueled up, it had to be pressurized to keep from collapsing.
22. As with all solid fuel rockets, the Saturn V's first stage is made up mostly of fuel and oxidizer tanks.
23. The control system is the system of the rocket that equates to the "brain".
24. The homing system is a guidance system that missiles use to fly along a beam to their intended target.

SHORT ANSWER

25. Apply Newton's laws of motion to rocketry.
26. What is Newton's law of universal gravitation?
27. What are two ways to increase the thrust of a rocket?
28. Define specific impulse for propellants.

Chapter 22

PROPULSION SYSTEMS

With a few exceptions, propulsion systems for rockets and spacecraft today use chemical propellants. These propellants can be solid, semisolid, gelled or liquid, depending on whether they are pressurized. However, they are most often in solid or liquid form.

How rapidly a solid propellant burns depends on how much of its surface is exposed to burning at any one moment. Of course, this depends on the design or molding of the solid-propellant charge within its container. It is relatively easy to throttle or change the thrust of a liquid-propellant rocket, but it is very difficult to control the thrust of a solid-propellant type. Why and how these conditions exist will be examined in this chapter. We will look at special factors and conditions influencing the use of liquid propellants and examine rocket engine (or motor) design and function.

bjectives

Explain oxidation.

State the difference between an oxidizer and a reducer.

Define cryogenics, hydrocarbons and a self-reacting compound.

State the difference between a propellant, a bipropellant and a monopropellant.

List the four qualities of a good propellant.

Explain why a rocket propellant does not need air.

Explain the difference between an air-breathing engine and a rocket engine.

Define hypergolic propellants, mass flow and low explosives.

Identify a way to get more force from a load of propellant.

Describe the purpose of the rocket engine.

Describe the function of the rocket motor throat and nozzle.

Compare the features of the liquid and solid-propellant chemical systems.

Name two systems that use solid propellants.

Describe the solid-propellant chemical system.

Explain how the burning rate of solid propellants is controlled.

State the purpose of a squib in a solid-propellant rocket.

Describe a liquid-propellant engine system.

Discuss the combustion chamber of a liquid-propellant system.

Explain the function of the coupled valve in a combustion chamber.

Explain the function of the injector in a liquid-propellant engine.

Describe the hybrid propellant system.

State the advantages of a hybrid propellant system.

Oxidation and Combustion

Combustion is nothing more than very rapid oxidation, but what is oxidation? Oxidation is the combination of oxygen with another substance. The time it takes for this combining process to take place determines whether the substance rusts or corrodes, burns as a fire or explodes violently.

A chunk of rusting iron and the heat, pressure and light of a functioning rocket engine are doing the same thing. It just takes one longer to become oxidized than it does the other. Another similarity between these two extremes of oxidation is that both require oxygen (oxidizer) and a substance to be oxidized. The substance to be oxidized, the fuel, is also known as the reducer. Thus, the iron in the example is the reducer and the oxygen in the air touching the iron is the oxidizer. For the rocket, one chemical compound is the reducer (fuel), while the oxidizer is either another chemical compound or perhaps liquid oxygen.

Oxidizers and Reducers

Various combinations of oxidizer-reducers can produce an almost endless variety of oxidation reactions. When it comes to rocketry, however, a few elements occurring in a wider variety of compounds (molecular bonding of two or more elements) dominate the field.

Oxidizers. The element oxygen exists in air as two molecules. To use it in its pure form as an oxidizer for rocket fuels (or reducers), it must be chilled until it becomes liquid. This means that the oxygen must reach and be kept at a temperature of -297 degrees F. The reason why this temperature (or lower) must be maintained is that the oxygen will boil (become gaseous) at any higher temperature. Temperatures in this range come within a classification known as cryogenics.

Cryogenics is an area of science concerned with the production of low temperatures and the effect of such temperatures on matter. Thus, wherever you

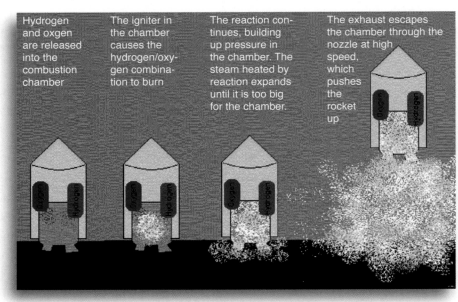

| Hydrogen and oxgen are released into the combustion chamber | The igniter in the chamber causes the hydrogen/oxygen combination to burn | The reaction continues, building up pressure in the chamber. The steam heated by reaction expands until it is too big for the chamber. | The exhaust escapes the chamber through the nozzle at high speed, which pushes the rocket up |

The chemical reaction of hydrogen and oxygen provides thrust for a rocket.

see cryogenics used with reference to an oxidizer, fuel or propellant, you know that the substance is "super cold."

There are other oxidizers that do not have to be kept at as low a temperature as pure oxygen. These are chemical compounds that contain oxygen atoms as part of their molecular structure.

Reducers. Any list of fuels (or reducers) must begin with the elements hydrogen, carbon and nitrogen. Certain compounds of hydrogen and carbon are called hydrocarbons. As you probably know, the fuels we use for heating and transportation are usually hydrocarbons that include coal and products obtained from crude oil.

The first stage of the Saturn V rocket used the hydrocarbon kerosene as its fuel. The remaining stages all used hydrogen. Pure hydrogen is an excellent rocket fuel, but it is even more cryogenic than oxygen. Hydrogen must be chilled to -423 degrees F to liquefy it.

In the atmosphere, nitrogen is inert, but it is highly reactive in other forms. Nitrogen is very important to the manufacture of high explosives and other high-energy compounds and mixtures.

Propellant Combinations. Since it takes both an oxidizer and a reducer to propel a rocket, it is correct to call either of them a propellant, However, the term propellant is most often used as a single reference to the oxidizer and reducer. For example, we could say, "the rocket uses an oxygen-hydrogen propellant." We could also say that a rocket uses 1,000 pounds of propellant. It is not necessary to say there are

Bipropellant Tank and Assembly

500 pounds of oxidizer and 500 pounds of reducer, nor is it necessary to say that they are stored within the same container or in separate containers.

Speaking of propellant storage, other terms are used to describe the storage arrangement of a propellant's oxidizer and reducer. If the oxidizer is stored in one container and the fuel (reducer) in another, the term bipropellant is used. Bipropellants are not mixed until they reach the engine's combustion chamber. Back to the Saturn V: the first-stage bipropellant was oxygen and kerosene; the second- and third-stage bipropellants were oxygen and hydrogen. For all three stages, the propellants were pumped into the combustion chamber of the engine where ignition and burning took place. The majority of liquid-propellant rockets use the bipropellant arrangement.

In some cases, the liquid oxidizer and fuel can exist together in the same storage tank. Here the propellant also is pumped into the combustion chamber of the rocket engine and ignited. However, the fact that separate storage tanks are not necessary qualifies the propellant to be called a monopropellant.

Chemically, when an oxidizer and a reducer occur in a mixture, they are considered to be two separate ingredients. There is such a thing as a self-reacting compound. In such a compound, one molecule contains atoms of both oxidizer and reducer and, upon ignition, reacts with itself, yielding energy as it breaks down or decomposes.

Combustion for Propulsion

The final objective in considering any combination of chemicals as a propellant is how much force can be obtained as the mixture oxidizes. However, there are other considerations that are recognized as the qualities of a good propellant: (1) the propellant must contain oxidizer and fuel, (2) it must ignite correctly every time, (3) it must produce energy in the form of force, and (4) the force produced must be controllable. Let's consider these four qualities individually.

Need for Packaged Oxidizers. Aside from propulsion in space, where no free oxygen is available, there is another reason for putting oxidizer in a concentrated package. An oxidizer-reducer mixture will burn forcibly in a confined or semi-confined space in which an air-breathing fire would be smothered.

People knew this fact for centuries without knowing the reason why and used it long before air-breathing engines were ever imagined. Old-fashioned gunpowder or "black powder" needs no air to burn its carbon and sulfur fuel ingredients because it has an oxidizer built into a third ingredient, potassium nitrate or saltpeter.

The ability of this mixture to propel a rocket or hurl a cannonball out of an

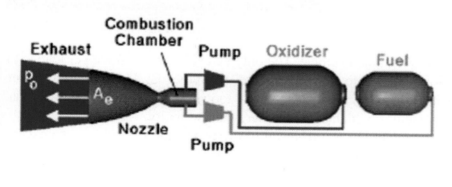

An Example of Rocket Thrust

iron tube was known and employed in warfare centuries before Lavoisier discovered oxygen and the principle of oxidation in the eighteenth century. To this day, all chemical rocket propellants, all gun munitions, and all chemical explosives contain an oxidizer, burn in confinement and do their work by bursting out of confinement or rushing out of semi-confinement.

Rushing out of semi-confinement describes rocket-propellant action. In a rocket-propellant mixture, the oxidizer outweighs the fuel on the order of 6 to 1 (for oxygen/hydrogen propellant combinations). Because the packaged oxidizer is expensive and a rocket propellant needs so much of it, the air-breathing engine is much less expensive to operate than any type of rocket engine. Still, the air-breathing engine cannot operate within both the atmosphere and space as does the rocket engine.

Ignition Characteristics. How fast a mixture burns is not necessarily related to how easily it starts. What properties of a propellant should be considered? Since the starting time of the rocket engine is important to controlling it, the propellant must start every time in the same way.

Another factor that must be considered is a choice between a continuous or restartable propellant. Some propellants can be started, but continue burning until all of the propellant is exhausted (a burnout). Others can be repeatedly started and stopped.

Safety is also a very important factor. This does not mean the propellant can stand up to any kind of rough or careless handling without igniting, but it does mean that its safety requirements should be known and feasible. Some propellants are ignitable the old-fashioned way with a match, flame or hot wire. Others require greater and more concentrated heat. Some require an explosive shock. Some are hypergolic; that is, under normal temperatures, the oxidizer and reducer burst into flame the instant they meet. The main safety requirement in this case is to keep the ingredients separated.

Energy for Force. Not light and not heat, but force is what we're looking for from a propellant's release of energy—the sheer momentum of moving molecules. What is desired is mass flow of combustion exhaust, but this mass can be no greater or less than the mass of ingredients before combustion.

Although a designer might wish to lighten the propellant load aboard a vehicle, there must be a certain amount of propellant on board to produce the needed thrust. This load alone constitutes most of the initial weight of a launch vehicle. The only way to get more force per load is to increase the velocity of the mass flow—that is, to get more "speed" per molecule. Therefore, it is better not to increase mass flow by means of heavier molecules that are too sluggish. The ideal exhaust gas consists of plenty of lightweight molecules, which excel in energy and velocity.

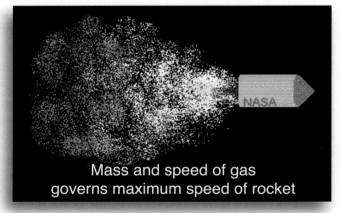

Mass and speed of gas governs maximum speed of rocket

Propellant Changes to a Gas

Controllable Force. When a propellant burns, the speed of the combustion should not be excessive. Fast, but not too fast, is the rule of thumb. How is this combustion process regulated? If a liquid propellant is used, the task of controlling the force is basically easy. All that is necessary is to govern the amount of propellant reaching the combustion chamber. This is similar to governing the amount of fuel/air mixture reaching the cylinders of an automobile engine through actions of the throttle and carburetor.

Controlling the force of a solid propellant is slightly more difficult. There are ways of controlling the force desired from a solid-propellant rocket. Basically, a solid propellant is selected (or developed) according to its ability to produce force without causing a massive, destructive explosion.

In fact, solid propellants sometimes are called "low explosives." Modern solid propellants are considerably more energetic than the black-powder-type propellant used with very early rockets. Yet, they have the black powder's property of burning so that each particle ignites its neighbor particle and the burning continues as a swiftly spreading reaction.

Pressure and Mass Flow

Adding pressure to a medium will increase its molecular activity and consequently, its temperature. Increase the temperature of a medium and its molecular activity and pressure will be increased— this is particularly true with a gaseous medium that is enclosed by a container. Thus, the purpose of the rocket motor or engine is to provide a container in which the temperature (of the oxidizing propellant) increases the pressure of the gaseous portion of the medium.

If some means were not provided to relieve the constantly building pressure of a burning propellant, the container would burst. Among the functions performed by the nozzle throat and nozzle of the rocket motor are to provide an exit for the burned propellant mass, reduce the pressure within the combustion area and direct the flow of the mass involved.

We can imagine what happens within the "business end" of a rocket on a molecular scale. The diagram below shows what happens to a single molecule that has been energized by combustion and pressure. Loaded with this energy, the molecule zips about at location A. It beats madly at its prison walls, creating pressure. However, there is a way out of its prison, and the molecule will get there along with a crowd of its highly active fellow molecules. We see it again at location B and again at location C. Note that its path continues to be erratic, but less and less so—more zig and less zag, one might say.

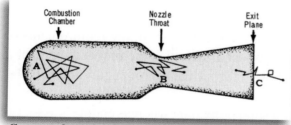
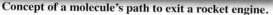

Concept of a molecule's path to exit a rocket engine.

Finally, it escapes.

This wandering molecule would seem to be going through a great deal of wasted motion and taking much too long to make its exit. Actually, it is making excellent progress. The whole journey is accomplished in a fraction of a second.

More significantly, at each stage of the journey it is traveling faster than before and in the right direction. Furthermore, the greater the pressure in the chamber, the greater the velocity through the nozzle. It is its speed out the nozzle that counts most. The net result, acceleration, is the essence of thrust. The mass of molecules is accelerating in respect to the motor, and the motor itself is moving. As long as combustion is going on inside and mass flow is passing out the nozzle, the motor adds velocity to velocity and accelerates.

Today, chemical systems are the most often used means of propulsion, When a lot of thrust is needed, rockets are usually propelled by a liquid fuel, such as kerosene and liquid oxygen (oxidizer). The propellants are mixed as they enter the combustion chamber to be ignited. A spark or small flame is used to start the ignition process. From then on, continuing combustion ignites the fuel and oxidizer as they enter the combustion chamber. The drawback to liquid chemical systems is that they require expensive plumbing, turbines, pumps, and engines.

Solid Propellants and the Solid Propellant Motor

Solid Propellants

The chemical system may have a solid rather than a liquid propellant. The fuel and oxidizer of a solid propellant are mixed together from the start. The skyrocket is a good example of a solid propellant; all it takes is ignition of the mixture. The combustion chamber and the propellant container are one and the same. This means that the solid-propellant chemical system is simple, much less costly than the liquid type and is very reliable. Today, solid propellants are used for our submarine-launched ballistic missiles, the Minuteman intercontinental ballistic missiles, and many space launch vehicles. Solid propulsion was also used on the MX (Peacekeeper) missile as well as the Space Shuttle solid rocket boosters.

Fuels used in solid propellants include asphalts, waxes, oils, plastics, metals, rubbers and resins. The oxidizers for solid propellants come from two general sources: the organic (the source of nitrocellulose and nitroglycerin) and the inorganic (the source of chemicals such as sodium nitrate and potassium perchlorate).

Chemical and Physical Properties

A look at the contents of a typical double-base propellant tells much about the requirements of a solid propellant. Typical of today's solid propellants are composites in which the fuel and oxidizer are two different compounds. Usually the oxidizer is crystalline in form (like salt or sugar) and is embedded in the fuel base.

In a solid rocket motor (motor usually is associated with solid propellant whereas engine is associated with liquid propellants), the propellant substance is molded into its motor and casing as a single solid mass called a grain. The shape and consistency of the grain determine its burning properties.

The polyurethane fuel base of the most common solid-fuel mixture is a type of synthetic rubber. It maintains about the same consistency as that of tire rubber. Various other rocket propellants have similar plastic consistencies. It is very important that this consistency be even and free from internal bubbles or surface cracks. Exposure of more burning surface than intended could result in the danger of uncontrolled burning or an explosion. The casing into which the grain is molded must be tough and heat resistant. A lining material is used as an insulator, and the case itself is made of various materials such as special steels, titanium and fiberglass.

Grain Design and Thrust Control

Once a solid propellant is ignited, it is going to burn. It can't be turned off and then restarted as is done with liquid-propellant systems. Some solid propellants can be stopped from burning by dousing them with water, but others cannot be stopped. So, how does one control the burning rate of a solid propellant? How can the amount of thrust produced be controlled? The primary way of doing this is to mold the propellant into a shape that will provide the desired burning rate.

The flame front (where actual oxidation is taking place) of a solid propellant always eats its way into the mass in a direction that is perpendicular to the surface. The flame eats its way into a mass at a fixed rate depending on the contents of the propellant. For example, a typical double-base propellant's burning rate is about 0.40 inch per second; a dense polyurethane composite burns at about 0.22 inches per second. Since these rates do not change, the only way to control the amount of force (or thrust) generated is to control the surface area exposed to the burning process.

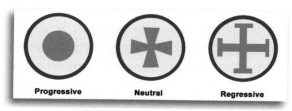

Grain Designs for Solid Propellants

The grain of a common skyrocket more than likely is a solidly packed propellant, with a space for ignition between the charge and the nozzle. Once ignited, this grain can burn only straightforward and the flame front is limited to the surface diameter. Thus, the burn rate (whatever it is) does not change until burnout. Since the burn rate doesn't change and the flame-front area doesn't change, the amount of thrust produced is constant. When this type of situation exists, the grain design is neutral.

What if a hole is bored the length of the grain, or charge, along its longitudinal axis? There will be an instantaneous spread of the flame-front along the entire surface of the hole. This, of course, provides a larger surface area of flame and greater force. As the grain continues to burn, more and more surface area is exposed so more and more thrust is produced. This is called a progressive burn rate.

Suppose a considerable amount of thrust is needed, but the designers want the thrust to be neutral. The design shown above might be used. Ignition produces a large amount of thrust very quickly, but the design keeps the surface area constant. Remember, the flame eats its way into the mass perpendicular to the surface.

The third design is one for a regressive rate. With this design, the most thrust is produced shortly after ignition, and it diminishes thereafter. A similar approach was used for the space shuttle's solid rocket boosters. The most thrust was produced upon ignition and during the first 55 seconds of the 2-minute burn. The grain of these boosters was shaped so that it then reduces thrust by approximately one-third until burnout.

There are other ways of controlling the amount of thrust or burn rate of a grain. The grain can be made up of different propellant mixtures that have different burn rates. Another method of control is to paint certain surfaces of the propellant with a heat resistant compound, leaving the other surfaces to burn at their regular rate.

Control of a solid rocket motor's thrust depends primarily on the design and composition of the grain, as indicated earlier. It is also possible to stop thrust in a solid propellant by injecting a high-pressure inert (or neutral) gas into the chamber. A grain stopped in this manner could be restarted. However, such arrangements have not proven worth the effort. So, once the grain is ignited, it continues to burn and produce the amount of thrust for which it was designed. Control of the direction of thrust is another matter. Thrust directional control for the solid-propellant rocket can be obtained from the same type devices used with liquid-propellant rockets.

Igniters

Solid propellants are ignited by a composition that both heats the grain to ignition temperature and increases the pressure in the combustion chamber until propellant reaction is assured. The heat produced by an electrical wire could ignite a few of the older solid-propellant mixtures. Today, this type of ignition device is sometimes found in model-rocket launching devices, but the real rockets use devices like the squib. The squib consists of an enclosure filled with a combustible powder that is ignited electrically. The flame of the burning squib, in turn, ignites the grain.

Two igniter compositions frequently used are common gunpowder and a metal-oxidizer mixture such as magnesium and potassium perchlorate. Each of these has advantages over the other. Each also has certain disadvantages. Gunpowder is inexpensive, but it tends to absorb moisture, which can adversely affect its performance. Metal-oxidizer igniters are generally more efficient and ignition delays are shorter. However, they are more hazardous to handle than black-powder igniters. If magnesium is used in igniter composition, surface oxidation is likely to occur. Once oxidized, the igniter doesn't work very well.

A critical part of an igniter is the case that contains the composition. Manufacturers of igniters have a variety of materials to choose from, ranging from paper to metal. The strength of the container must be sufficient for demands made upon it. For example, rapid ignition requires the container to be strong enough to remain intact, until all the composition has ignited. However, the container must be designed so that no part of it is large enough to block the exhaust nozzle. Such blocking could cause extremely high pressures and damage the motor. The location of the igniter depends upon the design of the grain.

Liquid Propellants and the Liquid-Propellant Engine

Liquid Propellants

You will remember that there are two general classifications of liquid propellants: bipropellant and monopropellant. When the oxidizers and fuels are separated, we refer to the two as a bipropellant. Any rocket that uses a bipropellant has a liquid-bipropellant propulsion system. However, it is not necessary for all liquid propellants to have their oxidizers and fuels kept separate. When a liquid propellant contains its oxidizer and fuel in one solution, it is called a monopropellant.

Bipropellants have an advantage over monopropellants in that they are more stable and capable of better performance. Bipropellants consist of two types: the nonhypergolic (nonself-igniting) and the hypergolic (self-igniting). Each of the two types of bipropellants has advantages and disadvantages. Malfunctioning of equipment and accidents involving a system using either type of bipropellant can be disastrous.

An ignition delay, even a brief one, results in a sufficient accumulation of nonhypergolic fuel and oxidizers in the combustion chamber to cause a damaging explosion. The components of a hypergolic propellant catch fire when brought into contact one with the other.

The design of a liquid-monopropellant system is much simpler than the design of a bipropellant system. A monopropellant system requires only half the storage, pumping and controlling equipment required by a bipropellant system. It doesn't require metering to keep the fuel and oxidizer in correct proportion.

The drawback of a monopropellant is its sensitivity to temperature and shock. This sensitivity results in instability and restricts its

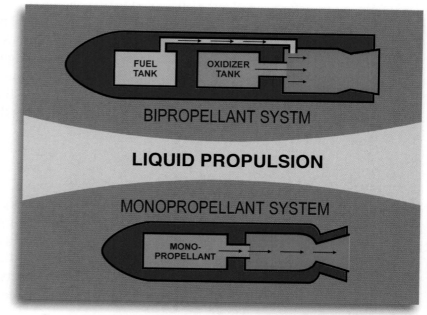

Comparison of Bipropellant and Monopropellant Propulsion Systems

handling. Generally, monopropellants also require more heat for ignition and react more slowly than bipropellants. These factors mean that monopropellants require larger combustion chambers.

Just as there are two general types of bipropellants, there are two general types of monopropellants: those that obtain energy by combustion and those that obtain energy by dissociation reaction (decomposition). A catalyst initiates the dissociation reaction.

To ignite a liquid propellant, it is necessary to raise the temperature of a small part of the mixture to its ignition point. The flame will then spread throughout the total mixture. Mixtures that contain liquid oxygen have a high reaction rate, so these mixtures are easy to ignite. For example, an ordinary spark plug can be used to ignite a flow of oxygen and alcohol.

One method of igniting a liquid-propellant mixture is to inject a limited amount of hypergolic fuel into the combustion chamber along with the oxidizer just before the main fuel flow starts. Another method uses a pyrotechnic fired electrically from an external circuit. If repeated ignitions are required during flight, a small precombustion chamber makes the ignition of a small amount of the propellant possible by means of a spark plug. The flow into the main chamber is delayed until the propellant in the precombustion chamber is ignited. The flame from the precombustion chamber is then used to ignite the mixture in the main chamber.

The Liquid-Propellant Engine

The essential units of a liquid-propellant system include propellant tanks, a combustion chamber and a means of forcing propellants from the tanks through control valves to the combustion chamber. The simplest liquid-propellant engine system transfers oxidizer and fuel from tanks to the combustion chamber by pressurizing the tanks with an inert gas such as nitrogen. More complex systems employ turbopumps to transfer propellants to the combustion chamber.

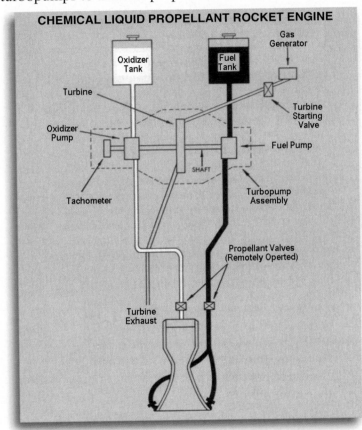

CHEMICAL LIQUID PROPELLANT ROCKET ENGINE

Major Components of a Liquid-Bipropellant Propulsion System

The nature of the propellant determines, to a great degree, the structural design of the engine or propulsion system. Quite often, the use that will be made of the liquid-propellant engine determines both the nature of the engine's design and the type of its liquid propellant.

There are many kinds of liquid fuels and a number of liquid oxidizers that are available for use in liquid propellants. It is possible for a single oxidizer to react with many different fuels. Also, a single fuel can react with a number of different oxidizers; for example, kerosene (a fuel) reacts with liquid oxygen, hydrogen peroxide or nitric acid. For this reason, many combinations of fuels and oxidizers are possible.

The basis for choosing a certain fuel-oxidizer combination might include economy, safety, ease of handling, and purpose. However, the fundamental factor underlying the choice of a propellant combination is generally the performance of such a combination.

Combustion Chamber

The combustion chamber is the "heart" of the liquid-propellant engine. Within this chamber, several phases of the combustion process take place. These phases include: (1) atomizing, (2) mixing, (3) preheating to ignition temperature, and (4) the reaction of the propellant.

A combustion chamber may be cooled or uncooled. Combustion temperatures of propellants used in uncooled combustion chambers frequently are under 1,000° C. When it is desired to construct uncooled combustion chambers that will withstand relatively high temperatures over a comparatively long period of time, they are given an interior ceramic or carbon coating.

There are several methods of cooling a combustion chamber, but the most commonly used method is by regenerative cooling. In this method, fuel or oxidizer is circulated within small passageways between the inner and outer walls of the combustion chamber, throat and nozzle. As the propellant flows through the passageways, it absorbs heat, thereby cooling the combustion chamber. The absorbed heat also adds energy to the fuel or oxidizer before it enters the injector and increases the velocity of injection into the combustion chamber.

Valves

A propellant system's tanks and plumbing must be constructed of materials that are not adversely affected by the nature of the fuel and oxidizer the system uses. The nature of the fluids a system uses also determines the kinds of materials used to make valves. The scope of both the operating temperatures and operating conditions to which they are subject makes it necessary to use high-precision techniques in valve manufacturing.

Valves used in propellant systems range in type and size according to their specific functions. Comparatively large valves, for example, are used to control the high flow of fuel and oxidizer. A coupled valve, consisting of two propellant valves opened by a single piston, operates through a crosshead, causing fuel and oxidizer to enter the combustion chamber at the same time.

Injector

The function of the injector of a liquid-propellant rocket engine is similar to that of the carburetor used with some automobile engines. Just as a carburetor atomizes (reduces to small particles) and mixes fuel and air, preparing the mixture for combustion, the injector atomizes and mixes fuel and oxidizer.

The type of injector used depends upon the type of propellant. Lightness, simplicity and low cost are factors that need to be considered by manufacturers of rocket-engine injectors. However, just as is the case with valves and other rocket-engine components, precision and exactness of construction of the injector are very important.

Two types of injectors are in common use. The difference between them is the difference between the methods each uses to mix fuel and oxidizer. In the swirl-jet type, each propellant is introduced into the chamber in an inverted-cone-shaped spray, finely atomized and sufficiently diffused for adequate mixing with the adjacent spray. In the impinging-jet type, the fuel and oxidizer enter the combustion chamber

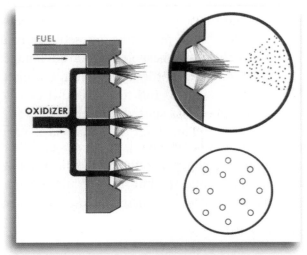

Operating Principle of the Impinging-Jet-Type Injector

directly through openings arranged in such a way that the streams of fuel and oxidizer strike each other (impinge on one another). Their collision causes the required atomization and mixing.

Improved injection systems have contributed to the development of throttleable (variable control) liquid-propellant engines. One such system mixes, in a specially designed manifold, gas under high pressure with liquid fuel before it is injected into the combustion chamber. Depending on the ratio of gas to liquid fuel, the engine may be throttled from a low to a full thrust, and may be stopped and started in flight.

Hybrid Propellants

Hybrid propellant systems use both liquid propellants and solid propellants in combination within the same engine. Thus, rockets that use this type of propellant system are called hybrid rockets. Usually, solid material is used as the fuel, and a liquid is used as the oxidizer. However, there are systems that use liquid fuels and solid oxidizers. When solid fuel is used, it is packed into the rocket engine as an inert material without its oxidizer. The liquid oxidizer is stored in a separate tank. To create combustion and generate thrust, the oxidizer is fed into the solid-fuel combustion chamber at a desired rate. In one such system, the solid fuel and the oxidizer do not come into actual contact. Instead, the heat of ignition vaporizes the oxidizer and the fuel. These gases, approaching each other from opposite directions, unite and burn just above the face of the fuel grain. The thrust produced by the hybrid rocket can thereby be increased or decreased simply by increasing or decreasing the flow of oxidizer over the fuel charge. Thrust is stopped when the flow of oxidizer is closed off.

The hybrid propellant system combines, in a single rocket, many of the advantages of both liquid-propellant rockets and solid-propellant rockets. It has the flexibility, controllability and high performance of liquid rockets, plus the simplicity, reliability and relative economy of solid rockets. Flexibility probably gives the hybrid rocket its biggest operational advantage. It can be throttled, like a liquid rocket, from zero to full thrust, and it can be stopped and started in flight.

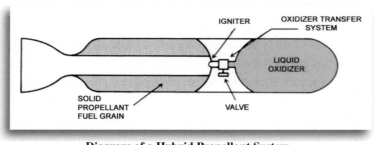

Diagram of a Hybrid Propellant System

The diagram above is a very simple diagram of how the parts of a hybrid propellant system might be arranged. In the system illustrated, the valve controls how much oxidizer is allowed to come in contact with the fuel. This amount, or rate of oxidizer to fuel, determines how much thrust the system produces. In this particular design, the grain has been molded for a progressive burn rate. To maintain a steady thrust could require less and less oxidizer as the process continues.

AEROSPACE PROPULSION TECHNOLOGY

Since the invention of the first heavier-than-air flying vehicle, designers, builders, pilots, war planners and commercial airlines have sought aircraft capable of higher and higher speeds. The requirements for faster vehicles have changed significantly since the early years of flight and the technologies used to achieve high speeds are undergoing significant advances.

The Air Force Laboratory's Propulsion Directorate has been the key national organization to develop and demonstrate these technologies. Since 1917, the Directorate and its predecessor organizations have been developing critical propulsion technologies, which have in turn, enabled revolutionary advances for the country's armed forces.

Aerospace Propulsion Technologies Defined

What are Aerospace Propulsion Technologies? Simply put – these are propulsion systems that utilize fuel and atmospheric oxygen for fuel combustion throughout all or part of their

Curtis V2-3 as used in WWI aircraft (courtesy of the Air Force Museum)

intended flight regime. Called air breathers, these propulsion systems are capable of at least Mach 5 and are categorized as hypersonic. These engines can range from single propulsion systems with single or dual mode combustion schemes up to multiple or combined cycle systems for multiple propulsion cycles with high speed turbines, scramjets, and rockets.

This publication focuses on current and future efforts to realize true, high speed endo-atmospheric flight, and specifically covers our efforts to develop and demonstrate high speed air-breathing propulsion systems. As the graph below indicates, enormous potential exists to expand the flight envelope of high speed air-breathing propulsion.

Hypersonic Airbreathing Propulsion Requires Advances in the Current State-of-the-Art. Only by advancing the state-of-the-art in turbine engine, ramjet/scramjet, and rocket technologies can true aerospace propulsion systems be realized.

AFRL's Propulsion Directorate leads the nation in the development of these critical technologies. Teaming with other government agencies and the propulsion industry at large, the Directorate has ensured technology research and development programs that address all technical challenges of aerospace propulsion systems.

High Speed Enables a Broad Range of Revolutionary Capabilities

There are several potential missions where high speed aerospace propulsion could have significant payoff. These missions are illustrated below.

Near Term – Expendable Systems – Supersonic, Long-Range Cruise Missiles. Small, supersonic turbine engines currently being developed can power a long range (thousands of miles), supersonic cruise missile. Produced in modular form, this Mach 3-plus capable missile can be assembled to match the required combat capability. Such a missile would provide a 4 times speed increase over fielded systems with a commensurate increase in range.

An early V-8 liquid-cooled aircraft engine.

Hypersonic, Hydrocarbon-Fueled Rocket Boosted Strike Missiles. Using higher speed air-breathing propulsion such as a ramjet or scramjet coupled with solid rocket motor boost, hydrocarbon fueled air-breathers can achieve Mach 7+ at high altitudes. Such performance enables the capability to engage time critical targets with a response time much less than current capabilities. These hypersonic weapons could also have long ranges and a majority of targets can be engaged by launch aircraft outside an adversary's national borders. The use of readily available and logistically supportable carbon fuel increases the readiness and availability of such systems. The kinetic energy available in such high speed systems make them ideal for penetration of deeply buried hardened targets.

Enable Space Lift. The technology developed for scramjet-powered high speed missiles form the foundation of low cost space launch systems for small payloads requiring short reaction time to launch.

Using hydrocarbon-fueled scramjets and solid rocket propulsion; these vehicles could be air launched and have the capability of inserting a 1000 pound payload into low earth orbit (LEO).

Mid- and Long-Term Reusable Systems.

The radial engine brought reliability and great power-to-weight propulsion systems to aircraft of the 20th Century.

While expendable high speed propulsion systems can take us through the entire ground-to-orbit flight regime, the most significant pay off will be realized from reusable high speed systems. That will allow frequent and reliable, high speed flight for systems ranging from global range, high speed reconnaissance vehicles to orbit – capable platforms.

Sir Frank Whittle's first jet engine. He personally provided the funds to patent this propulsion system and is credited with being the inventor of the first working jet engine prototype.

Significant advances in materials and manufacturing processes must be made to build vehicle and propulsion systems capable of withstanding the severe environment presented by hypersonic flight.

Cutaway Axial Flow Turbojet Engine of the '60s.

Advanced thermal propulsion systems and air frame structures must be developed. Vehicles in this class will operate much like military and commercial aircraft of today. They will take off and land from conventional runways.

Affordable, Reliable, Responsive Access to Space. The ultimate expression of aerospace propulsion technology combines scramjets with high speed turbines and rockets to form combined cycle engines capable of propelling a vehicle from take-off into low earth orbit. Such vehicles will have numerous advantages over pure rocket powered vehicles. They could operate from conventional runways and possess the ability to abort missions at any time during the mission flight profile. Because of this characteristic, a combined cycle vehicle offers a much faster operational tempo over current launch systems. This reduction in the cost of putting payloads in orbit leads to an enormously greater flexibility in the launching and utilization of space-based assets for both military and civil needs.

How Do Aerospace Propulsion Systems Provide Transformational Capabilities?

The Air-Breathing Advantage. The advantage of air-breathing hypersonic propulsion systems stem from the fact that they obtain oxygen for combustion from the earth's atmosphere. Unlike pure rocket-powered vehicles, the resultant vehicle does not have to carry the oxygen inside the vehicle.

Higher Propulsion Efficiency (Isp). Propulsion efficiency, designated Isp, is defined as the ratio of an engines thrust to the weight of fuel burned in one second. The higher the number, the more efficient the propulsion system. High bypass turbofan engines have the highest specific impulse that are capable of only modest velocities. High speed turbojets can generate appreciable velocities and the chart curves indicate the practical limits of pure turbo propulsion. Ramjets and scramjets take the Mach range out much further and using hydrogen as a fuel can theoretically accelerate a vehicle to Mach 25.

Improved Mass Fractions. With higher propulsive efficiency, more of the flight vehicle can be dedicated to performing mission requirements. This is typically defined as the vehicle systems mass fractions. As an example, a typical unmanned rocket powered launch vehicle has a mass fraction of about 10%. That means 90% of the vehicles total launch weight is made up of propellant. If scramjets were used as the primary propulsive system for a space launch vehicle, up to 28% of the vehicle weight could be dedicated to mission requirements, or over twice that of a conventional all-rocket powered launch vehicle.

Airplane-Like Design and Flight Characteristics. Using air-breathing propulsion for space access systems allows vehicles to be designed that operate like airplanes while in the atmosphere. This advantage allows for greater margin of safety in space launch vehicles whereby the mission can be terminated at practically any point of the flight profile (unlike a pure rocket, which has limited mission termination margin.) Vehicles can be made smaller and lighter for a given payload. This reduces the amount and cost of support infrastructure necessary to sustain flight operations.

America's First Operational Jet Fighter, the Bell P-59 Airacomet. (USAF Photo)

Earth-orbit capable systems can be made to operate more like aircraft and be truly reusable, thus increasing the frequency and reliability of space launch.

High Speed Propulsion Technology Challenges

The ultimate propulsion technology for high speed flight will combine the best of turbo machinery, ramjet, scramjet and rocket propulsion. When combined into one vehicle, such a propulsion system will enable systems to deliver unprecedented capabilities for swift delivery of munitions for time critical targets. Such a system will also create rapid response expendable space launch for small payloads' long range strike and reconnaissance; and low cost reliable, affordable and frequent access to space. To deliver such capabilities requires advances in all three firms of propulsion.

Turbine and rocket propulsion have proven their value operationally for over half a century. Supersonic combustion ramjets represent an emerging technology. These high speed air-breathing engines are the key to enabling the many advanced capabilities of aerospace propulsion.

Ramjets-A Building Block for the Scramjet. Ramjets were postulated in the first half of the 20th century and flew as early as the 1930's. A ramjet engine can be thought of as a long duct mounted to a supersonic vehicle in a suitably aerodynamically efficient manner. Incoming air enters the front of the engine and passes straight through and out the rear without the use of any rotating parts inside the flow path. The flow path essentially is open all the way through from front to back. The air is funneled and compressed – or rammed – into the engine inlet by the forward motion of the vehicle and by the shape of the front section of the ramjet. Once inside the engine, the air mixes with the injected fuel that is introduced part way along the flow path, and the oxygen in the air combines with the fuel and this provides ignition. The resultant hot gas exits out the rear of the engine to produce the needed thrust for the vehicle.

Since a ramjet relies on the forward motion of the vehicle to provide the needed compression of the air, some kind of booster or low speed engine is needed to accelerate the vehicle to the point where the ramjet can take over. The ramjet becomes effective only at speeds above Mach 2.

Once in operation, the ramjet is effective up to speeds of about Mach 5. Above this speed, ramjets start to lose efficiency for several reasons. It is necessary to change its mode of operation into that of a supersonic combustion ramjet, which is usable to much higher speeds. The next step involves scramjet technology.

Scramjets – Bridging the Speed Gap. The basic difference between a ramjet and a scramjet is

X-15, the First True Aerospace Plane. (NASA photo)

that in a scramjet, the air is allowed to exceed sonic (Mach 1) speed inside the engine. Like the ramjet, a scramjet is a visually simple machine. There are no moving parts in the flow path. The look, however, belies a complexity that is presented to engine designers when speeds significantly increase. In fact, the higher the speed, the tougher the problem.

There are several major challenges faced by the aerospace propulsion developers. By focusing initial development on missile-sized, expendable scramjets, significant progress has been made to overcome these challenges and to establish a solid technical base to extend toward large, reusable systems.

An exoatmospheric propulsion system

The legendary SR -71 use ramjet technology to reach and sustain Mach 3. (NASA photo)

The problem of mixing and burning the fuel in a supersonic flow. Lighting a match in a hurricane is easy compared to the problem of mixing and burning propellant in a scramjet. In a scramjet, the time required for mixing of the fuel with the incoming air and combusting it to produce thrust is roughly one millisecond or less. If not accomplished in this very short time, the reactions are likely to be quenched as the flow expands in the nozzle, greatly reducing thrust.

Survivable engine structures. The heat of scramjet operation is extremely high and requires innovative and robust structures. Materials must be high temperature capable and lightweight while maintaining the ability to preserve the critical geometry required for efficient flow path operation. Using fuel to cool combustion components has been commonplace in rocket engines for decades. The combination of pressure and temperature in a reusable rocket combustion chamber is required to maintain structural integrity of the engine. For much the same reason, a scramjet requires a fuel cooled structure and, in fact, requires more cooling because the run time for a reusable scramjet is longer than typical for rocket propulsion. Knowing how much fuel to use, the exact pressures and volumes, and at what locations is a challenging problem for high speed propulsion systems.

Fuels Technology. Fuel is the lifeblood of any propulsion system. For scramjets, the fuel plays a dual role – cooling the engine structure and providing the combustion energy to produce thrust. Choosing the right fuel is difficult. On the one hand, we need the highest available energy for the combustion process. Hydrogen, the simplest fuel

A Fighter for the 21st Century—
The F-22 Raptor (USAF photo)

Pratt & Whitney Rockedyne's State-
of-the-Art Rocket Propulsion System

has the highest energy and also the highest ability to absorb heat; however, it is volumetrically inefficient – it takes a large tank to hold the hydrogen. Larger tanks mean larger structures, which mean larger vehicles and the circle keeps on widening. Cryogenic hydrogen also requires insulation of the fuel tank, further reducing volumetric efficiency. Hydrocarbon fuels also have a lower rate of heat absorption.

Variable Geometry Inlet and Nozzle for Turbine and Scramjet Flow Paths. Scramjets need an inlet design that keeps the air flow supersonic. To operate over a broad range of mach numbers, scramjet inlets may require variable geometry. This represents a challenge in several ways: it adds complexity and weight to the vehicle, and the forces impinging on this variable geometry are enormous at hypersonic speeds requiring robust materials and control systems. The same challenges apply to variable geometry nozzles.

The major technical challenges for combined cycle engines include:
Airframe/Engine Integration.
Integrating the propulsion system with the airframe has been an important technical necessity

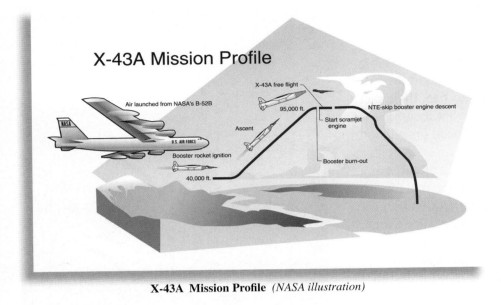

X-43A Mission Profile

Air launched from NASA's B-52B

X-43A free flight

95,000 ft.

NTE-skip booster engine descent

Ascent

Start scramjet engine

Booster rocket ignition

Booster burn-out

40,000 ft.

X-43A Mission Profile *(NASA illustration)*

for many decades. Piston engine-powered craft worked best when the frontal area of the aircraft could be reduced or at least streamlined to reduce the drag on the vehicle. The same problem was encountered at a more serious level with the introduction of the jet engine. In today's turbine-powered world, engine/airframe integration is a concept used to ensure the highest performance and reliability of the turbine engine.

In a hypersonic vehicle, this integration is so pronounced and critical that the airframe and engine are essentially blended. Many hypersonic vehicle concepts look very much the same. The reason is that the physical rules for hypersonic flight dictate designs such as is shown above where the front of the vehicle, in conjunction with a shock wave, forms the intake of the engine. The "engine" module is where the fuel is injected and combustion takes place while the rear of the vehicle forms the exhaust nozzle to allow for complete expansion of the combustion process. The aerothermodynamic performance cannot be decoupled from the propulsion performance since both share surfaces and the flow fields interact. In essence, we no longer look at an engine simply as a part that is mounted to the airframe, but rather as part of a complete aircraft system, the components of which must be designed in complete concert which each other.

Variable Geometry Inlet and Nozzle for Turbine and Scramjet Flow Paths. Advanced turbine engines are capable of speeds from Mach number zero (Mn0) to near hypersonic speeds (Mn4+) depending on the engine cycle chosen. Inlets for turbine engines are designed to keep the incoming flow at subsonic velocity. Scramjets are designed to operate with supersonic flows throughout the engine. Therefore, the inlet must have variable geometry to satisfy both propulsion cycles, bringing the complexity and need for robust control systems.

Integrated Scramjet/Rocket Nozzles. In order to generate thrust efficiency, the engine exhaust must be expanded through a nozzle. The challenge is designing a nozzle that provides near optimal expansion for the two different propulsion systems over a broad range of Mach numbers.

Low Drag Scramjet Injectors with Internal Rockets. A combined cycle powered vehicle has the potential to fly into orbit. At hypervelocity speeds (Mn15+), the energy of the flow begins to approach the energy of combustion. Any internal drag subtracts from the output of the engine in the airbreathing mode. Therefore, a fuel injection stream that allows for complete mixing and combustion at the velocities is required.

Thermal Management. A vehicle powered by combined cycle engines accelerating to orbital velocity spend a far longer time in the atmosphere than a pure rocket-powered vehicle, which "punches" straight through the atmosphere as quickly as possible. Because of this long residence time in the atmosphere, the vehicle will experience extreme thermal loads throughout. Managing this energy is critical to vehicle operation and, indeed, survival. A complete knowledge of the aerodynamic heating coupled with the heat generated through high speed turbine and scramjet combustion is required. Heat resistant materials capable of surviving the dynamic loads must be developed for both engine and airframe components. How the latent energy of the fuel is used is also part of the thermal balance equation and must be done correctly and efficiently for a hypervelocity airbreathing propulsion system to become a reality.

High Heat Sink Fuels and Actively Cooled Structures. The temperatures experienced in very high speed airbreathing engines exceed the limits of even the best high temperature materials. To preserve their structural integrity, these materials must be actively cooled. The most efficient way to cool these structures is by circulating the fuel through them prior to the fuel be used for combustion. Fuel characteristics play a critical role in the thermal management scheme. Ideally, the fuel should be endothermic. That is, have the ability to absorb the heat energy of combustion thereby cooling the engine walls. During the process of absorbing the energy, an endothermic fuel breaks down chemically into simpler, combustible species, which can be mixed and burned more rapidly than the complete fuel.

Long Life, Rapid Turn-Around Reusable Rocket Engines. Rocket engines have always been extreme machines. Producing the highest thrust to weight ratio of any propulsion system, their operating conditions are at the limits of the thermal/mechanical capability of the manufactured systems. For a vehicle to be truly reusable, the rocket engine component of the combined cycle engine must be as robust as the rest. Advances are required in nozzle design and materials, turbo pumps and control systems.

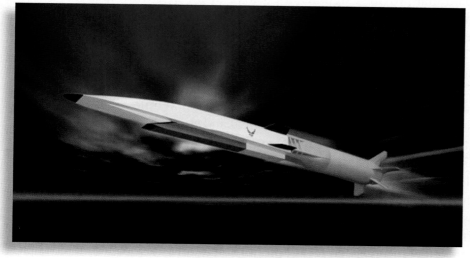

X-51 Scramjet Demonstrator (USAF illustration)

Our Response to the Challenge

The Propulsion Directorate is leading the work to deliver solutions to the development challenges presented by advanced aerospace propulsion. Our heritage and experience with all of the necessary propulsion components suggests to us that high speed aerospace propulsion technology development is at the same stage today as the turbine engine was in 1939.

When first introduced as an aircraft powerplant, the turbine engine was only marginally better than the best piston engines of the day. In the 25 years since its inception, turbine technology provided the

U.S. Air Force with revolutionary, high speed capabilities and holds even more promise as a critical component of advanced aerospace systems.

By using focused research and technology demonstrations, a technological revolution can begin that will transform the Air Force by providing a series of capabilities far beyond what we have today.

High Speed Today. After literally decades of scientific work, the Propulsion Directorate stands ready to begin the revolutionary change in capabilities for our national defense. The development and demonstration of the hydrocarbon fueled and cooled scramjet will introduce the first component of a radically improved aerospace capability.

High Speed 2034. In the future, we'll see a natural outgrowth of this early scramjet development maturing into aerospace propulsion systems capable of delivering routine, reliable access to any part of the earth in minutes.

To realize the future, the Propulsion Directorate is taking a stair step approach. This approach will add new capabilities on a planned, incremental basis by taking advantage of the high speed aerospace propulsion technologies as they can be demonstrated. Three propulsion system types form the backbone of this approach; small scram jets, medium scram jets and finally, combined cycle engines.

The first step will demonstrate the small scramjet currently being developed for a flight test vehicle called the X-51 Scramjet Engine Demonstrator or SED. Boosted by an available solid propellant rocket, the scramjet will take over the flight at Mach 4-plus and accelerate the vehicle to a cruising speed of over Mach 7.

The Directorate is well along the road to providing the propulsion system for this vehicle. We have demonstrated an engine flow path that provides significant positive thrust in a wind tunnel at Mach numbers 4.5 and 6.5. This engine, in its current form, is known as the Ground Demonstrator Engine, or GDE. It incorporates such features as a 2D inlet, 2D scramjet combustor, endothermic fuel-cooled metallic engine and uncooled Carbon/Silicon Carbide.

Part of step one will be to missionize the expendable scramjet into a hypersonic cruise missile. Such a missile, with a maximum speed of Mach 7 flying at over 100,000 feet altitude, will have few, if any, threats to successful mission accomplishment. With a range of well over 500 miles and transit times measured in minutes, these missiles can be employed against tactical and strategic targets. Their speed enables two important capabilities. The first is to destroy time sensitive targets from very long ranges. The second capability is the missile's ability to deliver high kinetic energy to destroy a hardened target. In addition, such weapons could be employed against 95% of strategic and tactical targets without the launch aircraft ever crossing an adversary's border.

Step two is to take the proven flow paths of the small scram jets and scale them up to medium size engines for expandable space lift vehicles. Such launch vehicles would capitalize on the high efficiency of air-breathing propulsion combined with advanced rocket propulsion to provide an on-demand capability for placing small payloads into low earth orbit.

Step three involves the much more difficult but very high payoff of development of the combined cycle propulsion system. Propulsion systems using a combination of turbine, ramjet, scramjet and rocket propulsion will engender radical capabilities when compared to our current state-of-the-art.

In 20 to 25 years aerospace vehicles using conventional runways will be able to conduct global range reconnaissance and precision strike missions on a frequent "sortie" basis.

With the addition of advanced rocket propulsion to the combined cycle system, airplane-like vehicles that are completely reusable will be able to perform multiple missions on a routine basis. Low-earth orbit using conventional runways as their bases of operations will be possible. These vehicles will likely be two-stage-to-orbit and will combine high speed turbine accelerators, turbo-ramjets, scram jets and advanced liquid rocket engines to provide almost immediate and frequent access to space for military missions. Such vehicles will not only revolutionize the military missions but commercial space launch as well. (This feature was generously provided for publication to the Civil Air Patrol by the Air Force Research Laboratory, Wright Patterson Air Force Base, Ohio)

HIGH ENERGY PROPULSION SYSTEMS

Current Technology Feature —
The Pratt & Whitney CECE Rocket Engine

Pratt & Whitney Rocketdyne Division is a company that has, for over 40 years, been one of the leaders in cryogenic upper-stage rocket engines. The company has been involved in the development of propulsion systems that support NASA's vision for future space exploration.

With permission granted to Civil Air Patrol by Pratt & Whitney Rocketdyne, one of their most advanced propulsion systems is featured. Under contract with NASA, Pratt & Whitney is developing the Common Extensible Cryogenic Engine, known as the CECE, which is a deep throttling 15,000 pound thrust-class cryogenic engine for use in multiple lunar exploration mission segments, including lunar orbit capture, planetary descent and landing, lunar ascent, and trans-earth injection.

These propulsion systems, which utilize the enhanced capabilities of the Rocketdyne RL10 upper-stage engine, will enable sustained exploration of our solar system by using common design elements. These elements can be easily tailored to meet specific mission requirements. The CECE system has the following specifications:

Propellants:	H2/O2
Thrust:	22,000 to 25,000 lbs
Specific Impulse	450-465 seconds
Starts:	A total of 50
Service Life	10,000 seconds
Weight	370-664 pounds

High Energy, In-Space CECE Rocket Engine

495

Current Technology Feature — The Pratt & Whitney RS-68 Booster Engine

The RS-68 is a throttable liquid hydrogen (H_2/O_2) booster engine for the Boeing Delta IV family of launch vehicles. The engine utilizes a simplified design that results in a reduction in parts compared to other cryogenic engines. The specifications are:

Thrust (vacuum)	578 Klbf
Thrust (sea level)	663 Klbf
Chamber pressure	1488 psia
Engine mixture ratio	5.97
ISP (vacuum)	409 seconds
ISP (sea level)	359 seconds
Expansion Ratio	21.5
Weight	14,876 pounds

RS-68 throttlable booster engine for the Boeing Delta IV launch vehicles

Hypersonic Propulsion Systems – Using the Atmosphere's Air To Achieve High Velocity

Pratt & Whitney has given the Civil Air Patrol permission to feature their state-of-the art ultra-high speed air breathing engines. At the heart of these systems is a dual-mode scramjet allowing the engine to function as a subsonic combustion ramjet for low supersonic speeds (Mach 3-5) and as a very high velocity supersonic combustion scramjet. This system allows aerospace vehicles to operate in ranges greater than Mach 5. Additionally work is being done on an air breathing combined-cycle engine based on the scramjet, which may contain either a rocket or gas turbine engine incorporated in the flowpath for low speed propulsion and rockets for orbital insertion.

Pratt & Whitney Rocketdyne and the U.S. Air Force have successfully run a flight-weight hydrocarbon–fueled scramjet Ground Demonstration engine known as the GDE-1. PWR is also developing propulsion system technologies applicable to hypersonic missiles, manned aircraft, unmanned aerial vehicle systems and access-to-space systems. Systems currently in the developmental stages are:

HySET (Hydrocarbon Scramjet Engine Technology) – is a three-phase program sponsored by the U.S. Air Force to develop and demonstrate a Mach 4-8 hydrocarbon-fueled scramjet propulsion system. Additionally, the program will serve as a stepping stone to developing a family of hypersonic vehicles, such as air-to-surface missiles, access-to-space systems and global strike/reconnaissance systems.

SED-WR (Scramjet Engine Demonstrator -Wave Rider) – The U.S. Air Force Research Laboratory selected PWR and the Boeing Phantom Works to flight-test the SED-WR. The team is exploring the air-breathing system-level potential of scramjets through multiple flight tests.

Scramjet Powered X-51 Mounted Under Wing Of B-52 Carrier Aircraft

497

Key Terms and Concepts

- Oxidation
- reducer
- oxidizer
- cryogenics
- propellant
- bipropellant
- monopropellant
- self-reacting compound
- combustion
- ignition characteristics
- low explosive
- solid propellants
- liquid propellants
- compounds
- crystalline

- progressive burn rate
- regressive burn rate
- igniters
- grain
- nonhypergolic
- hypergolic
- catalyst
- combustion chamber
- atomizing
- coupled valve
- swirl-jet type
- impinging-jet type
- hybrid propellant
- hybrid rockets

? Test Your Knowledge ?

SELECT THE CORRECT ANSWER

1. *To use it in its pure form as an* (**oxidizer / reducer**), *oxygen must be* (**chilled / heated**) *until it becomes a* (**liquid / gas**).
2. *A* (**neutral, progressive, regressive**) *burn rate design was used in the Space Shuttle' solid rocket boosters to provide maximum thrust in the first few seconds of launch.*
3. *Generally,* (**mono- / bi-**) *propellants require more heat for ignition and react more slowly than* (**mono- / bi-**) *propellants.*
4. *The majority of liquid-propellant rockets use the* (**mono- / bi-**) *propellant arrangement.*
5. (**Motor / engine**) *is usually associated with* (**liquid / solid**) *propellants.*
6. *Solid propellants are sometimes called* (**low / slow**) *explosives.*

FILL IN THE BLANKS

7. *Rust and corrosion, a burning fire and a violent explosion are all examples of* _____, *the combination of* _____ *with* _____.

8. The propellant substance is molded into its motor and casing as a single solid mass called _____.

9. _____ is the science concerned with the production of low temperatures and the effects of those temperatures on matter.

10. Bi-propellants are two types—_____(non-self-igniting) and _____ (self-igniting).

11. A _____ _____, consisting of two propellants _____ opened by a single piston, operates through a _____, causing both fuel and oxidizer to enter the _____ _____ at the same time.

12. Which is not a solid propellant rocket mentioned in the text?
    a. Submarine launched ballistic missile
    b. Minuteman intercontinental ballistic missile
    c. The main engines for the space shuttle
    d. The MX (Peacekeeper) missile

13. Which is not a drawback to liquid chemical systems?
    a. Their requirement for expensive plumbing,
    b. Expensive turbines,
    c. Expensive pumps and engines
    d. Costly igniters

MATCHING

14. **Match the terms with their correct definitions:**
    a. Propellant
    b. Bipropellant
    c. Monopropellant
    d. Self-reacting compound

    (1) Separate storage tanks are not required
    (2) Molecules contain atoms of both oxidizer and reducer
    (3) Requires separate storage tanks for oxidizer and reducer
    (4) A single reference to the oxidizer and reducer

TRUE OR FALSE

15. Nothing is gained or lost in an oxidation.
16. Solid propellants are more costly and less reliable than liquid propellants.
17. Controlling the thrust of a solid propellant motor is more difficult than controlling the thrust of a liquid propellant engine.
18. The phases in proper order in a combustion chamber are atomizing, preheating, mixing and the reaction of the propellant.
19. It is possible to stop thrust in a solid propellant rocket.

SHORT ANSWER

20. What are the four qualities of a good propellant?
21. How can the amount of thrust produced by a solid propellant engine be controlled?
22. Describe a squib. What type of propellant is it used with?

In this chapter, we will look at what happens when rocketry is used to send payloads into orbit or to destinations in space. Velocity is one major factor in this process. The other major factor is the direction of the trajectory. It is important to remember that these two factors always work with the forces of nature.

Objectives

Describe orbits and trajectories.

Define inertia.

Explain how a satellite remains in orbit.

Identify the closest and farthest points of an object in orbit about earth.

Identify the closest and farthest points of an object in orbit about another planet and about the sun.

Explain what happens if the velocity of an object in orbit is increased.

Identify the components that comprise the takeoff mass of a rocket.

Describe escape velocity.

Define burnout velocity.

Describe the effect of earth's rotational and orbital velocities on the launching of a satellite.

Define total velocity requirement.

Describe ballistic flight.

Describe a sounding-rocket flight.

Name the two basic types of orbits.

Describe why lower velocities are required for satellites to stay in orbit at higher altitudes.

Describe coplanar transfer.

Explain a circular orbit.

Explain the Hohmann transfer.

Explain the fast transfer method for launching a vehicle.

Describe a non-coplanar transfer.

Explain a geostationary orbit.

Explain why a satellite might be placed into polar orbit.

State a reason for placing a satellite into sunsynchronous orbit.

Describe the *Titan* IV launch vehicle.

Describe the *Atlas* and *Delta* launch vehicles.

Orbit and Trajectory Defined

The word orbit describes a path followed by one body in its revolution about another body. All matter within the universe is in motion. This motion begins somewhere down in what we might call the submicroscopic universe. An orbit is a balancing of forces. Where space is concerned, it is a balance between gravitational attraction and the inertia of a movement. Inertia is the property that causes a body at rest to remain at rest and, a body in motion to remain in motion in a straight line at a constant velocity. This tendency toward motion in a straight line, when modified by gravitational forces, results in motion in a closed orbit, forming what is called an ellipse. The path described by an orbiting body may also be called a trajectory. Trajectory is the path of a body through space. In general, application of the term trajectory through space includes the atmosphere. Thus, the terms orbit and trajectory are sometimes combined as orbital trajectory. A trajectory that does not result in an orbit (closed trajectory) must have a beginning and an ending. This is generally known as a ballistic trajectory, particularly if the flight of the object begins and ends on earth.

The Upper Atmosphere Research Satellite (UARS) in Orbit. (NASA)

Basic Orbital Trajectories

An orbit effects a balance between the gravitational and inertial forces. Newton's law of universal gravitation states that the attraction between any two bodies is directly proportional to their masses and inversely proportional to the square of the distance between them. Another way of saying the same thing is that the farther away two objects are from each other, the less effect their mutual gravitation will have. When applying this to earth, the force of gravity on the planet itself is less on a mountaintop than it is at sea level. Granted, there is very little difference, but the difference exists.

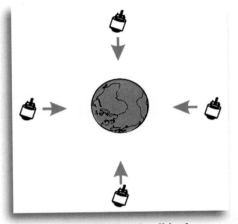
The earth's gravitational pull is always toward the center of the planet.

If an object is taken to an altitude of 100 or 1,000 miles above the earth and dropped, it would fall to earth. At 1,000 miles, the attraction would be even less than at 100 miles; therefore, the object would accelerate (or gain speed) more slowly. Nevertheless, it would still fall to earth. The only way to keep the object from falling to earth is to produce a force that is equal and opposite to the gravity and that balances the gravitational attraction. This is exactly what is done in keeping a satellite in orbit and the equal and opposite force is the inertial force or centrifugal effect. Inertia and centrifugal effects are both related to Newton's first and second laws of motion. The relationship between gravity and inertia in keeping a satellite in orbit can be visualized below.

Suppose you could build a tower on earth that was 100 miles high and you climbed this tower equipped with a supply of baseballs. If you dropped a baseball from the top of the tower, gravity would cause it to fall to the earth. If you threw a baseball from the tower, Newton's first law says that the ball would travel in a straight line (a-b) and at a constant velocity unless acted on by some outside force.

The outside force here is gravity. So the ball would start off traveling in a straight line, but gravity would pull it into a curved path and it would strike the earth at point c. Throwing the ball harder gives it more inertia and changes the curved path. The ball then would strike the earth farther from the tower (points d and e), but the result would be the same.

If it were possible to throw a ball from the tower at about 18,000 mph, it would have sufficient inertia

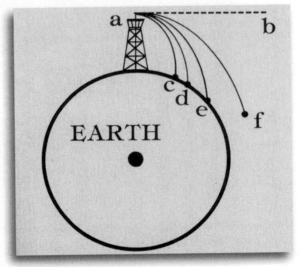
The Balancing of Inertial and Gravitational Forces to Achieve Orbit

to follow path f. Gravity would pull it toward earth's surface at about the same rate as earth's surface curves. The result is that the ball remains at a fairly constant distance (altitude) from the surface even though it is constantly falling toward the surface. This balance of forces continues only as long as the velocity is maintained. Slow the ball by some means and gravity will get the upper hand and pull the ball to the surface. Add velocity to the ball and something else will happen. There could be several trajectories that the ball would follow depending on how much force was applied and the direction in which the force was applied. Enough force in the right direction would accelerate the ball on a trajectory that might force it out of the solar system. Less force in a different direction might place it in a trajectory that would eventually bring it crashing onto earth again.

Listed below are definitions that will be used in future discussions:

Circular orbit—An orbit that maintains a virtually constant altitude above the earth's surface.

Elliptical orbit—Any closed orbit that is not circular. All elliptical orbits around earth have an apogee and a perigee.

Equatorial orbit—The satellite travels from west to east over the earth's Equator. Some satellite orbits incline to the Equator a certain number of degrees.

Escape trajectory—In launching a spacecraft to the moon or to another heavenly body, it is necessary to accelerate the spacecraft to its escape velocity (about 25,000 mph). The velocity of the spacecraft is so high and the inertia is so great that the spacecraft comes under the influence of another body's gravity before it reaches its apogee. The trajectory is the actual path the object takes as it travels through space.

Apogee—That point in the orbital trajectory or flight path where the orbiting body is most distant from the body being orbited.

Perigee—The opposite of apogee—that point where the orbiting body is closest to the body being orbited. (Apogee and perigee are used only to describe orbits around earth.)

By strict definition, the terms "apogee" and "perigee" should only be used when describing objects orbiting Earth (the "gee" originates from "geo" meaning Earth). It is not uncommon (even in the astronomical community) to use apogee and perigee to describe orbits around other planets besides Earth.

The orbit of a satellite may be elliptical in shape. The ellipticity is expressed by its closest

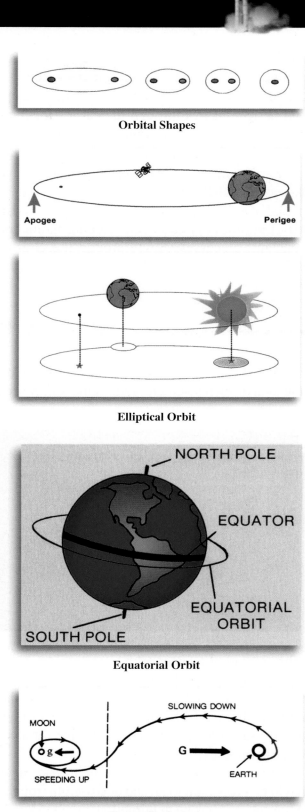

Orbital Shapes

Elliptical Orbit

Equatorial Orbit

Escape Trajectory

approach (p) to the earth called perigee and its farthest point (a) called apogee. The orbit lies within a plane called the orbital plane. The line connecting apogee and perigee passes through the earth's mass center. The angle between the orbital plane and the earth's equatorial plane is the inclination (i).

Earth rotates under the orbit, of course, making the satellite visible from many points on earth in the period of a day. Because the earth is slightly nonspherical, the orbital plane, while keeping its inclination constant, precesses slowly around the North Pole (with respect to the fixed stars) at a rate dependent upon inclination.

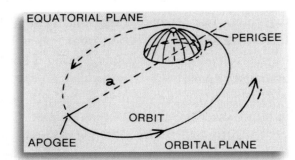

Elements for Describing a Geocentric Orbit

Velocity Requirements

Velocity requirement means the velocity required in order to travel a certain path. Here on earth, the idea of such a velocity requirement may seem odd. On the highway, your destination may be 100 to

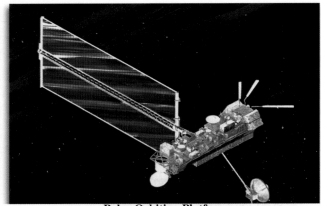

Polar Orbiting Platform

1,000 miles away, but you can take as much or as little time as you wish without fear of falling short of or overshooting your target. An airplane must achieve a certain velocity in order to keep flying. Within broad limits, it can also vary its airspeed without changing course. In space, on the other hand, how fast you go determines where you go.

Reaching the moon in the shortest possible time demands the complicated art of figuring the best trajectory to hit a moving target. Then apply exactly the right amount of thrust needed to propel the spacecraft along the chosen trajectory. Any increase in velocity is translated into a higher orbit instead of a faster orbit.

For example, let's suppose that we have a 90-minute circular orbit established. If we try to increase the vehicle's speed at any point in this orbit, the spacecraft is kicked out of the circular path and goes into an elliptical path. Though the spacecraft will travel faster than before at perigee, it will be considerably slower at apogee. The total time for a complete circuit of earth in this new orbit will be longer than 90 minutes.

In order to be used effectively in space missions, a rocket must have a satisfactory mass ratio. The payload, propellant load, and deadweight (total weight of the rocket structure) make up the takeoff mass. After the fuel has been burned, the payload and empty rocket are the remaining mass. By dividing the takeoff mass by the remaining mass you obtain the mass ratio. A goal of good rocket engineering is to make the mass ratio large. Therefore, the deadweight must be kept comparatively low.

The rocket must achieve circular velocity if its payload is to go into orbit, without further expenditure of propellant, around a planet such as the earth. The escape velocity is required for the payload to escape from the gravitational attraction of that planet. The circular velocity and escape velocity differ for each planet because they depend on the planet's mass. In the case of earth, the circular velocity is approximately 8 kilometers per second (17,856 miles per hour) and the escape velocity is 11 kilometers per second (25,560 miles per hour).

Burnout Velocity

At the moment a rocket engine ceases to produce thrust, it is at burnout. The velocity that is required to place a spacecraft on its intended trajectory must be attained at burnout. If something goes wrong and the proper velocity has not been reached by the time burnout occurs (either the propellant is exhausted or automatic cutoff is activated to cause burnout), the payload is not going to reach its intended destination—orbit, moon, planet and so on.

Today, this type of failure is not likely to occur unless there is a major breakdown in the system. (Rocketry systems have been perfected to the point where there is a great deal of control over what happens.) Whether or not direct control exists, the required velocity must be present upon reaching a certain point and/or time.

It is possible to start, stop and change the thrust of some rocket engines. This gives a great deal of flexibility to adjust the flight of a satellite or spacecraft. Suppose, however, that we had several one-shot, solid-propellant rockets and we wanted to use them to launch different types of space missions. In addition, let's consider each rocket capable of reaching a different velocity at burnout. The following velocities would be required to:

    a. place a satellite into a circular orbit at an altitude of 100 nautical miles (NM) (17,454 mph),
    b. place a satellite into orbit with 1,000-NM apogee and 100-NM perigee (18,409 mph),
    c. place a satellite into orbit with 10,000-NM apogee and 100-NM perigee (21,954 mph), and
    d. place a satellite into orbit with 100,000-NM apogee and 100-NM perigee (24,273 mph).

The above examples could be carried further, but suppose we wanted to send a payload somewhere other than into orbit about earth. What would be the velocity requirement? Of course, it would depend on the ultimate destination of the payload, but the minimum velocity to the moon is 24,409 mph—with burnout at 100-NM altitude. Such velocity requirements continue to increase until a velocity of more than 36,000 mph is required to leave the solar system.

Now, 36,000 mph is a respectable velocity, but it could take a velocity of almost twice this much to send a payload crashing into the sun. We tend to forget that earth's orbital velocity about the sun is more than 66,000 mph. Before any rocket is launched, we must remember that its initial velocity is the same as that of earth. To get a payload to the sun really means that the earth's velocity must be counteracted so that the sun's gravitational field will pull the payload into the sun.

All the velocity requirements stated previously are for a given set of conditions. No allowances were made for several variables. One variable is the velocity that can be added according to the direction of launch and another variable is the location of the launch site. If a launch vehicle is fired toward the east, it will have the velocity of the earth's rotation added to whatever velocity it obtains from the vehicle's propulsion system.

At earth's equator, this velocity is roughly 1,000 mph. A launch north or south of the Equator would reduce this added velocity. How much reduction there would be depends on the distance from the Equator of the launch site. The azimuth, or angle in relation to true east, would also affect how much natural velocity would be added.

Suppose the mission of a payload required that it be launched toward the west. Everything that we said about a to-the-east launch is reversed. Finally, what about a true-north or true-south launch direction? The specialists responsible for calculating the desired trajectory would still have to consider earth's rotational velocity because it would be more of a deflecting force instead of a force with a plus- or minus-velocity change.

Total Velocity Requirement

In planning a space mission, it is necessary to calculate total velocity requirements. This total figure represents the adding together of all the velocity requirements for all stages of the mission. It does not represent the velocity at which the vehicle travels at any one moment in its journey, but it would be in excess of that velocity. All the velocities in such a sum would not be in the same direction. Nevertheless, the sum is essential in computing the needed propellant for the mission.

Placing a payload into a low orbit about earth might be a one-shot deal. That is, the total required velocity would be realized at burnout, and the payload would be injected into the proper orbit. This could very well be the case for certain types of elliptical orbits. On the other hand, a trajectory for a very long spaceflight, or the need to change the shape of an object's orbit, will require a change in velocity—in other words, the application of thrust.

Perhaps we can better demon-

The space shuttle Challenger lifts off. *(NASA)*

506

strate the concept of the need to know the total velocity requirement by examining a flight to the moon and return. Injection into a trajectory that will take the spacecraft to the moon could require a burnout velocity of 36,000 feet per second (fps) (or 24,545 mph, with variables considered). To land the vehicle on the moon would require 8,700 fps (5,932 mph) of retrothrust (opposite-direction thrust). Another 8,700 fps would be required for liftoff and insertion into a return-to-earth trajectory.

In this example, we will go along with the technique of using earth's atmosphere to slow a returning spacecraft to soft-landing velocity, so no velocity requirements exist for the return trip. The earth's gravitational force has provided most of the velocity requirements. Thus, we have a total velocity requirement of 53,400 fps (36,409 mph).

If the flight plan did call for a slowing of the spacecraft prior to entering earth's atmosphere, this velocity requirement would have to be included. So would any velocity requirements for changing or correcting the vehicle's course on the way to or from the moon.

Saturn V, a three-stage vehicle, was used for manned Apollo lunar flights. In flying to the moon, Saturn's first stage, weighing nearly 5,000,000 pounds, lifted the second and third stages along with the spacecraft to a speed of 5,400 mph and to a point 41 miles above the earth. The second stage, weighing more than 1,000,000 pounds, then took over, increasing speed to more than 14,000 mph. At a point 120 miles above the earth, the second stage was jettisoned.

The third stage ignited briefly to accelerate the spacecraft to 17,000 mph, putting the spacecraft into earth orbit. The astronauts then reignited the single engine of the third stage, which burned for 5 1/2 minutes. This single engine cut off at an altitude of about 190 miles and a speed of 24,300 mph. From that point, the rocket traveled through space until it reached the vicinity of the Moon.

The total velocity requirement tells flight planners how much thrust is going to be needed for the trip. This thrust, and the vehicle and payload masses determine what kinds and sizes of engines will be needed and how much propellant will have to be used. The actual amount of propellant used will probably be slightly more than is calculated as the bare minimum.

Ballistic Trajectories

The term ballistic pertains to the science of ballistics. Ballistics is the study of the arc of a nonorbiting body. Ballistic flight is primarily concerned with propelling an object from one place on earth's surface to another place or target on earth's surface. The moment a bullet leaves the barrel of a rifle, the bullet is in ballistic flight. It is no longer powered so it is under the influence of natural forces only— primarily gravity.

The same ballistic-type flight occurs with rocket-propelled missiles used to hit a distant target. If there is no way to change the payload's flight path after main rocket burnout, the remainder of the flight is ballistic. On the other hand, if the missile is guided all the way to impact with the target, its trajectory cannot be considered ballistic. This is because any ballistic influences will be counteracted by the guidance and control systems.

All ballistic trajectories behave as if they were going into an elliptical orbit around earth's center of gravity. What keeps them from doing this is the presence of earth's surface. We can see this tendency to orbit the center of gravity if we examine the trajectory of a large ballistic missile.

Any missile that rises above the earth's atmosphere in its trajectory and is designed to reach its target in the shortest time possible is a ballistic missile. It must obey certain laws in its flight. Such a missile cannot be under continuous propulsion and guidance during the entire course of its flight. Its launch and trajectory, during the time the propulsion system is functioning, will be guided.

Burnout of the propellant system will occur well below the top of the missile's trajectory. The rest of the payload's flight will be like that of a bullet or an orbiting space vehicle—unpowered and determined primarily by the force of gravity.

It will describe a high, arching trajectory toward target, possibly reaching a peak of several hundred miles above the surface of the earth. The atmosphere will affect the path of the reentry portion of the flight.

The launch velocity of a ballistic missile is less than that required for an orbit, although in the case of a missile with a 10,000-NM range, it is only a little less. The missile is also launched into a higher flight-path angle than the more horizontal angle that is usual for orbital launches. Lacking the velocity to clear the earth, it will fall back to earth along a path determined by gravity. If it could continue falling—that is, follow an imaginary path within the sphere of earth—it would fall faster and faster to a perigee point and be carried by its own momentum right up through the earth back to the point where it started. This trajectory is impossible, but the fact remains that the actual flight of the missile does describe the exterior portion of such an imaginary orbit around the center of the earth.

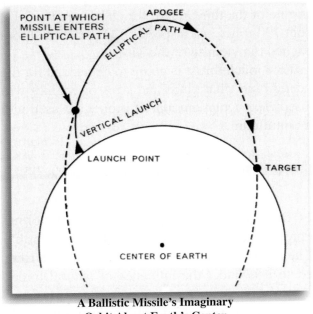

A Ballistic Missile's Imaginary Orbit About Earth's Center

Therefore, the missile's ground track—that is, the route of its trajectory projected downward and plotted on the surface of the earth—would be a part of a great circle, somewhat modified by the effect of the earth's rotation. The missile could not follow a trajectory due east or due west along some parallel of latitude other than the Equator (which is a great circle) nor could it follow an eccentric or irregular path designed to fool an enemy defense system.

These facts tell us two things about ballistic missiles. One is that propulsion and guidance are available to place a missile into a trajectory toward any target on earth with great accuracy. The second is that since the route the ballistic missile must fly is predictable, defense measures can be taken against it.

Sounding-rocket Flights

If the trajectory of a rocket does not send its payload into orbit, or to some destination well beyond earth or to another point on earth's surface, where does the rocket send its payload? The only direction left is straight up. Essentially, this is the trajectory of a sounding rocket—straight up.

Sounding is an old term associated with measuring or sampling the depths of a body of water. Somehow, and at some time, this same term was applied to sampling earth's ocean of air. Thus, a rocket sent into, or even beyond the atmosphere, on a one-way trip to gather information is now identified as a sounding rocket.

Instruments carried aboard a sounding rocket are designed to observe and measure various natural phenomena at different altitudes above the surface and transmit these findings to ground stations. After reaching its maximum altitude, the rocket simply falls back to earth and is destroyed by either reentry and/or impact forces. The total sounding rocket may not be destroyed in this manner every time. It is possible that at least part of the payload section could be designed to survive the force of reentry.

Launch velocity requirements for sounding rockets are of interest. These requirements are needed to reach a certain distance from earth's surface without going into orbit. For example, if the altitude chosen for the rocket's apogee is high enough, the thrust/burnout velocity is more than adequate to go into orbit. To reach a 1,000 NM altitude (100-NM altitude burnout) requires a velocity of 11,114 mph. This isn't enough velocity to achieve orbit (17,454 mph). Suppose a mission to sample the magnetosphere at 10,000-NM altitude had to be flown. The burnout velocity required for this mission is 31,000 fps or 21,136 mph—more than enough to achieve orbit.

Why does this very high-altitude sounding rocket not go into orbit? The reason is that a sounding rocket is launched at a very steep angle and does not have the horizontal velocity needed to put it into orbit. Like any other sounding vehicle, it eventually reaches a point where gravity overcomes its upward momentum, and it will return to earth. Its trajectory is not necessarily straight up and down, but is rather like a high, narrow arch with a return path that would not carry it beyond the earth. If the complete path of the sounding-rocket trajectory was plotted, it would show an extremely narrow ellipse within the earth, around the center of the earth's mass.

It does not require 10 times as much velocity to reach 10,000 miles as it does to reach 1,000 miles. Gravity's effect weakens with distance from its center.

Some economic factors can also be noted. Since the sounding-rocket velocity for 1,000 miles is suborbital, it is the cheapest way of reaching such an altitude. Using a sounding rocket to reach a height of 10,000 miles, however, is questionable. For reaching still higher altitudes, it is definitely more economical to put the vehicle into orbit.

Types of Orbits

As far as satellites of earth are concerned, there are two basic orbital flight paths involved: the elliptical and the circular. If you think about our previous introductory discussions on trajectories and orbital velocities, you will realize that an elliptical orbit can be achieved with one shot provided the angle used (to the vertical) is correct. Get away from the one-shot-type approach to orbital insertion and thrust will again be needed.

The lowest earth orbit that has been discussed is an approximate circular one at 100 NM altitude, for which an injection velocity (the velocity that will place it into orbit) of 17,454 mph is required. Therefore, let us use this orbit as a starting point for learning more about earth orbits. In this one instance, the injection velocity, the apogee velocity and the circular-orbit velocity are all the same. At this altitude, the pull of gravity is only slightly less than it is at the surface of the earth. The velocity represents the speed at which the vehicle must outrace the horizon as it "falls" around the curving earth, always maintaining the same altitude above it. It is important to note that the injection into orbit must be horizontal (tangent to the orbit). Any effort to extend range by giving the vehicle an upward trajectory without added thrust would only rob it of some of its vital forward velocity and bring it to earth before one orbit was completed.

For any higher orbit, we have this basic paradox. Higher and higher velocities are required to reach successively higher altitudes, but lower and lower velocities are required to stay in orbit at successively higher altitudes. This phenomenon is due to the weakening of earth's gravitational effect with distance.

A boost velocity of about 18,400 mph is needed to hurl a vehicle to an apogee of 1,000 NM. After burnout, the vehicle coasts outward along an elliptical path, moving slower and slower as gravitational pull gradually overcomes the force of the launch. At its planned 1,000-NM apogee, it will have a speed somewhat less than 15,000 mph and will begin to lose altitude. Sliding down the far side of the ellipse, it will move faster and faster as it approaches closer and closer to earth. It will then whip around perigee at top speed. Perigee in this case will be at the injection altitude of 100 NM and at the injection velocity of 18,400 mph. The vehicle will then begin another climb toward its 1,000 NM apogee. Discounting the slowing effect of faint atmospheric resistance at perigee, it will keep on swinging around this ellipse indefinitely without the need for burning an ounce of propellant.

Let us continue to assume that injection and perigee are at 100 NM. More and more launch power will shoot the vehicle out to more and more distant apogees. The orbits would describe successively longer ellipses.

Circular Orbits and Transfers

To change what is certain to be an elliptical orbit into a circular orbit when the satellite reaches an after-launch apogee requires the addition of thrust. This thrust must be applied toward a specific direction. That is, when the vehicle reaches apogee, its engine is restarted to give it some additional velocity to thrust it outward and circularize the orbit. Circular velocity minus apogee velocity gives the amount of kick needed to circularize an orbit at a given altitude.

To show how to figure the total velocity required to attain a circular orbit, let's work a problem using simple arithmetic. The velocity required to boost a vehicle to an apogee of 300 NM is 17,659 mph. To this number add the difference between apogee velocity and circular velocity at 300 NM (273 mph). The sum 17,932 mph is the total velocity requirement for launching a vehicle into a 300-NM circular orbit in two steps, but the vehicle never travels that fast. The total velocity requirement is merely an engineer's figure that is useful in determining how much energy is needed to perform a given task with a given payload weight. Spaceflight velocity usually is not given in miles per hour but in feet per second. However, to visualize the fantastic velocities required in spaceflight, we expressed it in miles per hour (an expression of measure with which everyone is familiar).

The velocities we have given are ballpark figures. In actual flight situations, much more precision is necessary. The amount and the point at which thrust is applied to an orbiting vehicle are critical. For example, if thrust applied at apogee is a little less than that required for circularizing the orbit, the result will be a wider ellipse with the same apogee and a higher perigee. If it is thrust a little more, the vehicle will be boosted to a higher apogee.

Achieving a circular orbit at any height above that of launch burnout (original perigee) is done in two steps—launching into an elliptical trajectory and applying another spurt of rocket energy at the desired altitude. It might also be done in three steps—the vehicle could be launched into a lower orbit called a parking orbit, then boosted to a higher apogee and then circularized at that apogee. Moving a vehicle from one orbit to another is called a transfer. Such maneuvers accomplished within the same orbital plane are called coplanar (same plane) transfers. All the movements are on the same plane, like the sheet of paper on which you see them. If viewed from the side, the plane would appear as a line.

The Hohmann Transfer

Back in 1925, when space travel was only a theoretical dream, the city engineer of Essen, Germany, published a scientific paper on the most economical way to boost a satellite into a chosen circular orbit. The method proposed by Walter Hohmann is quite similar to the one described above. It has been called the minimum energy transfer. The Hohmann transfer, or slight variations of it, is a practical method of space maneuver to this day. In a Hohmann transfer, the vehicle is first placed in a low-elliptical parking orbit. When the vehicle swings around to perigee, sufficient thrust is applied to push the vehicle to apogee at the desired altitude. When the vehicle reaches the high point of this transfer ellipse, thrust is applied again, and the vehicle moves out on a circle that is tangent to the transfer ellipse.

Discussion of ellipses, circles and tangents should remind us that all space travel is in curves. Moving in a straight line in space would require constant application of deflected thrust, a tremendous and wasteful expenditure of propellant. The curves that Hohmann chose are those that actually permit thrust to be applied in a straight line. A vehicle with a rigid engine or nozzle, incapable of changing direction of thrust would be able to accomplish a Hohmann transfer by thrusting straight ahead at the proper transfer points. Momentarily, the vehicle would move out on a straight-line tangent to its former course, but, almost immediately, the particular new balance achieved between the forward momentum and the pull of gravity would set the vehicle on a new curved trajectory.

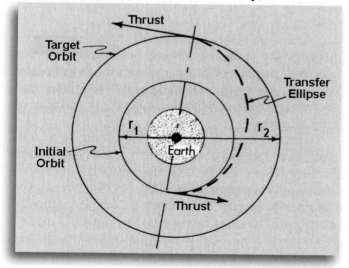

The Hohmann Transfer

Other Coplanar Transfers

There are other ways of accomplishing transfers and maneuvers within a given plane of orbit. One is the fast transfer applied in modern satellite maneuvering. Instead of choosing a transfer ellipse tangent to both the lower and higher orbits, a trajectory is chosen that intersects or crosses the two orbits. In a direct ascent, more launch velocity than needed would be built up to reach a given apogee. At the desired altitude, the kick would thus be applied lower than apogee, with deflected thrust, to aim it into the desired circle. Because all the energy would not be working in a straight line, extra energy would be needed to make the desired turn. The maneuver boosts the vehicle into higher orbit faster than a Hohmann transfer does. Actually, most fast transfers are only slightly different from Hohmann transfers. The turn is not very sharp at either transfer point.

Moving down from a higher to a lower orbit should also be mentioned. To do this, negative thrust (or retrothrust) must be applied to kill off some of the velocity that keeps the vehicle in the higher orbit. The vehicle is then drawn by gravity into an orbital path that matches its new velocity. As it moves lower, however, it moves faster. This is another interesting paradox—putting on the brakes in order to go faster. Actually, it is a practical maneuver. Suppose that two vehicles are attempting to meet (rendezvous) in the same orbit and one is a thousand miles ahead of the other. The chase vehicle can never hope to catch up with the target vehicle while both are in the same orbit. Therefore, the chase vehicle applies retrothrust to get drawn into a downward transfer ellipse. This allows it not only to follow a shortcut route but also to be moved by gravitational pull faster along that shorter, lower route to a point where the two orbits are again tangent. At this point, the two vehicles will come within maneuvering range of a rendezvous. The precomputed route selection, as well as the guidance and control mechanisms, used to accomplish the rendezvous itself must be extremely precise.

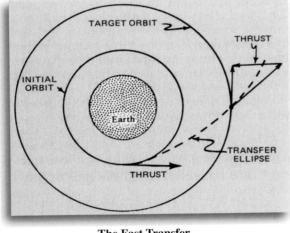

The Fast Transfer

Non-Coplanar Transfers

Up to this point, discussion has been given to satellites being in the same plane. In actual satellite flight, this is not true. We have earth satellites at many different altitudes and at various angles to the Equator. Some have circular orbits, but others are in elliptical orbits with apogees and perigees of varying distances.

The plane of any orbit around earth must pass through the center of earth. If a satellite is launched due east from Cape Canaveral in Florida (the launch site of many space vehicles), which has a latitude of 28.5° N, it is impossible for it to keep traveling due east around the world at the same latitude. Its orbital path will bring it south across the Equator to reach a latitude of 28.5° S before it swings north again. The orbital plane of such a launch is said to have an angle of inclination (slant) of 28.5° with respect to the plane of the Equator. Aiming the satellite at launch in any direction other than due east will produce a steeper angle of inclination, causing the satellite to overfly latitudes higher than 28.5° on either side of the Equator. A northward or southward injection will put the satellite into a polar orbit.

Obviously, no launch from Cape Canaveral could put a vehicle directly into an orbit around the Equator or at any angle of inclination less than the latitude of Cape Canaveral itself. To put a vehicle into equatorial orbit requires a non-coplanar transfer. The vehicle would first be launched at its minimum angle of inclination of 28.5°. Then, on either its first or a later revolution at one of two points where it crosses the Equator, thrust would be applied at the proper angle to put the vehicle into an orbit coplanar with the Equator. Think of this transfer maneuver as kicking the vehicle sideways instead of upward, as in the coplanar transfer. Similarly, any angle of inclination can be achieved by means of non-coplanar transfer, but not necessarily in one such transfer. If the angle of change is too extreme, the vehicle may have to orbit earth two or more times, changing its angle of inclination by a certain amount at each intersection of planes, before the desired inclination is achieved. If both a change of inclination and a change of orbital altitude are desired, the non-coplanar and altitude transfers can be achieved in one orbit by calculating the thrust angles three-dimensionally.

Special Orbits

A special orbit is our term for those orbits in which a satellite must be placed to accomplish a special mission. These orbits are mostly circular. This is especially true for those satellites that provide services in the forms of communications, environmental monitoring and navigation.

Geostationary Orbit

There are certain tasks that satellites can do best if they are in an orbit that will keep them stationed above one point on earth's surface. These are called geostationary satellites. The term means that the satellite is in an equatorial orbit at a distance where the satellite's period of revolution is the same as the earth's period of rotation—24 hours. Three geostationary satellites, spaced 120 degrees of longitude apart can give 24-hour around-the-world service over most of the surface of the globe.

For a satellite to be geostationary with the earth (that is, keep time with the rotation of the earth so perfectly that it always remains directly above a certain point along the Equator), it must have a circular orbit at one altitude. That altitude is 19,351 NM (or 22,300 statute miles), which gives it a period of 24 hours.

If such a satellite is launched from Cape Canaveral without a non-coplanar transfer, it will have an inclination of 28.5° and will not appear perfectly stationary over the earth. It can be timed to reach the

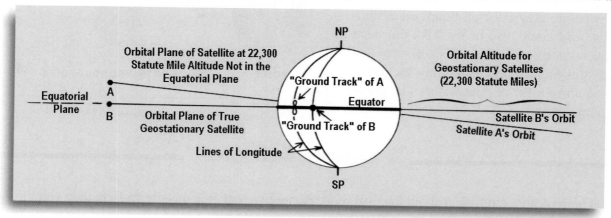

Examples of Geostationary Orbits

right orbit at the desired point, but its inclination will take it above and below the plane of the Equator by 28.5° in the course of its 1-day orbit. In other words, its ground track would describe a narrow figure eight crossing at the Equator and its top and bottom touching both 28.5° parallels. In order to make it remain stationary over one point on earth, it is necessary to plan for a non-coplanar transfer into the equatorial plane. The one point over which it hovers must be on the Equator and at no other latitude. This type of orbit is called a geostationary orbit.

These are the major maneuvers for positioning a geostationary satellite. However, once the satellite is in the desired orbital position, further and continuing adjustments to its position are necessary. After all, the satellite is subjected to varying gravitational influences of the sun-earth-moon system. In addition, the pressure of the sun's radiation disturbs the satellite's position. This means that station-keeping maneuvers have to be made periodically. The satellite's small-reaction control devices or thrusters effect such maneuvers.

Polar Orbit

As the name implies, a polar orbit involves a path that crosses or nearly crosses the North and South Poles during each orbit. This type orbit offers a satellite's cameras a chance to photograph earth's entire surface. The reason this is true is that earth is turning on its axis as the satellite sweeps over the poles and each orbit of the satellite puts it west of its previous sweep. (Earth is rotating toward the east.)

Sunsynchronous Orbit

This is another form of polar orbit that keeps a satellite exposed to constant sunlight. The earth is not a perfect sphere. It bulges slightly at the Equator and is flattened slightly at the poles. The resulting imperfect sphere contributes to the fact that earth's gravitational force is not constant at all points of a satellite's orbit.

A satellite placed into the proper polar orbit (direction and altitude) will remain exposed to constant sunlight as earth revolves around the sun. The sunsynchronous orbit is appropriate for those satellites that need constant sunlight to generate power for on-board operations. This orbit could also be used for those satellites that monitor the sun's activities, and the sunsynchronous orbit may be one of those chosen for in-space electrical power generation.

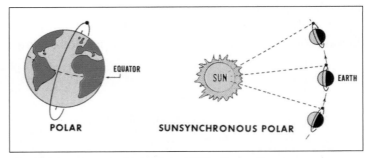

Polar and Sunsynchronous Orbits

Launch Vehicles

There is often confusion about the difference between a rocket, a missile and a launch vehicle. Many people will use one term when they are talking about the other. For example, many people use the term missile when talking about the Saturn rockets that carried people into space. Although there are no firm written rules that tell you when to use these terms, there are rules that are generally accepted by people who work in the field of rocketry. We are going to use these generally accepted rules in this textbook.

A rocket is a type of power plant that is used to propel something (payload). It produces its power by the principle of action and reaction (Newton's third law of motion). The exhaust gases that are expelled from the rocket at a very high velocity produce the action. The equal and opposite reaction forces the rocket and its payload in the opposite direction. Burning some type of fuel in the common types of rockets produces the exhaust gases. Some of the more advanced rockets produce the action in other ways.

In general usage, a missile is a rocket-propelled vehicle with a weapon or warhead as the payload. This warhead may be a nuclear weapon or a simple explosive charge. If the payload of a rocket is a satellite or a spacecraft rather than a warhead, the vehicle is called a launch vehicle or a booster. The same rocket may be used to carry either a warhead or a satellite. A rocket is called a missile while carrying a warhead and a launch vehicle when carrying a satellite. For example, the Titan II rocket was originally designed to carry a nuclear warhead and was called the Titan II missile. Later, NASA began using the Titan II to launch the Gemini spacecraft. It was then called the Titan II booster or the Titan II launch vehicle.

There are two basic categories of launch vehicles—expendable launch vehicles and reusable launch vehicles. Rockets that are only used once are considered expendable launch vehicles. These include the Atlas V and Delta IV, and until 2005, also included the Titan IV. For over thirty years, the Space Shuttle served as the world's only viable reusable launch vehicle (its final flight occurring in 2011). The space shuttle is the only reusable launch vehicle we have.

The satellites launched by the military are used to ensure our national security. They include navigational satellites to improve the navigation of military aircraft and ships, communications satellites,

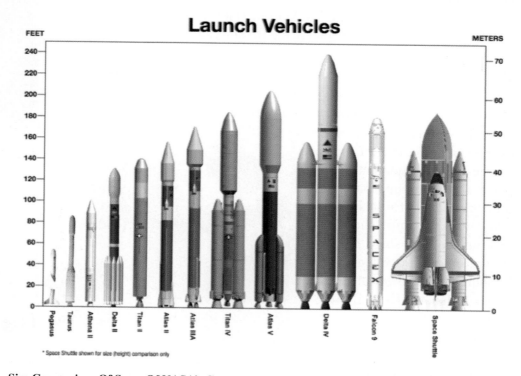

Size Comparison Of Some Of NASA's Current And Former Launch Vehicles Picture credit: NASA

surveillance satellites and nuclear-detection satellites.

The launch vehicles used by the military to place their satellites into space are the same as those used by NASA. The one exception to this was the Titan series of boosters. The Titan was developed by the military and only a few civilian spacecraft have ever been launched by it. The Titan was first launched in 1964 and since that time it has been produced in several versions. In fact, the Titan family of launch vehicles grew rather large over the years, to include the II, 23-G (a variant of the II), III-A, III-B, III-C, IIID, 34-D (a variant of the III-D), III-E, III-M, IV, IV-A, and IV-B. The Titan IV, the largest and most powerful of all the Titan versions, had a stretched first and second stage, two seven-segment solid strap-on boosters (for the IV and IV-A configurations), two three-segment (elongated) boosters for the IV-B configuration), and an Inertial Upper Stage (IUS) or Centaur Upper Stage (all versions of the Titan IV could also fly with no upper stage). The Titan IV could place 10,200 pounds into geo-

synchronous orbit or 31,100 pounds into near earth orbit. At one time, the Titans represented some of the most powerful expendable launch vehicles in the United States.

Nearly all of the early U.S. launch vehicles were based on military ballistic missile designs, the Thor and Atlas being two excellent examples. The Thor was developed in the 1950s as an intermediate-range ballistic missile and placed in service in Europe. When the Atlas ICBM became operational, the Thors were dismantled and returned to the United States. All were eventually converted into space boosters.

Beginning in 1959, Douglas Aircraft (later McDonnell Douglas, which then even later became part of the Boeing Company) was awarded a contract to develop a second and third stage for the basic Thor. The Thor, with its second and third stages, became known as the Thor-Delta, and this rocket launched many of our famous satellites. The first Delta could put a 480-pound payload into orbit about 300 miles above the

earth. The most current version of the Delta, the Delta II, was a three-stage booster that could place a 2,000-pound payload into orbit 22,000 miles high. This was accomplished by making the first stage longer (to hold more propellant) and by adding more powerful upper stages. Also, the Delta II used up to nine solid-fuel, strap-on rockets added to the first stage.

The Atlas became a launch vehicle in the same way as the

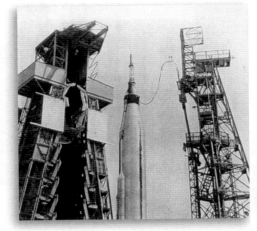

In 1962, an early version of Atlas thrusts a Mercury capsule into orbit.

For decades, the Delta II served as the workhorse for many NASA space missions

Thor. When the Atlas ICBMs were phased out in 1965, the missiles became available for other use. As they were needed, the Convair Division of General Dynamics Corporation at Vandenberg Air Force Base, California, refurbished them. More than 500 Atlas launches have taken place, including some very famous firsts. An Atlas launched the world's first communications satellite in 1958. The first US manned orbital flights in Project Mercury were boosted into space by the Atlas. The Atlas was also used to launch the first US spacecraft to Venus, Mercury, Mars and Jupiter.

At one time, NASA was responsible for launching all non-military spacecraft for the United States. This is no longer the case. With the establishment of the Launch Services Purchases Act, potential customers deal directly with the launch service provider. NASA itself has gone from being a launch service provider to being a customer. When it wants to launch a scientific satellite or space probe, it purchases services from a contractor, just as anyone else would do who wanted to put a payload into space. The current state of affairs represents the maturity of the technology required to launch payloads into space.

To illustrate, consider the following scenario. If NASA wants to ship a package cross-country, it does not design, build, and operate its own airline to do so; it simply hires FedEx or UPS (as examples) to transport it at a modest cost. The space launch arrangement is quite similar. The "package" is a satellite or space probe, and the "cross-country" destination is outer space. The launch services provider would be anyone of the current or emerging companies, such as United Launch Alliance or SpaceX. The launch vehicles that NASA currently uses to get its payloads delivered to space are the Pegasus, Taurus, Athena, Atlas V, Delta IV, and Falcon 9. NASA will enter into a contract with the appropriate company involved to arrange for the "service" of getting its particular payload to a specific destination.

A Titan IV with Centaur Upper Stage

A very impressive and imposing sight: a Titan III-M (M for manned) being prepared to launch a modified NASA Gemini spacecraft (USAF photo).

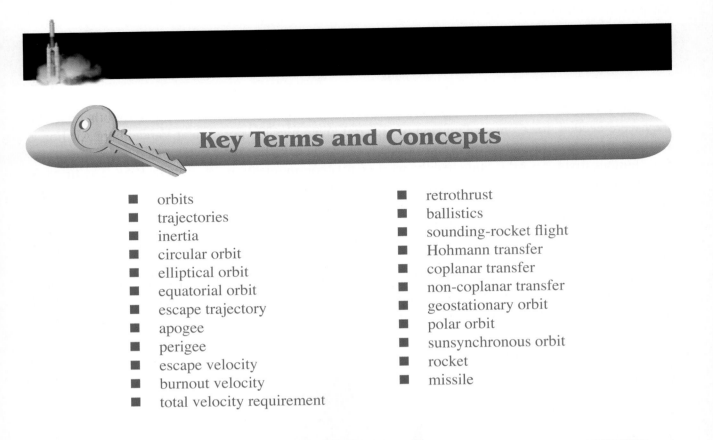

Key Terms and Concepts

- orbits
- trajectories
- inertia
- circular orbit
- elliptical orbit
- equatorial orbit
- escape trajectory
- apogee
- perigee
- escape velocity
- burnout velocity
- total velocity requirement

- retrothrust
- ballistics
- sounding-rocket flight
- Hohmann transfer
- coplanar transfer
- non-coplanar transfer
- geostationary orbit
- polar orbit
- sunsynchronous orbit
- rocket
- missile

? Test Your Knowledge ?

SELECT THE CORRECT ANSWER

1. *To take advantage of the speed from earth's rotation, rockets should be fired to the* (**north, south, east or west**). *If the launch is at the Equator, this adds roughly* (**500/1000/1500/2000**) *mph.*

2. *A* (**reusable launch vehicle/ sounding rocket**) *is sent on a one-way trip to gather information.*

3. *If the velocity of an object in orbit is increased, it* (**goes into a higher orbit/takes less time to travel the same orbit**).

4. *Moving from a higher orbit to a lower orbit requires the use of* (**thrust/ retrothrust**) *causing the vehicle to* (**speed up/ slow down**) *making it more subject to* (**gravity/ centrifugal force**), *but as a result of the lower orbit, the vehicle actually goes* (**faster/ slower**).

5. (**Polar/ Geostationary**) *orbits allow a satellite's cameras a chance to photograph the earth's entire surface.*

MATCHING

6. **Match the terms**
   - a. orbit
   - b. trajectory
   - c. inertia
   - (1) **Satellite travels west to east around the 0 degree latitude**
   - (2) **Path described by one body in its revolution about another body**
   - (3) **Path a body takes, accelerating enough to escape gravity's pull**

d. circular orbit   (4) **Point where a body orbiting earth is closest to it**

e   elliptical orbit   (5) **Property that causes a body in motion to remain in motion**

f. equatorial orbit   (6) **A non-circular path around a body**

g. escape trajectory (7) **Path of a body through space**

h. apogee   (8) **Maintained at a virtually constant altitude above the earth's surface**

i. perigee   (9) **Point where a body orbiting the earth is farthest from it**

7. Escape velocity is defined as _____.

8. The _____ _____ _____ represents adding together all the velocity requirements for all stages of the mission.

9. The moment a rocket engine ceases to produce thrust, _____ is said to have occurred and the velocity required to achieve the intended _____ must be attained.

10. Ballistics is the study of _____.

11. The trajectory of a _____ _____ is straight up.

12. Moving a vehicle from one orbit to another is called a _____; if accomplished within the same orbital plane, it is called _____ _____.

13. A Hohmann transfer is also known as a _____ _____ _____.

TRUE OR FALSE

14. The payload, propellant load and deadweight make up takeoff mass.

15. Retrothrust is defined as thrust in the opposite direction usually used to slow a vehicle.

16. Ballistic flight is concerned with propelling an object from the earth's surface to non-orbital space flight.

17. A bullet is a good example of ballistic flight.

18. Most fast transfers are only slightly different from Hohmann transfers.

SHORT ANSWER

19. Why are lower velocities required for satellites to stay in orbit at higher altitudes?

20. Briefly describe the Hohmann transfer.

21. What are the most notable differences between solid and liquid propulsion systems?

PART SIX

Space

SPACE ENVIRONMENT

Space. The Final Frontier. These are the voyages of the Starship Enterprise. *Its continuing mission—to explore strange new worlds, to seek out new life and new civilizations, to boldly go where no one has gone before!*

Gene Roddenberry, Introduction to Star Trek, The Next Generation

Space is the final frontier. Though we are a long way from building our first starship, we get closer every day. There are many reasons why we seek to explore and exploit space. From space we get a global view of the Earth and we can see the universe more clearly. Space also holds the promise of abundant resources such as solar energy and minerals from other planets. Finally, space provides a unique environment that is useful in making new materials.

The higher you are, the more you can see. Throughout history people have sought high places from which to observe the terrain around them. Armies have fought great battles to win the high ground to enable them to see, control and defend the land below.

Landowners built great towers from which they could survey the condition of their fields and to spot the approach of strangers and potential threats. Space offers the ultimate high ground above Earth. From space we can see large parts of the Earth's surface and orbiting satellites allow us to see the entire planet.

The universe is more visible from space. When we view the stars through Earth's atmosphere, they appear to twinkle or scintillate. This scintillation is caused by turbulence in the atmosphere that alters the light from the stars. The atmosphere also blocks some of the light. By placing observatories in space, we can get a clear view of the universe without atmospheric interference.

Exploitation of space offers new sources for minerals and energy. Scientists speculate that vast sources of minerals exist on the planets, Moons and asteroids in our Solar System. The Moon for instance, is rich in aluminum. Lunar soil is also rich in oxygen that might be used to sustain operations in space by providing breathable atmosphere. The oxygen in the soil might also be used as a rocket propellant. Energy from the Sun, unobstructed by the Earth's atmosphere, currently provides limitless power for spacecraft and may one day provide power for colonies in space.

Finally, the unique environment in space allows production of new metal alloys that are difficult, if not impossible, to produce in Earth's gravity. Objects orbiting around the Earth are actually constantly falling toward the Earth, but the path of their fall exactly matches the curvature of the Earth (see illustration). Because there is nothing to stop their fall, they are said to be in free-fall. And, with no opposing force, the object experiences weightlessness. We can experience the principles of this effect if we descend a tall building in a high-speed elevator. As we begin to descend, we briefly experience a sense of reduced weight. If the elevator descended fast enough, we would experience weightlessness.

It is this weightless condition that is so important to manufacturing new alloys. Combining different metals in exact proportion produces these alloys. Because the metals have different weights per given volume (also known as density), gravity tends to pull the higher density ones to the bottom, thus preventing a uniform mixture. In a

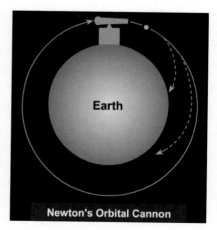

Newton's Orbital Cannon

Imagine a cannon firing a projectile horizontally from a tower high above the Earth. The projectile will follow a curved path as it falls back. If we progressively increase the power of the cannon shot, we will reach a point where the curved path of the falling projectile will match the curvature of the Earth. At that point, the projectile will have attained orbital velocity.

Picture credit: Astronomy 161, The Solar System

weightless environment, they all weigh the same so they can combine evenly.

While the space environment provides some unique advantages, it also presents some big challenges, as we shall see. There are millions of interesting objects in space. Astronomers look at them all and many are the subjects of our space programs. We will discuss many of the manned and unmanned programs, past, present, and proposed.

bjectives

List four reasons to explore and exploit space.
Define the lower limits of space.
Define cislunar space.
Describe the contents of cislunar space.
Describe interplanetary space.
Describe interstellar space.
Describe the characteristics of the Sun.
Describe the solar magnetic field.
Identify two solar cycles.
Identify the divisions of the Sun's atmosphere.
Identify three solar phenomena.
Define solar wind.
Identify three categories of solar emissions and their sources.
Describe the Earth's ionosphere.
State the causes of ionization.
Identify types of ionospheric behavior.
Define atom and ion.
Describe the general characteristics of the magnetosphere.
Explain the effect of solar wind on the magnetosphere.
Describe cosmic rays.
Describe the structure of the Van Allen radiation belts.
Identify the content and cause of the belts.
State the hazards identified with the belts.
Describe the characteristics of magnetic storms.
Identify the effects of the space environment of communications.
Identify the effects of the Earth's atmosphere on spacecraft.
Identify the effects of vacuum on spacecraft.
Describe the electrostatic charging that affects spacecraft.
Explain the dangers from collisions in space.
Identify the effects of the space environment on manned operations.

Definition of Space

What is space? Space is a place that extends infinitely in all directions and contains all of the stars, planets and galaxies in the universe. This is true, but is not a very good definition. The big question is "where does the Earth's atmosphere end and space begin?" There are several definitions of space but the most widely accept level is 62 miles above the Earth. When the Ansari family offered a $10,000,000 prize for a privately-funded aerospace craft to go in to and return from space, a parameter of 62 miles, or 100 kilometers was established as space. On the other hand, NASA awards astronaut wings to persons who fly above 50 miles altitude. Another phrase that has been used for years is outer space. The academic community defines this as the space beyond Earth's atmosphere to the ends of the known universe. The minimum altitude required for a satellite to sustain a stable orbit is approximately 100 miles above the Earth. Most shuttle missions require ranging from 115 to 250 statute miles. A one-way trip to the Moon is ruffly a quarter of a million miles.

Cislunar Space

Description

The dimensions of cislunar space, the space between the Earth and the Moon, vary from month to month since the Moon's orbit about the Earth is elliptical, with its closest distance (perigee) being 221,600 miles, and its farthest distance (apogee) 252,500 miles (values are close approximations).

This would be the same as traveling from New York to California 75 times. Since the Moon rotates around the Earth, the actual space that forms the sphere of … diameter of this sphere averages about 474,000 … with a circumference averaging approximately 1,489,000 miles. Thus, the Moon travels this distance in its orbit around the Earth as it establishes the outer border of cislunar space.

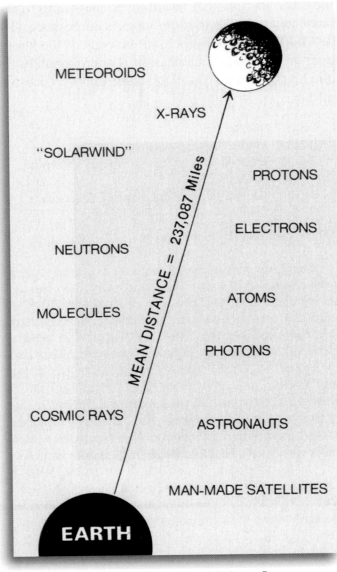

Dimensions and Occupants of Cislunar Space

Cislunar Space—Is it a void?

What would an astronaut find in this area called cislunar space? It is certainly not the void as portrayed in science fiction movies. The Earth's magnetosphere extends thousands of miles outward through cislunar space and onward to the Sun. The Sun's solar wind presses the magnetosphere and its contents beyond the Moon's orbit. So, a portion of Earth's magnetosphere is found within cislunar space. The magnetosphere also contains mass in the form of protons and electrons.

Magnetic lines of force from both the Earth and the Sun emanate into cislunar space. These magnetic lines of force are added to the Moon's very weak, but measurable magnetic field.

Besides the radiation storms emanating from the Sun, which bathe all of cislunar space, there are cosmic rays. These tiny charged particles cannot be seen, but the photons of the visible light spectrum generated by the Sun are visible. The Sun's photons can also be seen as some are bounced back through cislunar space after striking the Moon's surface. Photos from other stars in our Milky Way Galaxy travel through cislunar space to reach Earth.

Meteoroids, asteroids, comets and spacecraft, can all be found in this space. So it is not a void, it's just that most of its contents are invisible to the unaided eye.

Interplanetary Space

Interplanetary space is that region of outer space that extends spherically from the Sun past the outermost planet to what is known as the heliopause (defined as the region where the Sun's influence is no longer dominant). According to data sent back by the Voyager 1 space probe, the heliopause has been located at approximately 11 billion miles out from the Sun. Within the region of interplanetary space are the Sun, the known planets and their moons, a huge belt of asteroids, minor planets (to include Pluto), charged particles, magnetic fields, cosmic dust, and more.

Interstellar Space and Beyond

On clear nights, nights free of clouds and air pollution, the Milky Way is visible. This is a common name for the galaxy in which we reside, along with about 100 billion other Solar Systems and stars. The distance between the extent of one Solar System and the beginning of another Solar System is called interstellar space.

Distance between the stars and/or Solar Systems varies and involves such high numbers of miles that the imagination is staggered. In this case, distance is thought of in light years and parsecs instead of astronomical units (a single unit being the mean distance between the Sun and the Earth). A light year is the distance a photon can travel in one of Earth's calendar years. This amounts to 5 trillion 878 billion statute miles (5,878,000,000,000 miles). When the number of light years gets very large, parsecs are used; one parsec is 3.26 light years, or 19.2 trillion miles.

So, how far into this interstellar space would a person travel to find another Sun and/or Solar System? Astronomers believe a person would have to travel 4 1/3 years at the speed of light to reach it. However, this would be a nearby Solar System. Other stars and Solar Systems are much farther away.

Beyond Interstellar space is the realm of intergalactic space, or the space between the galaxys. It is the term that describes the broadest spatail dimensions used in astronomy. It is considered to contain the "emptiest" parts of the Universe, with very little cosmic dust or debis. Scientists have calculated that there is probably only one hydrogen atom per cubic meter (nearly a perfect vacuum).

Overhead view of our galaxy. Seen face-on, the Milky Way's central bulge of stars is surrounded by spiral arms.

Sun

Characteristics of Our Sun

The force at the center of our Solar System is the Sun. Although the Sun is only a medium-size star, its dimensions, power, composition, temperature and other factors stagger the imagination. The Earth has a diameter of a little less than 8,000 miles; the Sun's diameter is 864,000 miles. The Sun is the strongest gravitational force in the Solar System. Its gravity controls the orbital paths of all the objects in the Solar System. The Sun emits enormous amounts of energy. How does the Sun do what it does? No one has all the answers as to exactly how all the pieces of the solar puzzle fit together. It is generally accepted that the Sun is a giant thermonuclear reactor. Thermonuclear reaction is the nuclear fusion of atoms under pressure and heat into different atoms. This fusion process releases tremendous energy.

In the Sun, the fusion process is carried on as hydrogen atoms are fused into helium by the pressure and heat of the Sun's great mass. This helium may exist for only a billionth of a second before its protons disengage themselves with another release of energy. This process occurs over and over with each activity producing and absorbing energy.

The core of the Sun is so hot that no solid or liquid molecules can exist. Virtually, all atoms remain in a plasma state. The energy released within the core has to make its way to the surface, atom by atom. It's theorized if the Sun's fusion reaction were to suddenly halt, it would take more than 100,000 years before any effect would show on the surface.

While the Sun's gravity and energy emissions directly affect the space environment, the Sun's magnetic field affects it indirectly. Magnetic activity on the Sun affects how energy is released from the Sun.

The Sun's magnetic field is at least 100 times stronger than the Earth's. Unlike the Earth's magnetic field, the Sun's magnetic field lacks definite structure. The Earth's field flows between the North and South Poles. The Sun's is the net result of many small surface fields and the magnetic networks surrounding surging surface plasma. The Sun's rotation then alters these magnetic fields.

Because the Sun is plasma and not a solid body, its surface rotates at different rates. The generally accepted average time for one rotation is 27 days, but the Equator rotates 30% faster than the poles. Depending on where you measure, the Sun requires between 25 and 40 days to complete one rotation. These different rates cause the magnetic field lines to get twisted and sheared. The result is an increase in field strength and areas of stored energy. These areas are called active solar regions. **Sunspots, filaments, prominences,** and **flares** are solar phenomena associated with these active regions.

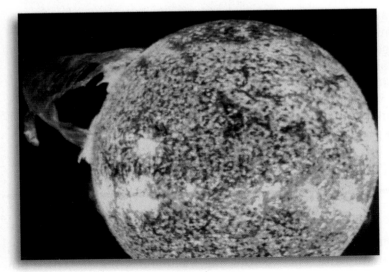

Solar Prominences

In addition to the 27-day rotation cycle, the activity of the Sun follows an 11-year cycle. Commonly called the Sunspot cycle, its actual length can vary between 8 and 15 years. These cycles are very important to space operations because they allow us to predict when solar phenomena may occur. During these occurrences, the Sun's stored up energy can be released suddenly and explosively. These sudden bursts can produce damaging amounts of particles and electromagnetic waves.

By compiling all the solar wind data gathered in the space age, NASA scientists have concluded that even though the solar magnetic field is constantly changing, it always returns to its original shape and position. Scientists now know that the Sun's magnetic field has a memory and returns to approximately the same configuration of each 11-year solar cycle.

The solar wind is composed of charged particles ejected from the Sun that flow continuously through interplanetary space. The solar wind carries part of the Sun's magnetic field into space. Before completing this research, scientists knew that features of the solar wind reaching the Earth tended to repeat about every 27 days. The new information pinpoints the repetition interval at 27 days and 43 minutes, and shows that the Sun has kept this steady rhythm, much like a metronome, for at least 38 years.

This pattern escaped previous detection because it is a very subtle statistical effect. There are many larger variations in the solar wind that come and go, which largely mask the underlying pattern. This repetitive behavior can't be seen if these data are examined for only a few months or years, but it was revealed through several decaded of opervation.

Unfortunately, not all phenomena are cyclic. Flares, potentially the most dangerous phenomena, are non-cyclic. The particles emitted during flares can harm satellites, ground systems, spacecraft and astronauts. We monitor the Sun's activity closely so we can react quickly when flares occur. The less dangerous electromagnetic radiation from a flare will reach Earth in less than 9 minutes. The more dangerous high-energy particles may take 15 minutes to 3 days to get here. Spacecraft operators must be prepared to act quickly.

Solar Atmosphere

The solar atmosphere consists of the photosphere, the chromosphere and the corona. Each has its own characteristics.

Photosphere. The portion of the Sun which gives light is a very thin shell called the photosphere. This is the portion of the star that exists in a gaseous form that is familiar to people. This shell is composed mostly of hydrogen and helium, and is very hot. Its temperature is more than 10,000° F, but its density is less than that of Earth's near-surface atmosphere.

Photographs of the Sun's photosphere depict a granular appearance. Each of these granules has a diameter of several hundred miles. The granules are massive clouds of super-heated gases that rise and fall with changing temperatures. Their brightness is also dependent on the temperature. Their motion can be generally equated with the rough seas produced by the winds of a hurricane, since these gases behave more like a boiling liquid than our terrestrial gases.

Sunspots are a phenomena associated with the photosphere. These spots are enormous areas where the photosphere is dark—somewhat like looking into a hole through the photosphere. Sunspots appear dark because they are cooler than the surrounding plasma.

There are many hot spots that show as bright blotches on ultraviolet pictures of the photosphere. Sometimes ionized gases condense and flow down magnetic field lines. What these gas flows are called depends on your perspective. When seen against

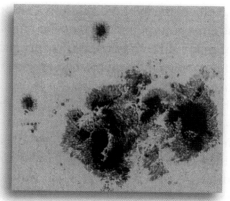

Sunspots

527

the black background of space, they are prominences. Against the solar disk, where they appear darker because they're cooler than the hot plasma of the solar disk, they are called filaments. Bursting from the surface are occasional solar flares. These phenomena extend through the Sun's chromosphere and into its corona.

Chromosphere. Above the photosphere is the chromosphere (sphere of color). It extends to about 15,000 miles. Considering the Sun's diameter of almost a million miles, you can see that the chromosphere is indeed a very minor shell. It is characterized by spicules that apparently jet straight up from the area of the granules described above. Astronomers believe that these spicules are part of the convective action taking place within the granules. At first, these hair-like spicules were thought to go only outward from the photosphere. However, later observations found some of them to be descending. This pink fringe of spicules has been described as appearing like blades of grass.

Corona. The next division of the Sun's atmosphere is called the corona (crown). The corona cannot be seen unless the solar disc is eclipsed (covered). This is also true for the chromosphere. Today, there is no need to wait for a natural eclipse to take place because astronomers have instruments, which contain an opaque disc for eclipsing the Sun. The corona is an enormous area of faint white light that visibly extends outward from the Sun's surface. It extends outward for 3 million miles during normal solar activity and more than 4 million miles when Sunspot activity is high.

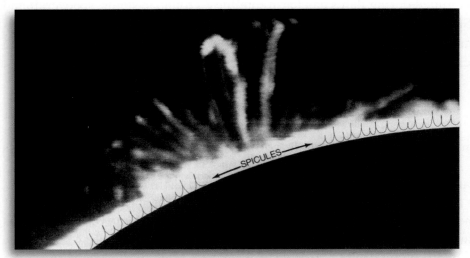

Solar Prominences and Spicules

Remember that this is visible light—that part of the electromagnetic spectrum that can be detected with the eye. There are other types of emissions from the Sun besides visible light. These electromagnetic emissions can be steady, cyclic or non-cyclic. We've already discussed the non-cyclic emissions generated by solar flares. Steady emissions are usually called solar wind and are made up of many different types of atoms and ions generated within the Sun. Solar wind is an extension of the Sun's corona into interplanetary space. Traveling at speeds from 300-1000 km/sec, its average speed near Earth is 400 km/sec.

Solar winds are also affected by the Sun's 11-year cycle. When strong localized magnetic fields build up, they sometimes extend out from the Sun. When this happens, they drag and accelerate particles away from the corona. This leads to areas of lower density in the corona, known as corona holes. These holes are the source of high speed solar winds. Because they follow magnetic lines of force, these high-speed winds cannot mix with other solar winds. The differing speeds create shock waves, which impact Earth and cause disturbances in Earth's magnetic field.

Our main source of information for learning about the Sun is SOHO, the Solar and Heliospheric

Observatory, launched in December 1995. The SOHO project is jointly operated by NASA and the European Space Agency (ESA). SOHO was designed for a nominal mission lifetime of two years. Because of its spectacular successes, the mission was extended five times (in 1997, 2002, 2006, 2008, and 2010). This allowed SOHO to cover an entire 11-year solar cycle (#23) and the rise of the new cycle 24. At the time of this publication, SOHO was currently approved for operation through the end of 2012. Source: ESA SOHO Fact Sheet. During the maximum sunspot occurrence of ... were also responsible for disrupting voice and other telecommunications on a global scale. Today, we are even more dependent on satellites and computers. Advanced microchips are more vulnerable to the Sun's electromagnetic effects and particles.

Located 1.5 million kilometers out in space, SOHO is the world's chief watchdog for the Sun. From its vantage point where the Sun never sets, the spacecraft can continuously observe solar activity. Images are sent to regional warning centers of the International Space Environment Service, which in turn alerts engineers responsible for power systems, spacecraft and other technological systems of impending effects on Earth's environment.

Earth

One of the most surprising discoveries resulting from SOHO observations was the occurrence of tornadoes on the Sun. Images and data collected from SOHO observations include at least a dozen tornadoes with steady wind speeds of 15 kilometers per second and with gusts up to 10 times faster. These tornadoes occur most frequently near the North and South Poles of the Sun and are almost as wide as the Earth. Hot gases in the tornado spiral away from the Sun and gather speed. Scientists are now studying the phenomena to determine how solar tornadoes might relate to observations of the fast solar wind farther out in space.

Space Environment Around the Earth

Ionosphere

Throughout history, people have wondered about the aurora borealis and the aurora australis. The aurora borealis (or northern lights) flashes brilliant colors in varying patterns across the northern skies. The aurora australis presents a similar display in the Southern Hemisphere. Observers have determined that these displays occur at heights ranging from 60 to 600 miles above the surface of the Earth.

It was only recently that people learned that these and other events may be associated with a zone of electrically conductive layers in the upper atmosphere called the **ionosphere**.

The ionosphere is a part of the atmosphere divided by its electrical activity. It gets its name from the gas particles that are ionized or charged.

Discovery of the ionosphere came with the invention of the radio early in the twentieth century. When radio waves were transmitted beyond the horizon, scientists theorized that a layer of atmosphere could act as a mirror to bounce waves back to Earth.

In the 1920s and later, a long series of observations provided a picture of the ionosphere. It was learned that the ionosphere contains reflecting layers. The lowest of these reflects long-wave radio transmissions, such as those of the standard commercial radio broadcast bands in the United States. Higher layers reflect short-wave transmissions. The higher the reflecting layer, the farther a signal can travel because it bypasses more of the Earth's curvature. Thus, short-wave radio can be used for international broadcasting and long-wave radio is preferred for local commercial broadcasting. However, long-wave stations may have ranges to approximately 1,000 miles, depending on power.

Characteristics of the Ionosphere. It is essential to examine the electrical peculiarities of the ionosphere. Why is the atmosphere at times ablaze with northern lights or other spectacles? Why are there reflecting layers that aid people in long-distance radio communications? Why are there black outs or garbled radio communications? Why do magnetic compasses spin instead of point steadily at the magnetic north? To understand both normal ionospheric behavior and sudden ionospheric disturbances, or SIDs, certain facts must be understood.

The Atom. An atom contains almost all of its mass in a central body or nucleus, which is a tight cluster of smaller particles called neutrons and protons. Neutrons have no electrical charge; protons carry a positive electrical charge. Around this central body, negatively charged electrons whirl in all directions. These electrons are so tiny that scientists formerly believed that they had no mass—that they were mere sparks of energy. Now, it is generally agreed that an electron has mass, approximately 1/1900 that of a proton or neutron.

Electrically speaking, however, the proton and electron are equal and opposite in charge; one charge balances the other. A normal atom is electrically neutral because the number of electrons exactly equals the number of protons. For example, a nitrogen atom has a nucleus containing 7 protons and 7 neutrons, giving it an atomic weight of approximately 14 and an atomic number of 7. The atomic number refers to the number of protons. Seven electrons revolve around the nucleus.

The Ion. An ion is an atom that carries a positive or negative electrical charge as a result of losing or gaining one or more electrons. The name is also sometimes given to a free electron, proton or other charged subatomic particle (particle smaller than an atom). Therefore, the ionosphere includes those zones of upper atmosphere and near space in which there are many charged or ionized atoms and numerous free electrons and other charged subatomic particles. These ions concentrate in certain layers to reflect radio waves of a given range or frequency.

Causes of Ionization. What causes ionization? In the ionosphere, the main causes are the powerful ultraviolet radiation of the Sun and the ultra-high-frequency cosmic rays from the stars of outer space. Above the shielding effect of the thicker atmosphere at lower levels, this radiation bombards the scattered atoms and molecules of nitrogen, oxygen and other gases, and knocks some of the electrons out of the outer rims of the atoms.

Ionospheric Behavior. Sunspots, solar flares and other disturbances on the surface of the Sun produce fluctuations in the output of the Sun's rays. These, in turn, produce SIDs and other variations in the behavior of the ionosphere. The normal rhythm of nights and days also affects the behavior of the ionosphere. SIDs, for example, will produce excess electrons in the atmosphere, and these will absorb radio waves. The magnetic forces of the Earth also have an effect on the behavior of the ionosphere. It is the interaction of solar radiation and the Earth's magnetism that produces the aurora borealis and aurora australis. Particles traveling swiftly toward the Earth's two magnetic poles produce these glowing displays.

The ionosphere is generally regarded as extending to more than 250 miles above Earth's surface, well beyond the altitude where most of the atmosphere exists. One name applied to space beyond the Earth's atmosphere is **exosphere** (outside sphere). The ionosphere blends into the exosphere, which must not be considered a dead vacuum. It contains atomic and subatomic particles. This is especially true of the Van Allen belts.

Magnetosphere and Solar Wind

Before studying the Van Allen belts in detail, a look at the Earth's magnetosphere and the effects upon it by the solar wind is essential. This is due to the Van Allen belts being closely related to the behavior of the magnetosphere.

Magnetosphere. The region of the Earth's atmosphere where ionized gas plays a big part in the dynamics of the atmosphere and where the geomagnetic field plays an important role is called the magnetosphere. The magnetosphere begins about 217 miles above the Earth's surface and extends 10 or 15 Earth radii to the boundary between the atmosphere and the interplanetary plasma.

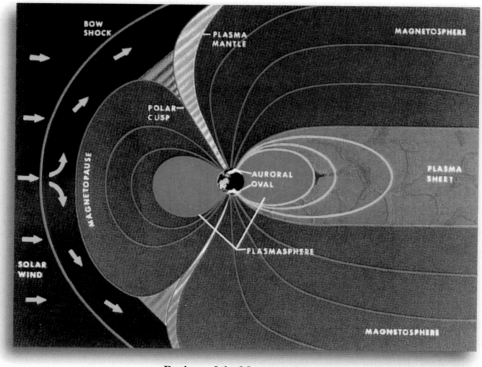

Earth, like most other planetary and stellar bodies, is surrounded by a tremendous magnetic field. Remember the experiment where a bar magnet is placed beneath a piece of paper on which there are iron filings? If the magnet is close enough for its magnetic field to affect the filings, they take on the shape of the magnetic field—that

Regions of the Magnetosphere

is, they align with the field of force. The filings sweep toward the magnet's North and South Poles, concentrating more or less at the poles and leaving relatively few filings toward the Equator of the magnetic force field.

If the bar magnet and the iron filings could be suspended in three dimensions, instead of the paper's two dimensions, the iron filings would probably, at least for a short time, form a sort of cloud around the magnet. This cloud would surround the magnet, but would leave a very deep depression at each of the poles as the magnetic lines of force swept downward carrying filings toward each of the poles (see picture at the left).

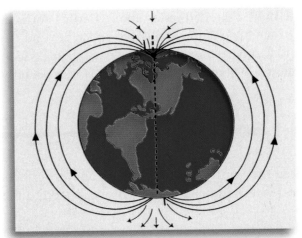

Earth's magnetic lines of force without outside forces acting upon them.

Earth acts as if it had a large bar magnet going through its center surfacing at the magnetic poles. The north and south magnetic poles are near the north and south celestial poles, which are sometimes referred to as the rotational axis. If the magnetic field could be seen, and if it were not for the effects of many other forces, Earth's magnetosphere would look something like the diagram to the left. However, forces such as the solar wind alter the patterns of the magnetic lines.

If a way could be found for space travelers to see Earth's total magnetosphere, it would probably look like a comet with an extended tail that always points away from the Sun. This pointing away from the Sun, of course, is caused by the pressure of solar radiation pushing outward from the solar sphere.

Solar Wind. The normal solar wind, or solar plasma, strikes the Earth's magnetosphere with considerable collective force. This force is such that it forms a bow shock wave where the magnetic lines of force of the magnetic field are struck by the solar plasma. The resulting bow shock wave distorts Earth's magnetosphere. The extent of the

Magnetosphere

distortion of the magnetosphere by the solar wind is not precisely known, but it is known that it sweeps the magnetosphere beyond the orbit of the Moon.

Actual, solid knowledge about the total magnetosphere and the solar wind continues to be received as the data is returned from satellites and other instruments. However, in 1958, a University of Iowa physicist, James A. Van Allen, announced the discovery of a large zone of space filled with electrically charged particles extending far beyond the limits of the ionosphere. This discovery was made with instruments of *Explorer* 1, the first US Earth satellite. Numerous other satellites and sounding rocket probes and scientific studies of the so-called Van Allen radiation belts have been made since then.

Van Allen Radiation Belts

Cosmic Rays

Energetic charged particles from all over the galaxy and beyond continuously rain down upon the Earth. These atomic particles, mostly electrons and the nuclei of atoms, are called cosmic rays. Even though they travel at nearly the speed of light, their flow is greatly reduced by solar wind. When solar wind is at a minimum, more cosmic rays enter into the magnetosphere. This increase in cosmic rays can disrupt spacecraft operations. Cosmic rays entering the atmosphere collide with atmospheric molecules and create secondary cosmic rays. While the cosmic rays coming from outer space are a concern to spacecraft, they rarely have enough energy to affect ground systems. However, secondary cosmic rays can be a major concern to ground systems.

Van Allen Radiation Belts

Like the ionosphere, the Van Allen radiation belts are filled with charged particles. Also like the ionosphere, the Van Allen belts are the product of interaction between the Sun and the Earth. Thus, some scientists regard these belts as an extension of the ionosphere, but the Van Allen particles are different from those prevailing at lower levels of the ionosphere. They also behave differently and fall into different patterns.

Structure of the Belts. The belts are thought to be crescent-shaped in cross section and composed of two shells. The "horns" of these crescents dip toward Earth's magnetic poles as the charged particles follow the magnetic lines of force. The horns of the internal belt lie close to where the magnetic line of force dips downward toward Earth's 45° latitude in both the Northern and Southern Hemispheres. The outer or external zone converges above Earth's surface between latitudinal lines 55° and 67°, with maximum concentration located at 62° latitude.

Content and Cause of the Belts. What is in these belts and what causes them? Primarily, the cause is the Sun. The Sun constantly emits charged particles that sweep outward in all directions and extend for unknown distances. These particles are mainly protons and electrons traveling at a million miles per hour as a plasma (a plasma is of much thinner consistency than a gas and is a conductor of electrical activity). However, this speed of a million miles per hour increases considerably when the Sun is active.

The Sun is considered to be active when solar flares and other solar disturbances are occurring. When these charged particles encounter Earth's magnetic field, many of them are trapped and bounce back and forth between the Northern and Southern Hemispheres.

Some say that both Van Allen belts are caused by solar activity with some influence by cosmic rays. Others believe that the outer belt is the result of solar activity while the inner belt has a different origin. The theory here is that the more powerful cosmic rays come into the upper layers (primarily the mesosphere) of the Earth's atmosphere where they are stopped when they collide with atmospheric molecules.

These collisions result in the release of neutrons, some of which travel outward from Earth. These neutrons decay into protons and electrons, which then become trapped by Earth's magnetic field. Thus, you can see that science is not positive as to exactly how the magnetosphere was formed or continues to function.

Radiation Hazards. Going outward from Earth's surface at the geomagnetic Equator (as opposed to the geographic Equator), radiation from the Van Allen belts begins to increase rapidly above 600 miles and then falls away rapidly near 30,000 miles out. This radiation increase goes up to about 10,000 counts per second (a measure of charged particles) and returns to 10 counts per second beyond what we might say is the outer fringe of the Van Allen belts. The maximum count (10,000 per second) occurs within the internal belt at the geomagnetic Equator and between 1,400 and 3,000 miles altitude.

Correcting this number of counts to roentgens, scientists tell us that the effect is between 10 and 20 roentgens per hour. The safe or maximum dosage of radiation is 0.3 roentgen per hour, so it is clear how lethal the internal belt would be to human habitation.

Actually, the combined energy possessed by one-radiation particle enables it to penetrate the human body and destroy or disturb a human body cell. Sustained exposure to these high-energy particles within the outer belt would kill too many body cells for the exposed person to survive.

Therefore, the concentrations of radiation within the Van Allen belts pose a hazard to astronauts. If it were justified to keep a manned space vehicle within this portion of the magnetosphere for any length of time, the occupants would have to be protected by heavy shielding.

During the Apollo Program, astronauts had to pass through both Van Allen radiation belts on the way out and on the return trip, but the exposure time was very short and insignificant. Orbits of manned spacecraft, such as Russia's Soyuz and the US Space Shuttle, are beneath the internal Van Allen belt because its altitude of 600 miles is much greater than the usual orbit.

What would happen, though, if a manned spacecraft were in polar orbit? Recalling that the radiation belts dip downward toward the surface of Earth, each orbit might involve flight through the four crescents. This could, in turn, build into a dangerous level of accumulated radiation effects on the astronauts' bodies even though they would be flying through a radiation-free zone near each of the Earth's magnetic poles.

The intense amount of radiation found within the Van Allen portion of the magnetosphere can be damaging even to satellites. However, satellites that are in synchronous equatorial orbit (22,300 miles altitude) are on the fringe of the outer Van Allen belt, so they remain functional for many years before replacement is necessary.

Effects of Solar Disturbances

Much of what affects the ionosphere, magnetosphere and Van Allen belts stems directly from solar activity. Most of the effects of solar activity on these regions occur during solar disturbances, a period when the Sun is active. These disturbances cause strange effects on the magnetosphere and in the ionosphere during what we call magnetic storms.

Magnetic Storms. Magnetic storms (also called electromagnetic or radiation storms) are characterized by a sudden onset of radiation bursts in which the magnetic field undergoes marked changes in the course of an hour or less. This is followed by a very gradual return to normalcy, which may take several days. Magnetic storms are caused by solar disturbances, although the exact nature of the link between the solar and terrestrial disturbances is not yet understood.

Magnetic storms are more frequent during years of high Sunspot activity and can sometimes be linked to a particular solar disturbance. In these cases, the time between the solar flare and onset of the magnetic storm is about one or two days. This suggests that a cloud of particles thrown out by the Sun carries the disturbance to the Earth.

Magnetic storms interfere with the reflectivity of the ionosphere and cause it to actually absorb radio transmissions rather than reflect them. Everything from telescopes to satellites monitor the Sun's activity

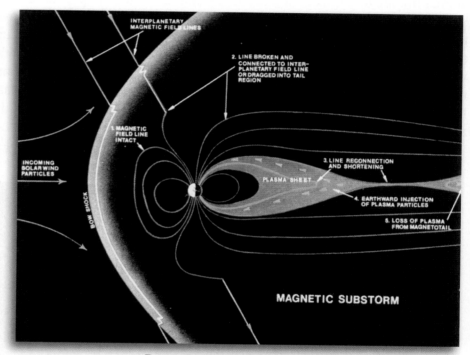

Process Involved in a Magnetic Storm

on a 24-hour, around-the-world surveillance system. When one of these solar storms occurs, it is detected immediately and word is sent out so that those who work with electronic communications can prepare for the effects of the storm.

In 1960, a solar outburst of great intensity took place. At 2:37 p.m. on November 12th, an astronomer discovered it. Approximately 6 hours later, this finger of hydrogen plasma (which was 10 million miles across) collided with Earth's magnetosphere and atmosphere. For over a week, there were interruptions and disruptions of electromagnetic functions on Earth.

The intensity of this solar outburst affected communications around the world. It blacked out long-distance radio communications for hours and made magnetic compasses spin erratically. This was a very serious blow to aviation since the magnetic compass is the primary reference for direction of flight.

To illustrate how powerful magnetic storms can be, during this outburst even the teletype machines printed nonsense instead of the messages sent. In northern areas of the country, electric lights flickered as if electrical storms were taking place; however, the sky was clear.

Solar outbursts of this intensity do not happen frequently, but when they do, similar effects occur. Even the transmission of electricity and telephone messages can be disrupted by such energy. It is now believed that solar activity of sufficient magnitude may have been responsible for electrical blackouts in the past. Solar activity has been known to induce currents in telephone circuits and cause automatic switching devices to open and close at the wrong time. So, when an outburst of solar energy strikes Earth, it temporarily affects many of the processes of civilization. The long-term effects on plant and animal life are unknown, but it seems certain that some are produced.

Earth does not receive the force of all solar outbursts. The Sun spins rapidly on its axis and has a tremendous magnetic field. When these outbursts or flares of energy occur, the net effect is a relatively narrow streaming out of plasma that may follow a curved trajectory (path). An example can be found with the common lawn sprinkler. Imagine cutting or separating a segment of the stream of water coming from the whirling sprinkler; this is what a stream of solar storm plasma is believed to be like. If Earth is in the path of this plasma stream's trajectory, communication and other problems arise and the auroras will be activated.

Polar Magnetic Storms. When the solar disturbances are observable only in the polar areas, they

Aurora Borealis

are termed polar magnetic storms. These polar magnetic storms produce sporadic radiant emissions from the upper atmosphere over middle and high latitudes. The visible emissions are called aurora borealis in the northern latitudes and aurora australis in the southern latitudes and appear as colored lights.

According to various theories, auroras are related to magnetic storms and the influx of charged particles from the Sun. The nature of the exact mechanisms involved is still being investigated, but it seems that the trapped particles from the Van Allen belts apparently play an important part. The protons and electrons dashing about within the Van Allen belts spill into Earth's upper atmosphere where the belts dip toward the magnetic poles. This spillage involves billions of collisions between the charged particles and the atoms that, in turn, cause the upper atmosphere's gases to glow and shimmer in different colors.

For example, radiation striking atomic oxygen at a certain altitude produces a green color. If atomic oxygen is struck at a higher level, where the oxygen atoms are less dense, a reddish glow will result. When molecular nitrogen is struck, a reddish glow different from oxygen red is produced. Occasionally, the green-glow oxygen bands will be fringed at the bottom edge by nitrogen red.

The auroras are brightest when the Sun is highly active. Long ago, the appearance and intensities of the auroras were discovered to be linked to solar activity. When a solar flare occurs, for example, people in latitudes from which the auroras can be seen are in for a spectacle. However, the spectacular nighttime visual displays are overshadowed by the problems caused, particularly on the Sun side of Earth, during the magnetic storms discussed earlier.

Environmental Effects on Space Operations

Communications

In addition to the problems caused by magnetic storms, several other environmental factors affect communications. First, not all radio frequencies are useable for uplink/downlink ground to satellite communications. The ionosphere absorbs low frequencies and water vapor absorbs high frequencies. Frequencies between 300 megahertz (wavelength = 1 meter) and 300 gigahertz (wavelength = 1 millimeter) are generally acceptable.

A second problem is scintillation. Electron density variations in the ionosphere cause rapid changes in radio signals. The effect is the same one mentioned earlier, which causes stars to twinkle. Three options exist to lessen the effects of scintillation. One is to only transmit when conditions permit such as during night hours. Obviously this limits the usefulness of the communication system.

The second option is to avoid transmitting in regions, such as the Equator and the poles, where scintillation is particularly strong. Again, depending on the satellite's orbit, this might not be a useful solution. The last option is to use a very high frequency to minimize the effects of scintillation. The problem with this option is the potential effects of water vapor we mentioned earlier.

A final environmental effect that hurts radio communications is caused by solar flares. Solar flares release large amounts of radio energy. The effect is referred to as "solar radio burst." It usually only lasts a few minutes, but during that time radio waves are effectively jammed.

Spacecraft

The space environment can be very hostile to spacecraft. The atmosphere, vacuum of space, charged particles and space debris all take their toll.

Atmosphere. Whenever a spacecraft passes through the Earth's atmosphere, it can be affected in two ways. The first effect is called drag, which slows the spacecraft down. This is the same force you feel pushing on your hand when you stick it out the window of a moving car. The second effect is oxidation from free oxygen atoms.

The most familiar type of oxidation occurs when iron is exposed to water. The oxygen atoms in water break away and combine with the iron. The result is rust. When oxygen atoms are free, the reaction is much faster. Normally, oxygen atoms exist as parts of molecules.

In the upper atmosphere, molecules are widely spaced. When radiation or high energy particles collide with these molecules, the atoms break apart. Often they are too far apart to recombine. The result is free oxygen atoms. These react with spacecraft surfaces to weaken components, change thermal properties and degrade sensors.

Fortunately, many free oxygen atoms find each other and form groups of three. These molecules are called ozone. Ozone is very effective at blocking radiation from reaching the Earth.

Satellites rarely orbit at a uniform distance from Earth. Instead they follow elliptical paths that bring them closer at one point, known as perigee, and farther away at another point, known as apogee. It is at perigee that the greatest effect from the atmosphere is felt. Any spacecraft perigee below 1,000 km will be affected. Temperature and atmospheric density determine the extent of the effect. However, the effect is fairly predictable and spacecraft designers plan for it.

Unplanned drag can occur when the atmosphere heats unexpectedly. When heated, it expands outward toward the spacecraft. Both electromagnetic radiation from solar events and particle bombardment that occurs during magnetic storms can heat up the atmosphere and create more free oxygen. Low Earth orbits and polar orbits are most affected.

Vacuum. Beyond the atmosphere, space is a vacuum. The emptiness of a vacuum can cause problems for spacecraft. Materials used in spacecraft can contain tiny bubbles of gas. Under atmospheric pressure, they stay where they are. Removing the pressure by exposing them to a vacuum can be like opening a can of soda. Eventually, the soda goes flat because all the bubbles escape. This is called outgassing.

We don't care about the spacecraft losing the bubbles, but sometimes the outgassing molecules settle on spacecraft surfaces. When these surfaces are delicate sensors and lenses, they can be damaged. Spacecraft, which might have this problem, must be placed in a vacuum chamber prior to flight to bleed off the gas.

Another problem the vacuum environment can cause is called cold welding. This occurs when moving parts fit with only a tiny air space between them. In a vacuum the tiny amount of air which kept them separated escapes and they weld together. Using a lubricant to maintain the space will solve the problem.

However, we must be careful to select a lubricant that won't outgas, freeze or evaporate in the vacuum of space. Dry graphite, like the lead in a pencil, is a good choice.

Electrostatic Charging. Electric charging, by itself, is not always a problem for spacecraft. But anyone who has ever scuffed across a carpet and then touched grounded metal can tell you how painful discharging can be. The small electronic parts of a spacecraft, particularly computer data bits, can be badly shocked. Spacecraft charging can be either "absolute" or "differential."

Absolute charging occurs when the whole craft is charged. It only becomes a problem if two spacecraft of different charges come together. Opposite charges cause a discharge. An example might be the shuttle retrieving a satellite. If it's charged up, it could discharge on contact with the shuttle.

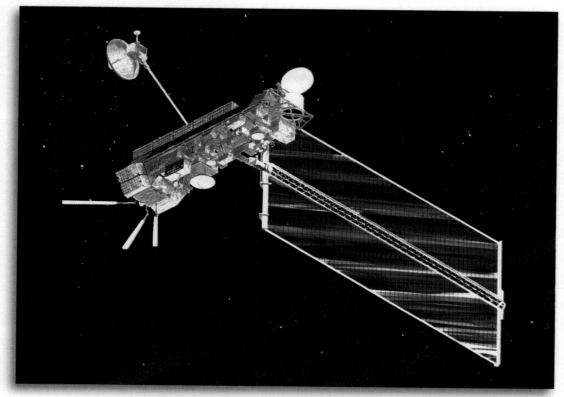

Polar Orbiting Platform

Absolute charging often occurs as a spacecraft passes through fields of plasma, such as solar wind. This plasma imparts a negative charge on the entire satellite.

Differential charging occurs when one part of a spacecraft gets charged and has a different charge than another part of the craft. One of the prime causes of this type of charging is called the photoelectric effect. It occurs when the Sun's electromagnetic radiation liberates electrons from the spacecraft surface leaving it positively charged. Spacecraft will usually have a negative potential on shaded areas due to plasma charging and positive potential on Sunlit areas.

If the surface of the satellite is conductive, these potentials will cancel each other out. If it's not conductive, they can build up to a point where they are much like the shoe scuffing example given earlier. This is very dangerous for the satellite. Unexpected discharges can cause total system failures, or "flipped bits," which can include false commands and memory changes.

Many designs have been used to counter the impact of electrostatic discharge. They include shielding to prevent charging, part selection to cancel it out, redundant systems, error detection and correction systems, and systems to intentionally discharge affected systems at regular times.

Collisions. You might think the most dangerous collisions in space are caused by meteoroids or perhaps other spacecraft. You would be close. Any object big enough to be seen would cause a lot of damage if it collided with a spacecraft at orbital speed. However, the vastness of space makes the risk of colliding with naturally occurring objects very low. Colliding with another spacecraft is also unlikely. There just aren't that many of them. But, getting hit by space garbage, now that is another story.

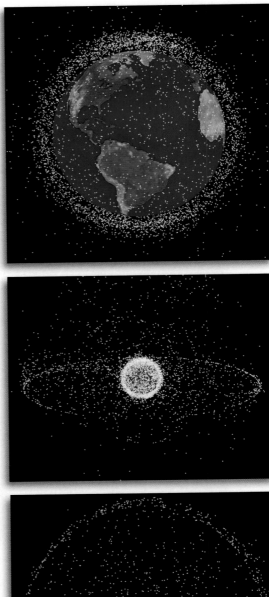

The space around Earth is full of junk left behind by previous space missions. The North American Aerospace Defense Command (NORAD) tracks more than 8,000 orbiting pieces of trash including broken satellites, booster parts and even an astronaut's lost glove. But, NORAD can only track objects baseball sized and larger. There may be as many as 40,000 golf-ball-sized objects and billions of much smaller pieces. Traveling at terrific speeds these tiny objects can hit with more energy than a rifle bullet. Even so, the odds of colliding with any of this debris are still fairly low.

The most common collisions are with high-energy particles from solar flares and cosmic rays. High-energy particles can cause direct damage to spacecraft surfaces and cause false sensor readings. Cosmic rays penetrate deep into spacecraft and ionize atoms as they pass through. This ionization is called deep charging and can disrupt electrical systems. They can also cause direct damage to internal parts. Protecting spacecraft from particle collisions isn't feasible because the necessary shielding is much too heavy. Designing triple redundant systems and doing recurring error detection and correction are the most effective solutions.

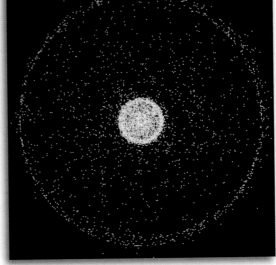

Space debris includes discarded hardware, abandoned satellites and released spacecraft items like separation bolts, lens caps and auxiliary motors. The three pictures illustrate the distribution of both operational satellites and space debris from different distances and perspectives.

Manned Operations

Human beings were not designed to live in space. We need air to breathe, the right temperature range, gravity and protection from radiation. In addition, living in isolation can be mentally taxing. We've already talked about the effects of radiation and we know we need to bring air and control the temperature. What can be done about weightlessness or the psychological effects of space?

Free Fall. Our skeletons, muscles and connective tissue all serve to support us against the pull of gravity. In space, we are still subject to gravity, but we don't experience the pull. We and our spacecraft are falling freely with nothing to resist our fall. We are in free fall and so is everything inside us. The inside parts of our bodies suffer from free fall. Our body's fluids shift, we experience motion sickness and all those tissues designed to support us in gravity get weaker.

On Earth, gravity pulls our body's fluids into our legs. In free fall, these fluids spread out evenly with less than normal in the legs and more than normal in the upper body. This causes several problems. First, the kidneys react to the increase in fluid in the upper body and eliminate it. This can cause dehydration so astronauts need to drink several quarts of liquid prior to returning to Earth.

Second, the heart doesn't have to work as hard and tends to weaken. Third, the downward shift of fluids when gravity is returned can cause us to black out or have the same feeling you sometimes get when you stand up quickly after sitting a long time.

Have you ever wondered why you get dizzy after spinning around in circles? It's because your internal balancing system gets confused. Normally, your eyes establish reference points to where you are, while tiny hairs inside your inner ear sense movement. By putting the two together, you are able to balance and sense where you are. When you spin around, your inner ear cannot react quickly enough and gets out of sync with your eyes.

This is what happens in space, only worse. Your inner ear is calibrated and takes gravity into account when it senses movement. In free fall, the calibration is wrong. What your inner ear senses doesn't match up with what your eyes see. You'll be motion sick until your inner ear can recalibrate.

Astronauts train for free fall by riding in NASA's "Vomit Comet." It's an airplane that flies as high as it can and then dives straight down putting its passengers in free fall for almost a minute.

The same faulty calibration, which affects your inner ear, also affects the rest of your body. Without the constant pull of gravity, your muscles and bones don't get exercised and atrophy. Muscles lose mass and weaken. Bones lose calcium and weaken. Vigorous exercise can help prevent muscle loss, but bone loss is still a problem. Long trips in space will probably require some sort of artificial gravity.

Psychology. When we first started sending astronauts into

NASA's "Vomit Comet"

space, they didn't stay there a long time. We needed them to get as much done as possible, so we designed very rigorous work schedules.

As missions got longer, the costs increased, so schedules continued to be grueling to get the most for our money. Eventually, even the best crews got exhausted. The crew of one United States *Skylab* mission got so frustrated they went on strike for a day to protest. The Russians have experienced similar problems aboard the *MIR* space station.

Extreme isolation and living in close quarters with the same people can cause problems as well. On long missions, we can expect individuals to experience bouts of depression, flaring tempers and periods of poor team performance. Mission planning must include breaks for the crew and provide diversions such as music or games. On long missions, frequent contacts with loved ones are necessary to combat isolation. Teams will need to be selected for compatibility.

Key Terms and Concepts

- space
- interplanetary space
- cislunar space
- the Milky Way
- light year
- solar flares
- solar winds
- Sunspots
- sudden ionospheric disturbance
- ion
- radiation hazards
- magnetic storms
- polar magnetic storms
- uplink/downlink
- scintillation
- solar radio burst
- atmosphere
- photosphere
- meteroid

- chromosphere
- corona
- magnetosphere
- ionosphere
- exosphere
- aurora borealis
- aurora australis
- vacuum
- outgassing
- cold welding
- electrostatic charging
- absolute charging
- differential charging
- free fall
- NASA's "Vomit Comet"
- Van Allen belts
- cosmic rays

? Test Your Knowledge ?

MATCHING

1. **Match the terms with their definitions:**

   a. *photosphere*
   b. *chromosphere*
   c. *corona*
   d. *ionosphere*
   e. *magnetosphere*

   (1) **composed mostly of hydrogen and helium**
   (2) **electrically conductive zone in upper atmosphere**
   (3) **characterized by spicules**
   (4) **ionized gas and magnetic field play an important role here**
   (5) **enormous area of white light emanating from the Sun's surface**

2. **Match the terms with their definitions:**

   a. *Sunspot*
   b. *spicules*
   c. *solar flares*
   d. *solar winds*
   e. *corona holes*

   (1) **Steady emissions made up of many different types of atoms and ions**
   (2) **Areas of lower density in the Sun's "crown"**
   (3) **Cooler area that appears dark on the photosphere**
   (4) **Hair-like phenomena that characterizes the chromosphere**
   (5) **Non-cyclic eruptions that can harm space assets**

SELECT THE CORRECT ANSWER

3. **(Interstellar/Interplanetary)** *is defined as the space between the extent of one Solar System and another.*

4. *The Sun's* **(gravity/energy emissions/magnetic fields)** *affect the space environment in our solar system. (Circle all that apply).*

5. *It is estimated that there are 100* **(thousand, million, billion, trillion)** *other Solar Systems just in our galaxy.*

6. *A parsec is defined as roughly* **(two/three/five/ten/twenty)** *times the distance of a light year.*

7. *Astronomers think it would take just over* **(2 / 4 / 6 / 10)** *light years to reach the nearest solar system in our galaxy.*

8. *The diameter of the Sun is more than* **(ten/one hundred/one thousand)** *times the diameter of Earth.*

9. *Appropriately, the Sun's magnetic field is also more than* **(ten/one hundred/one thousand)** *times the strength of Earth's magnetic field.*

FILL IN THE BLANKS

10. _____ _____ is the space between the Earth and the Moon.

11. USAF administratively defines _____ as beginning at _____ miles above the Earth because that is where it awards _____ _____.

12. Others define _____ as beginning at _____ miles above the Earth because _____.

13. The _____ _____ is the name given to our galaxy.

14. A _____ _____ is defined as the distance a photon can travel in 365 Earth days. It is 5.878 (**thousand, million, billion, trillion**) miles.

15. The surface of the Sun rotates at different rates, varying from _____ days at the Equator to _____ days at the poles, but it is generally accepted that the average is _____ days.

16. The _____ cycle also varies. It can vary between _____ and _____ years, but usually follows close to a/an _____ year cycle.

17. The less dangerous electromagnetic radiation from a _____ _____ can reach the Earth in as little as _____ minutes. The more dangerous high energy particles may take any where from _____ minutes to _____ _____.

18. The _____ begins 217 miles above the Earth's surface and extends 10 or 15 Earth radii to the boundary between the atmosphere and the interplanetary plasma. When struck by _____ _____, it is formed into a bow shock wave, distorting it and pushing it out past the _____.

19. _____ _____, made up mostly of _____ and _____ _____ _____, travel at nearly the speed of light, but have their flow greatly reduced by _____ _____.

20. The _____ _____ _____ are thought to be _____-shaped and composed of _____ shells. Their most significant threat to astronauts is _____, which may be as high as 65 times the safe exposure.

21. _____ _____ are characterized by a sudden onset of _____ _____ in which the _____ field undergoes marked changes in an hour or less.

22. _____ is caused by electron density variations in the _____ and results in rapid changes in radio signals.

23. _____ is when tiny bubbles of gas escape from the materials of the spacecraft due to the _____ of space.

24. Dry graphite may be used as a lubricant to prevent _____ _____, which occurs when the tiny amount of air escapes from between two surfaces of the spacecraft and they fuse.

25. _____ _____ occurs when one part of a spacecraft gets charged and has a different charge than another part of the craft.

TRUE OR FALSE

26. *There is strong agreement that space begins 82 miles above the Earth's surface.*
27. *The solar atmosphere consists of the core, photosphere, chromosphere and corona.*
28. *The Sun's output is fairly consistent and any variance does not impact space operations.*
29. *Short-wave radio is used for local broadcasting, while the long-wave radio is used for international broadcasting because it bounces off the ionosphere better.*

SHORT ANSWER

30 *List four reasons to explore and exploit space.*
31. *What are the main causes of ionization?*
32. *What is the primary cause of the Van Allen radiation belts?*
33. *List some of the characteristics of the Sun.*
34. *Describe an atom.*
35. *Describe an ion.*

OUR SOLAR SYSTEM

This chapter discusses the planets of our solar system. It is not an in-depth look, but it should give you a better understanding of some of the characteristics of the planets.

This chapter also takes into account moons of the planets and other bodies like asteroids, comets, meteoroids, nebula and novas. We discuss the planets in the order of their distance from the Sun, beginning with the planet that is closest to the Sun, Mercury.

Objectives

Describe the characteristics of Mercury.

Describe the characteristics of Venus.

Identify the different programs that sent spacecraft to observe Venus.

Describe some of Earth's characteristics.

State basic moon facts.

Describe the physical features of the moon.

Describe the basic types of moon rocks.

Describe the results of the *Mariner* probes of Mars.

Describe the results of the *Viking* probes of Mars.

Describe the characteristics of the planet Jupiter.

Explain the results of the *Pioneer* probes of Jupiter.

Describe the results of the *Voyager* probes of Jupiter.

Describe the characteristics of the planet Saturn.

Describe the ring system around Saturn.

Describe the characteristics of the planet Uranus.

Explain the results of the *Voyager* 2 probe of Uranus.

Describe the characteristics of the planet Neptune.

State the characteristics of Pluto.

Describe the location of the asteroid belt.

Explain the characteristics of an asteroid.

Describe the characteristics of a comet.

Identify the results of the probes of Comet Halley.

Describe the characteristics of the Milky Way.

Define nova, supernova, pulsar, black hole phenomenon, nebulae, light year and parsec.

Describe the scientific objectives of Messenger.

Describe the timeline of The Venus Express.

Explain why we are returning to the moon.

Describe Saturn.

Describe Sedna.

Mercury

The *Messenger* satellite entering orbit around Mercury.
(Illustration Courtesy of NASA)

Mercury is the planet closest to the Sun, yet it is difficult to see because of the Sun's glare on its surface. Mercury is slightly larger than our Moon, and it is the second smallest of the nine original planets.

Mercury is only 36 million miles from the Sun and orbits it every 88 days. It has a very elliptical orbit and moves approximately 30 miles per second. Mercury rotates very slowly and its "day" is 59 Earth days.

Mercury has a rocky, crust surface with many craters. This gives it the appearance much like our Moon. Many of these craters were formed when space objects crashed into its surface.

Within the solar system there are four planets that are categorized as "terrestrial" (or rocky). They are: Venus, Earth, Mars and Mercury. Everything about this planet is extreme and a new space probe, launched from Earth, has been sent to gather data on Mercury's density, geological history, core structure, atmosphere, surface chemistry, and its extremely dynamic magnetic field. The probe is all part of a program designated MESSENGER (Mercury Surface Space Environment Geochemistry and Ranging).

Messenger is the first spacecraft to orbit Mercury. It was launched on August 2, 2004, and entered into orbit around the planet on March 18, 2011. Pictures of Mercury were first taken by *Mariner* 10, in a flyby in 1974. Sensors on board the *Mariner* transmitted information that described Mercury as very hot with a loosely porous soil. It also gave indications that ice existed at its poles, in deep craters, where the Sun could not melt it. In the three *Mariner* 10 flybys, it was discovered that both a thin atmosphere and magnetic field existed.

***Mariner* 10 was the first space probe to fly past Mercury.**
(Illustration courtesy of NASA)

The four innermost planets compared, Mercury, Venus, Earth and Mars. *(Illustration courtesy of NASA)*

Venus

Moonless Venus is the second planet from the Sun and is nearest to the Earth in both distance and size. This is why it is often referred to as Earth's "sister" planet. The two are similar in size, gravity and density. Venus is covered with an opaque layer that has a highly reflective atmosphere with clouds of sulfuric acid and sulfur dioxide. This keeps its surface from being seen from space in normal visible light. The Venusian atmosphere also has a pressure that is about 90 times greater than that of Earth. The CO_2-rich environment creates a very strong greenhouse effect and this raises the surface temperature to over 400° Celsius, or 752° Fahrenheit. Venus has the most dense atmosphere of all the terrestrial planets. It has become so hot that any ancient water ocean would have totally evaporated.

The probe *Venus Express* in orbit around the planet. *(NASA Illustration)*

Venus' surface has been mapped in detail by the *Magellan* probe and shows only about 1,000 meteor craters, which is a very low number compared to the Earth or our Moon. It is a rocky body and the diameter is only 650 kilometers less than the Earth. About 80% of Venus' surface consists of smooth plains. There are two highland continents, which make up the rest of the surface. One is located in the northern hemisphere and the other is located south of its equator.

Since Venus is the closest planet to Earth, it has also

A globe of Venus from an image produced by the *Magellan* probe.
(NASA Photo)

been the most visited by our spacecraft. The following list summarizes the missions to Venus and some of the highlights of information collected:

- *Venera* 1 – (1961) launched by the USSR on a direct impact trajectory. Contact was lost seven days into the mission.
- *Mariner* 2 – (1962) confirmed the high surface temperature. This was the world's first successful interplanetary mission.
- *Venera* 3 – Soviet probe that crash-landed on the surface of Venus in 1966. Its communication system failed before it was able to return data.
- *Mariner* 5 – (1967) discovered a carbon dioxide-rich atmosphere and a surface pressure much greater than Earth's.
- *Mariner* 10 – (1969) determined the direction and speed (225 mph) of

cloud movement. This probe used Venus as a slingshot to give it enough energy to continue on to Mercury. It passed to within 5790 Km of Venus, returning over 4,000 images as it made its flyby.

- *Veneras* 9 & 10 – (USSR) revealed through radar images of the surface, that many large craters existed. This probe also showed surface wind speeds of only 1-3 mph.
- *Pioneer* 1 – identified, through radar mapping of the surface, tall mountains, plateaus and canyons.
- *Pioneer* 2 – discovered 4 distinct cloud and haze layers.
- *Magellan* – (1989) mapped 99% of the surface with a resolution down to 300 meters.
- *Galileo* – (1989) this outer Solar System probe flew past Venus to help it gain speed on its way to Jupiter

The Venus atmosphere as seen by ultraviolet imagery.
(NASA Photo)

- *Venus Express* – (2005) European Space Agency

Venus is currently being explored by the European Space Agency. The mission was scheduled to get underway in October of 2005; however, problems with the Fregat upper stage delayed this plan. It was finally launched on the 9th of November, 2005. It arrived at Venus on April 11, 2006. The *Venus Express* will study the atmosphere, clouds and its environment. Because of the success of the mission, it has been extended to through December of 2014.

Earth

In the previous chapter, we discussed earth's relationship to the solar system. We looked at how the earth was influenced by the affects of space. In this section, we will discuss some of the earth's characteristics and how they compare to the other planets within our solar system.

As far as we know, earth is the only planet that sustains life. Therefore, earth is a unique planet. Our atmosphere contains 78% nitrogen and 21% oxygen, with small amounts of argon, carbon dioxide, neon, helium, ozone and hydrogen. Our atmosphere contains clouds, and these clouds, along with the chemical composition of the atmosphere, help absorb some of the sun's radiation.

The Planet Earth

The surface of our planet is covered with over 70% water, with the Pacific Ocean accounting for over 50% all by itself. This water, in liquid form, is vital to life on earth.

Also, we have anywhere from smooth green pastures to hot dry desserts. Or, we have plateaus and small hills, to tremendous mountain ranges. We have acres of lush forests or areas with no trees anywhere in sight.

The earth revolves around the sun in 365¼ days. It rotates on its axis every 24 hours.

Earth's Moon

Basic Moon Facts

The earth has one moon. In the earth/moon relationship, the moon is situated in an elliptical orbit about earth. Because it is elliptical and not circular, the moon's distance from earth changes slightly. The distance varies from approximately 252,000 miles at its farthest point to 221,000 at its nearest point.

The moon's period of orbit around earth is 27 days 7 hours 43 minutes. Because the moon rotates about its axis in the same length of time as it takes to complete an orbit, it presents the same side toward earth at all times.

Between 1969 and 1972, six Apollo missions sent 12 astronauts to the moon's surface. They collected lunar rocks and soil to be brought back to earth to be analyzed.

The moon is less dense than earth (there is more matter in a given volume of earth than the same volume of the moon). Its gravitational pull is about one-sixth that of the earth's, and it does not have an atmosphere to protect it. Solar radiation, cosmic rays, meteoroids, and interplanetary dust bombard its surface without any interference. The surface temperature reaches 270° F during the 14 earth days that equal one moon day. During the lunar night, the surface temperature drops to -250° F.

From the earth, we always see the same side of the moon. The same force that causes the tides in the oceans–(gravity), causes this "synchronous rotation." The moon's gravity pulls on earth and earth's gravity pulls on the moon. This mutual attraction is strong enough to pull the water in the oceans slightly towards to the Moon, creating the tides. In return, the earth's gravity has slowed the moon's rotation on its axis. Therefore, the moon completes one turn on its axis in the same time it completes one orbit around the earth. Hence, the same side of the moon always faces the earth.

Physical Features

The entire surface is pockmarked by impact craters made by meteoroids. The size of craters ranges from very tiny to a 150-mile-diameter giant. These larger craters have walls that may average 8,000 feet above the surrounding terrain.

As is true with almost all other features of the moon, an explanation of the origin of the craters is unsettled. It is agreed that most of them are impact craters, but some are believed to be the result of volcanic action since they closely resemble volcanic craters found on earth.

Other features of the moon include very rugged ridges and mountains. Most of the mountains are less than 10,000 feet above the

The Moon

surface, but a mountain named Leibnitz rises to 30,000 feet above the surrounding terrain. In contrast to the mountains are the rilles, which are long irregular depressions similar to streambeds on earth. Most of these rilles are fairly shallow and narrow. The exception is called the Hadley Rille; it measures 1,200 feet deep and is 1 mile wide. What caused these rilles is still a mystery. The larger ones may have been caused by flows of lava many years ago and the smaller ones possibly were caused by large stones rolling across the surface after being blasted out by meteoroid impact.

Moon Dust

A fine dust covers the entire surface of the moon. On earth, sand, soil and dust deposits are the result of the erosion effect of wind and water, plus the transport of such particles by the movement of wind and water. The lunar environment apparently has never had a significant atmosphere, so how did so much dust get there? There are two theories—the explosive impact of meteoroids striking the surface pulverizes lunar matter into dust, which settles to the surface slowly and evenly, and other dust (cosmic dust) is picked up from space as it comes within the moon's gravitational influence.

Experiments with moon-dust samples produced some surprises. Tests on subsurface dust showed it had a sterilizing antibacterial effect almost as strong as that of a typical mouthwash. However, no other samples have produced this effect since then. Thus, scientists have one of many new moon mysteries to add to the old.

Moon Rocks

Certain dating techniques reveal lunar rocks may range in age from 3.0 billion to 4.6 billion years; thus, the older ones are older than any rocks on earth. Lunar rocks have remained exposed on the lunar surface for periods as long as 500 million years without being destroyed.

One discovery made during the Apollo lunar landings is that there are actually many different kinds of rocks on the moon. At first, it was believed that the surface of the moon would consist largely of primitive material. Although moon rocks have not gone through the weathering that earth rocks have and do not show as many variations, they do show evidence of melting and change.

Basalt. The moon basalt is a dark gray rock with tiny holes from which gas has escaped. It closely resembles earth basalt, but contains different mineral combinations. On the moon, basaltic lava makes up the dark, smooth surfaces of the lunar plains, which cover about half of the visible side of the moon. These plains can be seen from earth without a telescope and are popularly identified as the features of "the man in the moon".

Moon Craters Taken by *Apollo* 8

Anorthosite. Probably the most common rock on the moon is known as anorthosite. This rock is composed almost entirely of one mineral, feldspar. Anorthosite makes up the highlands of the moon, and they are seen from earth as the light areas. The highlands form the larger portion of the moon, thus comprising about half of the visible side and nearly all of the far side. Although anorthosite is common on the moon, it is rarer on the earth. It has been found in Greenland and is believed to be an ancient rock.

Other Rocks. Besides the two basic kinds of rocks described, a variety of other kinds and combinations of kinds of rocks were found on the moon. One of these, breccia, is a combination rock formed when meteoroids broke up the surface and the pieces were welded together by the heat and pressure of impact processes.

The astronauts observed an abundance of natural glass, a substance also extremely rare on the earth. Among the moon samples, scientists identified a rock they called KREEP, which has not been found on earth. Astronauts and scientists also identified deposits of quartz, granite and other rocks that are also found on the earth. Three new minerals were also discovered in the moon rocks that have never been found on earth—tranquillityite, armalcolite and pyroxferroite.

Mars

Mars is the fourth planet in our solar system. Also called the Red Planet, Mars appears as a small reddish light when viewed with the naked eye. When viewed in the telescope, it shows up as a predominantly reddish-colored disk with distinct markings. This color is due to the rock and dust covering the surface of Mars. It has been analyzed and found to have a high iron content, so it has a rusty look.

The surface of Mars is dry and rocky, and is covered with this reddish dust. The atmosphere is very thin and is composed mainly of carbon dioxide. Mars has about 1/3 of the gravity of Earth, so when the wind blows, the dust from the surface rises easily and gives the atmosphere a reddish pink appearance.

The surface of Mars is covered with deserts, high mountains, deep craters and huge volcanoes. One of Mars' volcanoes is the highest known mountain in our solar system. It is over 400 miles across and 17 miles high (about 90,000 feet high).

One day on Mars lasts slightly longer than earth's, at 24 hours 37 minutes. A Martian year is almost twice as long as an Earth year—about 687 Earth days. Mars has two moons, which are called Deimos (Terror) and Phobos (Fear), appropriate names for moons orbiting a planet named for the god of war. Both of the Martian moons are known to be extremely small (only 13.8 miles across for Phobos and 7.8 miles across for Deimos). The bodies are irregularly shaped and are most likely captured asteroids according to current theory.

It is possible that Mars once had an atmosphere, rivers, lakes and small seas. Scientists think that some pools of frozen or liquid water may be hidden underground. The north and south poles of Mars are covered with a frost that is made mostly of carbon dioxide (dry ice). Air pressure varies with the seasons on Mars. Winters are so cold that 20 to 30 percent of the entire atmosphere freezes out at the poles, forming a huge pile of carbon dioxide.

Mariner Mars Missions

The Mariner program was conducted by NASA in conjunction with the Jet Propulsion Laboratory (JPL) that launched a series of robotic interplanetary probes designed to investigate Mars, Venus, and Mercury from 1962 to 1973. Five of the Mariner missions were planned for Mars exploration, four of which were successful.

Mariner 4. *Mariner* 4, launched in November 1964, made a flyby of Mars in July 1965 and took

21 photos of the planet. Scientists were surprised when the pictures revealed a surface more like the earth's moon than the earth's. The pictures covered only a very small part of the planet, but they caused much excitement at the time because they were the first close-up photos returned to earth of another planet.

Mariners 6 and 7. The second and third probes of Mars, *Mariners* 6 and 7 launched as a pair of probes in 1969, were much more advanced. Together, these two spacecraft took over 200 photos. Pictures returned by *Mariners* 6 and 7 still gave no clues to the identity of the dark-line markings on Mars or of other puzzling features observed in the telescope.

Mariner 9. Since the flybys only photographed a portion of the planet at a particular time, *Mariner* 9 was designed to take pictures of the entire surface of the planet over a period of time. *Mariner* 9 revealed that at one time almost half the surface of Mars was affected by volcanic activity and extensive lava flows.

Viking I **Orbiter Mars Mosaic**

Viking Missions

The *Viking* program established a new benchmark in technological sophistication and quality of imagery. These craft consisted of orbiters and landers. The orbiters' role was to survey the planet on a global scale, and at the same time, serve as relayers of data and pictures gathered by the landers on the surface below.

The *Viking* 1 lander touched down July 20, 1976, and was followed by *Viking* 2 lander, which touched down on September 3, 1976. One of the primary missions of both landers was to determine if life—on a microscopic scale—existed on Mars. Unfortunately, the elaborate and automated experiments were not conclusive.

Considerably more water was found on Mars than had been expected. Analyses from orbit show the north polar cap to consist primarily of water ice; of course, carbon dioxide in frozen form is there too. Within some of the volcanic cones, water ice and carbon dioxide ice also exists. These frozen forms in the volcanic cones give way to clouds of condensate and vapor when heated by the sun. They return to ice when the sun sets.

Mars is cold. The daily temperature range measured at the *Viking* 1 lander site went from a high of -18° F to a low of -130° F (-191° F at *Viking* 2 site). The analysis of surface material near the lander showed a high content of silicon and iron, plus smaller amounts of aluminum, magnesium, calcium and sulfur. As mentioned earlier, the iron provides the red color of the Martian landscape.

Mars Pathfinder

On July 4, 1997, the *Mars Pathfinder* landed on Mars. The Pathfinder mission included a small exploration rover called *Sojourner* that moved around the surface of the planet to investigate the atmosphere and the composition of the Martian rocks and soil. The rocks analyzed by *Pathfinder* may be volcanic. Their pitted surface texture, presumably formed when gases trapped during cooling left small holes in the rock, suggests a volcanic origin. However, their silicon content classifies them as andesites.

One way that andesites can form is when a basaltic melt from the mantle intrudes deep within the crust of the planet.

Mars Sojourner

Crystals rich in iron and magnesium form and are separated from the melt, leaving a more silicon-rich melt that erupts on to the surface. The finding of these andesites was a great surprise to the scientists. Not all of the rocks on Mars are volcanic in origin, however, and there is evidence that liquid water was once stable and that the climate of the planet, therefore, was warmer and wetter than at present.

Mars Global Surveyor

The *Mars Global Surveyor* was launched on November 7, 1996, and entered orbit around Mars September 11, 1997. Designed to study climate and geology, the Surveyor's Mars Orbiter Laser Altimeter instrument collected exciting new observations of the north polar regions during the Science Phasing Orbit activities of the mission. These observations show the height of the Martian surface increases sharply by about 0.5 mile above the surrounding terrain at the edge of the polar cap. The elevation of the cap increases toward the pole and is 1.25-1.5 miles above the surroundings at the highest latitude sampled. A striking surface topography is composed of canyons and spiral troughs cutting through the upper portions of the northern polar cap to depths as great as 3600 feet below the ice surface. Vast dune fields surrounding the polar cap are similar to some forms of terrestrial sand dunes.

Mars Exploration Rovers (MER)

NASA Mars Exploration Rover Mission (MER) is an ongoing robotic space mission involving two rovers exploring the planet Mars. It began in 2003 with the launching of MER-A (later named Spirit) and MER-B (later named Opportunity) to explore the Martian surface and geology. The rover *Spirit* landed on Mars on January 4, 2004, at a place known as the Gusev Crater. *Opportunity* landed January 25, 2004. Its point of contact was on the Meridiani Planum. There was great excitement when, on March 2, 2004, NASA confirmed that liquid water once flowed on the surface.

On May 1, 2009, during its fifth mission extension, Spirit became stuck in soft soil on Mars. After nearly nine months of attempts to get the rover back on track, including using test rovers on Earth, NASA announced on January 26, 2010 that Spirit was being retasked as a stationary science platform. This mode would enable Spirit to assist scientists in ways that a mobile platform could not, such as detecting "wobbles" in the planet's rotation that would indicate a liquid core. Jet Propulsion Laboratory (JPL) last heard from Spirit on March 22, 2010, but continued to make communication attempts until May 25, 2011, at which time it declared the mission ended, bringing the elapsed surface mission time to 6 years 2 months 19 days, or over 25 times the original planned mission duration. Spirit traveled 4.8 miles on the Martian surface during its mission lifetime.

NASA announced on March 24, 2010, that Opportunity had traveled nearly 12.5 miles since the start of its mission. Since that announcement, it has traversed 8 more miles to Endeavour Crater where it continues its scientific observations. The total distance traveled represents an amazing accomplishment when considering that each rover was designed with a driving distance goal of less than half a mile.

In January 2005, Opportunity discovered the first meteorite to be found on another planet. It was lying just over half a mile from its landing site in the Mars Meridiani Planum area. The 1-foot (31-cm) diameter slug of iron and nickel gained the moniker "Heat-Shield Rock" due to the rover's discarded heat shield having come to rest

One of the Mars rovers on its way for a 263 million kilometer flight to Mars.

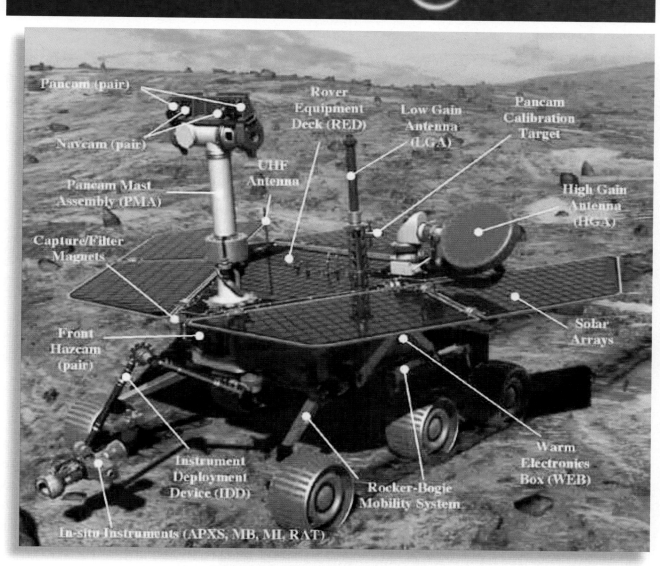

An artist conception of the Rover's Components. *(NASA)*

only 20 feet from the meteorite.

The unexpected longevity of *Spirit* and *Opportunity* has giving NASA a chance to field test some unexpected new capabilities. These tests will benefit current and future rovers. They have tested four new skills included in revised flight software uploaded to their onboard computers. One of the capabilities enables spacecraft to examine images and recognize certain features. It is based on software developed for NASA's Space Technology 6 "thinking spacecraft."

Spirit photographed dozens of dusty whirlwinds in action and both rovers have photographed clouds. Prior to the upgrade, scientists on Earth had to sift through many transmitted images from Mars to find those few. With the intelligence boost, the rovers can recognize dust devils or clouds and select only the relevant parts of the images to send back to earth. The increased efficiency will free up more

The Great Endurance Dunes of Mars. *(NASA)*

communication time for additional scientific investigations.

Another new feature, called "visual target tracking," enables a rover to keep recognizing a designated landscape feature as the rover moves. Khaled Ali, of NASA's JPL Division and flight software team leader for *Spirit* and *Opportunity,* said, "The rover keeps updating its template of what the feature looks like. It may be a rock that looks bigger as the rover approaches it, or maybe the shape looks different from other angles. Fortunately the rover still knows it's the same rock."

The combination of visual target tracking and the intelligence boost give *Spirit* and continues to give

The First Images of Mars as seen by the Spirit Rover. *(NASA)*

Photo confirmation of frozen liquid on Mars.

Mars Recon Orbiter

Opportunity a capability called "go and touch." So far in the mission, whenever a rover has driven to a new location, the crew on earth has had to evaluate images of the new location to decide where the rover could place its contact instruments on a subsequent day. After the new software has been tested and validated, the crew will have the option of letting a rover choose a target.

During its mission, *Spirit* returned 128,224 images from the Martian surface. To date, Opportunity has returned over 170,000 and continues to transmit pictures back to Earth. Visit http://marsrovers.jpl.nasa.gov for more about the available technology and to view more raw images from both of the rovers.

Opportunity discovered the first meteorite ever seen on Mars.
(NASA)

Jupiter

Jupiter, the fifth planet from the Sun, is by far the largest planet in the solar system. It has three times the mass of all of the other Solar System planets put together. In terms of volume, this equates to Jupiter being about 1,321 times larger than Earth.

Even though Jupiter is huge, it rotates very quickly, about every 10 hours. This causes a flattening effect at the poles and a bulging effect at the equator. This fast rotation also enhances the weather patterns on Jupiter. It creates high winds and giant storms.

Jupiter is a gas giant. Hydrogen is the most prominent gas, followed by helium, methane and ammonia. The outer core of Jupiter is composed of liquid hydrogen and helium, and these mix with the gaseous atmosphere to form belts of clouds. Jupiter has no firm surface (in contrast to Earth and the other terrestrial planets). The thick atmosphere gradually increases in density from gas to liquid. Astronomers have speculated that deep inside the planet there may exist a rocky core.

These belts are very colorful, but change rapidly due to the high winds associated with the quick rotation of the planet. These belts make Jupiter look like a striped ball with a giant red spot in the lower half. This red spot is a distinguishing feature of Jupiter and is called the Giant Red Spot. This spot is a giant hurricane-like storm that is 30,000 miles long and 10,000 miles wide.

Another feature of Jupiter is the moons. There are now 66 known moons orbiting the planet. Prior to the "Hubble era" of astronomical discoveries, that number hovered around 16. Utilizing Hubble's superior optics, astronomers have been able to discover dozens of smaller moons which proved to be too small to detect with Earth-based telescopes. The four largest moons, Io, Europa, Ganymede, and Callisto, were discovered in the early 1600s by astronomer Galileo Galilei. To honor their discoverer, these are now known as the Galilean satellites. Io is known to have active volcanoes and Europa has a deep ocean of liquid water. One of these moons has active volcanoes.

Jupiter has a diameter of about 88,700 miles, and it revolves in about 11 Earth years. Its temperature ranges from over 60,000° F at its center, to -220° F at the upper cloud layers. Except for Earth, Jupiter is the only planet known to have a strong magnetic field and radiation belts.

The *Pioneers* 10 and 11 spacecraft were the first investigations of the planet. Launched in the early 1970s, they made very significant contributions to our knowledge of the Jovian (Jupiter) atmosphere, magnetism and radiation, and satellites of the giant planet.

Atmosphere. The *Pioneers* discovered that the generally banded structure of the Jovian atmosphere is not present near the poles where oval circulation patterns develop. At the poles, a thick, particle-free (or blue-sky) atmosphere was found. The bright zones were found to consist of rising cloud masses at higher altitudes, while the belts are descending masses that allow a deeper view into the atmosphere. Detailed study showed rapid motions among the clouds and changes in the wind speeds. Between 1973 and 1974, changes in the flow patterns of the Giant Red Spot were also observed.

A great deal of atmospheric activity on Jupiter is similar to that of Earth. However, Jupiter's

Jupiter *(NASA)*

storms seem to be powered by the planet itself rather than by the Sun as they are on Earth. Jupiter's core still retains heat from the planet's original formation by collapse and compression and its storms develop from this internal heat source. Jupiter's heat reservoir of highly compressed hydrogen at its center causes the planet to emit almost 70 percent more heat than it absorbs from the Sun. This leads scientists to speculate that the source of Jupiter's stormy turbulence is the planet itself.

Magnetism and Radiation. The *Pioneers* detected a huge magnetic field on Jupiter. If the Jovian magnetosphere were visible in the sky from Earth, it would appear larger than our Sun or Moon. The *Pioneers* also revealed the fact that the Jovian magnetic field is 10 times stronger than Earth's and contains 20,000 times as much energy. However, the Jovian magnetic field is opposite to that of Earth—north magnetic pole is at the south pole of Jupiter.

The *Voyager* Spacecraft. On January 4, 1979, the first of two *Voyager* spacecraft was launched on a long mission to study the outer planets. These spacecraft were sent out to investigate the planets Jupiter, Saturn and Uranus as well as their moons. Besides sending back many superbly detailed photographs of Jupiter, these probes confirmed many observations from telescopes.

Satellites. Before the flights of the *Voyagers*, Jupiter had 13 known satellites, or moons. Four of these moons are large and bright enough to be seen through the higher-powered binoculars. Their sizes approximate those of the Earth's Moon and that of the planet Mercury. All of the outer moons (from the 15th on) revolve around Jupiter in a clockwise direction. This is opposite to the inner moons in that they behave as they are supposed to; that is, they revolve in a counterclockwise direction like the moons of Mars, and Earth and other planets.

The flights of the *Voyagers* revealed additional information about the Jovian satellites. First, three additional moons were discovered, raising the total to (at that time) 16 moons orbiting Jupiter. Volcanic eruptions were discovered in Io, the first evidence of active volcanism found outside the Earth.

Jupiter's atmosphere is very deep, perhaps comprising the entire planet and in some ways is similar to the Sun. Composed mainly of hydrogen and helium, with small amounts of methane, ammonia,

water vapor, and other compounds. At great depths within the planet, the pressure is so great that the hydrogen atoms are broken up and the electrons are freed so that the resulting atoms consist of bare protons. This produces a state in which the hydrogen becomes metallic.

Like all of the gas giant planets in our solar system, Jupiter has a ring system. However, it is a simple one in comparison to Saturn's intricate and complex ring patterns. The Jovian rings are tenuous and composed of dust particles kicked up as interplanetary meteoroids smash into the planet's four small inner moons. Many of these particles are microscopic in size.

These rings, which are not visible from Earth, and the Jovian moons exist within an intense radiation belt of electrons and ions trapped in the planet's magnetic field. These fields and particles make up the magnetosphere, which extends from 1.9 to 4.3 million miles toward the Sun and stretches at least as far as Saturn's orbit — a distance of 466 million miles.

Saturn

Saturn is the second largest planet in the solar system and the sixth from the Sun. It is the famous "ringed planet." The rings are easily the most recognizable features of Saturn. Through a telescope, the rings are spectacular! They are made of icy chunks of rock ranging from tiny particles to large boulders. The main rings are made of hundreds of narrow ringlets. The entire ring system is about 1 mile thick and extends about 250,000 miles from the planet.

Saturn's rings intrigue scientists and lay persons alike. There are seven distinct rings around Saturn. The rings are designated by the letters A

Saturn *(NASA)*

SATURN — *Cassini* **has produced some of the most spectacular images of any spacecraft to date.**
Cassini is a large spacecraft weighing in at six tons and stands approximately two stories tall. It was launched on October 15, 1997, and its flight covered a distance of 2.2 billion miles. A Titan IVB/Centaur rocket launched the Cassini *(and the Huygens investigation probe equipment) from Cape Canaveral.* Cassini *entered the new millennium and returned some of the most incredible images ever seen of a solar body beyond the moon.* Cassini *was scheduled to study Saturn and its moons for a period of four years and the project was managed by the Jet Propulsion Laboratory in Pasadena, California.*

through G. The first five rings were discovered by Galileo in 1610 and the final two by the *Pioneer* spacecraft.

The planet itself has an icy rock core surrounded by metallic hydrogen with an outer layer of hydrogen and helium. The hydrogen and helium are mainly liquid and turn to gas as they get to the lower atmospheric layers.

Saturn is a large planet, though not nearly as large as Jupiter. Like Jupiter, Saturn rotates at a very fast 10 hours. However, it takes over 29 years to revolve around the Sun. Also like Jupiter, the combination of fast

In this image, dark regions represent areas where *Cassini* is seeing into deeper levels in Saturn's atmosphere. The dark regions are relatively free of high clouds and the light at these particular near-infrared wavelenghts penetrates into the gaseous cloud-free atmosphere and is absorbed by methane. The image was taken with the *Cassini* spacecraft narrow angle camera on May 15, 2004, from a distance of 24.7 million kilometers (15.4 million miles) from Saturn.

rotation and gaseous and liquid atmosphere create very strong winds, clouds and storms. The winds of Saturn have been known to reach 1,100 miles per hour.

Atmospheric temperatures on Saturn vary from -218°F at 1 bar (1 Earth surface atmosphere) to -308°F at 100 millibars (1/10 Earth surface atmosphere). At an orbital distance of 900,000,000 miles from the Sun, Saturn does not experience the periodic temperature fluctuations between day and night like the Earth does.

Saturn has 62 known moons, all but one of which are covered with craters and icy surfaces. The one exception is Titan, which has an atmosphere of nitrogen and methane. It is the only moon in the solar system to have its own atmosphere.

Pioneer and *Voyager* Missions. The passage of these spacecraft past Saturn in the late 1970's and early 1980's has produced much information about the planet.

The planet's outermost region contains Saturn's atmosphere and cloud layers. The atmosphere has weak bands rather than the conspicuous belts and zones seen on Jupiter. Saturn's three main cloud layers are thought to consist respectively (from the top down) of ammonia ice, ammonia hydrosulfide ice, and water ice. Unusual atmospheric features discovered include a ribbon-like wave feature, large and small clouds, and a red oval similar to, but smaller than, Jupiter's Great Red Spot. *Pioneer* also discovered a magnetic field around Saturn that is larger than the Earth is but smaller than that of Jupiter.

Icy Rings of Saturn *(NASA)*

Saturn has 62 known moons. Of all of these known Moons, some were detected from Earth-based, observations, while others were detected during planetary exporation mssions such as *Pioneer, Voyager* and most recently, *Cassini-Huygens*. The *Hubble* telescope has also discovered several moons.

Titan, the largest of Saturn's moons and the second largest moon in the solar system, is the only moon known to have a dense atmosphere. The density of the moon appears to be about twice that of water ice and may be composed of nearly equal amounts of rock and ice. As with Earth, nitrogen is the most prevalent gas in the Titan atmosphere. Methane is the next most abundant gas. The thickness of the atmosphere is about ten times that of Earth.

One of the moons, Phoebe, orbits the planet in a plane much closer to the ecliptic than to Saturn's equatorial plane. It is quite red, roughly circular in shape, and reflects about six percent of the sunlight. It rotates on its axis about once in nine hours; thus, it does not always show the same face to the planet. Scientists believe that Phoebe, the only satellite of the planet to travel in a retrograde orbit, may in fact be a captured asteroid with its composition unmodified since its formation in the outer solar system. If so, Phoebe is the first such object that has been photographed at close enough range to show shape and surface brightness.

Saturn's magnetic field, unlike those of all other planets whose magnetic fields have been measured, is tipped less than one degree relative to the rotation poles. This rare alignment was first measured by *Pioneer 11* in 1979 and confirmed by the missions of *Voyagers* 1 and 2.

Saturn is the only planet in our solar system that is less dense than water (about thirty percent less). This means that Saturn would float if placed in a large enough ocean of water. The planet has a volume 764 times that of Earth, but weighs only about 95 times as much.

Uranus

Uranus is the third largest planet in the solar system. Like Jupiter and Saturn, it is a gas-giant world. Uranus has a rocky core surrounded by water, ammonia and methane, in both ice and liquid forms. The outer layer consists of hydrogen and helium gases. There is also methane in the upper atmosphere, and this gives Uranus a bluish greenish color.

Color Image of Uranus Produced in 1986 *(NASA)*

Uranus rotates once every 18 hours, but unlike the other planets, it spins sideways. The unusual position of the planet is thought to be the result of a collision with a planet-sized body early in the solar system's history.

Taking 84 years to orbit the sun, when the sun rises on the north pole, it stays up for 42 years and then is in darkness for 42 years. The sunlit hemisphere radiates large amounts of ultraviolet light. Voyager scientists have dubbed this phenomenon "dayglow."

The orbit of Uranus is nearly 2 billion miles from the Sun, about twice as far as Saturn. The temperature is about -340°F on Uranus.

Its environment is super cold because the amount of solar radiation reaching it is negligible. The *Voyager* 2 probe discovered Uranus' magnetic field is not in the usual north-south alignment, but is tilted 60 degrees and offset from the center of the planet. Astronomers initially discovered nine rings and five moons around Uranus. *Voyager* revealed the existence of 2 more rings and 10 more moons.

An Artist's Conception of the Rings of Uranus *(NASA)*

Neptune

Neptune, the outermost of the gas planets, is the fourth largest planet in the solar system. It was discovered in 1846 when scientists determined that something was affecting the orbit of Uranus. Neptune and Uranus are so similar they are sometimes called twins.

Neptune is about 3 billion miles from the Sun and it takes 165 Earth years to complete an orbit. A Neptune day lasts about 19 hours. The planet has a rocky core surrounded by water, ammonia and methane. The atmosphere consists of hydrogen, helium and methane. The methane gives Neptune a bluish color.

Pictures of the planet show that bright clouds of methane ice crystals are present. Pictures also indicate that Neptune has a very thin, faint ring system, which is hard to detect.

Neptune is a windy planet, the most windy in the solar system. Most of the winds blow in a westward direction, retrograde to the rotation of the planet. Storms similar to those on Jupiter were found during the *Voyager* missions. Several large dark spots were found during the mission; the largest of these storms, the Great Dark Spot, is about the size of the Earth and appears to be an anticyclone similar to Jupiter's Great Red Spot. Retrograde winds blowing up to 1,500 miles per hour, the strongest winds measured on any planet in the solar system, are found around the Great Dark Spot.

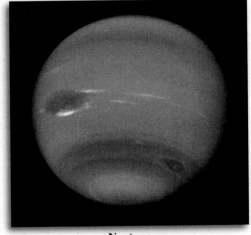

Neptune

The ring system around the planet is narrow and very faint. The rings are composed of dust particles that scientists believe were made by tiny meteoroids smashing into Neptune's moons. From ground based telescopes the rings appear to be arcs, but *Voyager* revealed the arcs to be bright spots or clumps in the ring system itself.

Neptune has 13 moons, the largest of which is Triton. Triton differs from all other icy satellites studied by the *Voyagers*. It is approximately three-fourths the size of Earth's Moon and circles Neptune in a tilted, circular, retrograde orbit every 5.875 days.

The moon shows evidence of a remarkable geologic history, and *Voyager* 2 images show active geyser-like eruptions spewing invisible nitrogen gas and dark dust particles several kilometers into space. The density of the moon is about 2.066 grams per cubic centimeter indicating Triton contains more rock in its interior than the icy satellites of Saturn and Uranus do. (For comparison, the density of water is 1.0 gram per cubic centimeter.) This relatively high density and the retrograde orbit of the satellite offer strong evidence that Triton did not originate near Neptune, but is a captured object.

If that is the case, tidal heating could have melted Triton in its originally eccentric orbit, and the satellite might even have been liquid for as long as one billion years after its capture by Neptune. While scientists are unsure of the history of Triton, icy volcanism is undoubtedly an important ingredient.

The Outer Solar System
Pluto

After 7 months of painstaking work, astronomer Clyde W. Tombaugh discovered Pluto on February 18, 1930. Less is known about Pluto than the other planets, but that is about to change with the launch of *New Horizons* space probe in 2006. It is a yellowish-gold in color and about 1,400 miles in diameter. It rotates on its axis in about 6.5 Earth days. The planet's orbit is inclined to the plane of the ecliptic 17 degrees. It has the most eccentric orbit of any planet in the Solar System, bringing it inside the orbit of Neptune for 20 of its 249-year orbit.

Pluto reaches its maximum distance from the elliptic, due to the 17° inclination, as it approaches perihelion (its closest approach to the Sun). This means it remains far above or below the plane of Neptune's orbit and there is no danger of the planets colliding. Pluto last crossed Neptune's orbit on January 21, 1979, made its closest approach on September 5, 1989, and remained within the orbit of Neptune until February

Artist's Illustration of New Horizons as it arrives at Pluto
(Courtesy of NASA)

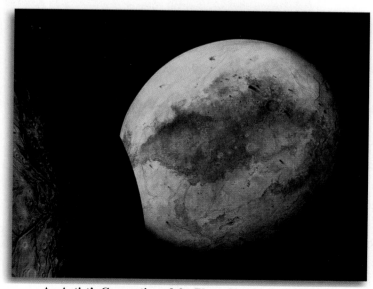

An Artist's Conception of the Pluto-Charon Binary Planet
(NASA Artwork by Pat Rawlings)

11, 1999. This will not occur again until September 2226.

Scientists believe that Pluto is 50-75% rock mixed with ice. Pluto can be as close to the Sun as 2.939 billion miles or as far away as 4.583 billion miles. The planet has a thin atmosphere that freezes and falls to the surface as it moves away from the sun.

Pluto's rotation period is 6.387 Earth days. Recent discoveries indicate there are millions of small rocky objects orbiting in the Kuiper Belt, a vast region that extends beyond Neptune. The Edgeworth-Kuiper Disk of "ice dwarfs," or minor planets, lies beyond Pluto.

567

Pluto-The Great Controversy

From the time of its discovery in 1930, until 2006, Pluto was considered the solar system's ninth planet. In the late 20th and early 21st centuries, however, many objects similar to Pluto were discovered in the outer solar system, most notably the trans-Neptunian object Eris, which is slightly larger than Pluto. On August 24, 2006, the IAU (International Astronomical Union) defined the term "planet" for the first time. This definition excluded Pluto and it was reclassified under the category of "Dwarf Planet." The definition of a planet by the IAU is: (1) a body that orbits the sun, (2) is large enough for its own gravity to make it round, and (3) has cleared its neighborhood of smaller objects. The new definition of "dwarf planet" includes Pluto, Eris and Ceres. There has been so much controversy over the new definition that as a result, it was put on the agenda of the 2009 meeting of the IAU in Rio de Janeiro.

By the current definition, Pluto is now the second-largest known dwarf planet in the solar system and the tenth-largest body orbiting the Sun. It is officially designated "134340 Pluto."

The composition of tiny Pluto is mostly rock and ice and is estimated to be 1,440 miles in diameter, or about 70% that of our moon. Pluto takes 249 years to make an orbit around our Sun and the distance of that journey is roughly 23 billion miles.

Scientists have described the orbit as a "squashed loop." Its orbit tilts up at a 17 degree angle whereas the other planets in the solar system revolve in a generally horizontal plane about the sun. Because of the eccentricity, Pluto's orbit will sometimes bring it closer to the Sun than the orbit of Neptune. The most recent occurrence of this phenomenon happened between February 7, 1979 and February 11, 1999.

Why Go There?

Pluto is moving farther away from planet Earth and because of deep space temperatures, its atmosphere will become completely frozen and will eventually fall to the surface. Once frozen, it won't thaw until early in the 23rd century. In the mid 1990s an unmanned Pluto exploration mission was approved by NASA. Known as the Pluto Kuiper Express, it would have reached its destination sometime in the 2012-2013 time period. The mission was cancelled, however, in 2000 due to budgetary reasons. In 2001 the mission was reinstated and renamed New Horizons.

**NEW HORIZONS AT LIFT OFF
ON JANUARY 19, 2006.**
(Image by Pat Corkery, Courtesy of Lockheed Martin)

Launched in 2006, it will reach Pluto in 2015. The probe has the distinction of being the fastest object ever launched into space. Leaving Earth at 36,373 mph, it whizzed past the Moon in only nine hours, and was crossing Mars' orbit only 78 days later. The image shown on page 568 is an artist's rendition depicting the New Horizons interplanetary spacecraft arriving at its destination.

Pluto is recognized as the second largest member of a region known as the Kuiper Belt and we now know that it has five natural satellites, the largest being Charon, first identified in 1978 by astronomer James Christy. In 2005, astronomers working with the Hubble Space Telescope discovered that Pluto also has two smaller moons. In 2006, their names, Nix and Hydra became official. These moons orbit Pluto at approximately 2-3 times the distance of Charon.

The Kuiper Belt

Our solar system is a magnificent collection of beautiful planets and various other bodies of lesser magnitude. There is a ring of bodies that exists billions of miles beyond the orbit of Neptune. This ring is called the Kuiper Belt and most of its inhabitants are small, icy bodies that are so far away, and dim, only the most sophisticated optical equipment is capable of capturing the reflected light. The majority of bodies within this Belt are smaller than Pluto, yet many have names and have been cataloged by astronomers. Due to improvements in ground and space based astronomical instruments, the number of known Kuiper Belt objects is now in the hundreds, 35 of which have been named. The greatest source of data has been gathered by the Hubble Space Telescope.

Another Space Telescope

The Hubble Space Telescope has had a few problems and a delicate, but successful "operation" brought it into usable operation. It continues to provide science with very important information about near and deep space. Another space telescope exists and collects its information in the infrared range. It is called the Spitzer Space Telescope and was launched into earth orbit in 2003. It has become extremely valuable for the collection of data of bodies within the Kuiper Belt. Due to depletion of on-board cryogenic cooling commodities, several instruments were rendered ineffective in 2009; however, Spitzer continues to provide data, although at reduced

Artist's concept of Eris with the Sun far away in the distance.
(Courtesy NASA)

capacity.

Another Mystery – The Tenth Planet

Scientist Michael Brown of the California Institute of Technology found what is believed to be the 10th planet in our solar system. The new body, designated 2003-UB 313, has been named Eris. This body has been classified as a dwarf and it has also been found to have a moon. This moon has been given the name Dysnomia.

Eris is approximately 1.5 times larger than Pluto and is located almost 10 billion miles from the Sun.

Bright red Sedna with the sun dimly seen in the distance.
(Courtesy NASA)

Michael Brown and Chad Trujillo of the Gemini Observatory and David Rabinowitz of Yale, used the Mt. Palomar Observatory near San Diego to photograph Eris on October 21, 2003. Another photograph, on January 8, 2005, spotted the planet. The astronomers calculated that it takes Eris 560 years to orbit the Sun. In approximately 270 years from this decade, it will be as close as the planet Neptune. Like Pluto, the surface is mostly made up of methane ice. Astronomer Trujillo made a spectrum analysis of the surface on January 25, 2005, and concluded that the surface had been in this state since the formation of the solar system. The planet's interior is most likely the same as Pluto's, i.e., rock and ice.

The Mystery Continues–The Discovery of Sedna

Located approximately 8 billion miles from Earth, approximately 84 billion miles from our sun, is yet another body that may someday be classified as either a dwarf or an actual planet. It is Sedna and is the most distant Solar System body yet recorded—it is an astounding 2.5 billion miles beyond Pluto. Sedna has a very unusual orbit that forms a long path about the Sun. Another astonishing fact is the body takes 10,500 years to make just one orbit around the sun.

Sedna has an unusual shiny red color. Astronomical calculations put the surface temperature at -400 degrees F. This means the temperature is just about 60 degrees away from being absolute zero (-459.69 degrees F). Scientists also found the size to be approximately 995 miles in diameter.

The name Sedna comes from the a mythical goddess of the sea. The connection comes from the story of how she was thrown into the icy Arctic waters by her father. Observations have concluded that the body Sedna is the coldest object in the solar system and that is how its name was connected to the mythical goddess.

**An Artist's Rendition Showing Sedna
located in the Kuiper Belt.**
(Courtesy of NASA)

The Mystery – Is There an Eleventh?

In the year 2002, astronomers Brown and Trujillo found yet another large body in the Kuiper Belt. They called it Quaoar (pronounced kwa war) a name taken from a Native American legend for their god of creation. The official designation is 2002LM60 and it resides at the edge of the Kuiper Belt in a field of icy bodies. The astronomers are not sure about the object, but they know it is a desolate, icy body that is larger than most asteroids with a diameter of approximately 800 miles.

Several other bodies have been discovered by the team of Brown, Trujillo and Rabinowitz. All totaled, more than 35 have been added to the "possibles." As the New Horizons approaches the Kuiper Belt and with extremely sophisticated optical equipment becoming available, there is no end to what they may find in and beyond the far reaching edge of our solar system.

An artist's rendition comparing the size of the Earth, Moon, Pluto, Sedna and Quaoar.
(Illustration Courtesy of NASA)

CREDIT: The source for much of the information in this section was provided by the outstanding web site, SPACE TODAY ONLINE.

Other Bodies

The Asteroids

Asteroids are rocky and metallic objects orbiting the sun, too small to be considered planets. Known as minor planets, they range in size from Ceres, with a diameter of about 623 miles, to the size of pebbles. Sixteen asteroids found in an area ranging from inside Earth's orbit to beyond Saturn's orbit are known to have a diameter of 150 miles or greater; however, the main belt of asteroids lies between the orbits of Mars and Jupiter.

Italian astronomer Guiseppe Piazi discovered the first asteroid in 1801. Since that time, more than 15,000 asteroids have been found and catalogued. Scientists speculate, however, that there are probably millions more asteroids in our solar system.

Asteroids are material left over from the formation of the solar system. There are several theories regarding their origin; one suggests that they are the remains of a planet that was destroyed in a massive collision during the formation of the solar system. More likely, they are materials that never coalesced into a planet. Scientists estimate that if the total mass of all asteroids was gathered together into a single object, the object would be less than 932 miles across—less than half the diameter of earth's moon.

Since asteroids are materials from the very early solar system, scientists are interested in their

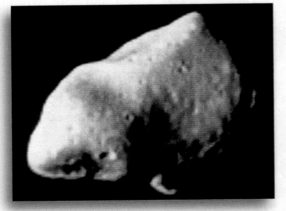

The Asteroid Gaspra

composition. Many of the asteroids have been studied through earth-based observations. Spacecraft that have flown through the asteroid belt have found that the asteroids are separated by very large distances. In October 1991, Gaspra was visited by the *Galileo* spacecraft, becoming the first asteroid to have high-resolution images taken of it. *Galileo* went on to a close encounter with Ida in 1993. Both Gaspra and Ida have been classified as S-type asteroids composed of metal-rich silicates. Photographs show them to be lumpy, potato-shaped rocks.

In 1997, the spacecraft *Near Earth Asteroid Rendezvous (NEAR)* made a high-speed, close encounter with the asteroid Mathilde, giving scientists their first close-up look of a carbon rich C-type asteroid. *NEAR* went on to an encounter with asteroid Eros in 1999 - 2000, discovering the existence of numerous boulders protruding above the surrounding surface. While some of these boulders are angular, others appear rounded, suggesting various origins or histories. Their non-uniform distribution seems not to correlate with any large craters or with gravitational laws on the asteroid.

Earth-based observation of the asteroids continues. In May 2000, scientists observed Kleopatra with the 1,000 foot telescope of the Arecibo Observatory. They collected the first-ever radar images of a main belt asteroid and discovered that Kleopatra was a metallic, dog bone-shaped rock the size of the state of New Jersey. Apparently a leftover from an ancient, violent cosmic collision, the scientists

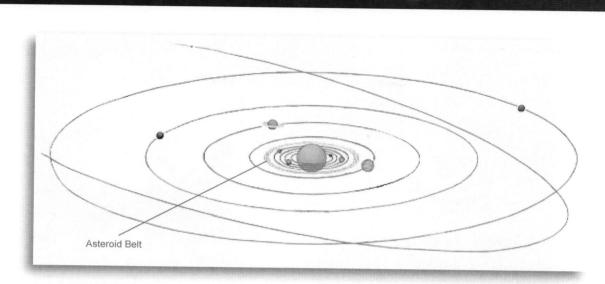

Asteroid Belt

theorize that Kleopatra is the remnant of an incredibly violent collision between two asteroids that did not completely shatter and disperse all the fragments. Radar observations indicated the surface of the asteroid is porous and loosely consolidated, much like the surface of earth's moon. Its interior arrangement and components are unknown. However, scientists believe its collision history to be extremely unusual.

Comets

A comet is a small, irregularly shaped body whose tiny nucleus is composed of water, ice, rock and frozen gases. Comets travel in highly elliptical orbits that take them very close to the Sun and swing them into deep space, often beyond the orbit of the planet Pluto. Comet structures are diverse, but all develop a coma (diffuse material surrounding the nucleus) that usually grows in size and brightness as the comet approaches the sun. Usually a small, bright nucleus will be visible in the middle of the coma; these two structures (the nucleus and the coma) form the head of the comet.

As a comet moves closer to the sun, it develops an enormous tail that can extend for millions of miles from the head, away from the sun. Far from the sun, the nucleus is cold and its material is frozen solid. It is this state that leads to comets being referred to as "dirty snowballs" since more than half of the material composing the comet is ice. But as the comet approaches the sun, the surface of the nucleus begins to warm and the volatiles evaporate.

The evaporated molecules boil off, carrying small solid particles with them. This is what forms the comet's coma of gas and dust. This cloud of dust and gas spreads out from the nucleus and reflects the sunlight. Thus a previously unnoticed, tiny speck suddenly becomes visible. As it continues to approach the sun, the stream of particles and radiation from the sun sweep the gas and dust away from the nucleus, forming a hazy head (the coma) and sometimes a tail as well. Some of the largest comets have had tails 100 million miles long—more than the distance from the sun to the earth.

Each time a comet visits the sun, it loses some of its volatiles. Eventually, it becomes just another rocky object in the solar system; therefore, comets are said to be short-lived, cosmologically speaking. Many scientists believe that some asteroids are comet nuclei that have lost all of their volatiles.

English astronomer Sir Edmund Halley first suggested that comets were members of our solar system. After studying historical writings of sightings of bright objects in the sky, he predicted the appearance of a comet in 1758. When it appeared right on schedule, it proved his theory and the comet was named

Comet West as Seen Above Table Mountain in California
(NASA Courtesy of the Jet Propulsion Laboratory)

after him. Halley's Comet continues to make regular appearances in our skies; it last approached the Sun in 1986 and will return in 2061.

Comets originate at the very edge of the solar system and are probably simply icy material mixed with dust that failed to come together to form true planets. The Oort Cloud is the source of long-period comets and possibly higher-inclination intermediate comets that were pulled into shorter period orbits by the planets, such as Halley and Swift-Tuttle. Comets can also shift their orbits as a result of jets of gas and dust that rocket from their icy surfaces as they approach the sun.

Although they can change their course, comets have initial orbits with widely different ranges. Long-period comets come from the Oort Cloud; Hyakutake and Hale-Bopp are two recent examples. The Oort Cloud itself is an immense spherical cloud surrounding the Solar System and extending nearly a full light year from the sun.

The cloud structure is believed to be a relatively dense core that lies near the ecliptic plane and slowly replenishes the outer boundaries. One sixth of an estimated six trillion icy objects are in the outer region of the cloud; the remainder are found in the core. The total mass of the Oort Cloud is estimated to be forty times that of earth. Scientists believe this matter originated at different distances (and thus at different temperatures) from the sun, thus explaining the compositional diversity in comets.

Many comets have probably slammed into the earth, causing widespread destruction (such as the extinction of the dinosaurs.) In 1994, Comet Shoemaker-Levy, broken up by Jupiter's massive gravity, impacted the planet. The *Galileo* spacecraft, about 150 million miles from the planet, recorded eight separate impact events. Preliminary spectroscopic data implies that the comet fragments did not penetrate

574

very deeply into the planet — little or no water was deposited in the stratosphere. Scientists presume that each comet fragment was vaporized in the impact and its constituent molecules were dissociated (broken apart) as was a considerable amount of the Jovian atmosphere along the explosion path.

Meteoroids

Bits and clumps of matter orbit the sun and cross, or exist within, the path swept by cislunar space as the earth/moon system revolves around the sun. The very small, dust-particle size bits of matter are called **micrometeoroids.** From this size upward, **meteoroid** is the name applied to clumps of matter in space.

Where do these meteoroids come from, and if they enter cislunar space what happens to them? No one is positive of the origin of meteoroids. The best evidence so far suggests they are parts of comets after the sun melted away some of the ice that bound them to the comet. Other meteoroids have a definite solar orbit because the earth/moon system keeps running into them on a very regular and frequent basis.

Then there are the random encounters with meteoroids, the origin of which can only be guessed. Those, which cannot be associated with the comet theory, may very well be parts left over from the formation of the earth, other planets or asteroids.

A Micrometeorite

When a meteoroid is drawn toward earth by gravitational attraction or when the two bodies collide and the meteoroid enters the outer fringes of earth's atmosphere, the meteoroid becomes a **meteor.** Friction causes the body to heat and glow, and begin to disintegrate leaving a trail of luminous matter.

Meteor showers occur when a great many meteors are seen in the sky over the course of an evening. The distinctive fiery trail left in the sky by the meteor as it burns up in the atmosphere is the reason for meteors being referred to as "shooting stars." Typical meteor tracks look like a streak in the sky. They fade away almost as soon as they are made. The particle making the meteor generally is about the size of a pea. As it travels through earth's atmosphere it quickly heats up and crumbles, causing a flare of light. Larger meteors can cause spectacular glowing tracks that last for longer periods of time.

Meteorites are the matter that remains when debris does not burn up completely as it passes through the atmosphere and lands on the surface of the planet. Scientists believe that many meteors hit the surface of our planet each year, but it is rare to actually see it happen. Most meteorites are basketball-size or smaller, but larger pieces can and do impact the surface of the earth. Some meteorites are small pieces of asteroids; others have proved to be material blasted off the surface of the moon following an impact on its surface. Other meteorites have been determined to originate on Mars.

The recent recovery of a carbonaceous chondrite meteorite from the Yukon has excited scientists who say that its very primitive composition and pristine condition may tell us what the initial materials were like that went into making up the earth, the moon and the sun. Only about two percent of meteorites are carbonaceous chondrites containing many forms of carbon and organics, the basic building blocks of life. This type of meteorite is easily broken down during entry into the earth's atmosphere and during weathering on the ground; therefore, recovery is quite rare.

A resident of the area over which the meteor exploded retrieved fallen fragments from the snow-covered ground, placed them in clean plastic bags, and kept them frozen. They are the only freshly fallen meteorite fragments ever recovered and transferred to a laboratory without thawing. (Keeping the meteorite fragments frozen minimizes the potential loss of organic materials and other volatile compounds contained in the fragments.) The 4.5 billion-year-old meteorite may help scientists understand the original composition of the entire solar system before planets formed.

Periodically, earth encounters a swarm of meteoroids called the Perseid cloud. The Earth passing through this cloud as it orbits the Sun is what produces the Perseid meteor shower (or simply the Perseids). The diameter of this swarm exceeds fifty million miles. However, the density of meteoroids is said to be only one for each million cubic miles. Even at this seemingly low density, there can be anywhere between 100 to over 150 encounters per hour during peak periods. This

A Meteor Shower

phenomenon, however, should not cause you to believe that cislunar space is crowded with meteoroids and other materials.

According to astronauts who have been there, space looks very much like the void it has been called. William Anders (Apollo 8) reported, "The sky is very, very stark. The sky is pitch black and the moon is quite light. The contrast between the sky and the moon is a vivid dark line."

The Milky Way and Beyond

On nights free of clouds and air pollution, the Milky Way is visible. This is the common name for the galaxy in which we live, along with about 100 billion other solar systems and stars.

The Milky Way galaxy is an enormous collection of stars arranged in a spiral shape. The Milky Way has a dense central bulge with four arms spiraling outward. The center of our galaxy contains older red and yellow stars, while the arms have mostly hot, younger blue stars.

Distance between the stars and/or solar systems varies and involves such high numbers of miles that the imagination is staggered. In this case, distance is thought of in light years and parsecs instead of astronomical units. A light year is the distance a photon can travel in one of earth's calendar years. This amounts to 5 trillion 878 billion-statute miles (5,878,000,000,000 miles). When the number of light years gets very large, parsecs are used; one parsec is 3.26 light years, or 19.2 trillion miles.

An extended halo of gas surrounding the Milky Way was generated by thousands of exploding stars as the galaxy evolved. Roughly football-shaped, this hot gas halo extends between five thousand and ten thousand light years above and below the galactic plane, thinning out with distance. Although the half-million-degree gas halo has been known for some time, scientists were not certain how it came to be there or remained hot.

Observations made with NASA's *Far Ultraviolet Spectroscopic Explorer (FUSE)* spacecraft revealed

Artist's concept of the Milky Way Galaxy

an extensive amount of oxygen VI in the halo. Oxygen six — oxygen atoms that have had five of their eight surrounding electrons stripped away — could only have been created through collision with the blast waves from exploding stars. Such star explosions are actually a record of star formation, and comparison of these supernovae-generated halos among galaxies may allow scientists to compare the star formation histories of the galaxies.

Novae and Supernovae

Nova (plural novae) is the term given to stars that suddenly and periodically brighten. Nova stars are typically part of a binary system wherein a white dwarf (essentially a dead star) pulls hydrogen from an active companion star. As the hydrogen builds up, the intense gravity of the white dwarf causes a fusion reaction to take place and therefore temporarily increases the star's brightness. Once the hydrogen is consumed, the star returns to its normal luminosity and the process begins to repeat. A supernova, on the other hand, occurs when a star gives up great mass in one giant explosion of light and energy.

Supernovae are the source of the heavier elements in the universe. The last-known supernova in the Milky Way was in 1604 and astronomers believe the next Milky Way supernova is overdue. Long-term supernova sequences obtained from SN1993J are helping astronomers understand supernovae in general as well as the remnants of ancient supernovae in our own galaxy. Detailed study of the stellar explosion twelve million light-years away showed a massive, morphing shock wave and provided scientists with a case study in the structure and evolution of the events in a stellar explosion.

Another supernova of particular interest to astronomers is SN1987A, located in the large Magellanic Cloud (a small companion galaxy to the Milky Way) located 169,000 light years away. A ring of gas believed to have been ejected by

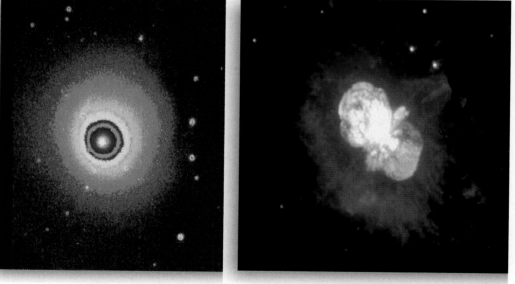

Nova   **Supernova**

the star 20,000 years ago (long before the star exploded) surrounds the supernova. This gas ring is being impacted by a never-before-seen violent collision of the fastest moving debris from the stellar explosion, causing the gases in the ring to glow as they are heated to millions of degrees and compressed by the blow of the forty million miles-per-hour blast wave. In 1997, astronomers observed the first impact between the shock wave and the ring. It appeared as a single knot in the ring shining like a bright diamond. The *Hubble Space Telescope* has been used by astronomers in the monitoring of SN1987A since it was launched in 1990.

Quasars and the Formation of the Universe

Quasars, extremely luminous bodies, were much more prevalent in the early universe. In a volume roughly equivalent to our solar system, a quasar emits up to 10,000 times the energy of the entire Milky Way galaxy. Scientists believe quasars are fueled by gases such as remnants of stars spiraling into super massive black holes at the center of galaxies; black holes that eject enormous amounts of energy as they consume surrounding matter. A recently discovered quasar in the constellation Cetus is among the earliest known structures ever to form in the universe.

In images, quasars look very much like stars, but a spectral analysis of the light reveals the true nature of the quasar. The quasar's redshift measures how fast it is moving away from us as the universe expands, and it is a good indicator of cosmic distances. The faster it moves away, the more its light shifts toward the longer wavelengths in the red part of the spectrum. That means the faster an object appears to move, the farther away it actually is.

Light from the Cetus constellation quasar, with a redshift of 5.5, takes about 13 billion years to travel to earth. Thus the ancient quasar in the Cetus constellation, in existence at a time when the universe was less than eight percent of its current age, is one of the universe's first structures. High redshift quasars are extremely important to understanding how the universe developed. The young universe is believed to have begun in a hot, dense state shortly after the Big Bang. Matter was ionized (electrons were not bound to protons) and over time matter cooled enough for electrons and protons to combine and become neutral. The formation of the first stars and galaxies reheated matter between galaxies and created the ionized intergalactic medium of today's local universe.

As a quasar's light travels toward earth, the light is absorbed by any matter lying in its path. Clouds of neutral hydrogen absorb more than half of a quasar's light at high redshift in the early universe, a finding essential to the understanding how and when super massive black holes, quasars, and other structures condensed from large, high-density clouds of hydrogen soon after the Big Bang.

The Cetus constellation quasar will also help astronomers determine how matter was distributed at earlier stages of cosmic history. Since quasars are more luminous than distant galaxies at the same redshift, they allow astronomers to study everything that has ever developed between us and the quasar. Continuing missions such as the International Space Very Long Base Interferometry Space Observatory Program (Space VBLI), combine satellite- and earth-based radio antennas to create a telescope more than two-and-a-half times the diameter of the earth. This provides one of the sharpest views yet of the universe and the most detailed images of quasars ever seen.

Common in galaxies and much more luminous and massive than our sun, tightly packed groups of hundreds to thousands of stars are known as star clusters. The Very Large Array (VLA) radio telescope has afforded astronomers a glimpse of what may be the youngest massive star clusters ever observed. Providing astronomers with a look inside the stellar nursery, massive star clusters estimated to be as young as 500,000 years and in their very earliest stages of development, are seen in their infancy. These observations may show astronomers the types of environments where globular clusters form.

For years, astronomers have searched for vast amounts of hydrogen that were cooked up in the Big Bang but somehow managed to disappear into space. The *Hubble Space Telescope* uncovered the long-sought hydrogen, which accounts for nearly half of all the "normal" matter in the universe, while the remainder is locked up in myriad galaxies. Astronomers believe that at least ninety percent of the matter in the universe is in dark form and has not yet been seen directly.

Pulsars

A pulsar is also known as a pulsating star because it flashes electromagnetic emissions (radio or other waves) in a set pattern. The astronomers who first discovered a pulsar first thought earth was being sent signals from intelligent life in another solar system. Today astronomers believe the phenomenon occurs in a manner similar to that in the pictures below. The body's magnetic poles are located at its equator. Its magnetic field keeps powerful radiation from escaping except at the holes created at each of the magnetic poles. As the star rotates about its axis, electromagnetic emissions stream out from the holes like the beams of light from a double-light beacon.

Pulsar (artist's rendering) Picture credit: NASA

Hundreds of pulsars, found in supernovae nebulae, are now known. After a supernova explosion, stars more than 1.4 times the size of our sun leave behind a large core of solid iron. The absence of fusion reactions allows the core of the star to collapse and presses the remaining star matter into a smaller space where it continues to degenerate until only neutrons remain. The result is a dense neutron star, about twenty miles across, in which matter is extremely dense (one cubic centimeter of matter would weigh one billion tons).

Spinning neutron stars have an axis of rotation that does not coincide with the axis of the magnetic field of the star. This causes its radio beams to sweep across the sky and deliver short pulses of radio waves to any receiver in its path.

Nebulae

Nebula is the Latin word for cloud and there are many dark and bright nebulae within our own galaxy, the Milky Way. The dark nebulae simply are vast clouds of matter which have not yet formed into stars. The bright nebulae may be studded with stars, and thus, send forth brilliant arrays of color. Some bright nebulae are the remnants of supernova; one such example is the Crab Nebula seen below left. Perhaps the best example of a dark nebula is also shown below right.

Several types of nebulae exist within the universe. In dark nebulae, both visible and ultraviolet light are almost totally absorbed by dust within the nebula itself, making the nebula appear as a dark smudge against the background. The dust within reflection nebulae reflects and scatters sufficient starlight to make the nebula visible and causes it to glow faintly. The most visible nebulae, emission or glowing nebulae, are three-fourths hydrogen (and nearly all the rest helium) heated by ultraviolet radiation from nearby hot stars; energy is re-emitted in the form of visible light.

After a star has evolved into a red giant, it enters a brief phase in which the outer layers are blown off. Eventually these layers become visible as a thin shell of gas around the star. Early astronomers observed that some of these shells of gas were the shape and color of the planets Uranus and Neptune, and so called them planetary nebulae. The nebulae, however, have nothing to do with planets. Many, but not all, nebulae are the places where stars are born.

Formed out of gas clouds, stars are large gaseous balls of hydrogen and helium along with a few other elements. As gravity pulls the star's materials inward, the pressure of it's hot gas drives it outward, resulting in an equilibrium that exists in all main sequence stars. Deep in the core, hydrogen atoms fuse together to create helium, a process that continues for billions of years as the star exists in the prime of its life.

The Crab Nubula

The Horsehead Nebula in Orion

Black Holes

A black hole probably began as a large star that exhausted its nuclear fuel and collapsed inward upon itself. The theory is that if gravitational force builds at the proper rate, the force itself keeps an explosion from occurring. So much matter is compressed into such small volumes that everything is together and nothing is allowed to leave because the resulting gravity is so strong. There are no x-rays, ultraviolet rays, radio waves, or visible light–nothing is coming from this dense body. If it can't emit some type of radiation, it is known as a black hole.

Mounting circumstantial evidence suggests black holes occupy the center of most galaxies and astronomers have used the *Hubble Space Telescope* and innovative imaging techniques to investigate swirling masses of interstellar dust believed to feed super massive black holes as it spirals into the center of nearby galaxies.

Black holes are considered active when their powerful gravity tears material apart, releasing radiation and brightening the galaxy's center. Only about one percent of galaxies that should contain super massive black holes appear to be in an active state. Astronomers calculate that black holes must consume stars, gas, or dust in amounts up to the mass of our sun every year to remain active.

Some astronomers and scientists doubt that these mystery stars even exist. If energy cannot escape from a black hole, how is one detected? Astronomers can detect gaseous matter being pulled into a black hole from a nearby star. Just before the matter disappears, it sends out strong bursts of x-rays that can be measured.

Black Hole

Black holes are perplexing to scientists because everything about them must be guessed. Anything sent to investigate could not send its messages back to earth because the black hole would absorb the radio transmissions.

Other Galaxies

Beyond our system of stars or galaxy, there seems to be an endless number of other galaxies. Each time our scientists develop techniques of seeing farther into space, they find other galaxies beyond the range limit of previous instruments.

Even the galaxy-to-galaxy relationship is in motion. In general, all of these individual galaxies and groups of galaxies seem to be moving away from each other. This movement also seems to be moving away from a common point. However, when the movement began is not certain, and the outermost extent of this expanding universe is not yet known. According to current theory, based on observations and the most accurate measurements available, the age of the universe is placed at approximately 13.75 billion years.

According to astronomer Douglas Richstone, "The formation and evolution of galaxies are intimately connected to the presence of a central massive black hole. Radiation and high-energy particles released by the formation and growth of black holes are the dominant sources of heat and kinetic energy for star-forming gas in protogalaxies."

Researchers have noted that nearly all galaxies with spheroidal distributions of stars (that is, bulges in spirals) seem to have massive black holes that appear to correlate with the mass of the central part of the host galaxy, pointing to a connection between the massive black hole and the galaxy. Additionally, comparisons of the history of star formation in the universe with the history of quasars reveals that quasars developed well before most star formation in galaxies. Astronomers believe the massive black holes now seen in the centers of galaxies are relics of these quasars, indicating that the black holes must have been present at the height of the quasar epoch when the universe was about one billion years old.

A Universe of Galaxies

Astronomers theorize that as galaxies formed in the early universe, powerful gravitational attraction pulled huge amounts of gas together at their center to create a black hole. Gas and any close stars were sucked in and converted to gas in the process. As the gas swirled into the black hole in a huge vortex, it became hotter and hotter and glowed more and more brightly. Just before plunging into oblivion, it became a quasar, emitting a burst of radiation, including massive flashes of x-ray and ultraviolet radiation.

Although the universe is still expanding, the combined gravity of its dark matter may be sufficient to halt the expansion. If this happens, then gravity may pull all the galaxies together again in a massive Big Crunch. The more we explore, the more we discover we still have much to learn.

Key Terms and Concepts

- moon
- crater
- rille
- moon dust
- moon rocks
- basalt
- anorthosite
- Mars
- *Mariner* and *Viking* probes
- asteroids
- Jupiter
- Saturn
- Uranus
- Neptune
- Pluto
- *Pioneer* and *Voyager* probes
- comets
- galaxy
- Milky Way
- interstellar space vs. intraga-
- lactic space
- nova and supernova
- pulsar
- black hole
- nebulae
- Hubble Space Telescope
- Eris, Sedna and Quaoar
- Rovers Opportunity and Spirit

? **Test Your Knowledge** ?

MATCHING

1. older than rocks on the earth
2. found mainly on the moon's plains
3. composed mostly of feldspar
4. abundant on the moon; rare on earth
5. can't find on earth
6. three new minerals discovered
7. makes up the highlands of the moon

a. **lunar rocks**
b. **anorthosite**
c. **basalt**
d. **pyroxferroite**
e. **natural glass**
f. **armalcolite**
h. **tranquillityite**

MATCHING

8. means starlike
9. first to be discovered
10. small, irregular shaped body composed of water, ice, rock and frozen gases

a. **comet**
b. **asteroids**
c. **Ceres**

MATCHING

11. refers to the space within galaxies
12. unstable stars; their action makes them appear to be winking
13. exploding star
14. flashes electromagnetic emissions
15. the ultimate star, which cannot radiate anything
16. clouds of matter not yet stars
17. a spiral-shaped galaxy of which the earth is a part

a. **black hole**
b. **intragalactic space**
c. **nebulae**
d. **supernova**
e. **nova**
f. **pulsar**
g. **the Milky Way**

FILL IN THE BLANKS

18. It takes _____ days for the moon to _____ the earth.
19. Since the Moon is less massive than the earth, its _____ is only one-sixth that of earth's.
20. Day and night on the moon can have a difference of _____ °F.
21. From earth we see only _____ side of the moon and it's always the _____ side.
22. Besides having mountains, plains, and craters, the moon has _____, which are long irregular depressions.
23. The Martian day is _____ to a day on earth.
24. The reddish areas on Mars were thought to be _____.
25. Mariner 4 took the first _____ of another planet.

26. Saturn's rings contain mostly
    a. rock.
    b. gases.
    c. ice.
    d. a and c above.

27. The exact number of Saturn moons is
    a. 17
    b 15
    c. 11
    d. we're still not sure

28. The orbits of most comets are
    a. eccentric.
    b. circular.
    c. consistent.
    d. none of these.

29. Comets have been observed
    a. since 1910.
    b. only recently.
    c. since ancient times.
    d. in the last 200 years.

30. The comet's tail forms as it nears
    a. the sun.
    b. the moon.
    c. the earth.
    d. Uranus.

TRUE OR FALSE

31. Vikings 1 and 2 consisted of orbiters and landers.
32. The existence of water was found in liquid form on Mars.
33. The highest content of surface material on Mars is silicon and iron.
34. Iron provides the red color of the Martian landscape.
35. By virtue of its size, Jupiter makes up about 70 percent of the mass of all the planets.
36. Due to its size, Jupiter rotates very slowly.
37. Of all the planets, Jupiter has the most intense radiation belts.
38. Nine rings encircle Uranus.
39. Neptune and Uranus are very similar.
40. In 2004, two rovers landed on Mars; their names are Spirit and Faith.
41. Some scientists have reclassified Pluto as a dwarf planet.
42. The Kuiper Belt is a ring of celestial bodies that extends billions of miles beyond the orbit of Neptune.

UNMANNED EXPLORATION

At the end of World War II, the team of German V-2 rocket experts (led by Dr. Wernher von Braun) surrendered to American troops to avoid being captured by Russian troops. The United States seized a V-2 assembly plant and 100 partially assembled V-2 rockets. These events formed the nucleus of US rocket research during the late 1940s and early 1950s, and marked the beginning of the "space race" between the United States and the Soviet Union.

 bjectives

Discuss America's early space efforts.

Discuss the Soviet Union's early space efforts.

Describe America's reaction to the Soviet launch of *Sputnik* 1 in October 1957.

State one of the biggest reasons for the space race between the United States and the Soviet Union.

Discuss the establishment of the National Aeronautics and Space Administration.

Describe the sources of space law.

Describe the significance of *Sputnik* to space law.

Describe the three principles of space law.

Identify two significant provisions of the 1967 Outer Space Treaty.

Explain the significance of the 1972 Anti-Ballistic Missile Treaty of space operations.

Explain the significance of the National Aeronautics and Space Act.

Explain the significance of the Commercial Space Launch Act.

Explain the significance of the Land Remote Sensing Commercialization Act.

Describe the function of the International Telecommunications Union.

Describe the 1976 Bogota Declaration.

Describe the International Space Station Agreement.

Identify three issues addressed by the International Space Station Agreement.

Define a satellite.

Identify four categories of satellites.

Identify uses of communications satellites.

Define an active communications satellite.

Define a passive communications satellite.

Describe the purpose of the Global Positioning System (GPS).

Describe the elements required for global positioning.

Identify GPS uses.

Identify three types of observation satellites.

Match examples of data to the satellite type most likely to observe and record it.

Identify examples of weather satellites.

Identify examples of multi-spectrum imaging satellites.

bjectives (continued)

Identify four types of reconnaissance satellites.
Identify two purposes of scientific satellites.
Describe the *Explorer* Satellite Program.
Identify the contributions of the *Orbiting Astronomical Observatory* and the *High-Energy Observatory*.
Explain the missions of the *Dynamic Explorers* and the *Solar Mesosphere Explorers*.
Explain the purpose of the *Infrared Astronomy Satellite*.
Explain the purpose of *X-ray Timing Explorer*.
Describe the *Hubble Space Telescope* Program.
Define a probe.
Identify examples of fly-by and landing-type probes.
Describe the purpose of the *Ranger* probes.
Explain how the *Surveyor* probes helped the *Apollo* Program.
Identify the planet that the *Mariner*, *Pioneer*, *Viking* and *Voyager* probes investigated.
Describe the *Mars Pathfinder* and *Mars Surveyor* missions.
Rovers, Spirit and opportunity launch

The Space Race Begins

The US Army assembled a team of scientists and engineers at the White Sands Proving Ground, New Mexico, in 1946 for the purpose of conducting scientific research on the upper atmosphere. This effort was a joint program involving the Army, Naval Research Laboratory, Air Force, General Electric Company, and several universities and scien-tific institutions. In the closing days of World War II, German rocket scientist Dr. Werner von Braun gathered together many of his V-2 rocket team members and surrendered to American forces with the hope of continuing his rocket research in the United States. After the war, many V-2 rockets were launched from White Sands Proving Ground (now Missile Range) for research purposes. In 1949, a U.S. Army WAC Corporal sounding rocket was added as an upper stage to the V-2 and the new configuration was known as Bumper. Six Bumpers were launched off of White Sands and the remaining two were sent to

**WAC Corporal Rocket Atop
a V-2 Rocket**

Cape Canaveral, whereupon they had the distinction of being the first two rockets to be launched from that new test facility.

Beginning in the 1950s, the different branches of the military began going their separate ways in rocket research. The Naval Research Laboratory contracted with the Martin Company to build an improved V-2 called the Viking. They also contracted with Johns Hopkins University to build a research rocket called the Aerobee. In 1951, both were launched successfully. The Viking reached an altitude of 136 miles, and the Aerobee flew to 80 miles altitude.

The Army moved Dr. von Braun's team to Redstone Arsenal in Huntsville, Alabama, in 1950. The Army viewed rockets as an extension of its artillery, so they gave the von Braun team the job of developing a battlefield missile based on the *V*-2. The result was the Redstone missile, which was first flown in August of 1953. The Redstone had a 200-mile range and reached a speed of 3,300 mph. In 1946, the Air Force began research on the first intercontinen-tal ballistic missile (ICBM). The project had to be canceled in 1947 due to a lack of money. From 1947 to 1951, the Air Force did not have an active ICBM Program. Shortly thereafter, two major occurences changed the national priorities and money became available to restart the Air Force ICBM Program.

Werner von Braun

Mercury Redstone Launch Vehicle

Atlas Launch Vehicle

First, in 1949, the Soviet Union exploded its first atom bomb, and the United States lost its nuclear monopoly. Second, in 1950, the Korean War started. In 1951, the Air Force gave a new contract to Convair to build an ICBM. They called the missile the Atlas.

In 1953, scientists developed a way to build nuclear warheads small enough to be mounted on missiles. In 1954, based on studies from the Rand Corporation and the Air Force Strategic Missile Evaluation Committee, the Atlas Missile Program was the Air Force's highest priority. The missile became operational on September 1, 1959.

By 1955, the Navy perfected the Viking and the Aerobee, the Army had a successful Redstone, and the Air Force was beginning production of the Atlas. In August 1955, President Dwight D. Eisenhower announced that the United States would place several small satellites into orbit during the International Geophysical Year (IGY), which started on July 1, 1957. This project was called Vanguard.

At this time, the United States had two vehicles able to put a satellite into orbit. One was the Navy Viking (with an Aerobee second stage and a solid-fuel third stage) and the other was the Army's Redstone (with an upper stage). The Navy's entry was selected in 1955 to launch the Vanguard satellite.

Soviet Union Efforts

As for the Soviets, they also had captured partially built German V-2 rockets at the end of the war.
However, as mentioned earlier, von Braun and his team
had escaped to the United States. The Soviet Union
captured only a handful of German engineers and
hundreds of technicians. The Soviets also got a list of the
manufacturers who supplied the parts for the V-2 and, from
these manufacturers, the Soviets obtained enough parts to
build a few of the rockets.

The Soviet Union also began upper atmosphere research
using captured V-2s. Because they had so few, they had to
begin building their own much sooner than the United States.
In 1949, the Soviets developed an improved V-2 called the
T-1 and in 1954, they started working on a large multistage
rocket.

In a 1956 speech, Premier Nikita Khrushchev stated the
Soviet Union had developed an ICBM and would soon have
missiles with nuclear warheads. In August 1957, the Soviet

**Replica of *Sputnik* 1 Suspended
in a Soviet Museum**

Union successfully test-launched its ICBM and on October 4, 1957, using the same rocket, they launched
Sputnik 1, the world's first artificial satellite. On November 3, they launched Sputnik 2, which carried
a dog named Laika. The Soviets were winning the race into space.

American Reaction

The reaction in the United States was immediate. The Senate began an investigation, and
the White House announced that the Navy was
preparing for the *Vanguard* 1 launch at Cape
Canaveral. In reality, the Navy was preparing
for a test launch of the Viking/Aerobee rocket
and was not ready to launch *Vanguard* 1. On
December 6, 1957, when the Navy made its test
launch, the *Vanguard's* first stage exploded, and
the whole world saw America's disastrous entry into the space age via television.

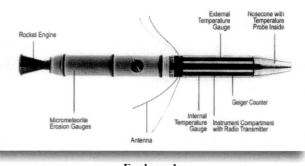

Explorer 1

In November 1957, the Secretary of Defense revised the Army's Redstone proposal and advised
Dr. von Braun to prepare to launch as soon as possible. The Army had a Redstone with solid propellant upper stages, which it had been working on as a test rocket (renamed Jupiter
C) to study some of the problems of reentry heating. The Army placed a satellite developed
by the California Institute of Technology atop a Jupiter C (renaming it Juno I) and successfully launched *Explorer* 1. This was America's first satellite. The date was January 31, 1958.

The Space Age

The Soviet Union entered the space race first because it had developed a rocket large enough and powerful enough to place very heavy objects into orbit. For example, *Explorer* 1 weighed 31 pounds while the Soviet's *Sputnik* 2 weighed 2,926 pounds. Eventually, the large rockets would prove to be the Soviets undoing, because they were not forced to develop the miniature electronics and other lightweight materials that the United States was forced to produce. When America finally caught up with the Soviet Union in large rockets, the United States was far ahead in the amount of equipment that could be taken to the moon or into space with a single rocket.

This space race was occuring during the Cold War between the United States and the Soviets. One of the biggest reasons for the space race was international prestige. The ability to put satellites into space was impressive, but even better was manned space flight.

NASA Established

As mentioned earlier, the Soviet Union launched *Sputnik* 2 on November 3, 1957, with a dog aboard. This was a clear indication that the Soviet Union's goal was to place people into space. The launch of *Sputnik* 3, 6 months later, demonstrated they had the booster power to do it.

This knowledge prompted a reevaluation of America's national priorities in the area of scientific research and leaders in the United States began looking for an agency to head up a space exploration program.

The military services had different ideas about what the priorities should be in space research. Their primary respon sibility was the defense of the United States. This led to a final decision that a space exploration program be headed by a new civilian agency.

On July 29, 1958, President Eisenhower signed the National Aeronautics and Space Act into law, creating the National Aeronautics and Space Administration (NASA). NASA was established as the agency to lead America's civilian space program, while the Department of Defense retained responsi-bility for space projects necessary for national security. The 8,000 employees of the National Advisory Committee for Aeronautics became employees of NASA on October 1, 1958.

Space Law

Space by its very nature is an international concern. Virtually all nations have an interest in space. However, only a few nations have the technological means to exploit space. What protects the interest of those that do not? How are conflicts resolved between those that do? International law provides broad guidelines for dealing with these conflicts. International law is drawn from several sources. Some of those are more powerful than others.

The most powerful source of international law are treaties. These are written agreements that are legally binding on those who sign them. Penalties for breaking them are often spelled out in detail. They may be bilateral or multinational. Bilateral means the agreement is between two nations. Multinational treaties are generally more powerful because they involve many nations. Most space treaties are multinational.

When disputes arise between nations they often refer them to an international court, such as the International Court of Justice. Unfortunately, there is no effective enforcement of these decisions. They are only binding if the nations involved agree to abide by the court's findings. Nevertheless, these decisions made by international courts are a second, important source of international law.

Along the same lines as international courts, the legal opinions of noted scholars and respected authorities are another source of international law. These opinions, called opinio juris, may be based on previous court cases. When there is no related case law, the opinio juris is simply the consensus opinion of the experts in the field. As with international court decisions, there is no method of enforcement. Because opinio juris lacks the formality of a court, it is a less powerful source of international law.

The least powerful source of international law is sometimes the most effective. This source is customs. Customs are those practices accepted by nations as the right way to act. They are rarely written down. They are also rarely violated. Sometimes they are based on tradition or long-standing practice. Sometimes they are simply based on common sense. Customs can slowly occur over time or they can occur quickly.

Space Shuttle Docking with Russian *Mir Space Station*

The launch of the first Russian satellite, *Sputnik*, is an example. *Sputnik's* first orbit established a very important new custom. It established the right of satellites to fly over countries without permission. This right to freely fly over nations is reflected in the first principle of space law.

There are three principles of space law that appear in both national and international space laws. Sometimes the principles are spelled out exactly. Sometimes they are only implied. The first of these principles is freedom of use. It is the idea that all nations should have access to space. Thus, no nation should be allowed to prevent another from gaining access.

The second principle concerns ownership. It is called non-appropriation. The idea is that no one owns any part of space. Appropriation of space by anyone would preclude freedom of use by all.

The third principle is that of common interests. It concerns the use of space. Since space belongs to all mankind, all nations should share its benefits. This vague notion is found in many United Nations (UN) resolutions. In reality all nations do benefit from the many common uses of space. Examples include navigational aids, communications, geological data and weather information.

Treaties

As we just discussed, treaties are an important source of space law. Over the past several decades, space operations have grown enormously. In the early years, basically, only two nations, the United States and Russia, were involved. Today, virtually the entire world is involved in space activities. As the activities in space increased, the need for regulations to avoid conflicts increased. Many treaties were made to meet this need. We'll look at the ones that continue to have a major impact on space activities. Some of these are between parties that no longer exist. For example, bilateral arms control agreements between the United States and the former USSR remain in force.

Outer Space Treaty

The first treaty we'll look at is one of the most significant; called simply the 1967 Outer Space Treaty. Its full title is " The Treaty on the Principles of the Activity of States in the Exploration and Use of Outer Space, Including the Moon and Other Celestial Bodies." In the midst of the space race between the United States and the Soviet Union, both countries sought a politically acceptable way to regulate space activities. The treaty grew out of a series of conferences on space activities and UN resolutions. The UN General Assembly approved it in 1966. It went into force in 1967. Approval was unanimous. Over ninety nations agreed to abide by it.

Many important issues were addressed in the Outer Space Treaty. It established the principle of freedom of use and called space the "province of all mankind." It also stated that exploration of space should benefit all countries.

Lunar Outpost Concept

Other issues it addressed were emergencies and accidents. It referred to astronauts as "envoys of mankind." It further stated those landing in foreign territories were to be treated as such and returned to their home nation. Nations, and not the organizations, that launched objects were held responsible for damage from accidents and returning objects. It stated that space would be used "exclusively for peaceful purposes," but allowed military personnel to conduct scientific research.

While many of the provisions in the Outer Space Treaty remain important, two merit special emphasis. First, the treaty documents the three principles of space law in written form. Secondly, it legitimizes a military presence in space.

ABM Treaty

The Outer Space Treaty provided for only peaceful use of space. Intercontinental Ballistic Missiles (ICBMs) threatened to breach this provision. Systems for destroying missiles before they reached their targets were proposed. It was thought these systems might make nuclear war more likely. As long as everyone knew both sides would be de-

Astronaut acknowledging that the United States of America has been there.

stroyed in a war, no one would attack. Anti-Ballistic Missile (ABM) systems offered a potential defense against attack.

The treaty on the limitation of Anti-Ballistic Missile systems was signed on May 26, 1972. Both the US and the USSR agreed not to develop or test ABM systems. This included space-based systems. However, the ABM Treaty is not significant to space operations because of what it prohibited. Military systems were already prohibited. It is important because it specifies monitoring treaty compliance from space. It sanctioned monitoring other countries from space. Thus, while *Sputnik* established the right to fly over a country without permission, the ABM Treaty establishes the right to gather treaty compliance information while doing it.

National Space Law

In addition to international law, space operations must also comply with national laws. United States' space law is only binding on US nationals and US organizations. It addresses many issues such as safety and liability. However, much of it is concerned with easing commercial entry into space. This is where we'll focus our attention now.

National Aeronautics and Space Act (NASA Act)

The National Aeronautics and Space Act was the first effort to regulate space in the United States. It was signed into law in 1958. Best known for establishing the National Aeronautics and Space Administration, it is the legal basis for military and civil space activities. It defines civil and military responsibilities, and provides a process for coordination between the two.

Commercial Space Launch Act (CSLA)

The purpose of the CSLA is to promote private sector activity and investment in space. It sought to create a single agency to regulate commercial space. NASA was not considered because they were in direct competition with commercial interests. The Department of Transportation (DOT) was designated the lead agency. The Office of Commercial Space Transportation was created within DOT to manage the effort.

Under CSLA, any US citizen or organization must be licensed to conduct space operations. The payload launch vehicle, and launch facility must all be licensed. The license is required even if the launch occurs in another country. During the process, the mission and safety are reviewed. The mission review ensures the payload and purpose are consistent with national policy. Applicants must also show proof of insurance before a license is granted.

The most important part of the act concerns the use of military launch facilities. CSLA authorizes the military to provide facilities and support for commercial launches. The launch company must only pay for the cost of the service. The military pays for maintaining the facilities. It saves commercial interests from having to build and maintain their own launch facilities.

Land Remote Sensing Commercialization Act (LANDSAT Act)

This act was designed to commercialize the government *LANDSAT* Program. *LANDSAT* is an earth observation satellite that produces special digital images. The images are valuable for monitoring crop growth, pollution and deforestation. *LANDSAT* didn't have many customers because it was less competitive than foreign systems. Whether or not the act succeeded in its design is not important. Its rules on remote sensing are what is important. It allowed the sale of government data. It also set limits on the level of quality that could be sold without harming national security. Finally, it prohibited selling to the

U.S. Space missions typically fly hardware adorned with the American flag.

highest bidder or to preferred customers. It directed that data be provided to all customers at the same cost.

International Space Issues

Space is a very big place. However, the orbital space around earth has limits. Some orbits are more useful than others and, thus, are in great demand. Earlier, we looked at types of orbits. We learned that a geostationary orbit allows a satellite to remain over the same point on the earth's surface. This is extremely valuable for communication uses. Transmitters and receivers can lock onto the satellite and never lose contact. Many, many users compete for the limited number of geostationary orbital positions. Therefore, some method of assigning positions is necessary. Radio frequencies used by geostationary satellites must also be regulated. Otherwise, satellites would be jamming each other's signals.

The International Telecommunications Union (ITU) is a United Nations organization that regulates international communications. The ITU was originally created to regulate radio frequencies and to set common standards. The ITU began regulating geostationary orbits in the 1960s. They assigned orbits and frequencies on a "first-come, first-served basis." Not everyone recognized the authority of the ITU to allocate orbital position. The "first-come" policy conflicted with the "equal access for all" principle of space law. Those with the means to access space would gobble up all the choice orbits. Also, because geostationary orbits remain fixed over a single point, some of the countries below claimed ownership, conflicting with the principle of non-appropriation.

These spacecraft are only 210 feet apart. (NASA)

Eight equatorial nations issued the Bogata Declaration in 1976. In it, they claimed sovereignty over the geostationary orbits above their territories. They argued that these unique orbits depended on the gravity of the earth below. In other words, each unique position was tied to the land below. They insisted that all countries needed their permission to place a fixed satellite above their land. No major space powers recognized their territorial claims.

However, the conflict focused attention on the problems of uncontrolled growth in satellite communications. Countries without space capability realized they could be squeezed out of this limited resource. They feared there would no longer be room when they were ready to launch their own satellites. As a result, they demanded "equitable access" provisions in ITU policy.

The ITU held two World Administrative Radio Conferences to address the problem and they came up with a solution. First, developing nations were guaranteed orbital slots. Current satellite operators were granted access rights for at least 20 years. No nation was guaranteed a specific slot, but they were assured access to a suitable segment of the orbital arc.

International Space Station (NASA)

The ITU also recognized that other useful orbits may eventually become overcrowded. Military, civil and commercial systems all vie for a limited spectrum of radio frequencies. And new orbits are being used. Communication systems are being designed for low earth orbits. The Iridium system consists of 77 satellites in low earth orbit. These factors led the ITU to consider allocations in low earth orbit.

Space as a limited natural resource is not the only issue that plagues nations. The cost of exploring and exploiting space is another. Some projects are simply too large for a single nation. The *International Space Station* is a prime example of such a combined effort. Proposed in 1993, the first International Space Station Agreement was signed that same year. The United States provides overall management of the program.

The United States also provides the infrastructure and operating subsystems. Subsystems consist of life support, power, laboratory and habitation modules. Japan, European Space Agency (ESA) and Canada were to be other participants. Each was to provide elements of the station. Russia joined the team in 1993 and, in 1998, a new agreement was signed. The new agreement includes Russian participation and provides for more international involvement. It also reflects design changes made to reduce costs.

The Space Station Project is the largest and most complex international science and engineering program ever. A multitude of issues needed to be settled. Most of them concerned how the members would work together. They detailed who would do what and who would bear the costs. These were fairly straightforward issues. Issues concerning the use of the station are another matter.

The first issue was managing the use of the station. All countries agreed to do this through consensus. If consensus cannot be reached, the dispute is forwarded to a Multilateral Coordination Board for a decision. The United States chairs this board.

The second issue of use refers to ownership of intellectual property. Who owns inventions and discoveries made on the station? Under the terms of the agreement, each state retains jurisdiction over its own station elements. A state's patent rights and copyrights apply to creations its nationals make while in their own modules. Ownership is determined on a terrirorial basis. Whose laws apply when a multinational team makes a discovery is unresolved.

The third issue on use concerns military involvement. Initially, the partners were very reluctant to have US Department of Defense involved. They preferred a purely scientific, non-military platform. However, many of the most experienced astronauts are military members. To restrict them from the station would hurt the effort. A compromise was worked out. The owner of each module decides whether activities occuring within that module are for peaceful purposes. The compromise did not completely relieve the concerns, but it did provide a workable solution.

Satellites- Unmanned Spacecraft

A satellite is a natural or artificial object that orbits the Earth or other planetary body. An example of a natural object in space is the moon. In fact, it is the earth's only natural satellite. Artificial means man-made,and as we know, *Sputnik* was the first man-made satellite in space. Astronomers and other scientists still refer to either a natural or man-made object in space that orbits the earth as a satellite.

Thousands of satellites now occupy various orbits. There are so many old satellites that concern has been expressed for the survival of new satellites being placed into certain orbits. The fear is that collisions could occur between the new craft and those now considered "space junk."

Many of the older satellites have continued to function well beyond their intended lifetimes. Some of these craft have had to be silenced because no funds were available to continue processing the data they returned. We'll take a look at some of these old satellites and their contributions to the space program. We'll also look at some current satellite systems. But first, let's see what purposes satellites serve.

The first satellites were experiments. They were designed simply to tell us how to make better satellites. Today, satellites serve a huge variety of purposes. Very few are experimental systems. Satellite technology has become very sophisticated. Virtually, all satellites gather, relay or provide information for our use. Some analyze cosmic radiation. Some look at earth's cloud cover. Others allow us to exchange ideas all over the world. Still others tell us where we are and what time it is.

All of these purposes can be divided into four broad categories. The first is communication. These satellites relay and amplify signals. The second category is navigation. These satellites send positional data and timing to special receivers, which can then calculate their own position. The third category is observation. These satellites look at the earth, collect information and relay it to ground stations. The last category is scientific. These satellites collect information about the universe.

Communications Satellites

The Communications Satellite (SATCOM) System began in 1958 when taped messages were broadcast from orbit. The *Score* satellite operated for only 13 days. But its messages excited the people of our nation. Since then the system has grown extremely complex.

Echo 1 was a very large reflective balloon placed in orbit in 1960. It extended the range of line-of-sight signals by bouncing them back to earth. It was an example of a passive communications satellite. Its function was nothing more than to reflect radio and television signals. Active satellites amplified the relayed signals. Because the satellite was in low earth orbit, it could only be used for a short time as it flew over broadcasting and receiving stations.

The *Courier 1B* also orbited in 1960. This active early communications satellite was the first of the repeater types. It received signals from ground stations, amplified them, then rebroadcast the signals to receiving stations on earth.

Telstar 1 was the first test of the commercial value of comunications satellites. In 1962, *Telstar* 1 was placed into orbit for Bell Telephone. It was an active satellite that amplified and retransmitted as many as 60 two-way telephone conversations at one time. *Telstar* 1 obtained the electrical power it needed to receive and transmit signals from banks of solar cells mounted on panels attached to the satellite. Ground stations were established in the United States, England and France.

A few months later, *Relay* 1 was launched for the Radio Corporation of America (RCA). It added Italy and Brazil to the growing list of countries receiving broadcasts from satellites in outer space. *Telstar 3D* was deployed from the *Discovery* orbiter in 1985.

Today, the large SATCOM business con-tinues to grow as national and international corporations provide financing for growth. They construct, launch and operate several types of SATCOMs. The uses of commuications satellites are also growing. They are still used for media transmission such as radio and television, as well as for pure data transmission such as the internet. Another use is for personal comunication systems such as cellular phones. And finally, a fourth important use is to provide links to other spacecraft. Examples of these uses are described below.

INTELSAT

INTELSAT is both a series of satellites and an organization. Standing for the International Telecommunications Satellite Organization, INTELSAT has

INTELSAT **IV rescued to be repaired and returned to space.**

more than 140-member nations and over 40 investing entitities worldwide. It operates as a commercial cooperative, linking the world's telecommunications networks together via a global satellite system of geostationary satellites. It has been in business since 1964 and now brings global access to over 200 countries and territories around the world.

Early satellites had the capability of relaying the output of two television channels. They could also relay 12,000 simultaneous telephone conversations. In 1978, INTELSAT provided coverage of World Cup football matches obtaining a record-setting global viewing audience estimated at 1 billion people in 42 countries. Both the organization and the system have continued to grow, launching a new generation of high-powered satellites in 1995. Today they have 17 advanced satellites in orbit and with orders placed for several new ones, they continue to be a leading wholesaler of satellite communications.

TDRSS Ground Antenna

Galaxy Series

The Galaxy series of satellites relays video, voice, data, and facsimile information worldwide. *Galaxy* 1 was dedicated to distributing cable television programming. The fleet has since grown to include many variations with names other than *Galaxy,* all relaying telecommunications. In 2006 Galaxy 16 was successfully launched. This was the 43rd communication satellite since Galaxy 1 and broadcasts the clearest cable network signal yet.

The Tracking and Data Relay Satellite System (TDRSS) consists of three satellites and a ground station. *TDRSS-East* and *TDRSS-West* are active satellites. The third is an on-orbit spare.

The ground segment is at White Sands, New Mexico. The system is designed to provide simultaneous full-time coverage for the Space Shuttle and up to 25 other NASA low-earth-orbiting spacecraft. The system relays data and communications to and from the International Space Station and other satellites

At 5,000 lbs. (2,260 KG), the TDRSS satellites are some of the largest, most complex communications satellites ever built. Each measures more than 50 feet (15 meters) from one tip of its solar array to the other.

Tracking and Data Relay Satellite (TDRS)
Picture credit: NASA

The TDRSS antenna is designed only to point at spacecraft up to 7,500 miles high. Providing communications to spacecraft above this level requires help. The system, which assists in NASA's Deep Space Network (DSN), consists of three deep space communication complexes. They are located at Goldstone, California; Madrid, Spain; and Canberra, Australia. The complexes provide continuous links for planetary spacecraft as the earth rotates.

The DSN has supported all the deep space probes since its beginning in 1959. It also supported all of the Apollo lunar missions. When the *Voyager* 2 spacecraft flew by Uranus, the DSN antennas received the signals. They provided 29,000 bits of information per second, equivalent to a color picture every 5 minutes. The result was hundreds of color pictures during the brief encounter. The Australian station viewed the spacecraft longer than either the Goldstone or Madrid stations, since Uranus was in the southern part of the sky in 1986.

The military also operates a variety of communications satellites. These satellites are exclusive to military missions. The Defense Satellite Communication System (DSCS) is a continuous long distance message service. It provides exclusive communications services to the highest levels of the US government. Transmissions can be voice, teletype, video or digital data. The Ultra High Frequency Follow-On (UHF F/O) satellites provide the Department of Defense with continuous worldwide communications. They link aircraft, ships, submarines, and ground stations to military commanders and the National Command Authority. *MILSTAR* combines many communications services in one family of satellites. *MILSTAR* satellites provide command and control of military forces at all levels of activity. They are designed to survive nuclear war.

Navigation Satellites

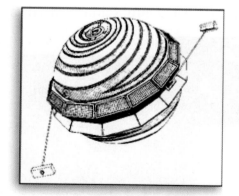

In the early 1960s, the Air Force and Navy actively pursued the idea of using radio signals from satellites for navigation and positioning. They envisioned a continuously operating space-based system that could also serve as an all-weather global system. Believing this could be a highly accurate system, the Navy sponsored both TRANSIT and TIMATION, two early programs designed to meet that vision.

Johns Hopkins University developed TRANSIT. It was designed to update the inertial navigation system on Polaris submarines. It became operational in 1964. In 1967 it was made available to non-military users. It is still working today, providing intermittent navigation information to ballistic missile submarines and surface ships.

TIMATION was a two-dimensional navigation system. It used high stability oscillators and time transfer capabilities to determine longitude and latitude. The Air Force was conducting its own research at the same time. Their project was called System 621B. System 621B was designed to identify longitude, latitude, and altitude. It was a three-dimensional system with a design that allowed it to run continuously.

In 1974, the Air Force was directed to oversee the creation of a new global navigation system. It would combine the best features of the previous programs. The new system was called NAVSTAR Global Positioning System. All the military services would participate in the program, assisted by the Defense Mapping Agency. The first NAVSTAR launched in 1978.

The NAVSTAR Global Positioning System (GPS) is a space-based radio-positioning system managed by the NAVSTAR GPS Joint Program Office at the Space and Missile Systems Center, Los Angeles Air Force Base, California. It provides navigation and timing information to both civilian and military users worldwide. Position, velocity and time can be precisely determined by GPS users. GPS satellites emit continuous navigation signals as they orbit earth every 12 hours. The GPS positioning accuracy will vary depending on the user's equipment as well as atmospheric conditions. Current accuracy levels for civilian users have been reported at better than 3 meters in the horizontal plane. The U.S. military has access to multi-channel GPS which further improves accuracy for

NAVSTAR Global Positioning System Satellite (GPS)

those users. The system consists of a constelation of 24 orbiting satellites, a worldwide satellite control network and GPS receiver units that pick up signals from these satellites and translate them into position information. The satellites act as precise reference points and continuously broadcast position and time data. These satellites are spaced in orbit so that a minimum of six will be in view at any one time.

The control network is made up of ground stations operated by the US Air Force; the master control station is in Colorado. Five monitoring stations and three ground antennas located throughout the world all work together to track the satellites and send the data to the master control station. This data is used to adjust the satellite positions if that should be necessary.

Every user of the system has a receiver, each one of which uses the broadcast signals to calculate its position. The entire system is based on ranging the satellite, a process of determining how far away it is. The satellite broadcasts its location and the time that the signal was sent. The receiver then measures how long it took to receive the signal, thus determining relative distance.

Highly accurate atomic clocks are the key to the NAVSTAR GPS. On board each satellite are three of these clocks, which lose or gain only one second in 36,000 years. Any receiver with a minimum of three GPS satellites in view and an atomic clock can calculate a three-dimensional position, which is given in latitude, longitude and altitude. If no atomic clock is available, a

**Backpack and Hand-held
GPS Receivers**

fourth satellite must be in view in order to calculate the three-dimensional position. Since atomic clocks are expensive, most GPS receivers rely on getting signals from four or more satellites.

GPS is rapidly replacing all other navigational means. Virtually all ships and airlines rely on it. Trucking fleets and law enforcement agencies use it. It is an all-weather location system that has become critical for search and rescue. US military forces rely on it to locate enemy positions as well as their own. Farmers use it to lay out their fields. Many fishermen, hunters and hikers favor it over a compass.

Observation Satellites

Satellites orbiting the earth in space have a great view of earth. Military "spy satellites" have been keeping an "eye in the sky" on potential adversaries for decades. But, there is a lot more to look at and learn. Today, these remote observers serve many other purposes. For convenience, we'll divide observation satellites into three broad types.

Weather Satellites

The first type is the weather satellite. Most of us are very familiar with the satellite images shown on the evening news. But, these observation satellites look at a great deal more. Weather satellites measure temperatures at the surface and in the atmosphere. They also measure cloud cover and moisture levels. Some even measure lightning strikes.

The United States launched its first weather satellite, *Tiros* 1, in 1960. Ten Tiros satellites were launched. Their cameras provided the first large-scale weather photographs of earth. An improved type of weather satellite, *Nimbus* 1, was launched in 1964. *Nimbus* 6 was launched in 1975. It measures radiation in the earth's atmosphere. This data is used to determine climatic changes.

The National Oceanic and Atmospheric Administration (NOAA) series of weather satellites are advanced *TIROS N* craft. They also carry special search and rescue instrumentation. The TIROS program is a cooperative effort of NASA, NOAA, the United Kingdom and France.

NOAA's on-board sensors measure earth's cloud cover, surface temperature, atmospheric temperature, moisture and electric particle flux. A data system collects environmental information from sensors on land, at sea and in the air. In 1986, an *Atlas E* booster carried the NOAA 10 weather satellite into polar orbit. This satellite is equipped with an L-band search and rescue payload that pinpoints distress signals from ships and aircraft.

The information gained from NOAA satellites can be used in several areas. For example, data has been used to help fire fighters control forest fires and to provide analyses of ice conditions at sea to the US Coast Guard. The NOAA satellites have detected volcanic eruptions in remote areas.

The pictures you often see on television of the earth's surface and cloud cover are transmitted from the GOES system. GOES stands for Geostationary Operational Environmental Satellites. Aboard the GOES spacecraft are instruments that provide cloud-cover pictures. Pictures in visible light and in infrared are possible. The infrared pictures are very useful in determining the intensity of storm systems. An instrument known as VAS collects data on the water vapor content. It also measures the temperature of the atmosphere. It provides data at various altitudes in the atmosphere. Meteorologists need this type of information for weather forecasting.

The US military has weather satellites as well. The Defense Meteorological Satellite Program (DMSP) provides weather data exclusively to the military. DMSP satellites use an optical system to gather data. They provide visual and infrared cloud data, as well as solar and oceanographic data.

Multi-spectrum-imaging Satellites

The second type of observation satellites is called multi-spectrum-imaging satellites. That's a long name for a satellite that observes radiant energy. This can be energy that is reflected from the surface of the earth. It can also be energy generated by objects on the earth. Either way, they give us some very useful data including information about crops, ocean currents and natural resources. Farmers and resource managers use the data extensively. Map makers also find satellite imagery much faster and cheaper than land surveys.

LANDSAT **4 is a Natural Resources Satellite**

One of the best-known satellite systems of this type is the *LANDSAT* series of satellites. *LANDSAT*s locate natural resources and monitor other conditions on the earth's surface. New mineral resources have been, and continue to be, discovered by *LANDSAT* imagery. Placed into polar orbit, one *LANDSAT* can examine conditions on earth's total surface every 12 hours.

Agricultural conditions are monitored by *LANDSAT*s and, thus, provide very important data to farmers, researchers and governments. Information relayed back to earth can show the rate of crop growth and allow accurate predictions of crop yield.

Healthy crops radiate at a known wavelength and produce a certain pictorial image. Any change in this image signals disease or damage, and corrective measures can be taken early. Similarly, grasslands for cattle can be monitored for overgrazing or to locate grazing areas, which could provide more nutritious food for cattle. Worldwide soil conditions can and have been evaluated. Thus, better use of available soil is made possible.

Land-use information is important to governments at all levels. For example, the study of *LANDSAT* imagery can point out the best areas for the future development of cities or the expansion of existing cities. Urban planners can use land areas that are the least suitable for crops. Laws can be passed that forbid construction of new homes or businesses on land that would be more valuable for some other use.

Federal and state governments find *LANDSAT* imagery particularly useful in the management of coastal resources. Effects of the tides, the status of industrial and waste pollution entering coastal waters and many other conditions are readily monitored. This allows corrective actions to be taken at proper times.

Fresh water is essential to life, and the availability of fresh water has diminished over the years. The problem lies in the fact that the demand for fresh water increases yearly with a higher standard of living and an increasing population. *LANDSATs* have been used to discover new sources and amounts of water. Its pictures of snowfall amounts provide specialists a measure of the fresh water that will result when the snow melts. In turn, very accurate estimates can be made of how much water will be in reservoirs before the dry seasons begin, how much will be available for growing crops, and so forth. This allows planners to prepare for any water shortages that may develop in certain areas of the country.

Another well-known series of multi-spectrum imaging satellites is France's SPOT system. *SPOT* 1 was the first in the series. It was very advanced for its time. This Earth resources mapping satellite was launched in 1986 atop *Arianne* 1. It carried visible and infrared sensors capable of much finer resolution than the comparable *LANDSATs*. This spurred better *LANDSATs*. The competition between them has resulted inexceptionally good imaging products. The more images they produce, the more uses are found for them.

A single scene from the Thematic Mapper of *LANDSAT 4* contains six times more data than a similar-sized area from the first *LANDSATs*. This image is of the Washington DC/ Baltimore, Maryland area.

Reconnaissance Satellites

The third type of observation satellite is the reconnaissance satellite. These satellites monitor the activities of people on the surface of the earth. Generally, they serve military purposes. There are four major purposes: providing early warning by detecting enemy missile launches, detecting nuclear explosions, electronic reconnaissance and photo-surveillance.

These satellites monitor radio and radar transmission from the countries they pass over. Satellites that do photo-surveillance can be either high or low-resolution pictures. Satellites designed for high resolution are called close-look satellites. Expert analysts can distinguish minute details, using these pictures, such as different models of aircraft on the ground. Those designed for low resolution are called area-survey satellites. These pictures are generally used to provide general terrain information.

The names and details of most surveillance satellites are not released to the public. The existence of early warning satellites may be an exception. Publicizing these satellites lets adversaries know their launches can be detected. They also are used for treaty compliance. One example is the Defense Support Program (DSP) satellite system. The details of this system were declassified in 1974. Many believe the reason for this was to let the Soviet Union know United States' capabilities. The purpose of DSP is to monitor ballistic missile and space launches. However, it is also capable of detecting nuclear detonations.

Scientific Satellites

Scientific satellites orbit for the sole purpose of gaining information. Scientists in several fields then use the information gained in an effort to better understand the total aerospace environment. There have been many scientific satellites orbited since the capability to do so was developed. Each series or individual satellite has had more or less a specific job. The growth of technology now allows satellites to conduct multiple missions from one spacecraft. All of these missions can be divided into two broad categories. The first is orbital astronomy. Examples

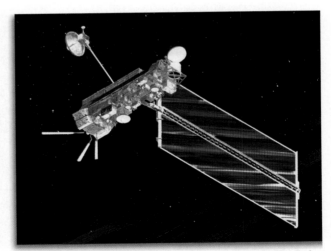

An Artist's Concept of the Scientific Satellite *NASA Polar Orbiting Platform* (NPOP-1)

include *Explorer, Orbiting Solar Observatory (OSO), Orbiting Astronomical Observatory (OAO), High-Energy Observatory (HEAO), Rossi X-ray Timing Explorer (RXTE),* and the *Hubble Space Telescope.* The second type is environmental analysis. Examples include *Solar Mesosphere Explorer (SME)* and *Earth Radiation Budget Satellite (ERBS).*

The Explorers

The first of this series of satellites was orbited in 1958. *Explorer* 1 discovered the Van Allen radiation belts. The *Explorer* 3, also orbited in 1958, provided more information about radiation in space. It also investigated micrometeoroids in its flight path. In 1959, *Explorer* 6 gave us the first photograph of earth from space. Other Explorer satellites have looked at conditions from earth's atmosphere to thousands of miles into space. They have looked at radiation and solar flares of the sun. The Explorers were particularly essential to understanding the space environment prior to sending astronauts into orbit and to the moon.

Orbiting Solar Observatory (OSO)

The sun has been, and continues to be, studied by different types of scientific satellites. One early group was called *Orbiting Solar Observatory (OSO)*. The *OSO* 1 was launched in May of 1962. For over one year, it transmitted data on 75 solar flares that occurred during its lifetime. Later, orbital flights of the *OSO* series made further studies of the sun's production of x-rays, gamma rays and other radiation. The *OSO* 4 gave us the first pictures of the sun in the extreme ultraviolet wavelength.

Orbiting Astronomical Observatory (OAO)

The *Orbiting Astronomical Observatory (OAO)* broadened scientists' understanding of the universe. The first of the series was orbited in 1968. It studied the stars in the ultraviolet, infrared, gamma, and x-ray wavelengths. The OAOs were able to extend scientists' knowledge of interstellar gases. *OAO* 2 discovered the existence of huge hydrogen clouds around comets. Astronomers had predicted such clouds. They could not confirm this and many other theories until the flights of the OAOs.

High-Energy Astronomy Observatory (HEAO)

Named for their special missions, the *High-Energy Astronomy Observatory (HEAO)* series were orbited to investigate the sources and intensities of high-energy radiation that are at the very far end of the electromagnetic spectrum. Among the many discoveries of this satellite family were the bursts of gamma rays and jets of the x-rays coming from the galaxy Centaurus A. From within our own galaxy, sources of gamma ray bursts were discovered. Pictures of a pulsar, or rotating neuron star, were made from the x-rays generated by the star.

The why and how of the data received from each *HEAO* satellite may keep astronomers busy for years. Each question answered through study of the data invariably generates more questions. For this reason, other satellites with *HEAO* capabilities have been and will continue to be sent into space.

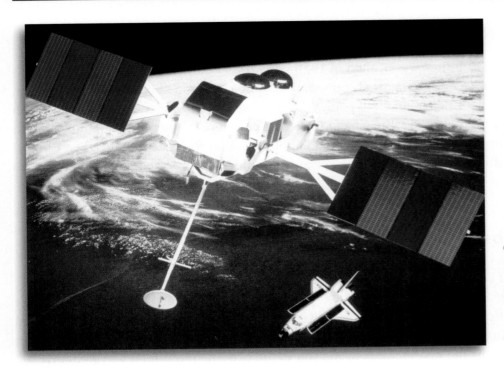

Gamma Ray Observatory (GRO) is equipped with four detectors to study gamma rays, the atomic messengers that tell the story of cataclysmic events in our universe.

Rossi X-ray Timing Explorer (RXTE)

The *Rossi X-ray Timing Explorer (RXTE)* satellite is an explorer-class spacecraft. It's a continuation of the great strides already made in x-ray astronomy through the use of satellites. Astronomers are particularly interested in x-ray emissions coming from galaxies. They believe that the study of such x-ray emissions from groups of galaxies will help them understand how giant systems of galaxies form.

RXTE was launched into a low earth orbit in 1995 and its mission continues today. The spacecraft carries three science instruments including high-energy x-ray timing equipment, an all-sky monitor and a Proportional Counter Array. It is able to detect x-ray sources that are 50 to 100 times weaker than those sources detected by earlier searches. The *RXTE* is studying a variety of x-ray sources including white dwarfs, accreting neutron stars, black holes, and active galactic nuclei.

The Hubble Space Telescope

Earth's atmosphere limits the usefulness of our best astronomical telescopes. The atmosphere interferes with light rays by scattering, bending or blocking some of them out before they reach a telescope lens. Another problem is light pollution. Light pollution results from the interaction of the atmosphere and man-made lights. Light pollution can be experienced when you look for the stars in the sky at night while in a city. Only the brighter stars can be seen.

The *Hubble Space Telescope* is built to work similar to a ground observatory. It operates from an altitude of about 310 miles above the earth. At this altitude, it is free of the atmospheric interference. Astronomers are able to detect faint objects that are 50 times better than those seen from earth-based

The *Hubble Space Telescope*

observatories. The astronomers are also able to see objects much more clearly. The clarity is about seven times better than ground observations.

Initally the Hubble Space Telescope was scheduled to operate for 15 years, but it has been such a valuable tool that its time has been extended. Hubble was designed to be deployed and periodically serviced by the Space Shuttle. The servicing task was accomplished five times during the Shuttle program, the most recent occurring in 2009. As a result of the superb maintenance performed over the years, Hubble may live nearly twice its initial expected service life of 15 years.

Chandra

In July 1999, *Chandra* was launched as NASA's new x-ray observatory. This probe was named after Subrahmanyan Chandrasekhar, one of the most prominent astrophysicists of the 20th Century. *Chandra* is solar powered and has only three major parts. The x-ray telescope contains eight mirrors that focus x-rays emitted by space objects. The scientific instruments on board the satellite include a high-resolution camera

Chandra – An artist's illustration of a space based observatory that is proving that truth is more exciting the fiction. It has been giving science data that is more dramatic than anything Hollywood could produce. *(NASA illustration)*

that records x-ray images and a spectrometer that determines the energy level of the x-rays. The spacecraft itself provides a safe environment for the telescope and the instruments. It is operated by the Chandra Flight Operations Center at the Smithsonian Astrophysical Observatory in Cambridge, Massachusetts. *Chandra* records observations of the universe in the high energy end of the electromagnetic spectrum. The x-ray images that *Chandra* records are 25 times sharper than previous x-ray images taken by other telescopes. *Chandra's* extraordinary capabilities make it possible for scientists to study high energy objects such as supernovae and black holes in much greater detail. As of this writing, the observatory continues to operate and may continue to do so through 2014.

Solar Mesosphere Explorer (SME)

SME is an example of an environmental analysis satellite. The mission of this satellite was to study the reactions between sunlight and earth's atmosphere. Of par-ticular interest to scientists were reactions between sunlight and the ozone layer of the atmosphere and other chemicals.

Astronauts F. Story Musgrave and Jeffrey A. Hoffman teamed up to perform servicing tasks on the *Hubble Space Telescope*.

Earth Radiation Budget Satellite (ERBS)

ERBS is a scientific satellite designed to study earth radiation and the interaction of the earth with radiation energy received from the sun. It was deployed by the shuttle orbiter *Challenger's* manipulator arm in 1984. The satellite's own hydrazine thrusters burned for long periods to boost it into its operational path. A pair of solar panels provides power.

Earth Observing System (EOS)

In 1991, NASA initiated a program to study the earth as a complete environmental system. The program was initially called Mission to Planet Earth, and is now known as NASA Earth Science, of which EOS is an integral component. NASA has been studying the earth since 1958. They believe the key to understanding the global environment is exploring how the earth's systems of air, land, water and life interact. The program has three parts: a series of observations satellites, advanced data systems, and teams of scientists. Specialized *Earth Observing System (EOS)* satellites will also gather data. *EOS* is the first system to provide integrated measurements of earth systems.

Probes

There have been many spacecraft sent to investigate the moon and various planets within the solar system. Some have even been sent beyond our solar system. We refer to all of these spacecraft that either fly by, orbit or land on a celestial body, other than earth, as probes. Each flight deserves a full explanation, but only a brief summary can be provided here. Similar to the families of satellites discussed earlier, the probes are grouped by name.

The Rangers

This was an early series of probes intended to investigate the moon by taking pictures of the moon as the spacecraft approached on a direct impact course. Several of the craft failed, but three of them provided the first close-up pictures ever seen of the moon's surface.

The Surveyors

Attention to the moon became more concentrated when the series of Surveyor probes landed on its surface during the period 1964 to 1968. These were soft-landers in that they carried retro-rockets that slowed them sufficiently to land undamaged. Of the seven launched, five landed as intended on different areas of the moon's surface. The probes sent hundreds of pictures back to earth. They also sampled the lunar soil for its chemistry and other characteristics.

Planners of the Apollo landings depended very heavily on the information gathered by the Surveyors. They had to know what the Apollo lunar module would encounter upon its descent to the moon's surface.

Lunar Orbiters

In approximately one year, 1966 to 1967, five orbiter-type probes were launched to the moon. All of the probes were successful, and they did their job of providing high-quality photographs of the moon's entire surface. From these photographs, maps of the moon were made.

This effort, like those of the Ranger and Surveyor programs, was in preparation for the Apollo landings. To make certain there would be no danger of collision with the Apollo vehicles near the moon, each of the orbiters was sent crashing into the moon's surface after it completed its mission.

The Mariners

This family of probes was used to investigate the inner planets. *Mariner* 2 made a flyby of Venus in 1962, confirming that Venus had a very hot atmos-phere near its surface and that it had neither radia-tion belts nor a magnetic field. In 1967, *Mariner* 5 provided confirmation of the first flyby findings and provided more information about the planet's atmosphere. *Mariner* 10 flew by Venus and Mercury in 1973 and this gave us the first pictures of the circu-lation pattern of the Venusian cloud cover and the cratered surface of Mercury. Additional information on *Mariner* missions can be found in the Mars section of Chapter 25.

Mariner **10 Mars Observer**

An Artist's Concept of *Pioneer* Leaving the Solar System (NASA)

The Pioneers

The Pioneers have probed both the outer and inner planets. *Pioneer* 10 gave us the first close-up pictures of Jupiter in 1973. The craft continued past Jupiter on its journey out of the solar system.

Pioneer 11 was the second probe of Jupiter. It flew past the Jovian system in 1974 and began a trajectory to Saturn. The first pictures and data from Saturn were received on Earth in 1979.

The Vikings

In 1975, NASA launched two space probes, the *Viking* 1 and *Viking* 2, to explore the environment of Mars. Each probe consisted of an orbiter and a lander.

Objectives for the Viking mission included analyzing the Martian atmosphere and photographing the planet's surface. But, the primary emphasis was the search for life. Each of the landers took samples of the Martian soil and submitted the samples to various tests for evidence of life processes within the soil. The experiments were not conclusive.

Although life was not found, scientists did obtain enough information to make several conclusions about the status of Mars, such as the fact that the polar ice caps are largely made of water ice. Thousands of photographs were taken of the Martian landscape from orbit and from landers' positions on the surface. In appearance and in content, the surface was found to be somewhat like desert soils on earth. Additional information on *Viking* missions can be found in the Mars section of Chapter 25.

Voyagers 1 and 2

The Pioneers opened the way to outer-planet investigations, but the Voyagers gave us greatly improved pictures and data. Both craft were launched in 1977, and both encountered Jupiter and Saturn. The *Voyager* 1 was launched after the *Voyager* 2 because it was placed on a faster trajectory to Jupiter.

The *Voyager* 1 reached Jupiter in March 1979 and flew on to Saturn, arriving there in November 1980. *Voyager* 1 completed its planetary encounters and is traveling toward interstellar space on a path away from the ecliptic plane. We can look forward to further investigations by the *Voyager* 2. *Voyager* 2 flew by Jupiter in 1979 and Saturn in 1981. It flew within 63,000 miles of Saturn and headed toward an encounter with two other planets.

The *Voyager* 2 spacecraft flew by Uranus in January 1986. The spacecraft's closest approach was 107,000 km from the planet. The *Voyager* 2 flew in and out of the Uranian system in a matter of hours.

A planned 1987 firing of *Voyager's* onboard thrusters was adjusted to retarget its August 1989 flyby of Neptune from a miss of 1,280 km to 4,800 km to avoid possible ring debris and radiation belts.

Both Voyagers are continuing on out of the solar system. They will continue to send information as long as power supplies last. We expect to learn a great deal about the edge of the solar system as they pass into interstellar space. Scientists are very interested in the area where the interstellar wind is equal to the solar wind. This area is called the Heliopause Boundary. They want to study the magnetic interactions of solar wind plasma and interstellar wind particles.

This painting shows *Voyager's* encounter with Uranus. (NASA)

Giotto

In 1985, the European Space Agency launched *Giotto* on an Ariane launch vehicle. It was sent to explore Halley's Comet. It streaked within 450 km of Halley's nucleus. Bombarded 100 times a second with particles weighing up to .001 gram, *Giotto* was, by encounter's end, coated with 26 kg of dust.

The Soviet Union launched *Vegas* 1 and *Vegas* 2 that flew past the comet and provided final targeting data for *Giotto*. They also suffered severe dust erosion of solar arrays. Japan launched the *Suisei* and *Sakigake* probes. *Sakigake* provided images from 7.1 million km (4.4 million miles).

The closest and most hazardous approach was made by *Giotto*, which was targeted to fly through the tail of Halley's Comet and behind the nucleus in order to obtain images with the highest possible resolution. The scientific instruments aboard measured neutrons, ions and dust particles, and recorded dust impacts. An on-board camera took color pictures of the nucleus from about 1,000 km. The probe sent back more than 2,000 images.

Mars Global Surveyor

Mars Global Surveyor (MGS) was launched in November 1996. It was the first of NASA's several low-cost planetary Discovery missions. It was designed to orbit Mars for a two-year period. Its purpose was to map and collect information about the surface of Mars. It also collected data on Martian atmosphere, gravity and magnetic fields. The data will be used to investigate such things as Martian geology, resources, climate and weather. NASA lost contact with MGS on November 2, 2006; contact was never reestablished.

Mars Pathfinder

Mars *Pathfinder* was the second of NASA's low-cost planetary Discovery missions. It consisted of a stationary lander and a surface rover. The primary objective is proving the feasibility of low-cost landings on and exploration of the Martian surface. It has provided atmospheric entry data, long-range and close-up surface images. It has also done rock and soil composition experiments.

Mars *Pathfinder* proved low-cost landings could be accomplished. During the landing, the craft was surrounded by four air bags that formed a protective ball. Once on the surface, the bags were deflated. After some maneuvers to clear an airbag out of the way, ramps were deployed and the rover rolled out onto the surface. The mission continued to send images and results from experiments until September 1997, when communications were lost for unknown reasons.

Galileo

Named for the discoverer of Jupiter's inner moons, the *Galileo* spacecraft was launched by NASA in 1989. After a 6-year journey, it entered orbit around Jupiter in 1995.

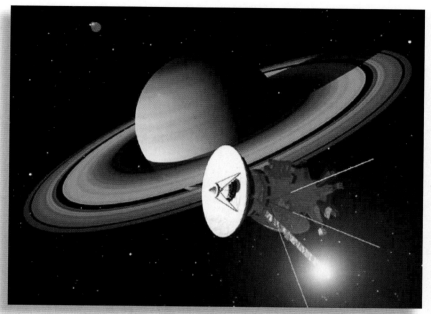

Artist's Illustration of the Space Probe *Cassini* Orbiting Saturn

The mission was the first to take direct measurements from within Jupiter's atmosphere. When it arrived, it injected a probe into Jupiter's atmosphere. The probe measured cloud temperatures, chemistry and electrical activity. Atmospheric pressure was also a part of the measurement taken. The orbiter continued to send a steady stream of images and scientific data for two years. This was its primary mission. It then began a secondary mission to explore two of Jupiter's moons. On September 21, 2003, ground controllers transmitted commands to deorbit Galileo and sent it crashing into the planet, thus ending the mission.

Cassini

In 1997, this two-story robotic spacecraft began a journey for Saturn. *Cassini* is an international project involving NASA, the European Space Agency and several European academic and industrial partners. It went into orbit around Saturn in July of 2004 and will observe the planet and its moons for many years, and is targeted to operate at least through 2017. Cassini

An actual image returned from *Cassini* taken of the rings of Saturn
(Courtesy of NASA)

carried a landing craft named Huygens which it released on December 25, 2004 and headed for Saturn's largest moon, Titan. The Huygens probe was named after the 17th century Dutch astronomer who discovered Titan, Christiaan Huygens. The Huygens probe descended through Titan's atmosphere by parachute and gently landed on the surface, transmitting data for approximately 90 minutes.

Phoenix

In August of 2007, NASA launched a space-craft, known as the *Phoenix Mars Lander.* This probe was designed to claw down into the icy soil of the red planet's northern plains. The robot investigated whether frozen water near the Martian surface night periodically melt enough to sustain a livable environment for microbes.

Phoenix Mars Lander (Illustration by Corby Waste, NASA)

To accomplish that and other key goals, *Phoenix* carried a set of advanced research tools never before used on Mars.

"Our 'follow-the-water' strategy for exploring Mars has yielded a string of dramatic discoveries in recent years about the history of water on a planet where similarities with Earth were much greater in the past than they are today," said Doug McCuistion, director of the Mars Exploration Program at NASA Headquarters, Washington, D.C. "*Phoenix* will complement the strategic exploration of Mars by being our first attempt to actually touch and analyze Martian water—water in the form of buried ice."

NASA's *Mars Odyssey* orbiter found evidence in 2002 to support theories that large areas of Mars, including the arctic plains, have water ice within an arm's reach of the surface. "*Phoenix* has been designed to examine the history of ice by measuring how liquid water has modified the chemistry and mineralogy of the soil," said Peter Smith , the Phoenix principal investigator at the University of Arizona, Tucson.

"*Phoenix* can assess whether this polar environment is a habitable zone for primitive microbes. This is just another step toward our efforts to see if life ever existed on our sister-planet," said Jean Cesarone, aerospace educator, about the importance of this mission in our never-ending effort to find life beyond planet earth.

Key Terms and Concepts

- scientific approach
- application spacecraft
- satellites
- probes
- manned spacecraft
- National Aeronautics and Space Administration (NASA)
- international treaties
- international laws
- international courts
- international customs
- United Nations resolutions
- 1967 Outer Space Treaty
- ABM Treaty
- NASA Act
- Commercial Space Launch Act (CSLA)
- Land Remote Sensing Commercialization Act (LANDSAT Act)
- geostationary orbit (GEO)
- International Telecommunications Union (ITU)
- Bogata Declaration of 1976
- International Space Station Agreement
- European Space Agency (ESA)

- active vs. passive communications satellites
- International Telecommunications Satellite (INTELSAT)
- Tracking and Data Relay Satellite System (TDRSS)
- Defense Satellite Communication System (DSCS)
- Global Positioning System (GPS)
- National Oceanic and Atmospheric Administration (NOAA)
- Defense Meteorological Satellite Program (DMSP)
- multi-spectral imaging
- Defense Support Program (DSP)
- *Orbiting Solar Observatory (OSO)*
- *Orbiting Astronomical Observatory (OAO)*
- *High-Energy Astronomy Observatory (HEAO)*
- *Rossi X-ray Timing Explorer (RXTE)*
- *Solar Mesosphere Explorer (SME)*
- *Earth Radiation Budget Satellite (ERBS)*
- *Earth Observing System (EOS)*
- *Mars Global Surveyor (MGS)*

? Test Your Knowledge ?

SELECT THE CORRECT ANSWER

1. *The* **(1967 Outer Space Treaty / Anti-Ballistic Missile Treaty of 1972)** *stated that space would be used "exclusively for peaceful purposes."*

2. *The* **(GPS / DSP)** *permits users to instantly determine their position, provides their velocity and time, and is more accurate than any radio system.*

MATCHING

3.

a. Earth Observing System	1) Discovered the Van Allen Radiation Belts
b. Earth Radiation Budget Satellite	2) Studied the sun's protection of x-rays and gamma rays
c. Explorer I	3) Improved knowledge of interstellar gases
d. High Energy Astronomy Observatory	4) Discovered burst of gamma rays from Galaxy Centaurus A
e. Hubble Space Telescope	5) From LEO, studies white dwarfs, black holes, active galactic nuclei
f. Orbiting Astronomical Observatory	6) Solved the problems of light pollution and atmospheric interference
g. Orbiting Solar Observatory	7) Studied the reaction between sunlight and earth's ozone layer
h. Solar Mesosphere Explorer	8) Studies interaction of earth and radiation energy from the sun
i. X-ray Timing Explorer	9) Studies how air, land, water and life interact on earth

MATCHING

4. **Match the probe type with its contributions:**

a. Cassini	(1) Provided the first close-up pictures of the moon
b. Galileo	(2) Information gathered helped Apollo planners know what to expect
c. Giotto	(3) Flyby missions investigated Mercury and Venus
d. Lunar Orbiters	(4) Launched in 1966-1967, five probes provided high-quality photographs of the moon's entire surface
e. Mariners	(5) Provided the first close-up pictures of Jupiter and Saturn
f. Mars Global Surveyor	(6) Investigated Mars using both orbiters and landers; tested soil samples
g. Pathfinder	(7) Flew past Jupiter, Saturn, Neptune, Uranus, now headed for interstellar space
h. Pioneers	(8) Launched by ESA to investigate Halley's Comet
i. Rangers	(9) Launched in 1996 to investigate Martian geology, resources, climate and weather
j. Surveyors	(10) Put the first rover on another planet to perform rock and soil composition experiments
k. Vikings	(11) Launched to take direct measurements of Jupiter's atmosphere and explore its moons
l. Voyagers	(12) International robotic probe sent to Saturn to study rings, atmosphere, magnetosphere

FILL IN THE BLANKS

5. _____ are unmanned exploratory spacecraft traveling beyond earth's orbit; _____ are spacecraft that orbit the earth.

6. _____, the first Soviet satellite, established the rights of satellites to _____.

7. _____ communications satellites reflect the radio or television signals while _____ communications satellites amplify the signals before return.

8. The GPS positioning accuracy will vary depending on the user's _____ as well as _____ _____ .

9. Identify the satellite type with its function (*weather, multi-spectrum imaging, reconnaissance*):
   a. DMSP   _____
   b. DSP   _____
   c. GOES   _____
   d. LANDSAT   _____
   e. NIMBUS   _____
   f. SPOT   _____
   g. TIROS   _____

10. The International Telecommunications Union Policy of "first come, first served" in assigning _____ conflicted with the _____ principle of space law.

11. Eight equatorial nations responded to the ITU Policy with the _____, in which they claimed sovereignty over the _____ above their territories.

12. The acronym DMSP stands for _____, which provides _____ data exclusively to the _____, using an/a _____ system to provide _____ and _____ _____ data.

13. The two purposes of scientific satellites are _____ and _____ .

14. Identified as L4 and L5, these points in space where a body will be in equilibrium are the most likely potential place for _____.

MULTIPLE CHOICE

15. Which of these spacecraft launch agencies has only recently been acknowledged to exist?
    a. Commercial
    b. Military
    c. Civilian
    d. National security

16. Which of the following is **not** a source of space law?
    a. Customs
    b. Treaties
    c. UN decrees
    d. International courts
17. The Land Remote Sensing Commercialization Act did which of the following?
    a. Allowed the sale of government data
    b. Set limits on the quality of the data that could be sold
    c. Directed that data be provided to all customers at the same costs
    d. All of the above
18. Which member of the 1998 International Space Station Agreement started participating in 1993 and signed the new 1998 agreement?
    a. Japan
    b. Russia
    c. Canada
    d. European Space Agency (ESA)

TRUE OR FALSE

19. Scientific application satellites gather information that may or may not have immediate use.
20. Telstar 1 was the first telecommunications satellite.
21. TRANSIT and TIMATION were precursors to the Global Positioning System.
22. Taking photos and infrared observations are the only activities of reconnaissance satellites.

SHORT ANSWER

23. Describe the three basic principles of space law.
24. What were the two most significant provisions of the Outer Space Treaty of 1967?
25. Briefly describe the situation that led to the ABM Treaty and explain why it is significant to space operations.
26. How did the National Aeronautics and Space Act help space exploration in the United States?
27. How did the Commercial Space Launch Act aid the development of commercial space activities?
28. What three issues were at least partially resolved by the International Space Station Agreement?
29. Name four categories of satellites.
30. Name four uses of communications satellites.
31. List three segments of GPS and their functions.
32. What are three types of observation satellites?
33. What are the four purposes of reconnaissance satellites?
34. What are some of the potential reasons to construct space colonies?

Chapter 27

MANNED SPACE EXPLORATIONS

The space race between the United States and the Soviet Union, and the early satellite launches paved the way for the continuing exploration of space. It was only a matter of time before manned exploration became a reality. The United States and the Soviet Union both had manned space exploration programs.

bjectives

Identify the contributions of the US manned space flights and their missions.
Describe the Soviet manned space flights and their missions.
Identify the American and Soviet joint manned spacecraft mission.
Describe astronaut and cosmonaut individual accomplishments.
Identify the three major parts of the Space Shuttle.
Describe *Spacelab*, *Long-Duration Exposure Facility*, and the *International Space Station*.
Describe the living and working conditions in space.
Describe the different space suits.
Define the X-Prize.

US Manned Space Program

The United States, through NASA, developed a systematic manned space flight program. Five programs were successfully developed from 1961 through 1975.

Project Mercury

The United States launched its first satellite in 1958, and by 1961, the United States was ready to attempt manned space flight. America's first manned space flight program was called Project Mercury.

Seven U.S. pilots were chosen as the original astronauts: Scott Carpenter, Gordon Cooper, John Glenn, Virgil Grissom, Walter Schirra, Alan Shepard and Donald Slayton. *Mercury's* mission was to find out if a human could survive space travel and what, if any, effects would space travel have on the human body.

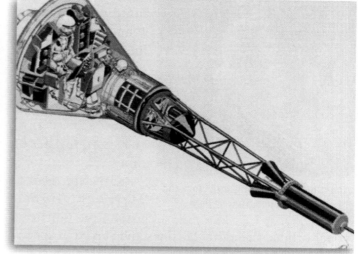

A Cutaway of the *Mercury* Capsule

The Seven Original NASA Astronauts Selected in 1959 for the Mercury Program

Alan Shepherd Suiting-up before the First Manned Space Flight

Project Mercury lasted four years and consisted of six manned flights. *Mercury* also conducted 19 test flights before the capsule was ready for manned space flight. The first flight involved sending one astronaut into space. This first flight was suborbital and lasted for only 15 minutes. May 5, 1961, astronaut Alan Shepard became the first American in space.

Project Mercury's third flight was also its first orbital flight. During this flight, astronaut John Glenn became the first American to orbit the earth. He remained in orbit for 4 hours and 55 minutes, circling the Earth three times.

On the final *Mercury* flight, astronaut Gordon Cooper orbited the earth 22 times and stayed in space for about 34 hours. Project Mercury accomplished its

John Glenn enters his capsule, *Friendship* 7

mission by answering basic questions about survival in space.

While the original goal of Project Mercury had been to put someone into orbit for a day's flight, the six flights of the program proved that the basic flight sequences that had been developed were sound and that a pilot had a place in orbital flight. Even though astronauts could not maneuver the capsule, they had proven they could take over controls to keep the capsule steady in flight and to direct it to its splash-down point. Project Mercury did a superb job of paving the way for the next manned space program.

Project Gemini

The next manned space flight project was known as *Gemini*. *Gemini's* objectives were to improve techniques needed for a lunar mission, put two persons in space, rendezvous and dock with another spacecraft, and achieve the first walk in space (also known as extravehicular activity, or EVA).

In 1961, President John F. Kennedy committed America to putting an astronaut on the moon before the end of the decade. Accomplishing the objectives of *Gemini* would determine if America would meet that commitment.

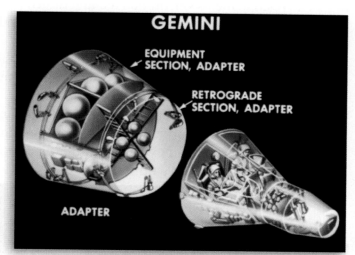

The Two-Man *Gemini* Capsule

There were a total of ten manned *Gemini* flights. *Gemini* was the first two-man capsule and it did achieve the first American walk in space. The *Gemini* flights also gathered additional information about the effect of space flight on the human body. The astronauts studied the effects of weightlessness and were involved in an exercise program. At times, they removed their space suits and relaxed in short-sleeve shirts.

Because the flights lasted for several days, the astronauts were able to establish routines for sleeping and eating. Enough information was gathered to convince scientists that a space flight could safely last for several weeks or even months. These *Gemini* flights were very valuable in America's plan of placing a man on the moon.

Gemini IV's astronaut, Ed White, made a 22-minute space walk.

Project Gemini had been designed with three primary goals: a flight duration of 2 weeks, the development of techniques for a rendezvous in space, and advancement in the understanding of performing EVA. Both of the objectives were of paramount importance if a lunar landing were to be made. Project Apollo was already in the planning stages when the Gemini missions were begun. By the time its missions were completed, the astronauts had the skills necessary to make a moon landing and to meet the national goal set by President Kennedy more than 5 years earilier.

Project Apollo

After the *Gemini* missions were completed, Project Apollo took center stage in America's space program. From the early 1960s, it was known that *Apollo*'s mission would be to put a man on the moon. So, the *Apollo* flights were conducted with that overall goal in mind. Two of the early *Apollo* flights traveled to the moon, orbited it and returned to earth. It was not until *Apollo* 11 that the mission was accomplished. *Apollo* 11 landed on the moon, and on July 20, 1969, Neil Armstrong was the first man to walk on the moon.

A few minutes later, Edwin "Buzz" Aldrin also stepped off the ladder of the *Lunar Module* and joined Armstrong on the moon. Many have called that landing the greatest scientific and engineering accomplishment in history.

After *Apollo* 11, there were six more *Apollo* flights to the moon. Five of them resulted in successful moon landings. The only flight of the six that didn't land on the Moon was *Apollo* 13. *Apollo* 13 had to be aborted due to an explosion in the spacecraft. However, *Apollo* 13 did make a successful emergency landing back on earth.

Buzz Aldrin pictured
next to the American flag

The *Apollo* 11 astronauts were Neil Armstrong,
Michael Collins, and Edwin E. "Buzz" Aldrin.

Aldrin joins
Armstrong on
the surface of
the moon.

Early in the Apollo program, numerous unmanned flights were made for equipment testing. Plans progressed to send astronauts into space to continue testing, but the program was halted for almost 2 years when astronauts Gus Grissom, Ed White and Roger Chaffee were killed in a launch pad fire as they were testing the command module on the *Saturn* booster. The January 27, 1967 tragedy stunned the nation.

In order to eliminate the fire threat that had killed the astronauts, NASA modified both the command module and the astronauts' space suits. These changes and new flight suits were all tested. Finally, in October 1968, the manned *Apollo* flights commenced and the nation was poised to meet the national goal of a man on the moon before the end of the decade.

Project Skylab

Project Skylab, the next space flight project, used a lot of left over equipment from the *Apollo* missions. Skylab's mission was to put a laboratory into space. Scientists had been interested in continuing their studies of the effects of long-duration space flights using a manned orbiting laboratory. This was accomplished when *Skylab* was launched in May 1973.

Skylab had about the same amount of room as a three-bedroom house. It also contained all of the food, water and oxygen needed to support the entire mission. A close look at the picture at the left will show what the living conditions were like. The astronauts slept standing up in restraints that resembled vertical sleeping bags. For eating, knives and forks were secured with magnets. To keep stationary, the astronauts had special triangular cleats on the bottoms of their shoes which would engage in the triangular grid of the floor. For breathing, the air was a combination of oxygen and nitrogen, so the astronauts could move around without their space suits.

Three different crews spent time in the lab. The first Skylab crew spent 28 days in space, the second 59 days, and the final crew spent 84 days in space (84 days being a world record at that time). The main lesson that came from *Skylab* was that people could live and work in space for at least 3 months with no ill effects.

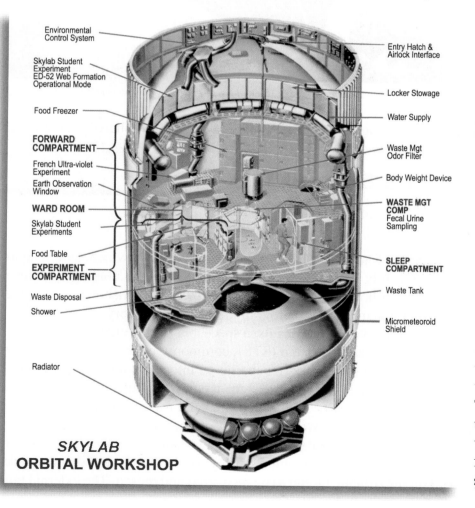

SKYLAB ORBITAL WORKSHOP

Environmental Control System

Skylab Student Experiment ED-52 Web Formation Operational Mode

Food Freezer

FORWARD COMPARTMENT

French Ultra-violet Experiment

Earth Observation Window

WARD ROOM

Skylab Student Experiments

Food Table

EXPERIMENT COMPARTMENT

Waste Disposal

Shower

Radiator

Entry Hatch & Airlock Interface

Locker Stowage

Water Supply

Waste Mgt Odor Filter

Body Weight Device

WASTE MGT COMP Fecal Urine Sampling

SLEEP COMPARTMENT

Waste Tank

Micrometeoroid Shield

Apollo-Soyuz Test Project (ASTP)

After the *Apollo* flights, the last manned space launch before the *Space Shuttle* was the Apollo-Soyuz Test Project. This occurred in July 1975, and involved a linkup in space of an American and a Soviet manned spacecraft. As depicted in the illustration to the right, this was a unique moment in history. These two superpowers, that had been involved in a well-publicized space race for 15 years, meeting and shaking hands in space was indeed a special moment.

The two crews docked together and spent 2 days moving between the capsules helping each other with scientific experiments. The American crew consisted of mission commander Thomas Stafford, veteran of the Gemini and Apollo programs, Donald Slayton, one of the original Mercury astronauts, and Vance Brand (ASTP would be the first space flight for both Slayton and Brand—Slayton having been grounded for a number of years due to medical reasons). Among the Soviet crew was Aleksei Leonov, the first man to walk in space. Back in 1965, Leonov walked in space 2 months prior to the American walk in space. This joint venture truly was an historic event.

Cutaway View of Docked Apollo and Soyuz Spacecraft.

Apollo-Soyuz marked the end of an era. It marked the end of the expendable spacecraft and launch vehicle. A new era was being ushered in, the era of the reusable space vehicle, the *space shuttle*.

US Second Era

Space Shuttle

For more than thirty years, the Space Shuttle has been the primary means by which American astronauts were launched into space. On July 21, 2011, with the completion of the final Space Shuttle mission, that era came to an end. The following section chronicles the accomplishments and other significant events of the longest running manned space program in American history.

From 1975 until 1981, the U.S. didn't have any astronauts in space, but that changed with the *space shuttle*. In April 1981, the Space Transportation System (STS), commonly called the *space shuttle*, was launched. The *space shuttle* provided a system for transportation into space and a return back to earth. This was considered a major advantage of the shuttle since it could be used again and again.

The *space shuttle* consisted of three main parts: the orbiter, the solid rocket boosters and the external tank. The orbiter looked like an airplane and was about the same size as a DC-9 jet. The orbiter carried the crew and the payload. The other two parts were required to launch the shuttle into space. The boosters would burn out after approximately two minutes. They would then be jettisoned and descend by parachute, landing safely in the Atlantic Ocean to be recovered and reused. The external tank would be jettisoned after its propellant was consumed (after approximately 8½ minutes into the flight) and impact in a remote ocean location. The tanks were not recovered.

In order to return to Earth, the crew would fire the orbital maneuvering system (OMS) engines in the direction opposite to their path of travel (retrograde). The maneuver would only slightly reduce the vehicle's velocity; however, it would significantly lower its altitude, and thus bring it into the upper fringes of the atmosphere where aerodynamic drag would slow it down. Friction heating would produce outside temperatures approaching 3,000°F while the elaborate thermal protection system (TPS) would keep cabin temperatures at a comfortable level. As atmospheric pressures increased, the vehicle would transition for spacecraft to aircraft, completing it mission with a runway landing.

The first *Space Shuttle* orbiter was actually the *Enterprise*, but it was only used for atmospheric flight tests. It was not designed for going into space. The other

The Liftoff of the Space Shuttle Dis*covery*

The *Hubble Space Telescope*

five orbiters have all gone into space and have been used for a variety of missions. They were the *Columbia*, *Challenger*, *Discovery*, *Atlantis* and *Endeavour*.

The first four flights of the *Columbia* were mainly tests. Most of the concern centered around how the *Columbia* would handle reentry into the earth's atmosphere and how its protective shields would perform. STS-5 was declared the first operational flight, and it occurred in November 1982. From orbit, the *STS-5* launched 2 satellites.

Over the years, the *space shuttle* has been used in many ways to further our knowledge of space. The first American woman in space, Dr. Sally Ride, was aboard the *Challenger* for STS-7. STS-9 delivered the first European Space Agency Spacelab into space. The 11th *Space Shuttle* mission placed the *Long-Duration Exposure Facility (LDEF)* into space to conduct experiments. A few years later, the *LDEF* was retrieved and the many experiments analyzed.

On January 28, 1986, less than 2 minutes after launch, the *Challenger* exploded on the 25th Space Shuttle mission. The entire crew of seven died. A leak in one of the solid rocket boosters was the cause. After the *Challenger* accident, the shuttle program was suspended for over 2 years. After design changes were made, and safety procedures and precautions taken, on September 29, 1988, the *space shuttle* flights resumed.

In April 1990, the shuttle *Discovery* deployed the *Hubble Space Telescope*. The *Hubble Space Telescope* is operating at over 300 miles above the earth and is free of any atmospheric interference. Therefore, the objects are seen much more clearly than from ground observations.

Atlantis, with mission STS-34, placed the *Galileo* probe into space. The probe investigated Jupiter for nearly eight years. In 1993, STS-55 carried the European developed *Spacelab* into orbit. Many useful experiments were conducted from the *Spacelab*.

As you can tell from the few examples that have been mentioned, the *space shuttle* was designed to be the workhorse of our space program, and indeed it has been. The Space Shuttle has served our nation well during its 30-year, 135-flight history. Our knowledge of space has increased tremendously with the help of the *space shuttle*.

A second tragedy, however, befell the Space shuttle program when on January 16, 2003 during the launch of STS-107 a piece of foam insulation broke away from the external tank and struck the leading edge of the left wing of the orbiter Columbia. The estimated weight of the foam chunk was 1.7 lbs. and analysis showed it impacted the wing at approximately 775 feet/sec. (or 528 MPH). Determined by post-flight testing and analysis, the force was found to be sufficient to punch a hole in the leading edge of the wing; however, due to the rapidly decreasing aerodynamic pressure (Columbia was heading to the vacuum of space) the damage did not impair the vehicle's ability to achieve orbit. The impact was recorded by ground cameras, and NASA and contractor engineers tried desperately to convince management to obtain clearer images on orbit, to further and more accurately assess the result of the impact. All requests went unheeded and no attempt was made to obtain additional data. Columbia continued on its mission for nearly 16 days, and on February 1 fired its engines to return to Earth. While streaking across the western United States heading for a landing at Kennedy Space Center, the effects of the damage that occurred on January 16 came shockingly into view. The resulting hole in the leading edge of the wing allowed hot gasses generated by reentry heating to melt the aluminum structure of the wing and break it apart. The vehicle then rapidly disintegrated and showered debris on east Texas and western Louisiana. None of the crew survived. NASA suspended Space Shuttle flights for over two years in an effort to determine the cause and take corrective action. Flights resumed on July 26, 2005 with the successful launch and flight of Discovery on STS-114.

The Crew

Prior to the *Space Shuttle* Program, all US astronauts were highly qualified pilots, and many were specialists in other fields as well. The shuttle had numerous diversified

The crew of the *Challenger* mission STS-7 included the first woman in space, Dr. Sally Ride.

The seven members of the *Challenger Space Shuttle* 51-L mission are: (back row, left to right) Mission Specialist El Onizuka, Teacher in Space participant S. Christa McAuliffe, Payload Specialist Greg Jarvis and Mission Specialist Judy Resnik; (front row, left to right) Pilot Mike Smith, Commander Dick Scobee, and Mission Specialist Ron McNair.

missions that required the knowledge and skills of several scientific fields. Hence, the pool of astronauts contained individuals with special skills, but not necessarily those of a pilot.

When NASA asked for volunteers in 1976, over 8,000 applications were received. From this number, 208 were selected as finalists. The finalists were interviewed and given medical examinations at the Johnson Space Center in Houston, Texas. Thirty-five of the finalists were chosen to undergo a 2-year training program, after which they would join the existing pool of more experienced astronauts.

The "new" astronaut candidates included women and men, pilots and non-pilots, and civilian and military personnel. There were 21 military officers and 14 civilians. All were grouped for assignment

The crew of the *Discovery* Space Shuttle Mission STS-95 included the 77-year-old Payload Specialist, Senator John H. Glenn, Jr. Glenn was the first American to orbit the earth in his *Mercury* capsule *Friendship 7* in 1962.

The other crew members are: (back row, left to right) Mission Specialist Scott E. Parazynski, M.D.; Payload Commander Mission Specialist Stephen K. Robinson, PhD.; Mission Specialist Pedro Duque; Payload Specialist John H. Glenn, Jr.; (front row, left to right) Pilot Steve Lindsey, Lt Col, USAF; Payload Specialist Chiaki Mukai, M.D., PhD.; and Commander Curt Brown, Lt Col, USAF.

as either pilots or mission specialists. The pilots were trained to fly the *space shuttle* orbiter while the mission specialists were trained according to the needs of programmed missions. However, with systems as complex as the Space Shuttle's, there had to be a certain amount of cross training.

Imagine the amount of training astronaut candidates must have experience to qualify as a full-fledged astronauts. They had to understand the organization and structure of their employer, NASA. They certainly must be familiar with the systems and structural aspects of the spacecraft. They had to be physically fit. They had to understand the aerospace technology associated with the *space shuttle* in order to support technical or scientific assignments. They also were taught what to expect physiologically and psychologically while in orbital flight.

Pilot astronauts kept their flying skills sharpened with lots of flight time in jet aircraft. Mission specialist astronauts were trained in navigation, communications and other subjects related to aircraft flight. They also would get flight time. Their flights in the T-38 jet aircraft were as "rear seaters" to help the pilots with planning navigation and communications. Mission specialists with little flight experience would become accustomed to high altitude and the unusual sensations of various flight attitudes. Rides in NASA's *"Vomit Comet"* were essential to their learning to adjust to free-fall.

Once they were fully qualified, the astronauts would continue training according to need. For example, after an astronaut team was selected for a flight, each person received intensified training for the flight's mission. The missions differed for every flight and there were numerous submissions to be accomplished. Thus, learning occupied a large segment of an shuttle astronaut's time.

The payload specialist was a specially trained person considered to be an expert for a particular payload. Most of the payload specialist's training was received from the payload developer and pertained to a highly technical or scientific project. However, every payload specialist did get some training from NASA. This training was conducted at the Johnson Space Center and involves about 150 hours of classroom time. The training was sufficient to familiarize the payload specialist with the spacecraft and payload support equipment, crew operations and emergency procedures.

The Space Shuttle Orbiter *Endeavor*

The Craft

The orbiter was the largest, most sophisticated manned spacecraft ever devised. It had a wingspan of 78.06 feet. Its total fuselage length, to include its engines and vertical stabilizer, was 122.2 feet. The orbiter's payloads could weigh a total of 65,000 pounds on a single flight. With lighter-weight payloads, the craft could reach an orbital altitude of approximately 400 miles.

The orbiter carried the crew and payload to and from space. Like a conventional aircraft, the orbiter's fuselage was constructed in three major sections: the forward fuselage, the mid-fuselage and the aft-fuselage.

Astronauts and payload specialists occupied the forward fuselage. While the forward fuselage was further subdivided into smaller units, two decks formed the cabin of working and living quarters. The flight deck was where control of the craft and manipulation of most payloads occurred. Below the

***Endeavor* crew members capture the *INTELSAT* VI communications satellite.**

flight deck was the mid-deck which contained the crew's living quarters. Here we find the astronauts' living quarters.

The mid-deck hads storage space for food, a galley where the food was prepared for consumption, sleeping stations for four crew members at one time, multiple storage lockers, a toilet, wet trash storage and an air lock. The air lock was used to transfer from mid deck into the payload bay area when required. The air lock was where extra-vehicular activity (EVA) suits are stored. It was a cylinder that is about 7 feet high and slightly more than 5 feet wide.

An astronaut going for EVA entered the air lock and would put on the very complex suit, which contained its own life-support system. Once the suit was checked out, pressure inside the air lock was reduced slowly until a space environment was achieved. The hatch leading into the payload bay is then opened for EVA. Astronauts completing an EVA returned to the mid-deck in reverse manner, storing their EVA suits within the air lock. The center-fuselage section (or mid-body) contained the payload bay. The payload bay was about 60 feet long and had a diameter of about 15 feet. Its doors were opened and closed by a mission specialist working on the flight deck.

A very important unit located within the payload bay area was the remote manipulator system's manipulator arm. This arm also was controlled from the flight deck, and it was the action portion of a very complex system. It could deploy, retrieve or otherwise affect a payload without the need of an EVA. The arm had a special light and television camera so that its human operator could see the detail of what was taking place as the system was operated. It was possible for two manipulator arms to be located in the payload bay if required by a mission. However, only one arm could be operated at a time.

The orbiter's aft-fuselage primarily contained, or had attached to it, units for orbital propulsion and aerodynamic flight control. The craft's main propulsion system engines, orbital maneuvering system engines, and aft reaction control system engines were found within the aft- fuselage. The vertical stabilizer was attached to the topside of the aft fuselage, and the body flap was attached to the bottom side of the aft-fuselage. The vertical stabilizer's attached rudder was sectioned so that it could be "spread" and served as a speed brake in atmospheric flight. The body flap also served as a speed brake during the return flight to earth.

The craft's wings were attached to the center- and aft-fuselages, with the major portions joined to the center-fuselage. The wings' function did not begin until the upper atmosphere was encountered upon reentry. The primary function of the wings, of course, was to provide aerodynamic lift for the craft. Recall from earlier discussions of space definitions that this occurs at approximately 62 miles above the earth. However, they first served as a brake and energy dissipater to slow the craft to aerodynamic flight speed.

In addition to acting as speed brake and lift producers, the wings housed the craft's main landing gear. To provide the craft a means of aerodynamic control, the wings were fitted with elevons. These elevons were located along the wings' trailing edges and function as either elevators or ailerons, according to how they are moved.

Payloads

The shuttle could carry a variety of payloads into space. At one time, it was thought satellites could be deployed from the shuttle more efficiently than from expendable launch vehicles. The original plan was have the Space Shuttle serve as the common carrier for virtually all payloads going to Earth orbit, cislunar, or interplanetary space. In order to accomplish that goal, the vehicle would have to be able to launch frequently and routinely. The original flight goal was to have 50 launches per year from three pads (two in Florida and one in California). This was later reduced to 26, and after the Challenger disaster of 1986, it became apparent that the program would never meet such a high flight rate. The highest flight rate ever achieved by the program was nine during 1985. The California launch pad that was built for west coast flights at a cost of $5 billion was never used during the program. It was a result of the Challenger disaster investigation that NASA refocused Space Shuttle missions to those that required the unique presence of an astronaut crew. Two notable ones were the Spacelab and the Long Duration Exposure Facility missions.

Long-Duration Exposure Facility (LDEF)

Long-Duration Exposure Facility (LDEF)
during deployment from shuttle.

The *Long Duration Exposure Facility* was designed to provide long-term data on the space environment and its effects on space systems and operations. Constructed of aluminum, *LDEF* was a nearly cylindrical 12-sided regular polygon 30 feet long and just over 14 feet in diameter. Fifty-two experiments were mounted in 86 trays around the periphery and on both ends.

One of the largest payloads ever deployed by the shuttle, *LDEF* was placed into orbit by Space Shuttle *Challenger* on April 7, 1984. The facility remained in space for 69 months, completing 32,422 orbits of earth before it was retrieved by Space Shuttle *Columbia* on January 11, 1990. The retrieval of *LDEF* and its experiments was accomplished about 1month before the facility would have reentered earth's atmosphere and been destroyed.

The 5-plus-year flight of the facility was a direct result of the suspension of all shuttle operations follow-ing the loss of *Challenger* in 1986. The result was that the facility, having been launched during a solar minimum and retrieved at a solar maximum, remained in orbit through half of a solar cycle. This lengthened stay increased the scientific and technological value toward our understanding of the space environment and its effects.

The experiments carried by *LDEF* involved the participation of more than 200 principal investigators representing 33 private companies, 21 universities, seven NASA centers, nine Department of Defense laboratories and eight foreign countries. Following the de-integration of each experiment from *LDEF*, research activities included a radiation survey, infrared-video survey, meteoroid and debris survey, con-tamination inspection and extensive photographic documentation. After these activities were completed, the experiment trays were returned to the laboratories of each principal investigator. Post-flight special investigations and continued principal investigator research resulted in a total number of investigators of between 300 and 400, and provided a broad and detailed collection of space environment data.

Post Shuttle Era

Astronauts not on flight status for a mission have other duties to perform. These duties may include assignments in mission control or other support functions. Some of the astronauts assist with public understanding of the *space shuttle* flight missions by appearing with news media personnel and providing expert commentary.

When missions are not being flown, it is also the astronauts' duty to respond to requests for public appearances. Their knowledge of present systems and plans for future manned space flights is in considerable demand by various organizations. These public appearances are a key part to increasing public awareness of the space program. Astronauts provide the public with insights into space exploration and the value of spending billions on the space program.

Spacelab

Spacelab was an orbiting laboratory designed by the European Space Agency to be flown in the space shuttle's cargo bay. Designed on a modular principle, the *Spacelab* was comprised of a long or short pressurized cabin inside which astronauts could work on experiments. Between one and three U-shaped pallets could be added to the laboratory, allowing experiments to be exposed directly to the vacuum of space.

These pallets were special modular containers in which the experiments could be placed. *Spacelab's* environment provided payload specialists with a "short-sleeve-shirt environment" that allowed them to work on experiments without a space suit. To facilitate entry to the *Spacelab*, a tunnel was attached to the airlock; entry to the module was through the orbiter's airlock and this tunnel.

Spacelab missions addressed a wide variety of scientific topics including astronomy, microgravity, life sciences, biomedicine and industrial technology. The flights were discontinued in 1998 as preparations were made for the Space Station Project.

Cutaway View of Spacelab Installed in Payload Bay of Shuttle Orbiter

Legacy

In spite of the two catastrophic failures, during its 30-year life, the Space Shuttle had become a worldwide symbol of American ingenuity and advanced technological ability. People from all over the world would come to the Kennedy Space Center to view a launch or tour the impressive facilities. A total of 135 missions were flown between April 1981 and July 2011.

The following statistical data gives an indication of the massive scope of the single biggest space project ever undertaken by any nation:

209,000,000,000: The estimated total cost (in U.S. dollars) of the program from development through its retirement.

3,513,638: The weight in pounds of cargo that NASA's space shuttles have launched into orbit (more than half the payload weight of every single space launch in history since 1957 combined).

229,132: The amount of cargo (in pounds) that NASA's shuttles have returned to Earth from space through 2010.

198,728.5: The number of man-hours astronauts spent in space during the 30-year history (about 8,280 days of manned spaceflight).

21,030: The number of orbits of Earth completed.

3,000: The scorching hot temperatures (in Fahrenheit) experienced in the hottest moments of atmospheric re-entry during landing.

1,323: Number of days in space spent for all orbiter vehicles.

833: The total number of crewmembers of all 135 space shuttle missions, with some individuals riding multiple times and 14 astronauts killed during the Challenger and Columbia accidents.

789: The number of astronauts and cosmonauts who have returned to Earth on a NASA shuttle orbiter. Some crewmembers actually launched into orbit on Russian Soyuz vehicles and returned home via shuttle.

355: The actual number of individual astronauts and cosmonauts who have flown on the space shuttle (306 men and 49 women hailing from 16 different countries).

234: The total number of days space shuttle astronauts spent at the International Space Station between 1998 and 2011, the construction phase of the orbiting laboratory.

180: The total number of satellites and other major payloads, including components for the International Space Station, deployed by NASA space shuttles.

135: Total number of NASA space shuttle missions that will have flown between 1981 and 2011.

52: The total number of satellites, space station components and other payloads returned from orbit on NASA shuttle missions.

37: The number of times a shuttle orbiter has docked at the International Space Station during the outpost's lifetime.

14: The number of astronauts killed during the space shuttle Challenger accident of 1986 and Columbia accident in 2003. They were: (Challenger's STS-51-L Crew) Commander Francis "Dick" Scobee, pilot Mike Smith, mission specialists Judy Resnik, Ellison Onizuka and Ron McNair, and payload specialists Greg Jarvis and Christa McAuliffe; (Columbia's STS-107 Crew) Commander Rick Husband; pilot William McCool; mission specialists Michael Anderson, David Brown, Kalpana Chawla and Laurel Clark, and payload specialist Ilan Ramon, Israel's first astronaut.

9: The number of times a shuttle orbiter docked at Russia's space station Mir between 1994 and 1998.

8: The greatest number of astronauts to fly on a shuttle at one time. It happened at least twice: during the STS-61A shuttle mission in 1985, then again in 1995 during the STS-71 flight's return from the Russian Space Station Mir.

7: The total number of missions by shuttle astronauts to retrieve, repair, and then redeploy a satellite in orbit.

5: NASA's final tally for the number of spaceworthy vehicles built for the space shuttle fleet. The orbiter vehicles that flew in space were: Columbia, Challenger, Discovery, Atlantis and Endeavour. Challenger and Columbia were lost during spaceflight tragedies.

3: The number of main landing sites for NASA space shuttles at the end of their missions (Kennedy Space Center in Cape Canaveral, FL, Edwards Air Force Base in California, White Sands Space Harbor, New Mexico). Only one mission landed at White Sands, STS-3. In addition to these three sites, NASA had a long list of airport runways that could be suitable for a shuttle landing in an emergency.

2: The total number of female space shuttle commanders after 30 years of shuttle flight (U.S. Air Force Col. (retired) Eileen Collins and U.S. Air Force Col. (retired) Pamela Melroy).

1: The number of NASA's Original Seven Mercury astronauts to fly on a NASA shuttle. In October 1998, Mercury astronaut John Glenn launched on the space shuttle Discovery during the STS-95 mission. At age 77, Glenn (then a U.S. Senator) was the oldest person ever to fly in space and continues to hold that distinction to this day.

The retired orbiter vehicles now have a less demanding (although some would argue and equally important) mission. They will reside in museums (no doubt for countless generations) with the intent of inspiring new generations of future space explorers.

Soviet Manned Space Program

The Soviet Union's space flight programs developed along the same lines as the American programs and occurred at approximately the same times. However, the Soviets had several firsts in the space race.

Vostok

As mentioned earlier, the Soviets launched the first satellite into space. After *Sputnik*, the Soviets launched nine more Sputniks in about 3 1/2 years. The last two were accomplished in preparation for their first manned space flight.

With the initial advantage of having large rockets, the Soviets put the first man in space on April 12, 1961. Major Yuri Gagarin, aboard *Vostok* 1, was the first man to escape from earth's atmosphere into space. Although he only stayed up for one orbit (108 minutes), he described sights no human eyes had ever seen before.

In June 1963, *Vostok* 6 had the distinction of carrying Valentina Tereshkova, the first woman, into space. She completed 48 orbits and was in space for 3 days before returning safely to earth. This was the last *Vostok* flight.

Pictured in the foreground is Yuri Gagarin
of the Soviet Union, the first human in space.

Voskhod

The success of *Vostok* led to the Voskhod series. The first *Voskhod* was launched in October of 1964, and was a three-man capsule.

On March 18, 1965, aboard the *Voskhod 2* spacecraft, Cosmonaut Alexei Leonov became the first person to "walk in space." He spent 12 minutes outside of his spacecraft. This space walk occurred about two months before the Americans walked in space.

Soyuz

Soyuz means "union," and the spacecraft were designed for docking in space. *Soyuz* consists of three modules: the Instrumentation/Propulsion Module, Descent Module, and Orbital Module.

Soyuz is capable of accommodating three crew members and has carried passengers from many nations including the United States. In fact, until a new vehicle is developed, the *Soyuz* will be the only means by which American astronauts will be able to travel to the *International Space Station*. *Soyuz* was developed as part of the USSR's Moon landing program. That program got off to a rocky start when in April 1967 *Soyuz* 1 was launched. The mission had many annoying problems from the start but ended in tragedy when the vehicle crashed on landing (due to a parachute failure), killing the sole crewmember, cosmonaut Vladimir Komarov. When the Moon program was cancelled, the Soviets decided to refocus their space program and use *Soyuz* for Earth orbital missions, as well as to transport cosmonauts to the *Salyut, Almaz,* and later *Mir,* space stations. Currently, the exclusive mission for the *Soyuz* is to transport crews to the *International Space Station* (ISS).

The Launch of the *Soyuz*

A flight begins with crew members entering the Descent Module (somewhat of a misnomer since members use the module for both ascent and descent portions of the mission). Once in orbit the crew can utilize the volume of the Orbital Module as they navigate to the ISS. Once docked, they transfer from the Orbital Module to begin their duties on the ISS. When their mission is complete, the crew exits the ISS and enters the Orbital Module of the *Soyuz*. They navigate away from the station, enter the Descent Module, and fire the retro rockets contained in the Instrumentation/ Propulsion Module. The three modules then separate, the Descent Module brings the crew safely back to Earth, while the other modules burn up in the atmosphere. The Descent Module lands on dry ground by parachute aided by small rockets that fire just before contact to help cushion the force of impact.

Soyuz has experienced two fatal accidents during its 45-plus year history—the inaugural flight described above, and a second in 1971 in which all three crewmembers died due to an unexpected cabin depressurization during reentry. Also noteworthy was the mission when the *Soyuz* saved its crew from almost certain death. In 1983, during ascent, a catastrophic launch vehicle explosion occurred and the on-board rocket escape system pulled the crew to safety. It has been over forty years since a *Soyuz* fatality, and as a result, it has gained a reputation of being a reliable workhorse for human spaceflight and will no doubt continue to launch space explorers from many nations for many years to come.

Upon reentry into the earth's atmosphere, the three modules would separate. Only the descent module reentered the earth's atmosphere intact. Forty *Soyuz* spacecraft were launched between 1967 and 1981.

China's Manned Space Program

China has become only the third nation to build and launch its own manned spacecraft. In the 2000s China joined a very elite group of nations by launching its first astronaut, Yang Liwei, into orbit. At this writing, China had completed four successful manned missions, with a fifth scheduled for 2013.

Shenzhou Spacecraft

Based on the Russian *Soyuz* design, the *Shenzhou* is similar in appearance; however, it has many significant improvements. The interior volume of *Shenzhou* is greater than *Soyuz*, and the Orbital Module can dethatch and perform autonomous orbital operations. Like *Soyuz*, *Shenzhou* can accommodate a crew of three. It is boosted into orbit using china's Long March launch vehicle.

Tiangong Space Laboratory

Similar in concept to the early Soviet Salyut station, *Tiangong* is entirely of Chinese design and construction. It can accommodate three crewmembers, but is not intended to be continually manned. It is intended, however, that *Tiangong* will be the forerunner of a much larger, permanently manned Chinese space station.

Space Stations

The basic objective of both the Soviet and American space stations was the physiological study of long-term manned flight. Again, the Soviets were the first to launch a space station. So, let us take a look at their program, and then we will discuss the American space stations.

Soviet Space Stations

Salyut

The Soviets launched their *Salyut* 1 space station on April 19, 1971, and on April 22, 1971, *Soyuz* 10 docked with the world's first space laboratory, although the crew of the *Soyuz* did not board the *Salyut*. In June of 1971, *Soyuz* 11 docked with *Salyut* 1 for 22 days. This was the mission that experienced the second *Soyuz* fatality described earlier.

By the end of 1976, the Soviet Union had put up six *Salyut* space stations. These stations were experimental laboratories and were the basis of the Soviet Union's long-term manned program. Despite setbacks in the program, they continued to pursue the *Salyut* Project. By the time *Soyuz* 23 failed to dock with *Salyut* 5 and had to make a quick trip home, there had been 7 failures in 11 attempts to complete space station missions.

In reality, *Salyuts* 2, 3 and 5 were classified Soviet military *Almaz* space stations. They were put in space for the purpose of conducting orbital reconnaissance. The USSR abandoned the program in favor of less expensive unmanned satellites.

For *Salyut* 6, the Soviets made a few changes, most notably a second docking port and a new propulsion system. These two changes made it possible to resupply, repair and refuel missions much easier. *Salyut* 6 was launched in September 1977, and it stayed in space for about 4 years.

Salyut 7, launched in 1982, had many more modifications. In 1984, Svetlana Savitskaya visited *Salyut* 7 and became the first woman to space walk. Also in 1984, a Soviet crew set an endurance record of 234 days in space. *Salyut* 7 fell back to earth in 1991.

Mir

The next Soviet space station model was the *Mir. Mir* (means "peace") was launched in February 1986, so it was in space before *Salyut* 7 fell to earth. *Mir* weighed approximately 220,000 lbs. compared to *Salyut's* weight of 40,000 lbs. *Mir* was much more advanced than *Salyut* in that it had a central node to which several modules could be attached. The ability to expand with additional modules gave *Mir* far more capability than *Salyut* was designed to have.

Mir

Mir was established to serve as a microgravity research laboratory, assembled by the USSR and, after the break-up, operated by Russia. During the time of its operation it was visited by crewmembers representing 12 different nations (including the United States). Between 1995 and 1998, as part of Phase 1 of the ISS program, seven American astronauts participated as crewmembers on board Mir. During that same period, Space shuttle orbiters docked with Mir nine times.

The *Mir* space station was originally planned to be followed by a *Mir 2*, but only the core module, *Zvezda*, became an integral part of the *International* Space Station. *Mir* went through de-orbit and broke up in the earth's atmosphere over the South Pacific in March of 2001.

American Space Station

Skylab

As early as 1970, the United States had made plans to establish a space laboratory program. This program was originally called the *Apollo* Applications Program, but was later renamed Skylab. The original intent of the program was to make some practical use of leftover hardware from the *Apollo* moon landings. Instead, it gradually grew into a vital step in our mastery of the space environment.

On May 14, 1973, the *Skylab* 1 unmanned orbital workshop was placed into orbit, 2 years after *Salyut*. There was a failure in the powered phase of the launch, which ripped off one of the solar array wings from the workshop. Stopgap measures were taken to control the solar radiation and prepare a repair kit for the astronauts who would go up and dock with *Skylab* 1.

Skylab was constructed partly from off-the-shelf hardware. Its main compartment, called the orbital workshop module, was constructed from a *Saturn* V rocket section. Within this section were the astronaut's living quarters, a work area and many of the vehicle's scientific experiments.

A second special module was an air-lock device used to exit and enter the station when necessary to perform work the station outside. This particular module proved very necessary when the astronauts had to erect a sunshade at the location of a micrometeoroid shield that had been torn off during the launch phase. A secondary function to the micrometeoroid shield was to serve as a sunshade to keep the laboratory/living quarters from overheating.

A third module was the multiple docking adapter. This portion was especially designed to accept the *Apollo* command module in airtight linkup so that the astronauts could transfer safely into the laboratory and back to the command module for return to earth.

Skylab was NASA's first orbited space station. Three different crews lived at different times in the *Skylab*. The last crew stayed for 84 days, which was the longest of the crews. During their stays, the crews conducted many experiments. They demonstrated that people could live and work in space. No other crews visited *Skylab*, but it remained in space for 6 years before reentering the earth's atmosphere and falling back to earth. Most of *Skylab* burned up on reentry, but some pieces landed in the Indian Ocean and western Australia. Some pieces were recovered.

Skylab

International Space Station (ISS)

The ISS evolved from NASA's *Space Station Freedom* project which was announced by President Ronald Reagan in 1984. The *Freedom* project was plagued by numerous budget cuts and hardware redesigns. By 1993, nearly $10 billion had been spent and not a single piece of flight hardware had been produced. In view of this, the administration of President Bill Clinton arranged to bring in Russia as a major partner and financial backer. As a result, the *International Space Station* was born. *Freedom* was not so much cancelled as it was folded in to the new ISS program, thus making use of much of the engineering research and development that had already been accomplished.

Assembly of the ISS is now complete. It

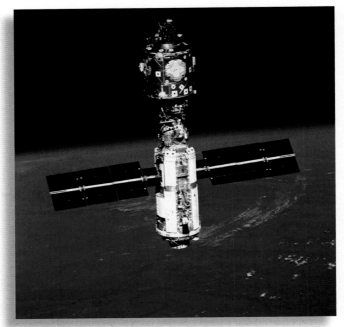

STS096-042-715 (3 June 1999)---A STS-96 crew member aboard Discovery recorded this image of the ISS during a fly-around to follow separation of the two crafts. Lake Hulun Nur in the China is visible in the lower left portion of the frame. A portion of the work performed on the May 30 space walk by astronauts Tamara Jernigan and Dan Barry is evident at various points on the ISS, including the installation of the Russian-built crane (called Strela) and the U.S. built crane. *(Courtesy of NASA)*

is the largest and most massive man-made structure ever assembled in outer space. With 29,600 cu. ft. of habitable volume, it has more living space than a large 4-bedroom home. Its physical dimensions make it larger than the playing surface of a football field.

Hundreds of scientific investigations have been conducted on the space station and much more scientific data is to come. Results from space station research, is available on the internet from NASA.

"One of the primary goals of the Space Station scientists is to develop technologies and capabilities that will allow humans to go places far away from Planet Earth. If we don't have these capabilities, we are pretty much destined to stay close to the Earth — and I don't think that's what humans are all about." (quote from *Expedition* 1 Commander Bill Shepherd)

"The *International Space Station* is a perfect stepping-stone for us to perfect the technology, to perfect the operational tempo, and operational parameters needed in order to make long duration missions successful." (quoted from Expedition 9 by Flight Engineer Mike Fincke).

The *International Space Station* continues to be the focal point for the advancement of technology in a realm with gravity. Over the years to come, this space-based laboratory will provide new and wonderful scientific information that will benefit all mankind and hopefully extend life beyond our home planet, Space Ship Earth!

S106-E-5318 (18 September 2000) backdropped against the earth's horizon, the *International Space Station* (ISS) is seen following it undocking with the space shuttle *Atlantis*. After accomplishing all mission objectives in outfitting the station for the first resident crew, the seven astronauts and cosmonauts undocked at 3:46 GMT on Sept. 18, over Russia near the northeastern portion of the Ukrain. When Atlantis was at a safe distance from the station, about 450 feet, astronaut Scot Altman, pilot, performed a 90 minute, double-loop fly around to enable the crew to document the station's exterior. He fired Atlantis' jets one final time to separate from the station at 5:35 GMT. *(Courtesy NASA)*

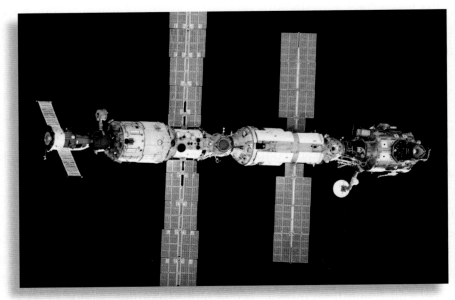

S97-E-5010 (2 December 2000) ISS against the darkness of space. This shows the progress of development in just a four month period.
(Courtesy NASA)

S114-E-7200 (6 August 2005) – The *International Space Station* **is backdropped against a heavily cloud-covered part of earth as the orbital outpost moves away from the space shuttle** *Discovery.* **Earlier, the crews of the two spacecraft concluded nine days of cooperative work. As the shuttle moved away to a distance of 400 feet, astronaut and pilot, James Kelly, initiated a slow fly-around of the station, while cameras on each space craft captured video and still images of the other. Undocking occurred at 2:24 a.m. (CDT) August 6, 2005.)**
(Courtesy NASA)

Living and Working in Space Stations

The space station has been a part of the manned space program for many years. The creation and assembly of the *International Space Station* provides a permanent laboratory where gravity, temperature and pressure can be manipulated to achieve a variety of scientific and engineering pursuits that are impossible in ground-based laboratories. It is a test bed for technologies of the future as well as a laboratory for research on new, advanced industrial materials, communications technology, medical research and more. On-orbit assembly of the station began as a cooperative effort between nations of earth's global community and its completion will be one of the largest international scientific and technological endeavors ever undertaken.

What is it like to live and work on the space station? Working in space presents its own unique challenges, not the least of which is microgravity. The force of gravity in low-earth orbit is almost as strong as it is on the ground. However, the outward force on the station as it orbits earth counterbalances the downward pull of gravity and this free-fall state creates an environment known as microgravity. The pull of microgravity is approximately

Weightless in Space

Foot restraints hold astronaut in place.

one-millionth the gravity on earth, but since all unsecured objects (including people) fall together within the station, they appear to be weightless and they float. Astronauts have learned how to function effectively in this apparent weightlessness and have adapted to working in a microgravity environment.

The atmosphere inside the space station is a mixture of nitrogen and oxygen, a better system than one using pure oxygen since earth's atmosphere is a similar mixture. The air pressure and temperature is also regulated and astronauts wear comfortable clothing such as T-shirts and shorts, or sports shirts and pants.

Much of the food aboard the station is dehydrated, saving both weight and storage space. A variety of tasty, nutritious foods and beverages are available; some foods may

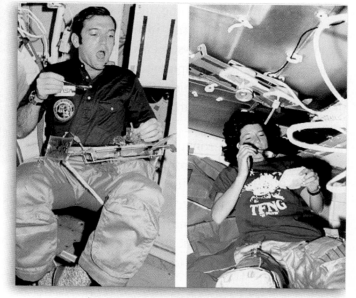
Astronauts eat their food strapped to their laps or to the cabin ceiling.

be eaten as is, while others can be heated before serving. Since the electrical power for the *ISS* is generated from solar panels rather than from fuel cells, there is no extra water generated aboard the station. Water is recycled from cabin air, but not enough for significant use in the food system. Hence the percentage of rehydratable foods will decrease and the percentage of thermostabilized foods will increase over time. Water is plentiful as it is a byproduct of the fuel cells when generating electricity; therefore, re-hydration of foods or beverages can be easily accomplished. Astronauts are able to anchor themselves in place for eating through the use of special floor restraints known as foot loops.

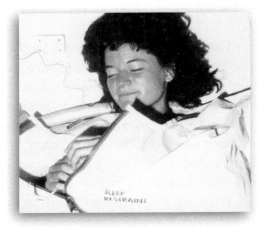

Astronaut Sally Ride in Sleep Restraint

A wide variety of choices in sleeping accommodations are available to the astronauts, including such options as sleeping in their seats, restrained in bunks, in sleeping bags or simply by tethering themselves to the wall. Sleeping bags would most likely be cocoon-like restraints that could be attached to lockers or walls, much like current shuttle systems. In microgravity, there is no "up," and astronauts can comfortably sleep either vertically or horizontally.

Recreation is an important factor in space station living. Along with regular exercise necessary to counter muscle atrophy that occurs in the microgravity environment, cards, games, books, taped music and videos are available to crew members.

Sanitation is vitally important within the confines of the space station. Since the population of some microbes can increase extraordinarily in microgravity, infectious illnesses could be easily spread. Eating equipment, dining areas, toilets, and sleeping facilities need to be cleaned regularly to prevent micro-organism growth.

On-Orbit Repair of Syncom Satellite

Work done by astronauts aboard the space station varies according to needs and missions, but, in addition to regular housekeeping chores, work involves developing and processing new materials, performing fundamental medical research, and performing long-duration research satellites and spacecraft in orbit.

Any activity outside the space station requires astronauts to wear space suits. The first space walk, or extra-vehicular activity (EVA), was accomplished by Aleksei Leonov in March 1965, when he went outside his *Voskhod* II spacecraft for about 12 minutes. In June of that same year, astronaut Ed White spent 22 minutes outside his *Gemini* IV capsule. By 1973, *Skylab* astronauts were setting duration records for EVAs with outside missions lasting more than 7 hours. Extra-vehicular activity allowed astronauts to retrieve satellites or to repair them while they remain in orbit. Missions such as the repair of the *Hubble Space Telescope* allowed earthbound scientists to continue making astounding new discoveries as they use orbiting satellites and telescopes to help them understand the universe.

In the 1930s, high-altitude flyers wore pressure suits; all of the *Mercury* astronauts wore a modified version of a US Navy high-altitude jet aircraft pressure suit. Mobility was quite limited in these suits. Later designs provided greater suit mobility. During the Gemini missions, a lighter weight, easily removable suit was developed and for the first time astronauts removed their spacesuits while in orbit. During the *Apollo* missions, the lunar surface EVA suits had a separate backpack-type life support system that had to be connected to the suit. The suit was also tailor-made for each astronaut, a time-consuming and expensive process. With the advent of the Space Shuttle Program, suits became lighter, more durable and easier to move around in. Manufactured in small, medium and large sizes, today's suits may be worn interchangeably by men or women. Life support systems are built into the torso of the suit; only the gloves continue to be custom-fitted for each astronaut.

Pressure suits worn by the seven *Mercury* astronauts.

Gemini Astronauts wore light-weight space suits.

Apollo astronauts wore a more advanced suit for moon walking.

The X-Prize

THE X PRIZE- PRIVATE ENTERPRISE FLIES INTO SPACE

The X-Prize Heritage — From the very beginning of aviation's rich history, prizes have been offered for numerous achievements. One of the most notable was the Orteig Prize and it was offered by a wealthy entrepreneur, Raymond Orteig, in 1919. He offered a $25,000 award to the first person who could fly from New York to Paris, non-stop. This was 1927 and the winner was Charles A. Lindbergh. Since it was a private venture, not one but nine different entries were involved. At the time, no one had any idea of how important Lindbergh's flight was to the development of aviation, but his flight is considered to be the beginning of the world's huge aerospace industry of today.

The Requirements — The 21st Century X-Prize took the Orteig Prize one step further by offering $10,000,000 to the first non-government organization to launch a reusable manned spacecraft that could fly into space (defined as 100 Km or 62 miles above the surface of the earth) and return within a period of two weeks. It also required that the vehicle carry the weight of three adult humans on each flight.

The People and Funding — The X-Prize was the brainchild of Dr. Peter H. Diamandis. He believed that a privately-funded flight into space could change the world. He was influenced by a gift, Charles Lindbergh's book *The Spirit of St. Louis*. In 1995, Diamandis established the X-Prize Foundation and

The *White Knight* "mother ship." *SpaceShipOne* is released
at 50,000 and the *White Knight* then returns to the airport.
*(Permission granted to Civil Air Patrol by Mojave Aerospace Ventures LLC,
photo by Scaled Composites. SpaceShipOne is a Paul G. Allen Project.)*

Inside *SpaceShipOne* during flight.
(Permission granted to Civil Air Patrol by Mojave Aerospace Ventures LLC, photography by Scaled Composites. SpaceShipOne is a Paul G. Allen Project)

his team set about getting financial support for the prize money. Several corporations and individuals contributed to the Foundation. This organization also included Erik and Morgan Lindbergh, the grandchildren of Charles A. Lindbergh. A substantial contribution made by the Ansari family helped make the prize a reality. As a result the original X-Prize was renamed the Ansari X-Prize.

The Winning Team — Several flight attempts were made, but on November 6, 2004, the $10M prize was officially awarded to Mojave Aerospace Ventures for meeting all of the requirements in an aerospace craft they called *SpaceShipOne*. Earlier, on June 21, 2004, test pilot Mike Melville flew *SpaceShipOne* to a record-breaking altitude of 328,491 feet, making him the first private pilot to earn NASA's coveted astronaut wings. The X-Prize set a parameter of 62 miles, or 100 kilometers, as the line defining space. On the final flight of *SpaceShipOne*, test pilot Brian Binnie, flew the vehicle to another record-breaking altitude of 367,442 feet, or 69.6 miles, above the earth's surface. With the necessary payload, this flight met all of the requirements to win the $10,000,000 Ansari X-Prize. It was made on October 4th, the 47th anniversary of the Soviet Union's launch of *Sputnik*.

"This flight begins an exciting new era in space travel," said Paul G. Allen, sponsor of the SpaceShi-

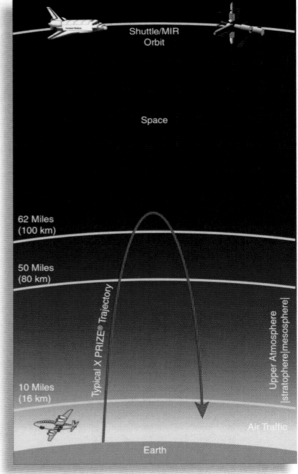

This artist illustration shows a typical X-prize flight trajectory as it enters space 62.14 miles above the earth.

645

pOne program. He continued, " Burt Rutan and his team at Scaled Composites are part of a new generation of explorers who are sparking the imagination of a huge number of people worldwide and ushering in the birth of a new industry of privately-funded, manned space flight." Burt Rutan commented to the press, "Today's flight marks a critical turning point in the history of aerospace…we have redefined space travel as we know it." In fulfillment of his dream, Dr. Peter Diamandis said, "Today we have made history. Today we go to the stars."

The Flight Crew of *SpaceShipOne***. From left to right, top to bottom, Brian Binnie, Pete Siebold, Mike Melvill, and Doug Shane. They are pilots whose fame is right up there with Charles A. Lindbergh. Godspeed Gentlemen.** (*Permission granted to Civil Air Patrol by Scaled Composites*. SpaceShipOne *is a Paul G. Allen Project*)

SpaceShipOne **returns from one of several test flights.** (*Permission given to Civil Air Patrol by Mojave Aerospace Ventures LLC, photographs by Scaled Composites.* SpaceShipOne *is a Paul G. Allen Project.*)

Legendary Aerospace pioneer, Burt Rutan (right) discusses the program with fiancier, Paul G. Allen (left). (*Permission given to Civil Air Patrol by Mojave Aerospace Ventures LLC. Photographs by Scaled Composites.* SpaceShipOne *is a Paul G. Allen Project.*)

Future Manned Spacecraft

The future is now–at least part of it. The commercial satellite industry is booming. Hundreds of new satellites are scheduled for launch in the next few years. We are in the middle of a communications revolution that may continue for a decade or more. While the United States may now be considered the leading information society, soon the whole world will have access.

The space station will be a permanently manned laboratory in space where men and women will be aboard full-time, 24 hours a day, 365 days a year. The space station's microgravity environment, high levels of power and extended time in orbit will enable scientists to make new discoveries in materials, research and life sciences. NASA's current focus is to move beyond Earth's orbit for human exploration and scientific discovery. As NASA Administrator Michael Griffin says, "the International Space Station is a stepping stone along the way." Astronaut crews will continue to learn how to live and work in space and also build hardware that will help the astronauts on a voyage from Earth to Mars.

With the termination of the Space Shuttle program, the United States is faced with the inability of providing a means of sending its own astronauts into space. For a number of years, we as a nation, will have to rely on the Russian Soyuz to transport our own astronauts to the ISS. In development, however, are several new launch vehicles and spacecraft that should help America regain its leadership in the human space launch arena.

NASA has awarded contracts to three aerospace companies for the purpose of developing new manned spacecraft and launch vehicles. They are: Boeing, Space Exploration Technologies (also known as SpaceX), and Sierra Nevada. Boeing and SpaceX are developing capsules, while Sierra Nevada is developing a small reusable winged vehicle (similar in appearance to the shuttle orbiter, but much

smaller). SpaceX has developed its own launch vehicle (the Falcon 9) to boost its capsules, while Boeing and Sierra Nevada will be using the proven Atlas V launch vehicle. SpaceX has successfully launched its Falcon 9 several times and has even sent an unmanned version of its capsule to the ISS.

Space Colonies

Far beyond the concept of space stations is that of permanent colonies for some of earth's people. It will be a

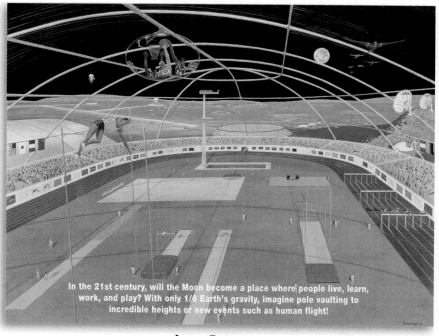

In the 21st century, will the Moon become a place where people live, learn, work, and play? With only 1/6 Earth's gravity, imagine pole vaulting to incredible heights or new events such as human flight!

Lunar Outpost

long, cautious road to the eventual construction of space colonies, and there seems to be no reason to doubt that the colonies will become a reality. Why should they be built? One of the primary reasons is that extensive materials processing and manufacturing can take place without polluting the earth's environment. Another reason is that more unique and better products can be developed in space. Still another more far-reaching promise is that the space colony approach could lead to people's existence in other solar systems that do not have habitable planets. However, the overpowering reason probably is that space is indeed a new and different frontier, and history has shown that new frontiers have always attracted explorers and settlers.

Serious work continues in an effort to define the best locations and missions for space colonies. As early as 1975, in summer workshops, scientists, engineers and others concluded that colonies in space are feasible and could be a great boom to human life.

There are two points in space which seem to be the best locations for eventual, sophisticated space colonies. These points are designated L4 and L5. The L of the designation signifies Lagrange, after Joseph Louis Lagrange. In 1772, Lagrange pointed out that there are points in relation to two large planetary masses where a body will be in gravitational equilibrium. The Lagrangian points would be a precise location around which space colony structures could orbit. This orbit within an orbit is necessary because of the gravitational influence of the sun.

When exactly will space colonies be in orbit at L5? No one really knows. But the 1990s television series Babylon 5 is based on the prospect. Just knowing that advances in space construction techniques and propulsion systems could eventually lead to the colonization of space should reinforce our hopes for the future.

Key Terms and Concepts

- manned spacecraft
- National Aeronautics and Space Administration (NASA)
- Apollo Space Program
- Project Mercury
- Project Gemini
- Space Shuttle
- *Hubble Space Telescope*
- *Skylab*
- Apollo-Soyuz Test Project

- Space Transportation System (STS)
- extra-vehicular activity (EVA) suit
- *Spacelab*
- *Long-Duration Exposure Facility (LDEF)*
- *Soyuz*
- *Salyut*
- *Mir*
- *Vostok*
- *Voskhod*

? Test Your Knowledge ?

SELECT THE CORRECT ANSWER

1. The (**Mercury/Gemini/Apollo**) *Program landed a man on the moon.*
2. The (**Mercury/Gemini/Apollo**) *was the first US manned space flight.*
3. The (**Mercury/Gemini/Apollo**) *was the first US space flight to place two persons in space.*

MATCHING

4. **Match the following:**

   a. Mir   **1) Transports up to three cosmonauts to and from space**
   b. Gagarin **2) First space station intended for prolonged occupancy**
   c. Salyut   **3) First man into space**
   d. Soyuz   **4) Second-generation Russian space station**

FILL IN THE BLANKS

5. _____ _____ *was the first American to orbit the earth.*
6. _____ _____ *was the first Russian to walk in space.*
7. *On July 20, 1969,* _____ __ *landed on the moon and* _____ _____ *was the first man to walk on the moon.*

8. _____-_____ involved a linkup in space between an American and a Russian manned spacecraft.
9. The _____ _____ _____ is commonly called the space shuttle.
10. The _____ was the first space shuttle, but it was only used for atmospheric flight tests.
11. Name the other five space shuttle orbiters: _____, _____, _____, _____ and_____.
12. The _____ _____ _____ is operating at 300 miles above the earth and is free of any atmospheric interference.

TRUE OR FALSE

13. A space walk is also referred to as an extravehicular activity.
14. The Long-Duration Exposure Facility is used for experiments up to 30 days.
15. The first space walk lasted for 60 minutes.
16. The Spacelab was built by the European Space Agency.
17. The air inside of space stations is a mixture of oxygen and nitrogen.
18. Astronauts inside the space shuttle would have to leave their space suits on at all times.
19. Skylab used a lot of left over parts from the Apollo missions.
20. Alan Shepard was the first American in space.
21. The X-Prize was awarded to Mojave Aerospace Ventures.
22. The aerospace craft that won the X-Prize was called the Sputnik.

"Test Your Knowledge" Answers

Chapter 1

1. Daedalus
2. Chinese
3. Chinese
4. f
5. c
6. e
7. b
8. g
9. a
10. d
11. T
12. F
13. T
14. T
15. T
16. F
17. F
18. T
19. T
20. T

Chapter 2

1. Robert Esnault-Pelterie
2. Alberto Santos-Dumont
3. English Channel
4. Rheims, France
5. Igor Sikorsky
6. heavy
7. e
8. d
9. a
10. b
11. f
12. c
13. F
14. T
15. T
16. F
17. F
18. T
19. F
20. F
21. F
22. F
23. T
24. F
25. T
26. T
27. F
28. T

Chapter 3

1. Pulitzer Trophy Race
2. Pulitzer Trophy Race
3. Bendix Race
4. Ninety-Nines
5. Woodrow Wilson
6. School of Aeronautics at New York
7. Igor Sikorsky
8. Charles Lindbergh
9. many disasters
10. Treaty of Versailles
11. b
12. c
13. d
14. a
15. F
16. F
17. T
18. T
19. T
20. T
21. T
22. F
23. F
24. F
25. T
26. T
27. F
28. F
29. T
30. T
31. F
32. T
33. T
34. T
35. F
36. T
37. T
38. F
39. T
40. T
41. F
42. T

Chapter 4

1. Japanese
2. cripple the American fleet
3. increased
4. civil service employees
5. F

6. T
7. F
8. T
9. T
10. F
11. T
12. F
13. F
14. T
15. T
16. T
17. T
18. F
19. F
20. F
21. T
22. F
23. F
24. T
25. T

Chapter 5

1. T
2. F
3. F
4. F
5. T
6. F
7. T
8. T
9. F
10. F
11. It was the only country possessing the atomic bomb, and it felt secure with that weapon.
12. nuclear deterrence
13. when the Soviet Union prevented any surface transportation in or out of the city
14. North Korean
15. The atomic arsenal was not enough to prevent involvement in war.
16. B-52
17. F-100
18. DeHavilland Comet 1
20. b
21. d
22. e
23. c
24. a
25. French
26. Kennedy

27. Tonkin Gulf Resolution, Johnson
28. Television
29. Tet Offensive
30. Precision guided munitions, smart bombs
31. Rolling Thunder, Linebacker
32. Strategic Air Command (SAC)
33. Civil Reserve Air Fleet (CRAF)
34. KC-135, KC-10
35. command, control
36. The Cold War was defined by the antagonistic and competitive relationship between the former Soviet Union (USSR) and the United States. The USSR's political and economic ideologies were communism and socialism, whereas the US preferred democracy and capitalism. The war was "cold" because the two countries did not directly fight each other with military forces.
37. The Soviets cut off the city of West Berlin from the "free world" in an attempt to make it another Soviet satellite. The U.S. was able to airlift enough supplies to the city so its people could survive. The airlift was so successful that the Soviets ended their siege.
38. Key airpoer role in the Korean War included close air support, interdiction, and air superiority.
39. American pilots did so well in the Korean War because they were well trained.
40. WW II improvements to aviation included: better instrumentation, better navigation equipment, better safety devices, and larger airports (just to name a few).
41. As aircraft approaching the sound barrier experienced severe vibrations and control problems.
42. Swept-wings allowed aircraft to fly faster, but landing at high speeds was very dangerous.
43. New missile technology allowed pilots to strike targets far out, making them less susceptible to enemy defensive fire.
44. B-52 bombers and KC-135 tankers extended the range of US nuclear attack capability, The U-2 was used in a reconnaissance role, B-2 bomber (stealth) was designed to elude nemy radar.
45. Unlike Vietnam's Rolling Thunder, where the US gradually escalated hostilities, the Desert Storm strategy was to hit hard and hit fast. Also, the conduct of Desert Storm was left to the military leaders and not to the President, as was the case with President Johnson during Vietnam. Finally, centralized control and decentralized execution was practiced as a result of lessons learned in the Korean War and during the North African Air Campaign during World War II.
46. Not only did E-8 JSTARS aircraft spot Iraqi tanks moving towards Saudi Arabia, AC- 130s demolished the tanks. Air power squashed the Iraqi counterattack.

Chapter 6

1. T
2. F
3. T
4. T
5. F
6. T
7. T
8. F
9. T
10. T
11. F
12. T
13. XB-70
14. X-15
15. X-15
16. c
17. a
18. b
19. d

Chapter 7

1. e
2. g
3. a
4. b
5. h
6. d
7. c
8. f
9. leading edge
10. camber (curvature)
11. trailing edge
12. chord (chord line)
13. weight, thrust
14. camber, airfoil
15. stall
16. shock wave
17. maximum gross weight
18. useful load
19. T
20. F

21. T
22. F
23. T
24. F
25. F
26. T
27. T
28. Relative wind or relative motion is the movement of air with enough speed and from a direction that will produce lift as it flows over a wing.29. Airspeed is the rate of speed through the air. Ground speed is the time it takes to fly from A to B over the ground.
30. It will be greater.
31. By streamlining and polishing the airframe.
32. At the speed of sound, a shock wave is encountered which results in lost energy.

Chapter 8

1. wing
2. flap
3. vertical stabilizer
4. aileron
5. cockpit
6. fuselage
7. elevator
8. rudder
9. horizontal stabilizer
10. lateral (pitch), elevator
11. longitudinal (roll), ailerons
12. vertical (yaw), rudder
13. increases
14. takeoffs, landings
15. protrusion, leading
16. induced
17. laminar, induced
18. airfoil's lift
19. c
20. e
21. a
22. g
23. b
24. f
25. d
26. c
27. a
28. b
29. conventional
30. tricycle
31. tandem
32. Anti-skid brakes prevent brake failure due to over-heating and reduce the possibility of sliding on a slippery surface.
33. Fixed gear is less costly to build and maintain; plus the drag caused by fixed gear is not a big factor for slow-

moving aircraft, especially compared to the additional weight of retractable gear.
34. The fuel pump maintains a positive flow of fuel from the tank to the engine so the engine does not stall. The vent pipe prevents the tank from bursting when its pressure builds on a hot day. The fuel tank drain allows the removal of water from the tank that may have co densed from the air in the unfilled portion of the tank. The fuel strainer keeps any sediment from entering the fuel line that leads from the tank. The fuel selectors allow the pilot to manage what tank the fuel is coming from — helps keep the weight of the aircraft balanced.
35. T
36. F
37. T
38. F
39. T
40. cork
41. airspeed
42. attitude
43. engine, flight, navigational
44. mechanical, pressure, electrical
45. d
46. a
47. j
48. i
49. b
50. h
51. g
52. f
53. e
54. c
55. T
56. T
57. F
58. F
59. T

Chapter 9

1. coordinates
2. vertical, horizontal, letters
3. intersection (coordinate point)
4. elevation
5. contour lines, color tints, shading
6. air, sectional (map)
7. small black circle
8. picks, sledge hammers
9. magenta
10. radio navigation
11. prohibited, restricted
12. Military Operations Area, military
13. training routes
14. true course, north (variation), deviation, altitude, airspeed, speed, direction

15. visible landmarks
16. true course, 10, checkpoints, course
17. dead reckoning
18. VOR, wind
19. nautical miles
20. thunderstorms
21. radio
22. stationary, rotating
23. b
24. c
25. b
26. a
27. T
28. T
29. F
30. F
31. T
32. T
33. T
34. F
35. F
36. T
37. T
38. T
39. T
40. F
41. Parallels = latitude; Meridian = longitude (only parallel at the equator)
42. The magnetic poles, north and south, are not co-located with the geographic poles.
43. Metals; electrical power; the compass, being mechanical will require adjustment
44. 6, 7, 5, 8, 4, 9, 3, 10, 2, 1
45. The master station and the slave station
46. Accelerometers, gyroscopes, and computers; it is self-contained and provides continuous information on the aircraft's position.
47. The military uses the Precise Positioning System (PPS); the civilian public uses the Standard Positioning System (SPS).
48. Instrument Landing System (ILS); Microwave Landing System (MLS); Differential GPS Landing System

CHAPTER 10

1. a-8, b-4, c-1, d-2, e-6, f-5, g-3, h-7
2. Controlled, uncontrolled
3. Military
4. Blue
5. Approach
6. White
7. True
8. False
9. True
10. 26, 03, XX Left or XX Right or XX Center
11. Automated Terminal Information System; a voice recording telling pilots about local weather conditions, and runway restrictions; it allows the controller to direct their attention to controlling air traffic instead of filling the pilots in on local conditions.
12. Wildlife (usually birds) strikes, community encroachment, noise (abatement)

CHAPTER 11

1. Boeing 747
2. A-300
3. Boeing 727
4. 70
5. a-2, b-3, c-1
6. short distances, speed
7. Boeing, McDonnell-Douglas, Lockheed
8. fares, routes
9. commuter, 20
10. T
11. T
12. F
13. F
14. T
15. They all fly on regular schedules and transport people or cargo as a commercial business.
16. It freed airlines from having to provide service to airports where little or no profit was made; helped the generation of new airlines to serve these smaller airports; increased competition among air carriers; helped to lower ticket prices.
17. They were suddenly faced with competition (their monopolies were eliminated); the newer airlines could charge lower fares, partly because their labor was not unionized and had lower pay, fuel prices tripled due to the energy crisis; high interest rates on newly purchased aircraft while newer airlines were flying used aircraft (lower purchase price and less interest); the recession of the late 1970s/early 1980s; the air traffic controllers strike
18. Airbus
19. Containers are easier to handle and load, and reduced losses from theft.

CHAPTER 12

1. Ultralights
2. Cessna
3. FAA inspections, experimental aircraft
4. General Aviation
5. Fun or transporting family and friends, related to business
6. Small single engine aircraft
7. Cessna and Piper
8. Ultralights, soaring, ballooning, racing, gliding,

aerobatics, homebuilts, antique aviation
9. True
10. True
11. True
12. False
13. False
14. Instructional, personal, sport, business and commercial aviation
15. Small, two-seater with small engines for a low cruising speed. They are very easy to fly (to build confidence in new pilots), inexpensive to buy, operate and maintain.
16. Four-place, single piston engine, fixed wing
17. Flying for fun or some other purpose than transportation or business (relaxation, hobby, competition, or thrill)

CHAPTER 13

1. Air taxi/charter, pilot, aircraft, rental aircraft
2. peace of mind, reliability
3. Piper Malibu, pressurized
4. Air taxi/charter, transportation function
5. Agriculture applications, aerial advertising, aerial photography, fire fighting, fish & wildlife, patrol aircraft, industrial uses, industrial uses
6. True
7. True
8. True
9. True
10. False
11. The use of a private or company owned general aviation aircraft for business purposes
12. Who is flying the plane—business person for business and professional pilot for executive
13. Almost certainly a piston-powered aircraft with a 75% chance of being single engine, 4 seater, similar to a typical personal aircraft except better equipped so it can fly in bad weather
14. Usually twin engine, either turbine or piston powered
15. Fuel efficiency—high cost of fuel and potential shortages; Noise—limitations on it by the Federal Government and airports closed at night to jets due to noise; Cost Effectiveness—it is more effective to buy a plane that will cover the range of most of your travel and use the airlines for the longer, less frequent trips.
16. A segment of general aviation which deals with using general aviation aircraft for hire as a commercial business.

CHAPTER 14

1. Heavier
2. A-10
3. F-117
4. E-3
5. S-3A
6. C-9A
7. c
8. b
9. d
10. c
11. Combat, noncombat, combat
12. Strategic, tactical
13. C-17
14. Bomber; Electronic attack-second in series; electronic fighter; experimental intended as bomber; cargo or passenger; reconnaissance fighter; tanker/cargo or passenger
15. Better training and better technology
16. False
17. False
18. True
19. True
20. False
21. Long term benefits of technology transfer among allies, a common use aircraft for NATO nations, increases the supply and availability of repair parts for the F-16 in Europe, and improves the F-16's combat readiness
22. The airplane dominates all aspects of warfare, control of the air is a prerequisite to winning on the ground as proven in wars since World War II

CHAPTER 15

1. 4000
2. Hybrid, compound
3. STOL, VTOL
4. Vietnam
5. 50; 1500; 1500; 50
6. c
7. a
8. a
9. V-22 Osprey, hybrid, US Military
10. Newton's 3rd Law of Motion
11. Exhaust vectored downward, the entire propulsion unit turns
12. Lethal, nonlethal
13. True
14. False
15. True
16. False
17. False

CHAPTER 16

1. CAB
2. FSS
3. NAFEC
4. NTSB
5. NASA
6. ICAO
7. Federal Aviation Agency, independent agency, Civil Aeronautics Administration, Commerce, safety regulations, enforcing, Federal Aviation Administration, Transportation
8. Air Traffic Control Tower, Air Route Traffic Control Center, positive control, Air Traffic Control Tower
9. Aircraft, airmen (or pilot, navigator, air traffic controllers, etc.), regulations, procedures
10. English
11. ICAO or International Civil Aviation Organization
12. Aircraft Owners and Pilots Association (AOPA)
13. Experimental Aircraft Association (EAA)
14. False
15. True
16. True
17. False
18. False
19. False
20. National Aviation Facilities Experiment Center; the FAA's research and development center; new types of airway navigational systems, a new instrument landing system, collision avoidance systems
21. Train personnel who operate the ARTCCs, FSSs, and airport control towers; train military and foreign controllers; train engineers and technicians who install and maintain the electronic equipment required for navigation, communication, and air traffic control; conduct initial and refresher training for their maintenance inspectors; develop examinations for airmen, airworthiness standards for aircraft, maintain records of airmen and aircraft.
22. National Transportation Safety Board; determining the cause or probable cause of any transportation accident
23. To explore, use, and enable the development of space for human enterprise; to advance scientific knowledge and understanding of the Earth, the solar system and the universe, and use the environment of space for research; to research, develop, verify, and transfer advanced aeronautics, space, and related technologies
24. Civil Reserve Air Fleet; allows DoD to use long-range jet transport aircraft belonging to the commercial airlines to move military equipment, cargo and personnel in times of national emergency or natural disaster on only 24 hours notice. The aircraft are supported by aircrews and maintenance personnel supplied by the airlines
25. Emergency Services—SAR missions for downed aircraft, lost outdoorsmen and children, disaster relief, and emergency airlift of sick and injured as well as blood and transplant organs; Aerospace Education—for the membership and general public to develop awareness and appreciation for aerospace world we live in; Cadet Program—for young men and women 12-21 interested in aerospace and community service

Chapter 17

1. is
2. institutes
3. two
4. formal technical education courses
5. voluntary
6. further training sponsored by the employer
7. d
8. a
9. c
10. d
11. b
12. aptitudes
13. occupation, aptitudes, succeed
14. Technical/vocational school
15. Terminal courses
16. Air Force Reserve Officer Training Corps
17. Professional Officers Course, General Military Course
18. Flight Instruction Program
19. True
20. True
21. False
22. False
23. False
24. It brought about change, it made it acceptable and popular to do research leading to the so-called knowledge revolution, the computer was developed to aid aerospace related industries, created a need for more and better trained people
25. It should be interesting, pleasant, provide satisfaction and self-respect, provide financial rewards

Chapter 18

1. aerospace
2. heat, thermometer
3. precipitation, condensation
4. condensation nuclei, water vapor
5. evaporation
6. spread
7. Earth's, solar
8. heat balance
9. lateral
10. Coriolis effect

11. d
12. b
13. c
14. a
15. b
16. c
17. a
18. a
19. b
20. d
21. T
22. T
23. F
24. T
25. F
26. T
27. F
28. Humidity equals the amount of water vapor in the air. Relative humidity equals the amount of water vapor that can still enter the air mass before it becomes saturated.
29. Transformed — heat energy can be absorbed or reflected by clouds or dust in the atmosphere; it can be absorbed by the Earth and converted into heat energy. Transferred — conduction, convection, advection, radiation.
30. 64°F
31. **a.** A new car door makes an airtight seal. As the door is closed, air is compressed and can not escape. Thus, the door will not close securely because of greater pressure inside.
b. The "pop" is caused by a tube behind the eardrum adjusting to the change in atmospheric pressure.
c. When you punch one hole in the can, the liquid does not flow out readily because a partial vacuum is produced. When you punch a second hole, the air enters the top hole and the liquid flows out the bottom hole. No partial vacuum

Chapter 19

1. c
2. a
3. b
4. d
5. f
6. e
7. h
8. g
9. weather
10. cumulus, stratus, cirrus
11. height (above the Earth's surface)
12. rain, snow
13. winds
14. cumulonimbus
15. cirrus, cirrostratus, cirrocumulus
16. fog, stratus (could be answered sratus and stratocumulus)
17. d
18. c
19. a
20. T
21. F
22. F
23. T
24. T
25. F
26. T
27. F
28. F
29. It is safer to fly on the windward side which has little turbulence. The leeward side will most likely have the turbulent downdrafts.
30. None. The rotor clouds will form on the leeward side.

Chapter 20

1. c
2. d
3. b
4. a
5. e
6. e
7. a
8. b
9. d
10. c
11. f
12. whiteout
13. cloud
14. blowing dust
15. hazardous (danger)
16. blowing sand
17. haze, smoke
18. blowing snow
19. towers
20. vortices
21. see
22. thunderstorm, cumulus
23. body, engine(s)
24. force, weather, uninhabitable
25. d
26. c
27. b
28. a
29. F
30. T
31. T
32. F

CHAPTER 21

1. Galileo
2. Galileo
3. Chinese
4. Goddard
5. World War I
6. 1-D, 2-C, 3-A, 4-B, 5-F, 6-E
7. 1-D, 2-A, 3-B, 4-C
8. B
9. C
10. C
11. D
12. Centrifugal effect
13. First, rest, motion, acted upon by some outside force
14. Third, an equal and opposite reaction
15. Riffling in the barrels
16. Payload
17. Liquid or solid
18. True
19. True
20. True
21. False
22. False
23. True
24. The first law means that, when launching the rocket vertically, the propulsion system must produce e nough force (thrust) to overcome the inertia of the l aunch vehicle (i.e. greater than the weight of the rocket).
    The second law means that the amount of force required to accelerate a body is proportional to the mass of the body.
    The third law is at the heart of rocketry. Before launch, the rocket is stationary. The "action" is firing of the engines. Upon launch, liftoff is the equal and opposite reaction (movement in the direction opposite to the thrust)
25. Two bodies attract each other with a force directly proportional to their mass and inversely proportional to the square of the distance between them
26. Increase the mass of the exhaust or accelerate the exhaust particles to a higher velocity
27. It is the number of pounds of thrust delivered by consuming one pound of propellant (oxidizer/fuel mixture) in one second.

CHAPTER 22

1. Oxidizer, chilled , liquid
2. Regressive
3. Mono-, bi-
4. Bi-propellant
5. Either (motor, solid) or (engine, liquid)
6. Slow
7. Oxidation, oxygen, another substance
8. Grain
9. Cryogenics
10. Nonhypergolic, hypergolic
11. Coupled valve, valves, crosshead, combustion chamber
12. c
13. d
14. 1-c, 2-d, 3-b, 4-a
15. True
16. False
17. True
18. False
19. True
20. It must contain oxidizer and fuel, ignite correctly every time, produce energy in the form of force, and that force must be controllable
21. By controlling the amount of the surface area exposed to the burning process
22. It is an enclosure filled with a combustible powder that is ignited electrically. The flame of the burning squib in turn ignites the grain of a solid propellant rocket.

CHAPTER 23

1. East, 1000
2. sounding rocket
3. goes into higher orbit
4. retrothrust, slow down, gravity, faster
5. polar
6. a-2, b-7, c-5, d-8, e-6, f-1, g-3, h-9, i-4
7. velocity required for the payload to escape from the gravitational attraction of that planet.
8. Total Velocity Requirement
9. burnout, trajectory
10. the arc of a non-orbiting body
11. sounding rocket
12. transfer, coplanar transfer
13. minimum energy transfer
14. True
15. True
16. False
17. True
18. True
19. Due to the weakening of the Earth's gravitational effect with distance, although higher velocities are required to achieve the higher altitude.
20. The vehicle is first placed in a low-elliptical parking orbit. When it swings around to perigee, enough thrust is applied to push the vehicle to apogee at the desired altitude. When it reaches the high point of this transfer ellipse, thrust is again applied and the vehicle moves out on a circle that is tangent to the transfer ellipse.

CHAPTER 24

1. a-1, b-3, c-5, d-2, e-4
2. a-3, b-4, c-5, d-1, e-2
3. interstellar
4. all
5. billion
6. three (actually 3.26)
7. four
8. 100
9. 100
10. cislunar space
11. space, 50, astronaut wings
12. space, 80, it's the point where an orbiting object will stay in orbit
13. Milky Way
14. light year, trillion.
15. 25, 40, 27
16. sunspot, 8, 15, 11
17. solar flare, 9, 15, 3 days
18. magnetosphere, solar winds, orbit of the moon.
19. cosmic rays, electrons, nuclei of atoms, solar winds
20. Van Allen belts, crescent, two, radiation
21. magnetic storms, radiation bursts, magnetic
22. scintillation, ionosphere
23. outgassing, vacuum
24. cold welding
25. differential charging
26. False
27. False
28. False
29. True
30. We get a global view of the earth, we can see the universe more clearly, potential for abundant resources (solar energy, minerals from other planets), a unique environment to make new materials not able to be developed on earth.
31. Powerful ultraviolet radiation of the sun and ultra-high frequency rays from the other stars
32. The sun
33. about 108 times as large as the earth; a giant thermonuclear rector; gravity and energy emissions affect the whole solar system directly, magnetic field indirectly; average rotation time 27 days (varies between 25-40 depending on location on surface); sunspot cycle runs 8-15 years averaging 11 years; solar flares can hit earth within 9 minutes (low energy) or 15 minutes to 3 days for high energy particles)
34. Contains almost all its mass in a central nucleus (a tight cluster of protons and neutrons) encircled by whirling negatively charged electrons.
35. An atom that carries a positive or negative charge from losing or gaining electrons

Chapter 25

1. a
2. c
3. b
4. e
5. d, f, h
6. d, f, h
7. b
8. b
9. c
10. a
11. b
12. e
13. d
14. f
15. a
16. c
17. g
18. 2.27, orbit
19. gravitational pull
20. 520
21. one, same
22. rilles
23. similar
24. deserts
25. photos
26. d
27. d
28. a
29. c
30. a
31. T
32. F
33. T
34. F
35. F
36. F
37. T
38. F
39. T
40. F
41. T
42. T

CHAPTER 26

1. 1967 Outer Space Treaty
2. GPS
3. 1-c, 2-g, 3-f, 4-d, 5-i, 6-e, 7-h, 8-b, 9-a
4. 1-i, 2-j, 3-e, 4-d, 5-b, 6-k, 7-l, 8-c, 9-f, 10-g, 11-b, 12-a
5. probes, satellites
6. Sputnik; fly over countries without permission
7. passive, active
8. Selective Availability, Precise Positioning Service

9. Weather—A, C, E, G; Multi-Spectral Imaging—D, F; Reconnaissance—B
10. Geostationary Orbits (GEO), equal access for all
11. Bogata Declaration (1976), Geostationary Orbits (GEO)
12. Defense Meteorological Satellite Program, weather, military, optical, visual and infrared cloud
13. Orbital astronomy and environmental analysis
14. Placement of future space colonies.
15. d
16. c
17. d
18. b
19. True
20. False
21. True
22. False
23. Freedom of use—all nations should have access to space; Non-appropriation—no one owns any part of space; Use of space—since space belongs to all mankind, all nations should share its benefits
24. It documented the three principles of space law in written form and it legitimized a military presence in space by allowing military personnel to conduct scientific research
25. The ICBMs of the Superpowers could reach each other with mass destruction and Anti-Ballistic Missiles were under development to protect each nation, thereby increasing the likelihood of a first strike in nuclear war. To prevent this, both countries agreed not to develop ABM systems, including in space. The treaty is important because it specifies monitoring compliance from space, thus sanctioning monitoring other countries from space.
26. It formed NASA and defined civil and military responsibilities and provided a process for coordination between them.
27. It authorizes the military to provide facilities and support for commercial launches. The launch company only has to pay for the service while the military pays to maintain the facilities.
28. Manage the use of the station through consensus; each nation's own copyrights apply to creations of its citizens while aboard; and each nation decides whether the activities aboard their section are for peaceful purposes (allowing military members to serve)
29. Communication, navigation, observation, and scientific
30. Media transmission (radio and television), pure data transmission (Internet), personal communication (cellular phones), and providing links to other spacecraft
31. Satellites, which act as precise reference points; Control System, operated by USAF to adjust the satellite positions if necessary; Receivers, use the broadcast signal to calculate its position, velocity, time
32. Weather, Multi-Spectrum-Imaging, and Reconnaissance
33. Provide early warning by detecting enemy missile launch; detecting nuclear explosions; monitoring radio and radar transmissions; photo surveillance
34. Extensive materials processing and manufacturing can occur without polluting Earth's atmosphere, more unique and better products can be developed in space, could lead to human existence in other solar systems that do not have habitable planets, it's a new and different frontier

Chapter 27

1. Apollo
2. Mercury
3. Gemini
4. 1-d, 2-c, 3-b, 4-a
5. John Glenn
6. Aleksei Leonov
7. Apollo 11, Neil Armstrong
8. Apollo-Soyuz
9. Space Transportation System
10. Enterprise
11. Columbia, Challenger, Discovery, Atlantis and Endeavour
12. Hubble Space Telescope
13. T
14. T
15. F
16. T
17. T
18. F
19. T
20. T
21. T
22. F

Glossary

A

Absolute charging – occurs when the whole craft is charged.

Acceleration – when a body is subjected to the application of a force over a continuing period of time.

Ace – a pilot who shot down five enemy aircraft.

Active communications satellite – a satellite, such as Courier 1B, that received signals from ground stations, amplified them and then rebroadcast the signals to receiving stations on Earth.

Advanced technology jets – jets which used technology such as features which reduce noise levels, fuel use, and exhaust emissions and control by fly-by-wire throughout normal flight.

Advection – lateral heat transfer that is important in the global circulation of air.

Advection fog – fog formed when wind blows moist air over a cold surface and the surface cools the air to its dew-point temperature.

Aerial photography – a highly specialized photography using special films that can be used to spot and map crop damage due to disease or insects.

Aerial refueling – to refuel a plane in midair.

Aerobatics – stunt-flying involving an aircraft that can stand tremendous forces and that can fly upside down, right side up, and everything in between. It also requires a skillful pilot.

Aeronaut – balloonist.

Aeronautics – the science and art of flight through the atmosphere.

Aerospace – a compound term used to describe the atmosphere and space as one medium.**Aerospace

engineering** – prepares a person to work on either aircraft or spacecraft design and production programs.**Agricultural

applications** – aircraft that seed, fertilize, and apply pesticides to almost 200 million acres of farmland annually.

Ailerons – small flaps on the wings that help control the plane.

Airborne – transported or designed to be transported by air.

Aircraft carriers – commercial airlines that are considered common carriers and are in business to serve the public. They are closely regulated and controlled to ensure the safety of the public.

Airfoil – parts of an airplane, such as wings, tail surfaces, and propellers, designed to cause a dynamic reaction from the air through which it moves.

Airframe rocket system – serves to contain the other systems and to provide the streamlined shape.

Air pump – invented by Torricelli, Von Guericke, and Pascal to study vacuums.

Airspeed indicator – informs the pilot of the speed through the air in terms of miles per hour and/or knots.

Air superiority – complete command of the air.

Air taxis – aircraft that provides transportation on a nonscheduled or demand basis. Also used for emergency transportation.

Air traffic control – concerned with keeping aircraft safely separated to prevent accidents.

Airways – three-dimensional highways in the sky and another subdivision of controlled airspace.

Alto – middle altitude clouds where the stratus and cumulus shapes are found and called altostratus and altocumulus.

Altimeter – aneroid barometer that reads in feet of altitude and is calibrated to atmospheric pressure in inches of mercury.

Angle of attack – the angle created by the pilot during takeoff (the angle between the chord line and the oncoming relative wind).

Anorthosite – the most common rock on the moon composed of almost entirely one mineral, feldspar.

Antique aviation – involves either funding or restoring a vintage aircraft or building replicas of old airplanes from original plans.

Apogee – that point in the orbital trajectory or flight path where the orbiting body is most distant from the body being orbited.

Aptitude – the special talents and natural abilities which a person possesses.

Area Navigation System (RNAV) – more of a computer controlled navigation system than a set of stations and receivers. This system uses VOR-type radio stations or GPS as reference points, but allows the pilot or navigator to fly directly from the airport of origin to the destination airport without following the airways.

Asteroids – rocky and metallic objects orbiting the Sun, too small to be considered planets.

Atmosphere – sometimes called "an ocean of air surrounding the earth" or "a gaseous covering." A gaseous fluid that reacts to any force.

Atomizing – one phase of the combustion process.

Attitude indicator – a gyroscopic instrument that provides an artificial horizon to the pilot.

Aurora australis – colored lights, which appear in the southern latitudes.

Aurora borealis – northern lights. The visible emissions from polar magnetic storms which produce sporadic radiant emissions from the upper atmosphere over middle and high latitudes.

Autogiro – a rotating-wing aircraft that achieves slow flight and vertical takeoff by the use of a freely rotating rotor replacing or supplementing the wings but is driven forward by a conventional propeller.

Automated Terminal Information System (ATIS) – a voice recording of a tower controller that tells the pilot about the wind, clouds, visibility, and any other restrictions that the runways may have.

Automatic Direction Finder (ADF) – another type of radio receiver used to determine direction, but does not provide as much information as the VOR.

B

Ballast – a heavy substance for controlling ascent.

Ballistics – the study of the arc of a nonorbiting body.

Barnstormers – ex-military aviators who flew war-surplus aircraft around the country, circling over a village or small town to attract attention and landing on a nearby farm to offer rides to individuals for a fee and put on flying exhibitions. They also called themselves a "flying circus."

Barometer – measures the pressure of the atmosphere.

Basalt – a hard, heavy dark gray rock with tiny holes form which gas has escaped.

Beam-ride guidance – missiles that are built to fly along a beam that is aimed at or kept on the target.

Bernoulli's principle – states "as a fluid's speed increases, the pressure within the fluid decreases." So the pressure on top of an airfoil must be less than the pressure below.

Bipropellant – the oxidizer is stored in one container and the fuel (reducer) in another.

Black hole – probably began as a large star that exhausted its nuclear fuel and collapsed inward on itself resulting in gravity so strong that nothing is allowed to leave it.

Blitzkrieg – lightning war devised by Germans.

Bombers – large, long-range aircraft with a mission to reach into the enemy's homeland and destroy the ability to wage war.

Burnout velocity – the velocity required to place a spacecraft on its intended trajectory that is attained when the rocket engine ceases to produce thrust.

Business aircraft – 78 percent are single-and piston-engine aircraft and 21 percent are twin-and piston-engine aircraft.

Business aviation – the use of a private-or company-owned general aviation aircraft for business purposes.

Buzz bomb – bomb that produced a unique sound caused by a pulsejet engine mounted in a "stovepipe" above the fuselage.

C

Cambered – curved upper surface on a wing to increase lift.

Canards – horizontal surfaces forward of the main wings and are used for trim and control.

Cargo carriers – carriers that carry mainly freight, but now are also allowed to carry passengers.

Catalyst – a substance, which speeds up a chemical reaction but undergoes no permanent chemical, change itself.

Ceiling and visibility unlimited (CAVU) – when the sky is clear of clouds, the winds are calm, the air is cool, and there is no haze.

Centralized control – bringing together of all air assets as one unit.

Centrifugal force – a force moving or directed away from the center of rotation, which is a factor that affects the circulation of air or wind.

Charter services – aircraft and pilot hired by people who cannot afford to own their own aircraft but need to get somewhere in a hurry.

Chemical propulsion system – involves the mixing and burning of a chemical fuel and a chemical oxidizer to produce the hot, expanding gases needed to provide thrust.

Chemosphere – an important region due to a number of important photochemical (radiant energy and chemical) reactions which occur in it.

Chord (airfoil) – an imaginary line that connects the leading edge with the trailing edge of the airfoil.

Chromosphere – above the photosphere. This sphere of color extends to about 15,000 miles.

Circular orbit – an orbit that maintains a virtually constant altitude above the Earth's surface.

Cirrus clouds – clouds that are wispy, thin and lacy. They are high altitude clouds.

Cislunar space – the space between the Earth and the moon.

Civil Air Patrol (CAP) – a federally chartered, private, nonprofit corporation that is also the official civilian auxiliary of the U.S. Air Force. Its threefold mission is emergency services, aerospace education, and cadet programs.

Civil airport – airport operated or owned by citizens for private or business purposes.

Civil Reserve Air Fleet (CRAF) – composed of commercial airliners, which have been designated by the Department of Defense for use in time of national emergency.

Clear-air turbulence (CAT) – may exist at different places and altitudes but be completely invisible. The causes may be one or a combination of: convective currents, windshear, and obstructions (such as mountains) to wind flow.

Close ground support – air power used to support army ground operations.

Close support aircraft – aircraft that supports or cooperates with friendly surface forces, consisting of air attacks with guns, bombs, guided airborne missiles or rockets on hostile surface forces.

Cold front – when a cold air mass replaces a warmer air mass, the boundary is called a cold front.

Cold welding – when moving parts fit with only a tiny air space between them. In a vacuum the tiny amount of air which kept them separated escapes and they weld together.

Combat aircraft – aircraft used by the military such as bombers and fighters.

Combined arms operations – the army and air force used in combination with each other.

Combustion chamber – a chamber or cylinder-like assembly in a rocket engine, jet engine, or the like where the propellant is exploded.

Comet – a small, irregularly shaped body whose tiny nucleus is composed of water, ice, rock and frozen gases.

Command guidance – electronic guidance, outside the rocket, wherein signals or pulses sent out by an operator cause the guided object to fly a directed path.

Commercial aviation – a segment of general aviation which deals with using general aviation aircraft for hire as a commercial (money-making) business.

Compass deviation – the deviations caused by electrical power and metal in the airplane that affects the compass. The pilot must use the compass correction card kept in the aircraft if he flies by the magnetic compass.

Composites – super-strong, but lightweight, nonmetallic, epoxy graphite materials used in aircraft construction.

Compound helicopters – a conventional helicopter wit extra forward thrust provided by either a jet or propeller unit.

Compounds – molecular bonding of two or more elements.

Compression wave – a type of shock wave that is formed when the air must move aside as a leading edge passes.

Condensation – to change to a denser form as from a gas to a liquid.

Condensation nuclei – small particles that serve as surface for condensation of water vapor.

Conduction – heating by direct contact.

Conic projection – a type of map projection formed by projecting the surface of the earth on the surface of a cone and unrolling this to a plane surface on which the parallels of latitude are then concentric circles and the meridians equally spaced radii.

Continental air mass – a dry air mass.

Controlled airspace – airspace that has several subdivisions and is shown on aeronautical charts. It is subject to control by FAA air traffic controllers.

Control rocket system – the system that carries out whatever the rocket's guidance system dictates should be done.

Convection – heat transfer by vertical motion.

Conventional – landing gear consisting of two wheels forward of the aircraft's center of gravity and a small, third wheel at the tail.

Coplanar transfer – accomplishing transfers and maneuvers within a given plane.

Coriolis effect – rotation of the Earth influences any object moving over its surface such as the atmosphere in motion.

Corona – a division of the Sun's atmosphere known as the crown. An enormous area of faint white light that visibly extends outward from the Sun's surface.

Corporate jet – a turbojet called a bizjet that is expensive to buy and to operate.

Cosmic rays – rays of extremely short wave length and great penetrating power, which bombard the Earth from beyond its atmosphere.

Coupled valve – two propellant valves, opened by a single piston, operating through a crosshead, causing fuel and oxidizer to enter the combustion chamber at the same time.

Cowling – removable metal covering that houses the engine and sometimes also a portion of the fuselage of an aircraft.

Crater – a depression formed by the impact of a meteorite.

Cryogenics – an area of science concerned with the production of low temperatures and the effect of such temperatures on matter.

Crystalline – having the structure of a crystal like salt or sugar.

Cultural features – landscape marked by people such as mines, highways, and railroads.

Cumulus clouds – piled up lower altitude clouds that look "bumpy."

Cyclone – a hurricane that occurs in the Indian Ocean.

D

Dead reckoning – involves the systematic consideration of all factors that will and could affect the flight.

Density – how many molecules of air are squeezed into a given volume.

Density impulse – another measure of a propellant's thrust according to the volume involved.

Dew point – the temperature at or below which water vapor will condense.

Differential charging – occurs when one part of a spacecraft gets charged and has a different charge than another part of the craft.

Differential GPS Landing System – used to fit GPS approaches to the community's needs and still satisfy the aviator.

Dirigibles – rigid airships like large balloons. A lighter-than-air craft that can be propelled and steered.

Distance-Measuring Equipment (DME) – the time it takes a signal to go from the aircraft to the VORTAC and return, converted to nautical miles distance between the airplane and the station.

Dog fight – German and Allied aircraft battled in the air using an aircraft equipped with an interrupting gear which connected a machine gun to the aircraft engine and prevented the gun from firing when a propeller blade was lined up with the gun's muzzle.

Downlink – the communication link from the satellite to the earth station.

Drag – a slowing force acting on a body (as an airfoil or airplane) moving through air, parallel and opposite to the direction of motion.

Drag devices – devices such as speed brakes, air brakes, dive flaps or drag parachutes used to produce a significant amount of drag without affecting the airfoil's lift.

E

Earth's gravitational field – a region associated with any distribution of mass in which gravitational forces due to that mass may be detected.

Electrical system – a generator mechanically attached to an aircraft's engine that provides the electricity required to charge the battery, start the engine, operate the radios, and operate navigation and landing lights.

Electric propulsion system – uses magnetic fields and currents to propel matter in small amounts.

Electrostatic charging – charging related to static electricity. The small electronic parts of a spacecraft, especially computer data bits, can be badly shocked by electrostatic charges.

Elevator – control surface that is responsible for pitch.

Elliptical orbit – any closed orbit that is not circular.

Encroachment – the noise factor or any other considerations at airports that might intrude on the neighboring communities.

Engine instruments – keep the pilot aware of how his thrust-producing device is operating.

Equatorial orbit – the orbit a satellite travels from west to east over the Earth's equator.

Eris – some scientists call this the 10th planet in our solar system.

Escape trajectory – a spacecraft must accelerate to its escape velocity which causes the velocity of the spacecraft to be so high and the inertia so great that the spacecraft comes under the influence of another body's gravity before it reaches its apogee.

Escape velocity – the speed at which an object is able to overcome the gravitational pull of the earth.

European Space Agency(ESA) – an international organization composed of 14 European Member States which aims to provide cooperation in space research and technology.

Evaporation – the process by which liquid water molecules change to a gas or vapor state and enter the Earth's atmosphere.

Evaporation fog – steam that occurs when cold air moves over warm water; the water's normal evaporation process saturates the cooler air with water vapor, and the dew point is reached.

Executive aircraft – a typical executive transport is a twin-engine aircraft that is turbine-or piston-powered. The pilot must have special training, a multi-engine rating, and at least a commercial license.

Exosphere – the top of the atmosphere above the heterosphere. Known as the "region of escape."

Expansion wave – a shock wave that is formed when the air must fill back in as the trailing edge passes.

Extreme turbulence – turbulence where the entire aircraft may be tossed about and is practically impossible to control; structural damage to aircraft may result.

F

Federal Aviation Administration (FAA) – the United States Government agency, which is responsible for regulating air commerce.

Fighter escort – small pursuit aircraft used to escort large bombers and given the freedom to chase enemy fighters and shoot them down.

Fighters – aircraft that have the basic mission of destroying other aircraft.

Fixed-Base Operation (FBO) – a service station for airplanes.

Fixed landing gear – usually on less expensive, smaller airplanes because it is much less costly to build and maintain.

Flaps – attached to the trailing edge of the wing. When cruising, the flaps simply continue the streamlined shape of the wing's airfoil.

Flight instruments – inform the pilot of the altitude, the airspeed, and the attitude of the aircraft.

Flight Service Station (FSS) – provides all types of weather information for pilots.

Fog – a large mass of water vapor condensed to fine particles, at or just above the earth's surface.

Force – the cause of motion. Power or energy exerted against an object in a given direction.

Form drag – the shape of the aircraft that creates drag.

Forward-swept wings – wings sweeping which goes back more than 100 years. The design needed to be structurally stronger in high-speed flight.

Four-year colleges/universities – offers a broad education because students can choose from more electives in both humanities and science areas than those in junior college or vocational/technical schools can.

Fracto – a combining term which means broken and/or ragged.

Free fall – the motion of a body in space when the only force acting on it is that of a gravitational field.

Freezing level – may be around 15,000 feet during summer and perhaps as low as 1,000 feet above ground level on warm winter days.

Friction drag – caused by the friction of air particles rubbing against the parts of an airplane.

Frost – a feathery deposit of minute ice crystals or grains upon a surface or object, formed directly from vapor in the air.

Fuel system – includes everything that involves delivery of fuel to the engine including fuel tanks and fuel lines.

Fuselage – the basic structure of the airplane to which all the other parts are attached.

G

Galaxy – a grouping of billions of stars apparently merging into a luminous band that extends across the sky.

Gas-heating system – uses an external heat source to heat and cause the propellant to build the pressure necessary to provide thrust by exiting the exhaust nozzle at high velocity.

Gearbox – the gear including the change gear and the propeller shaft or driving chain by which power is transmitted from the engine to the live axle.

General aviation – all civil aviation other than flying done by scheduled air carriers and government agencies.

Geostationary orbit – an orbit stationed above one point on Earth's surface.

Glaze ice – formed and builds quickly as an airplane flies through supercooled rain droplets.

Global Positioning System (GPS) – consists of about 24 satellites in orbit around the Earth, several ground tracking stations, and a receiver in the aircraft.

Grain – a single piece of powder charge regardless of size of shape used in a rocket.

Gravitation – the term used to describe the force of attraction that exists between all matter within the universe.

Gravity – when gravitation involves Earth and a body or mass on or near the Earth.

Great circle – any circle on the Earth's surface that is made by a plane crossing through the Earth's center.

Grid system (graticule) – a system of coordinates that involves numbers across the top and letters down the left side. The Earth graticule uses 18 primary great circles going north-south and parallel small circles and two poles going east-west.

Ground speed – a measure of how fast the aircraft is going across the surface of the Earth. This is important in determining how long it will take to get from a start point to the destination.

Guerilla warfare – military actions carried out by small forces in the rear of an enemy with the purpose of harassing the enemy, interrupting his lines of communication, and destroying his supplies.

Guidance rocket system – a self-contained electronic unit that employs a computer and an inertial platform and may also have a star-tracking unit for space navigation.

Gyroscopic stability – a spinning flat weight that tends to line up on one of its axes. That axis is the one perpendicular to the face of the weight. Once the weight is aligned on the axis, it will remain there.

H

Hail – pellets or lumps of frozen rain or snow sometimes precipitated during a thunderstorm.

Hangers – a garage for airplanes which protects it from weather damage.

Haze – a concentration of water vapor, lighter than fog or clouds, but thick enough to reduce visibility.

Heading indicator – a type of compass with a gyroscopic device behind the compass card that tells the pilot which was he is flying.

Heat – the sum total energy of all moving molecules within a substance.

Heavy-lift – the largest and heaviest helicopters that were designed for military use.

Helium gas – a Very light inert gas used to inflate airships.

Hemisphere – half-sphere.

Heterosphere – begins at about 55 to 60 miles in altitude where the molecules and atoms of the gases are spaced much farther apart. At this level, gravity influences the gases according to mass with the heaviest found in the lower part and the lighter gases found in the upper part.

High-inversion fog – a low cloud fog formed by condensation of water vapor at or near the top of cool air that is covered by a warmer air layer.

Hohmann transfer – minimum energy transfer that was developed by a German engineer named Walter Hohmann and is a practical method of space maneuver to this day.

Homing guidance – require that the rocket "home in" on the target that is radiating heat or light.

Homosphere – extends from Earth's surface up to an altitude of about 60 miles. That region in which the gaseous composition and mixing are relatively constant.

Humidity – the amount of water vapor in the air.

Hurricane – a strong tropical cyclone (usually in the West Indies) with winds that often surpass 100 mph and have been clocked at more than 200 mph.

Hybrid helicopters – a variety of advanced helicopter concepts lumped together which, in one way or another, attempt to solve the problem of using the rotor for vertical takeoff and landing without impeding forward flight.

Hybrid propellant – systems that use both liquid propellants and solid propellants in combination within the same engine.

Hybrid rockets – rockets that use hybrid propellant systems.

Hydraulic system – may operate the brakes, lower the landing gear, move the flight controls, and extend and lower the flaps. The mechanical advantage of this system allows the pilot to exert great pressure on the aircraft control systems or structures.

Hydrogen gas – discovered by Henry Cavendish in 1766. A "flammable air" that is lighter than air and was first used to fill balloons.

Hydrographic features – water features.

Hypergolic – a biopropellant that is self-igniting.

I

Icing – the act or process of atmospheric moisture freezing upon the surfaces of an aircraft.

Igniters – any device, chemical, electrical, or mechanical, used to ignite.

Ignition characteristics – starting every time in the same way, choosing between a continuous or restartable propellant, and safety are all properties of a propellant considered for ignition.

Induced drag – caused by lift vector pointing in the same direction as the drag vector.

Induced lift – induced lower pressure on the top of the wing due to the camber.

Inertia – the force produced by the reaction of a body to an accelerating force, equal in magnitude and opposite in direction to the accelerating force.

Inertial guidance – a self-contained unit that automatically adjust the rocket after launching to follow a given flight path, the mechanisms reacting to inertial forces during flight.

Insolation – the rate at which the Earth's surface is heated by solar radiation.

Institutes – special schools that place more emphasis on subjects that are essential to doing the job that the student is preparing for. Students take several courses in the humanities and earn a bachelor's degree.

Instructional aviation – aviation that teaches a pilot how to fly, usually in small single-engine airplanes.

Instrument Flight Rules (IFR) – weather conditions at an airport during which a pilot must use instruments to assist takeoff and landing.

Instrument Landing System (ILS) – is used only within a short distance from the airport and only when the purpose is to land the airplane.

Interdiction – air attack directed on a route or area to deny its use to the enemy.

Intergalactic space – within the galaxy.

Internal Navigation – a self-contained unit located within the aircraft that needs only to be programmed for a starting point and destination.

International Civil Aviation Organization (ICAO) – an international organization dedicated to standardizing aviation functions.

International courts – a judicial assembly between or among nations.

International customs – a usual practice carried on by tradition and enforced by social disapproval of any violation, between or among nations. Those practices accepted by nations as the right way to act.

International law – the rules generally observed and regarded as binding in the relations between states or nations.

International treaties – written agreements or contracts between or among nations that are legally binding to those who sign them.

Interplanetary space – measured from the center of the sun to the orbit of its outermost planet.

Interstellar space – between or among the stars.

Ion – an atom that carries a positive or negative electrical charge as a result of losing or gaining one or more electrons.

Ionosphere – reflects certain radio waves, which allows them to be received at stations far away from the broadcasting station. An outer region of the atmosphere that consists of layers of ionized air particles.

Isobars – lines drawn on maps to join points having the same barometric pressure. When isobars are far apart, the wind is weak; when they are close together, the wind is strong.

J

Jet stream – a comparatively narrow current of air which moves around the Northern (and Southern) Hemisphere of the earth in wavelike patterns. Compared to a "river" of wind moving at high speed.

Joined wings – an aircraft with its main wing swept upward and backward connected at the tips to the rearward wing which would be swept forward and downward, resembling the shape of a diamond.

Joint-use airport – airport where civil aviation and military aviation share the runways.

Jumbo jet – wingspan was 65 feet longer than the 707, and its fuselage was nearly 90 feet longer and almost twice the diameter.

Junior college – a school giving training in only the first one or two years of the standard college course.

Jupiter – the fifth planet from the Sun and by far the largest planet in our solar system.

K

Kamikazes – Japanese pilots who gave their lives in suicide attacks against US naval ships. They were to crash their aircraft loaded with bombs into a Navy ship.

KREEP – a rock found on the moon which has not been found on Earth.

Kuiper Belt – a ring of celestial bodies billions of miles beyond Neptune.

L

Laminar air flow – smooth flow pattern of air around an object.

Land-sea breeze phenomena – convection currents along shorelines produce heated air rising upward, which cause advection currents (wind) to flow from the water over the warmer land during the day. During the night, convection currents develop over the warmer-than-land water and cause the wind to blow from the land toward the water.

Lateral axis – an imaginary line that runs from one wingtip through the fuselage and exits the other wingtip. Also called the pitch axis.

Latitude – planes of the Equator that are parallel small circles and two poles.

Leading edge (airfoil) – the edge that meets relative wind first.

Leeward – the part or side of an object (such as a mountain) that is sheltered from the wind or is farthest from the source of the wind and is usually dry.

Lenticular – clouds that have a lens-like shape (double convex) and usually form in the mountains.

Light-lift – helicopters used in the military for observation and transportation of personnel. In the civilian community, they are used as executive transport and for many commercial uses such as crop dusting, construction and hauling personnel and light cargo.

Light turbulence – turbulence usually found in hilly and mountainous areas, below 5,000 feet when the air is colder than the Earth's surface (soon after the passage of a cold front) and at anytime the wind is blowing about 20 mph.

Light-year – the distance a photon can travel in one of Earth's calendar years.

Liquid propellants – a propellant in a liquid state which may be bipropellant or monopropellant.

Long-haul jets – commercial jet airliners such as the Douglas DC-8 and the Convair 880 and 990.

Long-range bombing – bombing long-distance targets requiring aircraft with bigger engines and fuel tanks.

Long-range navigation – used by aircraft as a means of navigation using ground-based radio stations, a receiving unit aboard the aircraft and special LORAN navigational charts.

Low explosive – solid propellants that produce force without causing a massive, destructive explosion.

Lift – the upward force that opposes the pull of gravity.

Lighter-than-air – a concept that must be met to achieve flight. Balloonists were first to develop the concept.

Longitude – the 18 primary great circles going north-south.

Longitudinal – front to back of an aircraft. (roll)

M

Mach number – determined by Ernst Mach as being the speed of sound through a medium.

Magnetic course – the course according to the magnetic compass heading or direction. The difference between magnetic north and true north must be subtracted from or added to the true-course direction. Otherwise, the airplane will not follow the true course drawn on the chart.

Magnetic storms – (also called electromagnetic or radiation storms) are characterized by a sudden onset of radiation bursts in which the magnetic field undergoes marked changes in the course of an hour or less.

Magnetosphere – the region of the Earth's atmosphere where ionized gas plays a big part in the dynamics of the atmosphere and where the geomagnetic field plays an important role.

Major carrier – the largest carriers in terms of the number of passengers carried regardless of the length of the routes.

Manned spacecraft – spacecraft carrying one or more human beings.

Maritime air mass – a humid air mass.

Mars – the fourth planet in our solar system that is also called the Red Planet because it appears as a small reddish light when viewed with the naked eye.

Mass – the amount of material in an object.

Mechanical instruments – instruments that work by means of direct mechanical linkage (such as a gear attached directly to the engine to give a reading on how fast the engine is operating) or on the principle of the gyroscope.

Mercator projection – maps in which the earth's surface is shown as a rectangle, with the meridians as parallel straight lines spaced at equal intervals and the parallels of latitude as parallel straight lines intersecting the meridians at right angles but spaced further apart as their distance from the equator increases. The areas become increasingly distorted toward the poles.

Mesosphere – a region of the atmosphere starting at 30 miles up to about 50 miles altitude.

Meteoroid – any of the small, solid bodies traveling through outer space.

Microburst – caused when a column of air is quickly cooled (usually by rain) and rapidly falls toward the Earth.

Microwave Landing System (MLS) – broadcasts much wider beams than the ILS – both horizontally and vertically.

Missile – a rocket-propelled vehicle with a weapon or warhead as the payload.

Mission-adaptive wings – the wing changes to create its most efficient shape for a variety of conditions.

Moderate turbulence – turbulence that requires aircraft occupants to wear seat belts and unsecured objects move about.

Modular air vehicle – air vehicles from different aircraft sections that allow the airplane to do different missions. This mixing and matching of sections allows the vehicle to meet the needs of country defense.

Mojave Aerospace Ventures – winners of the x-prize.

Momentum – the product of mass and velocity.

Monocoque – French word meaning single shell. It depends on the covering or skin to provide the required strength to resist the stresses of flight.

Monopropellant – liquid oxidizer and fuel existing together in the same storage tank.

Moon dust – a fine dust that covers the surface of the moon.

Moon rocks – rocks on the moon that have remained exposed on the lunar surface for periods as long as 500 million years without being destroyed.

Multi-spectral imaging – a satellite imaging system that observes radiant energy. This imaging can give useful information about crops, ocean currents and natural resources.

N

Napalm bombs – a firebomb that was made of 110-gallon tanks of jelled gasoline, which when dropped, would explode and burn an area some 250 feet long and 80 feet wide.

NASA's "vomit comet" – an airplane that flies as high as it can and then dives straight down putting its passengers in free fall for almost a minute.

National Aeronautics and Space Administration (NASA) – a government organization with a threefold mission. First, to explore, use, and enable the development of space for human enterprise. Second, to advance scientific knowledge and understanding of the Earth, the solar system and the universe and use the environment of space for research. Third, research, develop, verify and transfer advanced aeronautics, space and related technologies.

Navigation instruments – help the pilot find the way from the point of departure to the destination.

Nebulae – any of several dark or bright misty, cloudlike patches seen in the night sky, consisting of groups of stars too far away to be seen singly.

Neptune – the outermost of the gas planets and the fourth largest planet in the solar system. It is eighth in distance from the Sun.

Neutrosphere – in this region, there is little ionization compared to that which takes place in the ionosphere.

New Horizons – an unmanned space probe launched toward Pluto in 2006.

Newton's First Law of Motion – states that a body in a state of rest and a body in motion tend to remain at rest or in uniform motion unless acted upon by some outside force.

Newton's Law of Universal Gravitation – states that two bodies attract each other with a force directly proportional to the square of the distance between them.

Newton's Second Law of Motion – states that the rate of change in the momentum of a body is proportional to the force acting upon the body and is in the direction of the force.

Newton's Third Law of Motion – for every action there is an equal reaction in the opposite direction.

Nimbo – the combining term to indicate that a cloud is at the moment producing precipitation or is capable of producing precipitation.

Noise abatement procedures – usually involve a very quick climb by the aircraft after takeoff. Also, the aircraft might try not to fly over certain areas on the ground.

Non-coplanar transfer – a transfer that does not occur in the same plane because Earth satellites are at many different altitudes and at various angles to the equator.

Nonhypergolic – a bipropellant that is nonself igniting.

Nova – stars that are not stable; they flare, subside, and flare again.

Nozzle (of a rocket engine) –a "bell-shaped" duct that allows the escaping exhaust to expand thereby lowering its pressure.

O

Oblique-wing aircraft – this aircraft wing changes form during flight for optimum lift under different circumstances and can be rotated to different positions for the best aerodynamic characteristics.

Occluded front – when a warm air mass, lying between two cold air masses, is lifted up by the cold air mass behind it. The rapidly lifted warm air cools and creates a low and severe precipitation can sometimes occur.

Opportunity – a Mars rover.

Orbits – paths described by one body in its revolution about another body.

Ornithopter – flying machines that are kept aloft and propelled by flapping wings, described first by Leonardo da Vinci.

Outgassing – bubbles escaping from a spacecraft which can cause damage to delicate sensors and lenses.

Oxidation – the combination of oxygen with another substance.

Oxidizer – either another chemical compound or maybe oxygen in pure form – liquid oxygen.

Ozonosphere – a special region of the atmosphere that performs the very important function of shielding us from ultraviolet and infrared radiation that could be fatal.

P

Para-frag bombs – bombs with small parachutes attached to fragmentation bombs so that the allied bombers could come in low over the airfield and drop their bombs without exploding the plane that just dropped the bomb.

Particulate matter – dust and very small particles of matter.

Passenger terminal – designed to handle passengers, baggage, and cargo. Most have large waiting rooms for passengers to relax as well as places to eat, purchase tickets, and rent cars.

Passive communications satellites – those satellites, such as Echo I, that does nothing more than to reflect radio and television signals.

Patrol aircraft – aircraft used by utility companies to inspect pipelines or power lines.

Payload – whatever the rocket is carrying.

Performance instruments – tells how the aircraft has responded to commands.

Perigee – the opposite of apogee – that point where the orbiting body is closest to the body being orbited.

Personal aviation – the use of an aircraft for other than business or commercial use.

Photosphere – the portion of the Sun which gives light. It is composed of mostly hydrogen and helium and is very hot.

Pilotage – navigating by reference to visible landmarks.

Pluto – the outermost planet of the solar system, discovered in 1930, ninth in distance from the Sun.

Polar air mass – a cold air mass.

Polar magnetic storms – solar disturbances observable only in the polar areas.

Polar orbit – involves a path that crosses or nearly crosses the North and South Poles during each orbit.

Powered flight – aircraft having, producing, or propelled by means of engines.

Precipitation – when visible water falls in the form of rain, sleet, snow, and hail.

Precise Positioning System (PPS) – the military's encoded signal.

Pressure – air at higher altitudes is under less pressure than air at lower altitudes. Standard day pressure is 14.7 psi, or 29.92 on a mercury barometer. All air molecules pressing down upon all the molecules below them. Pressure is exerted in all directions with a given volume of air.

Pressure gradient – the rate of pressure increase or decrease on any atmospheric plane, usually a horizontal plane, for any given distance.

Pressure instruments – uses the principle that pressure decreases with height to tell the pilot about the performance of the aircraft.

Prime meridian – the great circle line that passes from the North Pole to the South through Greenwich, England.

Probes – satellites or spacecraft that either fly by, orbit or land on a celestial body, other than Earth.

Progressive burn rate – an instantaneous spread of the flame-front along the entire surface of the hole and as more and more surface area is exposed by burning, more and more thrust is produced.

Propellant – the oxidizer and reducer which propel the rocket.

Propfan system – combines the air-moving efficiency of the turbofan engine with the thrusting efficiency of the propeller causing a dramatic reduction in fuel consumption while retaining the turbofan's high power and the speed it makes possible.

Propulsion rocket system – includes the propellant used, the containers for the propellant, all plumbing that may be required to get the propellant from the containers to the engine, and the rocket engine itself.

Pulsar – known as a pulsating star because it flashes electromagnetic emissions (radio or other waves) in a set pattern.

Pure jets – a jet using a type of propulsion where all of the thrust is provided by the jet exhaust.

R

Radar – radio detecting and ranging by means of emitting radio signals and observing and analyzing the minute signals reflected from an object to detect range, bearing, and other characteristics of the object.

Radiation – energy radiated in the form of waves or particles such as the heat energy of the sun that reaches Earth.

Radiation hazards – intense amounts of radiation found with the Van Allen portion of the magnetosphere that can be damaging to astronauts and to satellites.

Radial – each degree line, in a 360-degree circle, extending away from the site.

Radiation fog – fog that forms at night when land surfaces radiate much of the heat absorbed from the sun back into space.

Ramjet engine – the simplest type of all-jet engines because it has no moving parts. The force of inertia "rams" air into a streamlined chamber where it is compressed slowed down, mixed with fuel, ignited, and released.

Ramps – a large paved area for parking airplanes.

Reaction engine – a rocket engine where the action of the rocket's exhaust gases produces a reaction, forcing the rocket in the opposite direction.

Reciprocating engine – certain parts of the engine move back and forth in straight-line motion. This straight-line motion has to be changed to rotary motion for turning the propeller of an airplane.

Reconnaissance aircraft – aircraft used by the military to watch an enemy or potential enemy in order to keep track of what they are doing.

Reducer – the substance to be oxidized.

Regional-commuter aircraft – smaller airlines that carry passengers within a certain limited geographical region. They serve many of the smaller cities that the larger airlines have dropped.

Regressive burn rate – the most thrust is produced shortly after ignition, and it diminishes thereafter.

Relative humidity – the method used to tell you the amount of water vapor that can still enter an air mass before it becomes saturated.

Relative wind – opposite the flight path and impacts the airfoil at any angle to the chord line.

Retractable gear – landing gear that retracts in order to get them out of the airstream and thereby reduce drag.

Retrothrust – negative thrust (moving down from a higher to a lower orbit require negative thrust).

Rille – one of several long, narrow telescopic valleys on the surface of the moon.

Rime ice – form when the airplane is flying through super-cooled cloud condensate. If allowed to accumulate, it will reduce lift and become a danger to flight.

Rocket – operates on the same principle as the firework rocket, consisting of a combustion chamber and an exhaust nozzle, that carries either liquid or solid propellants which provide the fuel and oxygen needed for combustion. A type of power plant that is used to propel something (payload).

Rotary engines – an air-cooled engine with the cylinders arranged in a round fashion. The crankshaft was fastened solidly to the airframe and allowed the engine and the attached propeller to spin around the fixed crankshaft.

Rotary-wing aircraft – a large rotor (propeller) on top of a helicopter, which is made up of a number of blades, each like a wing, and as the rotor whirls, the blades move through the air causing, lift.

Rotor blades – the airfoils in the rotor of a rotary-wing aircraft.

Rotor clouds – clouds that show by their shape and motion that the air coming over the mountain is spinning on an "axis" that parallels the mountains linear shape.

Rotor hub – the central component of a rotor, to which the blades are attached and where the rotor is attached to the drive shaft.

Rotor system – a complete system of rotating airfoils that supplies all or a major part of the lift supporting an aircraft.

Rudder – a control surface that controls yaw (left and right movement) of an airplane.

Runway designations – runways are identified by a number which corresponds to a compass direction rounded to the nearest 10 degrees.

S

Satellites – a man-made object or vehicle intended to orbit Earth, the moon, or other celestial body for the transmission of space data.

Saturation – when the air is holding the maximum amount of water vapor for the existing temperature and pressure.

Saturn – the second largest planet in the solar system and the sixth from the Sun. Known for its famous rings.

Scintillation – the twinkling of the stars.

Scramjet engine – similar to ramjet engine except the air is not slowed to subsonic speeds within the engine.

Seaplanes – flying boats.

Sedna – a newly discovered celestial body that one day may be classified as either a planet or a dwarf planet.

Self-reacting compound – one molecule contains atoms of both oxidizer and reducer and, upon ignition, reacts with itself, yielding energy as it breaks down or decomposes.

Semimonocoque – a fuselage structure that uses internal braces to help the skin carry the forces generated.

Severe turbulence – turbulence where aircraft may at times be out of control, occupants are thrown against seat belts, and unsecured objects are tossed about.

Shock wave – the sudden displacement of air and the resulting wedge-shaped wave formed by the air.

Short-haul jets – smaller jets such as the Boeing 727 and the DC-9.

Short-Takeoff-and Landing (STOL) – the ability of an aircraft to clear a 50-foot obstacle within 1,500 feet of commencing takeoff and to stop within 1,500 feet after passing over a 50-foot obstacle when landing.

Slats – protrusions from the leading edge of a wing that, when combined with the flaps, result in a significant increase in lift.

Small circle – any circle other than a great circle.

Smart weapons – weapons preferred because pilots could launch them far away from the targets and thus stay away from enemy defensive weapons.

Smoke – the vaporous matter arising from something burning and made visible by minute particles of carbon suspended in it.

Solar flares – a sudden and temporary outburst of energy from a small area of the sun's surface.

Solar powered aircraft – aircraft powered by the sun's rays.

Solar radiation – a process which causes evaporation by heating the oceans and large bodies of water.

Solar radio burst – large amounts of radio energy released by solar flares, which causes radio waves to become jammed.

Solar winds – steady electromagnetic emissions that are an extension of the Sun's corona into interplanetary space.

Solid propellants – a propellant in a solid state which is less costly and more reliable than the liquid type.

Sound barrier – the speed sound travels through air. Before 1947, it was believed that the speed of sound created a physical barrier for aircraft and pilots.

Sounding rocket flight – a rocket sent into, or even beyond the atmosphere, on a one-way trip to gather information.

Space – a place which extends infinitely in all directions and contains all the stars, planets, and galaxies in the universe.

Special use airspace – some special but relatively small areas of the airspace that most pilots have to avoid. Prohibited airspace and restricted airspace are clearly marked on aeronautical charts.

Specific impulse – the number of pounds of thrust delivered by consuming one pound of propellant (oxidizer/fuel mixture) in one second.

Speed of sound – how fast sound travels through a medium such as air. The speed of sound in air is about 761 mph when the air temperature is 59 degrees F.

Spin stabilization – the ability of a projectile to be steadied in flight by a rotating motion about its longitudinal axis.

Spirit – a Mars rover.

Spoilers – device used to destroy lift. Found on top of the wing and in varying sizes.

Sports aviation – called "flying for fun." It is flying for some purpose other than transportation or business purposes.

Stabilizer (horizontal and vertical) – located on the tail with the horizontal stabilizer having the elevators attached and the vertical stabilizer having the rudder attached.

Stall – separation between the streamlines and the airfoil causing loss of lift producing low-pressure on the top of the wing.

Standard Positioning System (SPS) – the civilian public's signal.

Stealth bomber – an aircraft that is hard to see by radar.

Strafe – to rake (as ground troops or an airfield) with fire at close range and especially with machine-gun fire from low-flying airplanes or formerly with artillery fire.

Strategic airlift – transportation of personnel or cargo between the theaters of operation.

Strategic bombing – bombing enemy territory.

Stationary front – when air masses lose their "punch" and are not replacing one another.

Stratosphere – a region where temperature goes up with increase in altitude, beginning at 10 miles above the Earth and going to about 30 miles up.

Stratus clouds – clouds that stretch out/or cover as a layer.

Sublimation – happens when water molecules leave the frozen (solid) state and directly enter the atmosphere without first changing into a liquid.

Sudden ionospheric disturbance – produced by sunspots, solar flares, and other disturbances on the surface of the sun causing fluctuations in the output of the sun's rays. SIDs produces excess electrons in the atmosphere, and these will absorb radio waves.

Sunspots – any of the dark spots sometimes seen on the surface of the sun.

Sunsynchronous orbit – a polar orbit that keeps a satellite exposed to constant sunlight.

Supercritical wings – wing designed to delay the point at which an aircraft reaches supersonic speeds, thus delaying the increased drag.

Supernova – occurs when a star gives up great mass in one giant explosion of light and energy.

Supersonic – relating to speeds from one to five times the speed of sound in air.

Supersonic transports – a delta-wing aircraft, which could carry about 100 passengers and fly at about Mach 2.2 (such as the Concorde).

Swept-back wings – aircraft wings that are designed to be more efficient at high speeds for supersonic flight.

Swirl-jet type – a type, in which each propellant is introduced into the chamber in an inverted-cone-shaped spray, finely atomized and sufficiently diffused for adequate mixing with the adjacent spray.

T

Tachometer – an instrument that shows how fast the engine's crankshaft is turning (expressed in rpm).

Tactical airlift – transportation within a theater of operation.

Tail (empennage) – consists of the horizontal stabilizer and the vertical stabilizer.

Tandem – landing gear in an arrangement where the main gear consists of two sets of wheels, which are, located one behind the other on the fuselage.

Tankers – most of the time used for aerial refueling of bombers, fighters and attack aircraft. They can also transport passengers and cargo.

Taxiways – the roads that aircraft use to get to the runway.

Technical/vocational school – provide the majority of the formal technical education courses. In this type of school, many people learn the special trades and skills that are applicable to the industry they plan to join.

Temperature – the measure of the energy within a gas.

The Milky Way – the galaxy in which we reside, along with about 100 billion other solar systems and stars.

Thermosphere – a region of the atmosphere that begins at 50 miles up and extends outward to about 300 miles.

Throat (of a rocket engine)- the most constricted area or section of a duct or passage of a rocket nozzle that constricts the exhaust and thereby increases its velocity.

Thrust – the force exerted through the propeller shaft of an airplane due to reaction of the air on the revolving blades of the propeller and that moves the craft ahead.

Thrust vectoring – allows the thrust force to be pointed in any direction to assist lift, reduce the chance to stall, or allow the aircraft to fly at extremely high angles of attack and very slowly.

Thunderstorm – any storm accompanied by thunder and lightning.

Tilt-Rotor Research Aircraft (TRRA) – an aircraft where the entire propulsion unit turns.

Total velocity requirement – represents adding together of all the velocity requirements for all stages of the mission.

Trailing edge (airfoil) – the thin junction where the upper and lower surfaces come together at the rear of the wing.

Trainers – an aircraft used to train pilots.

Trajectories – the curved paths of objects hurtling through space.

Transport – its mission is to airlift personnel and material to wherever they are needed.

Tricycle – consists of three wheels, which make an airplane very easy to control on the ground.

Tropical air mass – a hot air mass.

Tropical weather – weather conditions in the tropics which can be continental (extremely varied) or oceanic (low pressure and light winds.)

Troposphere – that region in which people live, work, play, and fly, extending from the Earth's surface to about 10 miles above the Earth at the equator.

True airspeed – a measure of how fast the airplane is flying through the air.

True course – what the navigator indicates as the course the airplane will follow. This might include consideration of radio navigation stations, landforms such as mountains, or prohibited airspace.

Truss - a type of fuselage that is made of tubing welded in place to form a well-braced framework.

Turbine engines – use the force of hot flowing gases striking a turbine.

Turbofan engine – similar to turbojets except more air is pulled into the turbofan engine, they are much quieter, and more fuel-efficient. The limitations are speed and poor low-altitude performance.

Turboprop jets – a type of jet propulsion in which the gas turbine is fastened to a propeller that is used to propel the aircraft.

Turbulence – air that flows over the wing's surface and scrapes against the rough metal and is slowed down and churned up.

Turn-and-slip indicator – the turn indicator indicates the direction and rate of turn and the ball in the glass tube (inclinometer) indicates the quality of the turn.

Typhoon – a hurricane that occurs in the western Pacific.

U

Ultralights – small, lightweight aircraft, which began as, powered hang gliders.

Uncontrolled airports – airports with no control tower where the pilots must use common procedures to reduce the chances of collisions on the ground and in the air.

United Nations resolutions – formal statements of opinion or determination adopted by the United Nations such as those relating to the use of space and how all mankind should share its benefits.

Unmanned Air Vehicles (UAV) – small, pilot-less aircraft that perform missions, which do not require a pilot on board or which, are considered too dangerous or politically unwise for manned flight.

Unmanned spacecraft – research devices designed to add to our knowledge of the atmosphere and space.

Uplink – the communication link from the transmitting earth station to the satellite.

Upslope fog – fog that results when wind carries moist air up a mountain slope or sloping land until the air is cooled.

Uranus – the third largest planet in the solar system, seventh in distance from the Sun.

Useful load – subtract the empty weight from the maximum allowable weight from the maximum allowable weight to find how many pounds may be loaded into the airplane.

Utility aircraft – aircraft used by the U.S. Air Force to airlift important people or for operational support airlift.

V

Vacuum – completely empty space.

Vectors – a graphic mathematical illustration showing both direction and magnitude.

Velocity – the rate at which a body moves when a force is applied to it.

Vengeance weapons – two World War II German weapons called the V-1 and V-2. V-1 was nicknamed "buzz bomb" and V-2 was a rocket-propelled ballistic missile.

Vertical axis – an imaginary line that passes vertically through the meeting point of the longitudinal and lateral axes and is also called the yaw axis.

Vertical-Takeoff-and Landing (VTOL) – a method by which an aircraft can achieve forward flight, like a conventional aircraft, but can also takeoff and land without any horizontal movement at all.

Vertical velocity indicator- tells the pilot at what rate (in feet per minute) the airplane is climbing or descending.

Viscosity – a fluid's resistance to flow.

Viscous drag – when an object is placed in the path of moving air and the mutual attraction of molecules slows the rate of flow. This is transmitted to other air molecules that are actually touching the surface over which they are flowing.

Visual Flight Rules (VFR) – the general weather conditions the FAA considers a pilot can expect at the surface.

VOR receiver – a receiver that gives a pilot a way to tell where he is from a given ground point without actually seeing the point.

Vortices – form around the wingtips of an airplane and described as horizontal tornadoes. Strong swirling air currents.

V/STOL – vertical/short takeoff and landing aircraft could get into and out of small airports that were located close to the customer's destination.

W

Wake turbulence – a man-made turbulence caused by large aircraft in flight.

Warm front – when a warm air mass replaces a cold air mass, the boundary is called a warm front.

Wave drag – result of lost energy when air flows across a shock wave and undergoes a change in temperature, pressure, and velocity.

Waverider – a hypersonic or supersonic vehicle that has an attached shock wave along its leading fuselage edge. The vehicle appears to be riding its own shock wave.

Weather – the day-to-day changes in atmospheric conditions.

Weather radar – shows areas of precipitation, but its most important function is to show storm cells (thunderstorms) ahead.

Weight – force that directly opposes lift.

Windshear – an atmospheric condition in which changes in speed and direction of the wind occur.

Wind triangle – a tool used by the pilot to figure out where wind drift will cause the aircraft to fly over the ground. It can also be used to counter the effect of drift.

Wind tunnel – a device used in the design and development of virtually all aircraft flying today.

Windward – slopes of mountains that face the wind and are usually moistened with rain or snow.

Wing – primary source of lift with ailerons attached.

Winglets – small wings placed in a vertical position at the end of the wings to eliminate the vortices and improve the efficiency of the wing.

Whiteout – an atmospheric and surface condition in the Arctic in which no object casts a shadow, the horizon being indiscernible, and only very dark objects being seen. Snowfall which reduces visibility.

X-Prize – the prize awarded for a non-government organization spacecraft flying into space and returning within two weeks.

Y

Z